Aquaculture

Third Edition

JASPER S. LEE
Agricultural Educator
Georgia

GARY J. BURTLE
Extension Aquaculture Specialist
University of Georgia–Tifton

MICHAEL E. NEWMAN
Professor
Mississippi State University

AQUACULTURE

Third Edition

Jasper S. Lee — Series Editor

PEARSON

Prentice
Hall
Interstate

Upper Saddle River, New Jersey
Needham, Massachusetts

Cover Photo Credits

background
(Courtesy, Getty Images)

top left—tilapia in a divided tank
(Courtesy, Education Images, Inc.)

top middle—harvesting catfish
(Courtesy, U.S. Department of Agriculture)

top right—an attractive koi pond
(Courtesy, Education Images, Inc.)

bottom left—processing fish in a modern facility
(Courtesy, U.S. Department of Agriculture)

bottom middle—a fish ladder for salmon
(Courtesy, Education Images, Inc.)

bottom right—determining the average sizes and weights of different trout strains
(Courtesy, Agricultural Research Service, USDA)

Pearson Prentice Hall Interstate™ is a trademark of Pearson Education, Inc., publishing as Pearson Prentice Hall Interstate.

Interstate™ is a trademark of Pearson Education, Inc., publishing as Pearson Prentice Hall Interstate.

Prentice Hall® is a registered trademark of Pearson Education, Inc., publishing as Pearson Prentice Hall.

Pearson® is a registered trademark of Pearson plc.

ISBN 0-13-117077-5

1 2 3 4 5 6 7 8 9 10   08 07 06 05 04

Preface

Aquaculture, Third Edition, is an exciting, full-color revision of a book that has been highly popular book in U.S. high schools. (The first and second editions were entitled *Aquaculture: An Introduction*.) Widely expanded content and up-to-date technology will, no doubt, help this continue as the leading text. An expanded author team has been used to enhance further the book's content and usefulness.

The book emphasizes developing a basic understanding of the diversity of aquaculture and the potential it holds for the United States. A practical approach is used. Emphasis is on aquaculture as a profitable source of income. The book also emphasizes the undergirding science.

New areas of emphasis in the Third Edition include sustainable aquaculture, genetics, and use of the seafood list. Additional content on salt-water species, careers, recreational aquaculture, ornamental fish, freshwater species, and baitfish has been included. A large increase in photographs and line-art illustrations makes the book more appealing.

A science-based approach is used throughout. Research findings have been studied and used in preparing the book. Key terms in each chapter appear in bold italics and are carefully defined in relation to aquaculture.

The bottom line in any production endeavor is to make a profit. Principles of decision making and management are stressed throughout the book. Planning and marketing are steps that must be included in any thoughts about beginning an aquabusiness.

Many areas of aquaculture are new and untried in the United States. Much progress has been made in the last few years, but supplies of wild fish and other aquatic foods continue to be depleted. This means that emphasis on aquaculture will increase. Educational programs to prepare people for this new industry are certain to expand in popularity. Such programs must always be founded on basic principles and the application of those principles in real-world settings.

Teachers have responded most favorably to previous editions of this book. The Third Edition expands on the outstanding qualities. It also embraces the new format for books in "AgriScience & Technology Series." Careful research was used to identify the features students and teachers wanted in user-friendly books. The "AgriScience & Technology Series" has implemented those features for students and teachers to enjoy.

Aquaculture is exactly what students and teachers want and need. It is a tested book based on sound approaches to science-based education in aquaculture. The authors have carefully attempted to live up to the expectations of users. Go ahead and see for yourself by exploring and using this book.

Order copies of this book as follows:

- Call toll free: (800) 848-9500

- Mail: Pearson Prentice Hall Interstate
        Order Department
        P.O. Box 2500
        Lebanon, IN 46052-3009

Acknowledgments

Many individuals are acknowledged for their help with this edition and previous editions of this book. *Aquaculture* would not have been possible without contributions of businesses and agencies involved in aquaculture. Many of these are acknowledged at various points throughout the book; others are recognized here.

Special acknowledgment goes to the reviewers of the manuscript. These are Chad Nunley, of Greencastle, Indiana; Gordon Mengel, of Kentucky State University; Erwin Janszen, of the Palacios Marine Education Center, in Texas; and Steven H. Lazell, of Wilapa Bay and South Bend, Washington.

Many people in aquaculture helped the authors. These include Jim Steeby, of the Mississippi Cooperative Extension Service; Charles Collins, of the Fish Farming Experimental Station, in Arkansas; Nathan Stone, of the University of Arkansas at Pine Bluff; Larry Bottorff, of South Putnam School, in Indiana; and Ron Buckhalt, of Washington, D.C.

Other individuals to be acknowledged are Jeanne Hartley for assistance with line art and Eddie Harris, Kevin Fitzsimmons, Jimmy Avery, and LaDon Swann for help with photographs. David Harvey, of the Economic Research Service of the U.S. Department of Agriculture, was most helpful in providing statistical information. Staff members of the Gulf Coast Research Laboratory provided opportunities for the authors to get information on aquaculture. Gary Fornshell, of the University of Idaho, and Mack Fondren, of the Mississippi Agricultural and Forestry Experiment Station, were most helpful with photography opportunities.

Additional individuals acknowledged for special assistance with the Third Edition are Max Sherman, of Canby, Oregon; Danell Blair, of Molalla,

Oregon; and Nick R. Nelson, of Clackamas, Oregon. Students and teachers at the following high schools are acknowledged: Newton High School, Mississippi; Florin High School, California; Monticello, Tri-Valley, and Paxton-Buckley-Loda High Schools, Illinois; Turner Tech and Coral Reef High Schools, Florida; James Madison and Sandra Day O'Connor High Schools, Texas; and Park High School, Montana.

The assistance of Amanda R. Patrick, Cindy Williams, Jennifer Mason, and Karin Schauble, of Piedmont College, is gratefully acknowledged. Education Images, Inc., of Georgia, is acknowledged as the source of many illustrations in this edition.

Individuals at the Center for Environmental and Agricultural Research and Training (CAERT), Inc., are acknowledged. These include Dan Pentony, president, for his encouragement and support; Ron McDaniel for his editing skills; and Rita Lange, Kim Romine, and Jewel K. Martin for their design and typesetting expertise.

Appreciation is also expressed to the staff of the publisher, Pearson Prentice Hall Interstate.

To

Vernie L. Thomas

This book is dedicated to Vernie L. Thomas, of Danville, Illinois. No individual did more to provide quality learning materials for students in high school agriculture classes in the last decade of the twentieth century than Vernie Thomas. He is known throughout the United States for being a "friend to agricultural education."

Vernie has been involved in a number of ways in agricultural education. He was best known as the owner and president of Interstate Publishers, Inc. No individual knew more about publishing agriculture books than Vernie. If you had questions, he had answers!

Vernie, this book is dedicated to you for many reasons but most of all because of your untiring efforts, concern for others, and enthusiasm for life. The authors wish you the very best life has to offer.

Contents

PART ONE: THE DYNAMIC AQUACULTURE INDUSTRY

PART FIVE: PRODUCTION IN AQUACULTURE

PART SIX: AQUACULTURE AND PEOPLE

The Dynamic Aquaculture Industry

CHAPTER 1

Aquaculture Industry

OBJECTIVES

This chapter introduces aquaculture and the broad nature of the aquaculture industry. It has the following objectives:

1 Define aquaculture and explain the areas included
2 Distinguish between cultured and captured aquatic organisms
3 Describe how the types of aquaculture production systems vary
4 Trace the history of aquaculture
5 List and discuss the contributions of aquaculture
6 Describe the role of research in aquaculture

TERMS

aquacrop
aquaculture
bait aquaculture
brackish water
captured aquafood
closed system
cultured aquacrop
development
extensive aquaculture
food aquacrop

freshwater aquaculture
intensive aquaculture
mariculture
monoculture
offshore aquaculture
open system
ornamental aquaculture
polyculture
production intensity
raceway

recirculating facility
recreational aquaculture
research
scientific method
seafood
stock enhancement
tank
water enclosure
water recirculation

MORE fish and other aquatic foods are being eaten each year. Information about the important role of fish in promoting health is increasing the demand for fish products. This demand is greater than the natural growth in oceans, lakes, and streams. Some bodies of water no longer have the fish that were abundant just a few years ago. These waters have been over-harvested.

Demand for fish and other aquatic species has resulted in the emergence of aquaculture. Aquaculture helps prevent the loss of wild fish and assures quality food products. Aquaculture provides an expanding source of food and has lead to profitable new crops. Wholesome food is made available without depleting wild fish in oceans, lakes, and streams.

1–1. A producer is guiding a basket with 2,000 pounds of harvested food fish into a transport truck. (Courtesy, Agricultural Research Service, USDA)

Most people have favorite fish and seafoods. These foods are often fish, shrimp, or clams that are products of aquaculture. With aquaculture, we are assured of quality products.

AQUACULTURE

1–2. Appealing colors of some fish species, such as this queen angelfish, create demand for aquarium stocking.

Aquaculture is the production of aquatic plants and animals. More specifically, it is the culture and harvest of plants and animals that live in a water environment. The plants and animals are used for food, fiber, ornaments, medicine, and other purposes. Aquaculture is much like traditional farming on land, except it occurs in water. Another way of defining aquaculture is to say that it is "water farming."

Many new words are used in aquaculture. *Aqua* (meaning "water") is often used as a prefix in front of other words to create new words, such as *aquafarm*. When this is done, we know that water is involved. An **aquacrop**, for example, is a crop grown in water.

USES OF AQUACROPS

The plant and animal aquacrops produced in the United States are used in many ways. Five important purposes are for

1. Food—**Food aquacrops** are crops grown in water and produced almost exclusively for human food. Catfish, tilapia, trout, oysters, crawfish, and salmon are examples.

1–3. Steamed crab at Fisherman's Wharf in San Francisco.

2. Bait—***Bait aquaculture*** is the raising of small fish and other aquatic species for use as bait. In the wild, they are the food of other species. The fathead minnow and small crawfish are examples.

3. Recreation—***Recreational aquaculture*** is the raising of fish for sport fishing. The fish are grown for use in fee-lakes, for release into streams, or for use in stocking hobby ponds. Examples of such fish are trout, catfish, and bream. The operation of recreational facilities is also included in recreational aquaculture.

4. Ornamentals (or pets)—***Ornamental aquaculture*** is the keeping of fish, plants, and other species for aesthetic or personal appeal. Ornamentals are often found in aquariums or similar water containers. You likely have an aquarium in your home or school. Examples of ornamental species are goldfish, guppies, and angel fish.

5. Feed—Some species are used as feed or as ingredients in manufacturing feed for other animals. Fish meal, at least in small amounts, is needed in rations for most fish. Examples of fish used in feed are goldfish and menhaden, with the latter usually being wild marine fish. The by-products from processing aquatic crops may also be used in feed manufacturing.

Aquacrops are also used for many other purposes. Some are widely known; others might surprise you! We are all familiar with the use of pearls from oysters in making jewelry. Products from seaweed are used in food manufacturing. Some aquaculture products are used in making clothing and related items—for example, the skin of alligators is used in making boots. A few aquaculture products are used in biotechnology and human medicine. Others, such as bullfrogs, are used in science laboratories.

1–4. Boiled crawfish ready for peeling and eating.

SPECIES

Many species are produced as aquacrops. Aquaculture is more than the production fish. The production of aquaplants, such as watercress, is increasing. Kinds of aquacrops also vary by water temperature and salt content.

Aquaculture also includes the production of bullfrogs, crawfish (also called crayfish), alligators, seaweed, tilapia, turtles, and squid. Despite the large variety of aquacrops, four aquacrops (crops grown in water) account for more than 90 percent of the production in the United States. They are trout, salmon, catfish, and crawfish. Sometimes, exotic animals, such as seals and porpoises, are included.

Aquaculture includes many crops, terms, and subjects. It is a very broad area. Examples of aquacrops are presented in Table 1–1.

Table 1–1. Examples of Aquacrops
(All aquacrops listed have some potential for culture in the U.S.)

Common Name (Scientific Name)	Notes on Culture and Importance
Alligator *Alligator mississippiensis*	Grown in southern U.S., primarily in Louisiana and Texas; flesh is used for food, and skin is used for leather.
Bullfrog *Rana catesbiana*	Cultured for food and laboratory use; mostly imported to U.S.
Carp *Cyprinus carpio*	Many nations produce and consume; not particularly popular in U.S.
Carp, grass (white amur) *Ctenopharyngodon idellus*	Consumes huge amounts of vegetation; native to China.
Catfish (channel) *Ictalurus punctatus*	Widely grown in southern U.S.; most important aquaculture crop.
Chinese water chestnut *Eleocharis dulcis*	Plant grown for corms; production is experimental in U.S.; popular and successful in China; imported food to U.S.
Crawfish (red swamp) *Procambarus clarkii*	Primarily grown in Louisiana and Texas for food.
Eel (Japanese) *Anguilla japonica*	Popular food in Italy, Japan, and other countries; cultured in Taiwan, Japan, and other countries.
Goldfish *Carassius auratus*	Popular ornamental fish in U.S.; grown in Arkansas and Florida.
Freshwater prawn *Macrobrachium rosenbergii*	Experimental in U.S.; successful production in Asian and other countries.
Minnow (fathead) *Pimephales promelas*	Popular baitfish in U.S.; grown in Arkansas and other areas.
Oyster (American) *Crassostrea virginica*	Limited culture success in Chesapeake Bay area and Eastern Shore of U.S.; successful culture in Japan, Taiwan, and other areas.

(Continued)

Table 1-1 (Continued)

Common Name (Scientific Name)	Notes on Culture and Importance
Paddlefish *Polyodon spathula*	Limited culture success, though research is showing potential; primary use is for caviar; often captured wild from streams.
Salmon (chinook) *Oncorhynchus tshawytscha*	Popular food fish; harvested in several locations.
Shrimp (Chinese white) *Penaeus chinensis*	China is world leader in shrimp production; other species produced elsewhere.
Striped bass *Morone saxatilis*	Thought to hold much potential for culture, particularly its hybrids; still somewhat experimental.
Tilapia (blue) *Tilapia aurea*	Grow in warm water or intensive systems; sometimes considered a pest.
Trout (rainbow) *Salmo gairdneri*	Popular; produced in northern U.S.
Watercress *Nasturtium officinale*	Grown in temperate and subtropical climates, such as in Hawaii; the only aquatic foliage consumed on a regular basis in U.S. in raw salads or cooked.

Sources: *The Seafood List,* U.S. Food and Drug Administration, 1994; J. E. Bardach, J. H. Ryther, and W. O. McLarney, *Aquaculture: The Farming and Husbandry of Freshwater and Marine Organisms.* New York: John Wiley & Sons, Inc., 1972; H. K. Dupree and J. V. Huner, *Third Report to the Fish Farmers.* Washington, DC: U.S. Fish and Wildlife Service, 1984; B. Rosenberry, *World Shrimp Farming.* San Diego: Aquaculture Digest, 1990; Rick Parker, *Aquaculture Science,* 2nd ed. Albany, NY: Thomson Delmar Learning, 2002; and S. W. Waite, B. C. Kinnett, and A. J. Roberts, *The Illinois Aquaculture Industry: Its Status and Potential.* Springfield, State of Illinois, Department of Agriculture, 1988.

1–5. Seaweed grows naturally in the oceans and is cultured in some places. This shows nori (Porphyra leucosticta), which is often eaten for iodine and other nutrients. (Courtesy, Mike Guiry, National University of Ireland)

CHOICES

Producing aquatic plants and animals is an alternative to traditional agriculture. Growing aquacrops may be more profitable than other crops. Sometimes, however, large investments may be lost. Aquacrops may be grown in fresh water, salt water, or brackish water.

1–6. Trout being raised in round tanks. (Tanks usually involve a high stocking rate or intensity of production.)

1–7. A baitfish hauler is ready to make a delivery. (Note the flatbed semitrailer with tanks and oxygen system.)

Oceans and seas contain salt water. The production of aquatic crops in salt water is marine aquaculture, or *mariculture*. *Brackish water* is the water where fresh water and salt water run together. Crops adapted to one kind of water will not likely grow well in another. Some aquacrops require both fresh water and salt water, depending on their stage of growth. For example, freshwater prawns (a kind of shrimp) may grow well in fresh water but must be placed in salt water to reproduce. Aquacrops are frequently grown in ponds and tanks and in cages in oceans, lakes, and streams.

Seafood includes edible marine fish, shellfish, and other aquatic plants and animals, which may be either wild or cultured. Most often they are wild and are captured in the oceans, seas, and lakes.

Freshwater aquaculture involves growing aquacrops in streams, ponds, and lakes not containing salt water. It also includes super-intensive tank culture, where spring or well water is used. Trout, tilapia, catfish, and watercress are examples of freshwater aquacrops.

COMPETITION

Cultured fish and other aquacrops compete for markets with the wild crops caught in streams, lakes, and oceans. As aquaculture expands, the fishing industry may be threatened. Some companies involved with wild aquafoods are also getting into aquaculture.

The seafood industry is based on capturing wild fish that cost nothing to produce. No investment in feed and other production inputs is needed. Wild fish get their food from what is naturally available in streams, lakes, and oceans.

Aquaculture results in more good-quality water crops at the market. These products compete with the wild harvest. Further, some people think that cultured aquafoods are of better quality than those from the wild. This is because growers can control the quality of the water the crops are grown in and the kind of feed the crops receive. Would you prefer a wild or cultured aquafood?

1–8. Streams can no longer provide the quantity of wild fish to satisfy consumer demand. (Courtesy U.S. Fish and Wildlife Services.)

CULTURED AND CAPTURED AQUAFOODS

Aquaculture emerged over the years so aquafoods would be more readily available. Capturing wild fish in streams and oceans does not always provide a dependable source of food.

CULTURED AQUACROPS

A *cultured aquacrop* is a species raised or grown with human care. Cultured aquacrops often need expert attention to live and grow. This husbandry of plants and animals requires the application of scientific and management principles. Knowledge is needed in a wide range of subjects, including water management; fish breeding, feeding, and disease control; and harvesting and marketing. Much difference exists between growing traditional crops on land and producing crops in water.

1–9. A small commercial fishing boat in front of a cannery at Valdez, Alaska. (The water in this area is known for good catches of wild salmon.)

Compared with wild fish and other aquatic species, cultured aquacrops may require considerable investment. The producer must construct ponds, buy feed for fish, control diseases, and operate hatcheries. Wild fish do not usually require such investment, but the availability of a supply of fish is less certain.

CAPTURED AQUAFOODS

Captured aquafoods are plants and animals that grow wild in the oceans and streams, much as squirrel and deer grow wild in the forest. Commercial fishers catch the species by using nets, hooks, traps, and other means. Of more than 21,000 kinds of fish recognized by scientists, only a few of these are widely known as sources of food. The U.S. Food and Drug Administration has established regulations on the names used for seafood species sold in the United States. More details on the list are included in Chapter 11.

Some kinds of fish are produced in both wild and cultured forms. This often occurs when the supply of wild fish does not meet consumer demand. Proper equipment and knowledge are needed to culture fish. Some popular kinds of food fish are virtually extinct due to overfishing of the oceans and the lack of good culture methods.

Major progress has been made in the culture of salmon since the early 1960s. Salmon culture (also called salmon farming or ranching) was essential to meet demand for the product without destroying the wild fish populations. In 2004, 70 percent of all salmon was a product of aquaculture. The percentage is higher for fresh salmon.

ADVANTAGES AND DISADVANTAGES

The key factor in aquafarming is making a profit. Aquaculture must be economically feasible. In the past, many individuals invested in aquaculture only to fail and lose their money. Thorough knowledge, good planning, and sound management are keys to success.

Beyond making a profit, several important advantages and disadvantages of aquaculture should be considered. These are listed in Table 1–2.

1–10. A large catch of fish is shown on this ocean-going fishing vessel. (Courtesy, National Oceanic and Atmospheric Administration)

Table 1-2. Major Advantages and Disadvantages of Aquaculture

Advantages of Aquaculture	Disadvantages of Aquaculture
Helps ensure a supply of desired aquacrops. (Wild supplies may be very limited. Aquafarming helps ensure availability.)	Technology not available for many possible crops. (To water farm successfully, the aquafarmer must have information on how to do it. Such information is often not available, though considerable research is underway.)
Can control environment of production. (Feeding fish nutritional, wholesome feeds eliminates the possibility of contamination with harmful substances, such as pesticides.)	Lack of knowledge about aquaculture. (With aquacrops that have been adapted to culture, farmers need education in how to be successful in aquafarming. Farmers who go into aquaculture without good information may lose money.)
Helps provide nutrients essential in the human diet. (Fish have been shown to be good sources of protein and other nutrients.)	Competition from wild fish and seafood. (Since money is required to produce an aquacrop, the aquafarmer must be able to sell the crop at a price to recover costs and earn a profit. Wild fish usually have no production costs.)

TYPES OF AQUACULTURE PRODUCTION SYSTEMS

Several types of aquaculture production systems are used. These types can be distinguished by production intensity, kind of water facility, type of system (closed or open), water temperature, and kind of species cultured.

PRODUCTION INTENSITY

Production intensity is the density (crowding together) of the aquacrop being produced. The intensity may be extensive, intensive, or intermediate.

An *extensive aquaculture* system involves low population density, little control over the system, and little intervention by the producer. Extensive systems may be used in natural or artificial ponds or lakes. The number of fish or plants is at a level low enough for the natural food in the water to be sufficient. Almost no investment is made in feed, water management, and other areas. Of course, the volume of the crop harvested is low.

Intensive aquaculture is the production of aquacrops at a high rate of stocking. Considerable skill in management is needed. Tanks and raceways are commonly used with

1–11. An aerial view of a commercial aquafarm showing a system of ponds. (Ponds are mostly used for intermediate density of aquacrop production.) (Courtesy, Catfish Institute)

continuously flowing water. The producer must know and follow proper feeding, disease control, water management, and other factors. Considerable financial investment is often required. The potential for returns is greater than with an extensive system. Examples of fish produced with intensive systems are tilapia and hybrid striped bass.

Intermediate aquaculture systems involve some principles of both extensive and intensive aquaculture. Intermediate systems are between the two in level of intensity. Artificial ponds are primarily used. Fish are stocked at a rate requiring feed and water aeration but not in water that flows. Most fish aquaculture in the United States has used intermediate systems, but there is a trend toward more intensity in these systems. Most catfish farming uses intermediate systems.

WATER FACILITY

The kind of water facility refers to the design of the water enclosure and the water movement. Some facilities use flowing water; others do not.

1–12. Concrete vats are being used to grow baitfish on this Georgia farm.

Water Enclosures

A *water enclosure* is a facility in which aquaculture takes place. Water enclosures include ponds, cages, raceways, recirculating systems, and offshore facilities.

Ponds are sometimes divided into two groups: farm ponds and levee ponds. A farm pond may serve other purposes, such as providing a source of drinking water or a location for recreational fishing. A farm pond is often formed by building a dam across a hollow between two hills. A levee pond is carefully designed and constructed for fish culture. In whole-pond culture, the aquacrop is placed in the pond without restriction by cages or pens. In other types of aquaculture, cages are used to confine fish to a certain area of water. Cages may be used in streams, ponds, oceans, or other water areas. Water in a pond is usually static.

A *raceway* is a long, narrow structure that uses flowing water. Sometimes ponds are linked together in a series so water flows from one to another much as with a raceway.

1–13. A raceway facility used to raise trout in Virginia. (Hand feeding is underway in the photograph.)

CONNECTION

CELEBRATING AQUACULTURE

The Catfish Museum in Belzoni, Mississippi, has captured much of the history of catfish production. Not only does the museum depict the history of catfish, but it is decorated with art created from artifacts of the industry. Located in an area with a large aquaindustry, the museum hosts many educational events, such as the Catfish Festival.

The bottom photograph shows the front of the museum. The rectangular containers made into rounded art form were formerly spawning nests made from ammunition cans. The table-like structures on the inserted photo are hatching troughs.

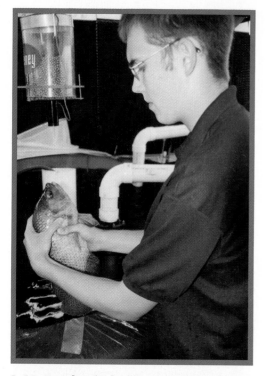

1–14. A student is checking on tilapia raised in a tank in Illinois.

A *recirculating facility* recycles water. The recycling involves restoring water quality for satisfactory fish production. Tanks are the most common recirculating facilities, though some raceways recirculate water.

A *tank* is a relatively small water facility. Tanks may be round or rectangular water enclosures and use flowing water. In recent years, the trend with tanks has been toward round tanks, 20 feet or so in diameter, with a considerable volume of flowing water.

Offshore aquaculture is the use of cages in seawater to produce aquacrops, such as cobia and red snapper. The Gulf of Mexico, the Atlantic and Pacific Oceans, and other bodies of water are being used for offshore production. Species produced offshore are saltwater fish and do not thrive in fresh water. An offshore facility must also have a land base for storage of equipment, launching of boats, and other needs. (Note: The focus of this book is on freshwater species; therefore, limited content is included on offshore aquaculture.)

Water Movement

Water movement is defined by whether the water in an enclosure flows. Ponds use static systems but are often artificially aerated with water sprayed into the air or with air or oxygen injected into the water. Aeration is necessary because fish, at the population levels used in aquaculture, need more oxygen than static water can provide. Tanks and raceways use flowing water. The density at which fish can be stocked depends on the rate of water flow.

WATER USE AND REUSE

Systems may be classified by the use and reuse of water. The systems may range from open to closed.

Open Systems

An *open system* is one in which the water is pumped in at one place and removed at another. The water is used once and discarded. This may involve running the water into a holding pond or into a creek or river. Environmental regulations may not allow certain water to be run directly into streams. As freshwater supplies have diminished, interest has increased in ways of reusing water.

Water may be reused by flowing from one tank or other water facility to another in a series. The water is not filtered to remove uneaten suspended feed or other waste matter.

Recirculation Systems

Water recirculation is the pumping of water back through the same water facility. In recirculation, the water is reconditioned. Reconditioning may involve filtering, aerating, or using other procedures to keep good-quality water.

Closed Systems

A *closed system* is one in which no new water is added. Filtering and recycling are used. The water from closed systems must be treated to remove uneaten feed, fish excrement, and other substances before recycling. Some aquafarms use a combination of recycled and "new" water in what is known as semi-closed systems. In practice, very few systems are completely closed. Most require the addition of some new water.

Reconditioning water used in a closed system is a difficult procedure. Better systems are being developed. Most of the systems available today are not fully satisfactory. Besides problems in making them operate properly, they are costly to set up and maintain.

WATER TEMPERATURE

Aquacrops have varying water temperature needs. Water may be cold, cool, or warm. Fish adapted to warm water will not thrive in cool or cold water; they may die. For example, tilapia thrive in water with a temperature of 80° to 90°F (26.7° to 32.2°C) but will die in water with a temperature below 50°F (10°C). The potential producer must select an aquacrop suitable to the environment. This requires study of the habitat needs of the species.

1–15. A filtration system is used here in a small aquaculture tank facility to prepare water for reuse.

Aquacrop Species

Some species of aquacrops are compatible with other species, and some are not. In addition, cultural practices may require that only one species be grown in a production system. For example, growing two different species of fish together in a pond may require sorting at the time of harvest. Processors of fish want to receive only uniform batches of fish. **Monoculture** is a production system in which only one species is grown at a time.

Polyculture involves growing two or more species together. The species need to be compatible in behavior and environmental requirements. In good polyculture, the species use different niches. They also do not directly compete with each other for food.

A good example of polyculture is the common farm pond. Bass and bluegill are frequently stocked together. Research into aquafarming is showing that some combinations of species of fish, and of fish and other aquacrops, may be satisfactory.

1–16. Monoculture of catfish promotes harvesting and processing. (Courtesy, Catfish Institute)

A BRIEF HISTORY

Although aquaculture is relatively new in the United States, various forms of aquafarming have been carried out for centuries.

China and the Far East

The earliest fish farming was in China, beginning before 2000 B.C. with the common carp. The Chinese learned that fertilizer would help ponds produce more fish. They used organic fertilizers, primarily manure.

From China, fish culture spread to Korea and Japan around A.D. 200. By 1700, the Japanese had started mariculture.

Today, areas of Asia are quite active in aquaculture. China is the leading producer. Japan, Taiwan, India, Korea, Vietnam, and other nations are increasing aquaculture production.

Australia and New Zealand are also involved, with salmon and rainbow trout among the most important finfishes. These are for sport fishing and food fish.

EUROPE

Aquaculture began in Europe during the Middle Ages. Fish were kept in the moats around castles. These moats became known as "stew ponds." Wild fish were caught and placed in the stew ponds until needed as food. Some fish remained longer than a few days and reproduced. People soon learned a simple form of fish farming.

Using the ocean to raise salmon, oysters, and other aquacrops has increased in recent years in Europe. Large cages are being used with salmon. Species with particular appeal in Europe are also being cultured. Turbot, a flatfish similar to flounder, is a popular food in some areas of Europe.

AFRICA

Africa has had a long history in fish culture. Most of the production is at the subsistence level, meaning that little enters commercial trade. Tilapia, walking catfish, freshwater shrimp, frogs, and several marine species are produced.

The first trout farm was established in South Africa in 1945. Since then, various other freshwater species have been produced, including ornamental species and carp.

1–17. Shells of aquatic organisms have been used to make necklaces.

NORTH AMERICA

In North America, interest in aquaculture began to emerge in the mid-1800s. This grew out of a need to restore depleted stocks of game fish in some natural waters. The early efforts focused on trout and carp.

Research in the 1930s in Illinois and Alabama was on how to produce larger crops of fish. This was followed in the 1950s by the farm pond program of the U.S. government, which encouraged the construction and stocking of farm ponds. These 2 million ponds, however, have been of little importance as a commercial source of food.

In the 1960s, catfish culture began to emerge in the South (primarily in Mississippi, Arkansas, Louisiana, and Alabama). Huge increases of acreage in catfish farming occurred in the 1970s, 1980s, and 1990s. Research and new technology have resulted in catfish becoming a major aquaindustry. Catfish farming is now a sizeable aquacrop in some areas.

Aquaculture received a boost from the National Aquaculture Act of 1980. This legislation established aquaculture as a national priority in the United States. It further stated that government agencies should work together in planning aquaculture development. Regional aquaculture centers have been set up to promote research and development work.

Tilapia, hybrid striped bass, sturgeon, and other species are now being cultured in the United States. Promotion of additional species occurred through many high schools that initiated aquaculture education during the 1990s. Research findings have also had major impacts on fish production.

Aquaculture is now a major production enterprise. Catfish, trout, tilapia, salmon, baitfish, ornamental fish, game and sport fish, mollusks (oysters, clams, and mussels), shrimp, and crayfish have been among the most popular species cultured. Algae, sea vegetables, and other fish species have made small contributions. The farm sales of these aquaculture products totaled approximately $1 billion in 2003.

Aquaculture in the United States has been threatened by imports from foreign countries. In 2003, the International Trade Commission (ITC) placed heavy tariffs on the importation of certain species, such as the "basa" and "tra" fish from Vietnam. These fish products were reported to have been labeled and marketed as farm-raised catfish fillets. They were sold in the United States at a price much lower than profitable to U.S. catfish producers. The species are not catfish!

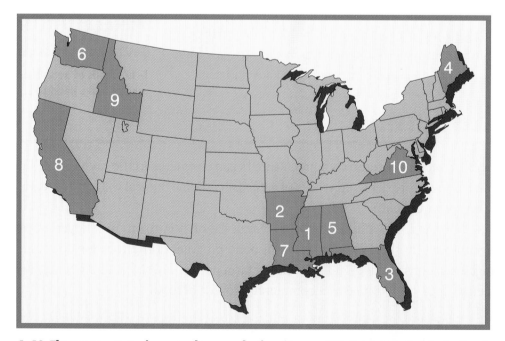

1–18. The top ten states in aquaculture production. (Source: U.S. Department of Agriculture)

Aquaculture appears to have a bright future. Current trends point toward at least a 20 to 25 percent shortfall in the worldwide supply of fish in the next few years. Demand for fish is predicted to continue to increase in the United States.

LATIN AND SOUTH AMERICA

An abundance of coastline areas suitable for aquaculture has resulted in major aquaculture activity in the Caribbean and the Atlantic and Pacific Ocean areas of South America.

Efforts in aquaculture began in the early 1960s in Latin America. These led to major aquaculture production enterprises in 2004. Shrimp production is the largest aquaculture activity in Latin America, including Ecuador, Mexico, Costa Rica, and Panama. These areas also produce some saltwater mollusks, red drum, pompano, and yellowtail. Freshwater species include rainbow trout and native species.

South American aquaculture developed somewhat parallel with that of Latin America. Chile and Peru produce mollusks. Chile placed greater emphasis on salmon production and was second in salmon production behind Norway by 2000. Production in South America now has major impact on world salmon and trout markets.

CONTRIBUTIONS OF AQUACULTURE

Aquaculture contributes to food supplies and the economy in several ways. These are briefly discussed here.

SOURCE OF HUMAN FOOD

The most important reason for aquaculture is to provide food for an expanding population. Some medical authorities support the health benefits of fish and seafood in the human diet. With a population in the United States of about 290 million people, aquafoods can be good sources of protein and other nutrients.

In the United States, per capita consumption of fish and seafood has been increasing, except in isolated years when there was a slight decline. For example, in 1910 per capita consumption of fish and shellfish was 11.2 pounds in the United States. This reached 15.2 pounds by 2000. An increasing share of this consumption has been from aquaculture, with wild catch declining. Even if per capita consumption remains constant, the total consumption will rise because of greater human population.

Table 1–3. Trends in Fish and Shellfish Consumption in the United States, Including Wild Catch and Aquaculture Products

Year	Per Capita (lb)	Year	Per Capita (lb)
1910	11.2	1960	10.3
1915	11.2	1965	10.9
1920	11.8	1970	11.7
1925	11.1	1975	12.1
1930	10.2	1980	12.4
1935	10.5	1985	15.0
1940	11.0	1990	14.9
1945	9.8	1995	14.8
1950	11.9	2000	15.2
1955	10.4		

Source: U.S. Department of Commerce / National Marine Fisheries Service, 2003.

Table 1–4. Fish and Shellfish Per Capita Consumption in Selected Nations (Live Weight)

Nation	Per Capita (lb)	Nation	Per Capita (lb)
Australia	45.0	Italy	50.5
Brazil	14.3	Japan	143.7
Canada	50.7	Kazakhstan	3.7
Chile	45.4	Mexico	21.2
China	53.8	New Zealand	66.1
Cuba	28.7	Norway	114.4
France	65.9	Somalia	5.3
Germany	28.2	Switzerland	32.0
Greenland	185.8	United Kingdom	44.8
Iceland	198.9	United States	46.7
Iraq	3.3		

Note: Pounds are in live weight before processing. Aquatic plants were included as applicable.

Source: Food and Agriculture Organization, United Nations, 2000.

VALUABLE NONFOOD PRODUCTS

Some aquaculture crops provide valuable nonfood products and by-products. Fine leather products are manufactured from eel skins and alligator hides. Cultured pearls from oysters are used in making valuable jewelry. Shells and skeleton parts may be incorporated into home and business decorations. Lower-quality, less-valuable shells may be used in paving roads or in ornamental landscaping. Educational programs may use frogs and other aquatic animals in the instructional process.

HUMAN HEALTH RESEARCH

Aquaculture helps with human health research. Some aquaculture animals are studied to try to understand the human body and how it functions. For example, the squid has been used in medical research since the early 1930s. Functions of the squid's nervous system have similarities to certain functions of the human nervous system. The University of Texas Medical School has been a leader in the use of squid in human research.

DEMAND FOR GRAIN CROPS

Feed for fish is often made from grain and by-products of grain processing. Soybeans and corn are widely used in feed. The result is greater demand for grain crops. This helps producers of grain find new markets.

1–19. Most commercial fish feed contains a number of farm-raised ingredients. (Read the label for details.)

JOBS AND ECONOMIC ACTIVITY

Many jobs are found in aquaculture. Thousands of people produce and market aquacrops. For example, one job is created in processing for every 20 acres of catfish ponds. Some 37,000 people are employed in the catfish industry

1–20. Many people have good jobs in fish processing and marketing. (Courtesy, U.S. Department of Agriculture)

1–21. Sport fishing is an important area of recreation.

alone. U.S. trout farmers received $58.3 million in 2002 for their crop. Catfish farmers in four states (Mississippi, Alabama, Arkansas, and Louisiana) received $386 million for their aquacrop in the same year. When the value from processing, merchandising, and restaurant sales is added, the economic impact is tremendous.

International trade involves several aquacrops, as well as captured fish and shellfish. Currently, 80 percent of the shrimp and 65 percent of the fish consumed in the United States are imported. Lobster, tuna, and frogs are examples of other imports. Some exporting also occurs. Crab and salmon are among the exports from the United States. Some catfish are exported.

RURAL AREA REVITALIZATION

Aquaculture can help revitalize rural areas. Many rural areas have experienced a decline in agricultural profits. People have quit farming traditional crops. A profitable aquacrop could stimulate the economy of an area.

RECREATION

The recreational aspects of aquaculture should be considered. People who sport fish are using fee-lakes stocked with cultured fish, particularly trout and catfish. The success of recreation fish-out ponds depends upon the convenience of the facilities to towns and cities. Management is needed to make the facilities attractive.

SCENIC BEAUTY

1–22. Aquaculture includes raising and keeping ornamental species. Goldfish in this bowl are being fed.

Scenic beauty can be enhanced with aquaculture. *Aquascaping* is the term applied to using aquaculture to add aesthetic beauty to an area. Work with wetlands in Florida has helped reclaim swampy areas and converted land into prime property. Underwater aquascaping has created tourist attractions. Aquatic ornamental plants and other features have been used in aquascaping.

WILD STOCK ENHANCEMENT

Aquaculture is used to raise fish and other species to release into streams, lakes, and oceans to replenish the wild population. Many state and federal government hatcheries release cultured fish into the wild of streams and lakes. This is often known as *stock enhancement.*

1–23. This Washington fish hatchery raises coho salmon for enhancing wild salmon populations.

RESEARCH AND DEVELOPMENT

Research and development (R&D) have been used to investigate and promote new practices in aquaculture. Much of the progress in growth of the aquaculture industry is based on R&D.

RESEARCH

Research is a systematic approach used to answer questions. The questions may be about production practices, biological processes, or water environments. The questions are carefully developed to reflect the scientific method.

Kinds of Research

Aquaculture research is of two major kinds: basic and applied. Basic research focuses on problems that may not have an immediate use. An example is research on the genetics of a particular fish species. The findings of basic research are often used in doing applied research. Improving fish stocks often involves using genetics information.

1–24. An example of research is the work underway on paddlefish at Kentucky State University.

1–25. The National Warmwater Aquaculture Center is a major source of research in aquaculture.

Applied research is used to answer questions or solve problems of aquaculture producers. The goal is to get information that will be useful immediately. An example would be to investigate the growth efficiency of fish when fed rations of varying levels or sources of protein. The goal would be to determine the protein level or source that promotes the most efficient growth.

Scientific Method

The *scientific method* is the step-by-step process of solving scientific questions or problems. It is composed of several steps:

- Identify a problem. (This is often based on the experiences of producers.)

- Investigate the problem. (Determine what other researchers have learned about the problem by reading books, journals, and Web sites and by other means.)

- Form a hypothesis. (A hypothesis is an educated guess about what will happen.)

- Design an experiment. (This is the method of testing a hypothesis.)

- Carry out the experiment. (This involves using precise methods and recording observations about what is happening.)

- Analyze the data and form conclusions. (This is examining what you observed and then making a judgment about your findings.)

- Report. (All research should be reported in an article or in some other way so that what is learned is shared with other people.)

Doing Research

Research is carried out by private companies, individuals, and research laboratories or experiment stations. These may also collaborate and share resources. For example, a feed manufacturer may contract with a research laboratory to investigate feed quality.

A major research facility is the National Warmwater Aquaculture Center (NWAC) in Stoneville, Mississippi. This facility has state-of-the-art facilities for carrying out research on problems faced by catfish producers. Both basic and applied research are conducted. The NWAC also has a diagnostic laboratory. This laboratory investigates diseases in catfish. Aquatic veterinarians perform analyses on fish tissues and recommend actions for controlling a disease outbreak or other problem. Often a producer will take a sick or dead fish to the laboratory for analysis.

A network of regional aquaculture centers has been established to help disseminate the findings of research to those who need it. These centers are shown in Figure 1–26.

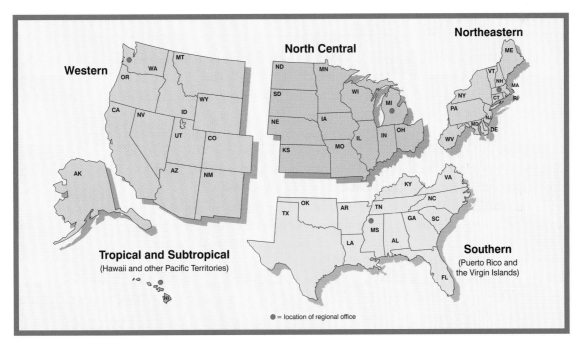

1–26. Regional aquaculture centers and areas served. The headquarters of each region is located as follows: Northeastern, University of Massachusetts; North Central, Michigan State University; Western, University of Washington; Southern, Delta Research and Extension Center; and Tropical and Subtropical, Oceanic Institute. (See Appendix B for more details.)

Development

Development is the use of information to create something new. The information often includes the findings of research. All areas of aquaculture have seen the results of development work—for example, in aerators, harvesters, and processing equipment.

Most development begins with an idea. Someone may wish to reduce the amount of hand labor required to process fish. Equipment is developed to take the place of the hand labor. An example is the development of a machine to remove the skin from fish. Such a machine has been in use for several years. The developer wanted a machine that would remove the skin without removing valuable meat. Automation in most of today's fish processing plants involves using this type of machine.

Many development ideas begin with the people who are involved in doing aquaculture work. The ideas lead to developments that help solve problems. The first paddle wheel aerator was likely developed because of the need to aerate large volumes of water very quickly and economically.

REVIEWING

MAIN IDEAS

Aquaculture is a source of food and other products. Various production systems are used to grow the crops. The species selected must be suited to the climate and production system.

Most aquacrops are used for one or more of five purposes: food, bait, recreation, ornamentals (or pets), and feed. By far, the most important use is food.

Cultured aquacrops have benefits over the wild captured aquatic species. The overall factor in deciding whether to go into aquaculture is profit. A producer must be able to sell a product for more than the cost of production. Imported fish sometimes depress prices. The International Trade Commission can impose tariffs on imported fish and shellfish.

The demand for aquacrops is increasing annually, resulting in a bright future for aquaculture. To be successful, a producer must learn as much as possible about the subject, make thorough plans, and follow sound management practices for the aquacrop selected. Assistance from authorities on aquaculture should be sought.

Research and development have been important in the emergence of aquaculture. Research is a systematic approach to get answers to questions. The scientific method is typically used by researchers. Information from research and practical experience is used to develop new ways or machines for doing work.

QUESTIONS

Answer the following questions, using complete sentences and correct spelling.

1. Contrast and compare aquaculture with traditional farming.
2. What are the five purposes for which fish may be produced?
3. What is an aquacrop?
4. Distinguish between cultured and captured fish.
5. Describe three advantages and three disadvantages of aquaculture.
6. Identify and describe five ways aquaculture production systems can be classified.

7. Where did aquaculture begin? How did it advance from its beginning?
8. Identify and explain nine ways aquaculture is important.
9. What is R&D? Why is it important in aquaculture?
10. What is the scientific method?

EVALUATING

Match the term with the correct definition. Write the letter of the term on the line provided.

a. polyculture   e. monoculture   i. research
b. mariculture   f. bait aquaculture   j. offshore aquaculture
c. aquaculture   g. ornamental aquaculture
d. water recirculation   h. production intensity

_____ 1. The production of aquatic plants and animals
_____ 2. The raising of small fish and other species used in catching other aquatic species
_____ 3. The keeping of fish, plants, and other species for aesthetic or personal appeal
_____ 4. The raising of species in saltwater
_____ 5. The density or crowding of an aquacrop being produced
_____ 6. The pumping of water back through the same water facility
_____ 7. The production of only one aquacrop species in a water facility
_____ 8. The production of two or more aquacrop species in a water facility
_____ 9. Aquaculture carried out in oceans away from land
_____ 10. A systematic approach in answering questions

EXPLORING

1. Tour an aquaculture facility in your area. Consider a hatchery, a fish farm, an ornamental fish store, or some other place where aquatic species are produced or marketed. Interview the manager to learn about the species. Use a digital camera to record interesting practices. Prepare a written report on your observations. Present an oral report in class. Supplement the report with electronic presentation of the images you made with the digital camera.

2. Visit the seafood department of a supermarket. Note the different products (species) on sale. Determine how the products have been prepared for sale to the consumer. Interview the person in charge of the department to learn how aquaculture products are refrigerated to prevent spoilage. Prepare a report on your observations.

3. Explore sources of aquaculture information. A good Web site with many links is the Aquaculture Network Information Center, also known as AquaNIC. The Web site address is **http://aquanic.org**. Prepare a report on your findings.

The Importance of Aquaculture

This chapter is about the importance of aquaculture in the United States. It has the following objectives:

1 Describe aquaculture as a food source

2 Explain the scope of aquaculture and the future potential

3 Describe consumption trends of aquaculture products

4 Explain the economic importance of aquaculture

5 Identify organizations in aquaculture

6 Identify research and educational agencies and programs in aquaculture

TERMS

agricultural education
commercial landing
consumption
high-density lipoprotein

high-density stocking
NMFS
NOAA
non-native species

omega-3 fatty acids
regulations
trade deficit
World Aquaculture Society

2–1. Live giant crab are for sale in this market. (Courtesy, National Oceanic and Atmospheric Administration)

AQUACULTURE products are popular foods. They give consumers safe, low-fat sources of essential nutrients. Restaurant consumption of aquaculture products has increased, along with home-prepared meals. New products are being used to help meet consumer demand.

Aquaculture is a business. Big business! Aquaculture production in the United States has a farm-gate value of nearly $1 billion a year. It provides jobs for an estimated 300,000 people in production and related industries.

Most experts feel that aquaculture will continue to expand in the United States. Several reasons support this contention: First, aquaculture produces a quality product. Second, fishery landings from oceans, lakes, and streams have declined somewhat while the demand for fish and seafood products has increased. Third, the health benefits of eating fish and seafood should result in a continued increase in demand for these products. Fourth, production technology is continuing to improve profit to producers.

AQUACULTURE AS A FOOD SOURCE

Consumer eating habits have been changing. Some people are switching from red meat to more fish, seafood, chicken, and turkey. Seafoods and other white meats have increasingly been recommended by health experts. White meat is lower in fat than other meat.

2–2. Cultured oysters are being shucked in this processing plant at Wilapa Bay, Washington. Aquaculture in the area creates many jobs and supports the community.

Newspapers, television, and magazines have contributed to this change in diet. Stories have focused on the health benefits of protein sources that are lower in fat. Aquacrops are often featured in the stories. Advertisements supporting aquacrops have also had a role in increased consumption.

Food scientists have found that fish and some other kinds of seafood have high levels of polyunsaturated fatty acids called **omega-3 fatty acids.** As a result, they have encouraged consumers to include more fish in their diets. Omega-3 fatty acids raise the level of **high-density lipoprotein** (HDL) ("good" cholesterol) in the blood and reduce the level of low-density lipoprotein (LDL) ("bad" cholesterol). Low-fat alternatives, such as poultry (with the skin removed) and veal, do not have this characteristic.

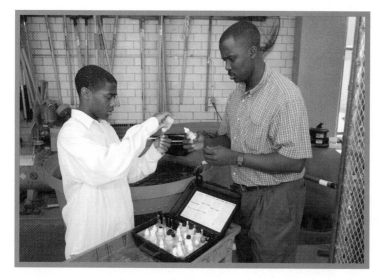

2–3. Water testing is used to assure water quality for food fish production.

Aquacrop foods are important because they fight high cholesterol levels. This helps prevent blocked arteries, heart attacks, and strokes.

The by-products of aquacrop processing are used in making feed for animals. The skin, internal organs, and other parts can be cooked and mixed with grain to increase protein content of feed. Research has shown that fish grow better if they get feed containing protein from a fish source!

Products of aquaculture may have an advantage over wild catch in terms of wholesomeness. Some wild fish and other aquatic organisms have been found to contain high levels of mercury, lead, and other pollutants. This is true also of sport fishing catches from lakes and streams, especially those subject to water runoff from areas where hazardous materials are found. Cultured fish and other species are raised in good-quality water that is normally free of hazardous substances.

Table 2–1. Per Capita Consumption of Seafoods in the United States*

Rank	Species	Per Capita (lb)
1	Shrimp	3.70
2	Tuna (canned)	3.10
3	Salmon	2.02
4	Pollock	1.13
5	Catfish	1.10
6	Cod	0.66
7	Crabs	0.57
8	Clams	0.55
9	Tilapia	0.40
10	Flatfish	0.32

*Includes wild catch and cultured fish and other aquatic foods.

Source: National Fisheries Institute, 2002.

SCOPE OF AQUACULTURE

For the past half-century, aquaculture has been the fastest growing sector in agriculture. Some years it has expanded at the rate of 20 percent. Part of the expansion is attributable to aquacrops being more profitable than traditional crops. In a few states, aquaculture production has been initiated to replace tobacco production.

Much of the growth in aquaculture has been in catfish production. Trout and salmon have also contributed to the increase. Several species just beginning to be cultured, such as tilapia and hybrid striped bass, are beginning to have impacts on production. Some increases have occurred in oysters, clams, and mussels. Increases in shrimp culture, including freshwater shrimp, have occurred.

2–4. Aquaculture got its start at fish hatcheries in the United States. The Issaquah Salmon Hatchery is a part of the Washington state system which began in 1895.

Offshore aquaculture of marine species has also created increased production with fish such as grouper and cobia.

Aquaculture in the United States is young compared with aquaculture in other countries. The United States is the fourth largest aquaculture-producing nation, behind China, Japan, and South Korea. These three nations have had aquaculture for hundreds of years.

Aquaculture production can have many facets. Here are three examples:

- Aquacrops may be produced as fingerlings to sell to food fish producers.
- Food fish producers raise fish on a large scale for processing or for on-the-farm retail sales in smaller amounts.
- Stocker fish may be raised for use in sport fishing lakes or to enhance populations in streams and lakes.

2–5. New technology in catfish harvesting reduces labor costs and helps assure a quality product from high-density stocking. (Courtesy, U.S. Department of Agriculture)

Several factors have contributed to the growth of aquaculture. These will likely continue to shape future growth. Three factors are

- Aquafarmers have learned to integrate vertically. (Vertical integration means that producers are also involved in feed manufacturing and in the processing of the fish.)
- Knowledge of reproductive physiology has made it possible to reproduce many fish.
- *High-density stocking* has been perfected. This allows crowding many more animals into a growing facility than would normally be found in nature.

SPECIES PRODUCED

Four species are most important in the United States: catfish, crawfish, trout, and salmon. These four account for 90 percent of U.S. aquaculture production, which is about 860 million pounds a year. Baitfish and ornamental fish are also important.

In 2003, nearly 1,000 farms produced catfish, with 190,000 acres in ponds. Production totaled 660 million pounds. Mississippi lead all states in catfish production, with 390 major producers having 110,000 acres in ponds. Alabama was next, with 245 major producers having 26,000 acres in ponds. Arkansas had fewer farms, but total acreage was larger, with 150 farms having 33,500 acres. Louisiana had 50 major catfish farms, with 10,000 acres in ponds. Other states with lesser production of catfish included Georgia, Texas, Oklahoma, Missouri, Tennessee, and California.

More than 60 million pounds of crawfish are produced each year, with most of the production in Louisiana. The value of crawfish is around $45 million annually.

Trout production in the United States averages almost 55 million pounds a year. Idaho is the leading state, with more than two thirds of the trout production, or 40 million pounds. North Carolina is second and is followed by Washington, California, and Pennsylvania. Trout are sold as food fish and for stocking in streams and lakes as replacements for fish caught by recreational fishers.

Pacific salmon production from aquaculture (both salmon farming and ranching) accounts for 20 to 30 million pounds a year. The commercial catch (also known as landing) of wild Pacific salmon is 600 million pounds a year. More than half the wild catch originates with private

2–6. Cobia (*Rachycentron canadum*) is a saltwater species increasingly cultivated. (This shows a female cobia used for spawning.) (Courtesy, National Oceanic and Atmospheric Administration)

Table 2–2. U.S. Aquaculture Production

Aquacrop	Weight (1,000 lb)	Value ($1,000)
Catfish	630,000	369,180
Crawfish	56,784	28,518
Trout	54,451	69,597*
Salmon	25,279	68,358
Oysters	24,399	76,139
Baitfish	20,574	63,033
Saltwater shrimp	6,614	26,455
Clams	6,125	12,096
Freshwater shrimp	350	2,006
Mussels	308	927
Ornamental fish	—	68,982
Other	24,713	194,727
Total value	—	978,012

*Includes value of eggs.

Source: Economic Research Service, U.S. Department of Agriculture, and Census of Agriculture. Data are primarily for 2002, though some are from earlier years.

and public hatcheries that release young fish to keep the stock from being depleted. Because of commercial landings, salmon is the major seafood export product of the United States.

Arkansas is the leading producer of baitfish. Some baitfish production occurs in many states, including Georgia and Missouri. Florida is the leading producer of ornamental fish.

Other aquacrops produced in the United States include tilapia, freshwater prawns, crabs, lobsters, mollusks (oysters, clams, mussels, and scallops), and gastropods. Coastal areas are often used for the culture of aquacrops requiring salt water, such as oysters and clams. More details on these and other species are given in later chapters.

The importance of aquaculture is expected to increase in the years ahead. Research will solve problems, resulting in more efficiency of production. Other species will likely increase in production in the United States, such as cobia, tilapia, redfish, hybrid striped bass, sturgeon, and walleye.

Table 2–3. Value of Aquaculture Products Sold, by Type and Region*

Aquaculture Product	Northeastern ($1,000)	Southern ($1,000)	North Central ($1,000)	Western ($1,000)	Tropical and Subtropical ($1,000)
Food fish	85,558	472,660	17,935	114,580	981
Baitfish	**	27,078	6,421	2,557	**
Ornamentals	5,130	58,578	2,844	1,740	690
Sport***	550	**	2,104	**	**
Crustaceans	2,361	27,164	**	**	5,499
Mollusks	26,758	24,712	**	36,606	**
Other animal aquaculture	5,619	22,846	**	14,548	**
Regional totals	125,976	633,038	29,304	170,031	7,170

*States in regions:

Northeastern—Connecticut, Delaware, Maine, Maryland, Massachusetts, New Hampshire, New Jersey, New York, Pennsylvania, Rhode Island, Vermont, and West Virginia

Southern—Alabama, Arkansas, Florida, Georgia, Kentucky, Louisiana, Mississippi, North Carolina, Oklahoma, South Carolina, Tennessee, Texas, and Virginia

North Central—Illinois, Indiana, Iowa, Kansas, Michigan, Minnesota, Missouri, Nebraska, North Dakota, Ohio, South Dakota, and Wisconsin

Western—Alaska, Arizona, California, Colorado, Idaho, Montana, Nevada, New Mexico, Oregon, Utah, Washington, and Wyoming

Tropical and Subtropical—Hawaii and island territories

**Not reported or insufficient data to include.

***Includes sport and game fish as permitted in aquaculture.

Source: 1998 Census of Aquaculture, USDA.

CONSUMPTION TRENDS

Consumption is the amount of a food people eat and of other products they use. Compared with people in other countries, people in the United States consume low amounts of fish and seafood. However, consumption is increasing. It went from 12 pounds a year in 1970 to nearly 15 pounds in 2003. At the same time, red meat consumption declined.

Why have people in the United States traditionally consumed less fish and seafood than people in many other nations? A productive agriculture has likely been a big factor—people have not had to use products from streams, lakes, and oceans for food. Sometimes, the products have not been available because people have not lived near a body of water. In other cases, people have not known how to prepare fish and seafood.

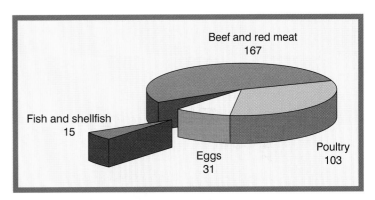

2–7. Per capita consumption of selected meat and egg products in the United States, in pounds.

PROXIMITY TO FISH AND SEAFOOD

People who live close to sources of fresh fish and seafood eat more of these foods than people who do not live near streams, lakes, or oceans. The increased consumption is probably of wild catch. Those who live in areas where aquaculture is practiced eat an increased amount of cultured fish.

2–8. A primary requirement of aquaculture is an abundant supply of suitable water. Salmon returning upstream to hatch must negotiate this "step" in the Cowlitz River in Washington State.

Table 2-4. Percentage of Animal Protein in Human Diet from Fish and Seafood for Selected Countries

Country	Fish as a Percentage of Animal Protein
Indonesia	67.9
Philippines	56.7
Bangladesh	52.2
Thailand	51.5
Malaysia	41.6
China	33.0
India	15.1
U.S.	8.4

Source: U.N. Food and Agriculture Organization, Rome, Italy.

The United States is a large nation, and many people do not live near natural bodies of water in which fish and other aquatic food grow. Before refrigeration was popular, fish could not be stored very long without spoiling. Good transportation helps in getting fresh fish products to people over long distances.

Improved methods of keeping fish fresh or frozen and quickly distributing it to the inland areas have increased the amount of fish eaten in these areas. Almost every supermarket in the United States now has a good selection of fresh and frozen fish and seafood products.

ALTERNATIVES TO FISH AND SEAFOOD CONSUMPTION

Some people have not eaten fish and seafood because they had a good supply of beef, pork, and other meats. These products were often priced below fish, especially in the midwestern United States. People without water facilities can produce beef, pork, and other meats for themselves.

As the nutritional benefits of fish and seafood have been recognized, and with improved availability, people are finding aquaculture products a good alternative. People are learning more about how to prepare these foods. With better-tasting foods, consumption will increase.

PROMOTIONAL EFFORTS

Another reason the consumption of aquacrops is expected to increase is the promotional efforts by aquaculture groups. Promotion involves encouraging people to consume fish and shellfish. This may be through advertising, price incentives, development of new recipes, and other means.

An example of promotion is that done by The Catfish Institute. As the informational arm of the Catfish Farmers of America, The Catfish Institute promotes catfish as a delicacy. Its promotional campaigns throughout the United States have lead to a wider acceptance of catfish in many fine restaurants and an increased market demand for the product. For additional information on The Catfish Institute, go to **www.catfishinstitute.com/**.

ECONOMIC PERSPECTIVE

The future of aquaculture in the United States looks very promising. Because Americans will be eating more fish and seafood as part of a healthier diet, the demand for these products will grow. As a result, the supply of fish and seafood must increase to meet the demand. The increase in supply might come from an increase in *commercial landing*, which is wild fish caught in their natural habitat but not cultured. The increase in supply might also come from an increase in imports from other countries or from an increase in aquaculture production in this country.

Aquaculture is providing an increasing percentage of the total supply of fish and seafood in the United States. The volume of catfish from aquaculture exceeds 90 percent. For salmon, the volume is 70 percent. The figure for trout, tilapia, shrimp, and other species is probably well above 50 percent, though the production history of the amount imported into the United States is unknown. Several factors suggest that aquaculture will play a much larger role if the demand for fish and seafood continues to increase. Here are some reasons for the future expansion of aquaculture:

- Increased per person consumption of fish and seafood
- Increased overall population in the United States and worldwide
- Depletion of reserves of wild fish in the oceans and in streams
- Trade deficit of the United States with other nations
- Improved aquaculture techniques that will make production more efficient
- Better knowledge about how to prepare fish and seafood
- Promotional programs to increase consumption

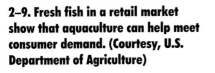

2–9. Fresh fish in a retail market show that aquaculture can help meet consumer demand. (Courtesy, U.S. Department of Agriculture)

IMPORTED FISH AND SEAFOOD

Since the mid-1960s, the United States has relied on other countries for more than half its edible seafood. During 2002, the U.S. Department of Agriculture reported that more fish and seafood were imported than exported. This leaves a negative in the balance of trade. An increase in aquaculture production in the United States could lower this *trade deficit,* the situation that occurs when more is imported than exported.

Shrimp leads the list of imports. Some 850 million pounds were imported in 2003, with a value of $3 billion. The demand for shrimp has increased in recent years. Landings of wild catch by the United States have decreased. Cultured shrimp production has not kept pace in the United States. As one example, food leader General Mills, the parent company of Red Lobster and Olive Garden restaurants, may import shrimp from as many as 40 different countries in one year. The potential for culturing shrimp and prawns appears strong. Better production techniques will expand their culture in the United States.

2–10. The freshwater prawn could replace some imported shrimp in seafood markets. Better production techniques are needed. Prawns grow well and to a good size.

Imports of tilapia have increased greatly and were up 43 percent in the first half of 2003 alone! Tilapia only became important enough in 1995 for the United States to begin keeping records. Total imports in 2003 were about 380 million pounds on a liveweight basis.

Importation of Atlantic salmon has been steady over the last few years. About 213 million pounds were imported in 2003.

Mollusks are characterized by both imports and exports. Some 10 million pounds of oysters, mussels, and clams were exported in 2003. At the same time, oyster and clam imports were up slightly at about 14 million pounds.

Some increase has been seen in the importation of ornamental fish, with a value of about $44 million in 2003. Some ornamental fish were exported, though the value was only about half that of imports.

2–11. The alligator is a species that holds potential in aquaculture for skins and meat.

ROLE OF AQUACULTURE IN MEETING INCREASED DEMAND

A worldwide shortage of fish and seafood has been predicted, according to officials of the Food and Agriculture Organization in Rome, Italy. New ways of producing fish and seafood should be developed to meet the demand. Some experts believe that aquaculture has the potential to meet at least 25 percent of the demand in the United States for shrimp and salmon. Other aquacrops can replace some major imported seafoods.

2–12. Eel culture is carried out in some areas and will expand to meet worldwide demands.

REDUCING FISHERY IMPORTS

Aquaculture can play a role in reducing the trade deficit in the United States. Export markets for trout, salmon, and catfish can help. Increasing demand for fishery products and higher incomes throughout the world will expand seafood demand.

Increased shrimp production can also help reduce the trade deficit. Because of their popularity as a food, shrimp are imported by processors and retailers.

The share of seafood consumption of domestic fish landings dropped 2 percent a year in the United States during the 1980s. The ocean supply of edible fish and seafood is near or at its maximum yield. This means that aquaculture has an opportunity to make up for the shortfall in wild fish catch.

BENEFITS OF AQUACULTURE

Providing a quality product on a year-round basis will continue to make aquacrops strong in the fish and seafood market. As oceans and streams become more polluted, the public will

2–13. Crawfish production benefits communities by creating jobs. (This shows crawfish being harvested on a Louisiana farm.) (Courtesy, U.S. Department of Agriculture)

become suspicious of fish and seafood from commercial landings. Many people will turn to aquacrops grown in clean water and fed a proper diet. In some areas, labeling aquacrops as such has resulted in willingness by consumers to pay higher prices.

Aquacrops can be planned for harvest on a year-round basis. This will provide processors and consumers products throughout the year. The availability of year-round products is important to restaurants, which like to keep an item on the menu all the time and not just "in season." Grocery stores and supermarkets also like the stability of being able consistently to offer a quality product to their customers.

RURAL ECONOMIC DEVELOPMENT THROUGH AQUACULTURE

Some rural areas in the United States have been depressed. Jobs have vanished, and people have moved away. Other rural areas have used aquaculture to revitalize the local economy. The success of a few producers often causes an industry to begin to develop and grow.

2–14. Aquaculture contributes to the economy of many areas. (This illustrates the importance of oyster culture in the South Bend, Washington, area.)

An excellent example of how aquaculture helps in rural economic development involves the catfish industry in the Mississippi River Delta. When the catfish industry began in the early 1970s, this was one of the poorest income regions in the nation. The catfish industry has brought jobs and new sources of income.

Mississippi alone now produces more than 300 million pounds of edible catfish each year. For every 10 million pounds of fish produced, 200 jobs are created in production and processing. Another 1,000 jobs are created in support industries, such as feed and equipment, services, transporting, and marketing.

OTHER BENEFITS OF AQUACULTURE

Besides producing an aquacrop for a profit, many producers have discovered other benefits of including aquaculture as part of their agricultural enterprise. Producers who use wastewater from fish operations to irrigate and fertilize their row crops and pastures realize even greater benefits from aquaculture than normal.

In Arizona, for example, producers can use irrigation and aquaculture combinations. The water can initially be used for growing fish in raceways and then, when nutrient rich, be used to irrigate crops.

LIMITATIONS TO GROWTH

Although the future of aquaculture looks promising, there are some limitations to the expansion. The main limitations are the high initial investment, lack of water, and regulations affecting aquaculture.

2–15. Dishes containing cultured pearls are shown beside an open oyster. (Courtesy, National Oceanic and Atmospheric Administration)

Though much progress has been made with some species, the lack of technology for producing many aquacrops is also a limitation. Production techniques for many possible aquacrops are still in the development stages. As a result, the production of some crops is risky. Many people are concerned about investing money before these techniques are perfected. Limitations on producing some species are covered later in the book.

AQUACULTURE ORGANIZATIONS

Associations have been important in the early development of the aquaculture industry in the United States. These associations will continue to fill important roles, especially when producers join together for a unified voice to the public and to government officials. An association with a large membership will have more power than individuals alone.

ROLES AND PURPOSES OF ORGANIZATIONS

Why are organizations important? They help people meet their needs in the aquaculture industry. Organizations have four roles:

1. Promoting products produced by members
2. Educating members about regulations and practices
3. Effecting policy related to their members and enterprises
4. Providing opportunities for the members to interact with each other

An effective organization usually has an elected board and officers made up of members. The board develops the policies of the organization, with approval of the members, and then develops a plan of work to carry out the policies. An administrative staff is often hired to oversee the everyday operations and to carry out the policies of the organization.

The organization must choose which issues to address. Some possible issues include promotion of aquacrops, international trade, market development, food safety, and government regulations.

EXAMPLES OF AQUACULTURE ORGANIZATIONS

Aquaculture producers can choose from a wide range of associations. Some represent the general area of aquaculture; others represent a particular species or interest. The associations may have international, national, regional, or state interests.

The **World Aquaculture Society** (WAS) is an international association for the promotion of aquaculture. Its main function is as a source of information and a representative of aquaculture interests around the world.

The National Aquaculture Association (NAA) represents all types of aquaculture. Leaders of other organizations that represent specific aquacrops formed the NAA to provide a unified voice for aquaculture in the United States.

Several species-specific associations also exist at the national level. These include the United States Trout Farmers Association, the Catfish Farmers of America, the American Tilapia Association, and the Striped Bass Growers Association.

In a state where a particular aquacrop is prevalent, a state association may be formed. Examples include the Catfish Farmers of Arkansas and the New York Trout Farmers Association. State associations usually affiliate with a national counterpart organization.

RESEARCH AND EDUCATIONAL AGENCIES AND PROGRAMS

Future expansion of aquaculture requires research and education. Government agencies and private industry are now involved in these areas. Research finds answers to questions; education disseminates the information to people who can use it.

RESEARCH AGENCIES

Universities and government agencies are leaders in aquaculture research. The research is often carried out in collaboration with private industry. Agricultural experiment stations in universities conduct research in disease control, nutrition, genetics, reproduction, product quality, facilities, and overall production systems.

Two federal agencies are involved in aquaculture research: the U.S. Department of the Interior and the U.S. Department of Agriculture. The Fish Farming Experimental Station in Arkansas operates through the Fish and Wildlife Service of the Department of the Interior.

The U.S. Department of Agriculture, through its Agricultural Research Service, promotes research into areas of aquaculture and collaborates with universities. The USDA also has five regional aquaculture centers, each of which coordinates research in the region

2–16. Researchers at the University of Maryland are shown investigating the use of artificial conditions to hatch oysters. (Courtesy, Agricultural Research Service, USDA)

2–17. An aquaculture scientist in Hawaii is showing the first harvest of moi from offshore cages in Hawaii. (Courtesy, National Oceanic and Atmospheric Administration)

served. Sea grant programs are operated in many coastal states and investigate some aquaculture topics.

EDUCATIONAL AGENCIES AND PROGRAMS

The two primary government-sponsored educational efforts are the Cooperative Extension Service and agricultural education in the public schools. Many states have aquaculture specialists on the staff of the Cooperative Extension Service. These specialists, along with local extension agents, provide informal education in aquaculture.

Agricultural education programs usually focus on formal classroom instruction in high schools, vocational centers, and community colleges. These programs may provide adult and young adult instruction.

REGULATORY AGENCIES

Various government agencies regulate aquaculture at the federal, state, and local levels. The regulations impact where and how an individual can go into aquaculture and how the business can be operated. *Regulations* are the interpretations by agencies of laws that have been enacted. A knowledge of regulations is needed before initiating aquaculture production. This information is available from different government agencies.

Federal Agencies

Several federal departments and agencies within the departments have responsibilities in aquaculture.

Besides supporting research and education, the U.S. Department of Agriculture regulates some areas of aquaculture. A main concern of the USDA is fish and seafood inspection. The inspection is to provide wholesome food products for consumers. The National Agricultural Statistics Service (NASS) within the USDA collects data on aquaculture production and issues reports. The USDA operates the Animal Welfare Information Center, which is concerned with the well-being of fish, shellfish, and other aquatic animals.

The Fish and Wildlife Service is a part of the U.S. Department of the Interior. The Service primarily focuses on natural populations of fish in lakes, streams, and coastal areas. In the past, it operated a number of hatcheries to provide fingerlings for stocking streams. Private hatcheries have replaced the federal fish hatcheries in most areas.

NOAA (the National Oceanic and Atmospheric Administration) has considerable responsibility for seafood and non-seafood products, including wild and mariculture harvest. **NMFS** (the National Marine Fisheries Service) is a part of NOAA and promotes sound mariculture practices. NMFS has developed a Code of Conduct for Responsible Aquaculture Development in the U.S. Exclusive Economic Zone. The focus is on the territorial waters outside the jurisdiction of the coastal states. The Code was released in 2002. Major provisions of the Code include a three-part strategy:

2–18. Students in a Texas high school aquaculture class are examining samples of fish raised in a tank that uses recirculated water.

2–19. All regulations, such as wearing a hairnet, must be met in processing plants to provide wholesome food.

1. Develop and implement environmentally sound aquaculture technologies and practices

2. Promote commercial breeding of at least seven new aquaculture species

3. Identify areas in coastal waters and the Exclusive Economic Zone suitable for environmentally sound aquaculture development

NOAA also includes The Fisheries Statistics and Economics Division, which collects information about fish, shellfish, and other aquatic species, primarily mariculture and wild harvest. The Seafood Inspection Program provides inspection services to assure compliance with all applicable food regulations. The Program can also apply official marks to seafood, such as "U.S. Grade A" and "Processed Under Federal Inspection (PUFI)." NOAA also collects and reports weather information as related to seafood. The National Sea Grant Program unites NOAA with 30 state Sea Grant programs and 200 universities. Sea Grant deals with scientific discovery, technology transfer, and other areas related to seafood and mariculture.

2–20. The National Oceanic and Atmospheric Administration assists offshore producers to assure a quality product and minimal environmental problems. This shows an offshore cage near an oil rig in the Gulf of Mexico. (Courtesy, National Oceanic and Atmospheric Administration)

The Food and Drug Administration (FDA) is concerned with the use of drugs to prevent disease in aquacrops and how these drugs affect the aquacrops. Before a drug can be legally sold for use with food fish, the use must be approved by the FDA. For example, the FDA ruled in 2003 to approve the use of formalin in a water bath for the control of certain external parasites on finfish and shrimp and fungi on finfish eggs.

The Environmental Protection Agency (EPA) regulates the use of pesticides and approves their use on certain aquacrops. The main problems with using pesticides in aquaculture are concerns over residues in the harvested product and over the effects of the runoff on streams and lakes in the area.

The U.S. Army Corps of Engineers is concerned with wetlands protection, among other areas. To construct an aquaculture pond or raceway, the owner must often obtain a wetlands permit from the Corps of Engineers. The Corps works with individuals and state agencies to assure proper development of wetlands.

The U.S. Department of Labor (DOL) regulates the use of hired labor in aquaculture. Aquaculture is defined as agriculture by the DOL. Therefore, aquaculture must comply with the same regulations.

The U.S. Department of Commerce promotes fair trade and practices in aquaculture and seafood marketing. This role is particularly important in protecting U.S. aquaculture from unfair competition from imported fish and other aquatic crops.

State and Local Agencies

Agencies regulating aquaculture at the state level vary, depending on the state and the nature and scope of aquaculture in that state. At the state level, departments of agriculture, commerce, health, and wildlife may be involved in some way.

State agencies generally focus their efforts on the regulation of ground and surface water use, pollution by discharges from an aquaculture facility, building and construction, and control of non-native species.

State agencies must often balance the interests of citizens groups with those of aquaculture. Environmental groups are concerned with the effects of aquaculture on the environment and on endangered species. Recreational boaters and fishers often do not want public lakes, streams, and coastal waters used for aquaculture.

Local government agencies often have regulations that influence aquaculture. Most county and city governments have planning and zoning commissions. Regulations may exist on drilling wells and using water from lakes.

Aquaculture producers must comply with legal regulations. Doing so is sometimes a formidable task.

EXAMPLE OF GOVERNMENT REGULATIONS

Suppose Mary Jones wants to begin aquaculture production using ponds and drilling a well for water. She will likely need to get permits from several state agencies beforehand. Mary will also need zoning and building permits from local agencies.

CONNECTION

CANNERY ROW: WHEN NATURE RUNS OUT

Monterey, California, was once a major canning area for sardines and other fish. The area prompted John Steinbeck to write a book about life in the fishing and canning industry titled *Cannery Row*. The water of the Pacific Ocean yielded many large catches. But, too many were taken, and nature ran out of fish!

Today, Monterey is mostly a resort area for tourists. Old canneries are now shops and museums. The tradition of a bountiful catch of wild fish is mostly a dream. The fishing heritage is used in naming restaurants and other local businesses.

Because Mary's farm will have some discharged water, she will need an NPDES (National Pollutant Discharge Elimination System) permit. To get one, Mary will have to apply to the Bureau of Pollution Control, usually located in the state Department of Natural Resources.

Mary's water needs require a well with a pipe of more than 6 inches in diameter. To drill a well this large, she will need a ground water use permit. This permit will also likely be available from the state Department of Natural Resources. She will also need a surface water permit for her ponds, especially when they are drained.

To build ponds, Mary will need a dam construction permit. This is available from the state agency that handles the ground water use permit. Some states exempt shallow ponds from the permit requirement.

Mary may need approval for the species to be produced. A permit to grow a non-native species is usually available from a state wildlife conservation office. (A *non-native species* is one that does not naturally grow in the area. Sometimes, a non-native species poses threats to the native species if it gets into streams and lakes. An example is tilapia. In warm climates, tilapia tend to destroy the native habitat in natural bodies of water.) If Mary operates a fee-lake, she will also need to get retail business permits and other licenses that may be required.

REVIEWING

MAIN IDEAS

The United States needs aquaculture to meet the growing demand for fish and seafood caused by changes in dietary habits. Its people are eating more fish and seafood! This increased demand cannot be met on a sustained basis by commercial landings or increased imports.

Aquaculture is the fastest growing agriculture industry in the United States. The main food aquacrops are catfish, crawfish, trout, and salmon. These four crops account for 90 percent of the aquaculture production in the United States. The baitfish and ornamental fish industries are also important.

A continued increase in aquaculture will lower the federal trade deficit and allow U.S. money to be used for U.S.-produced goods and services.

For aquaculture to continue to expand, producer associations must be supported by producers and must take an active role in promoting the benefits of aquaculture. Government agencies that regulate aquaculture must take a supportive stance.

QUESTIONS

Answer the following questions, using complete sentences and correct spelling.

1. What are the nutritional benefits of including more fish and seafood in the diets of Americans?
2. What percentage of edible fish and seafood in the United States is supplied by aquaculture?
3. What are the four major aquacrops in the United States?
4. What is the trend in the consumption of aquaculture products?
5. How can aquaculture help to reduce the national trade deficit?
6. What are the important economic advantages of aquaculture?
7. What roles can producer associations have in aquaculture?
8. What federal agencies have roles in aquaculture?
9. What are the three major strategies of the Code of Conduct for Responsible Aquaculture Development?
10. Contrast the value of food fish, baitfish, and ornamental fish of the region in which you live with the other regions. (Refer to Table 2–3.)

EVALUATING

Match the term with the correct definition. Write the letter of the term on the line provided.

a. agricultural education
b. commercial landings
c. consumption
d. high-density stocking
e. non-native species
f. omega-3 fatty acids
g. regulations
h. trade deficit
i. NMFS
j. NOAA

_____ 1. Good cholesterol that fights bad cholesterol

_____ 2. Interpretations of laws

_____ 3. A negative difference between imports and exports

_____ 4. The placing of more organisms into an environment than would exist in nature

_____ 5. Formal instruction in agriculture at the high school or community college level

_____ 6. Wild fish caught in their natural habitat with no culture involved

_____ 7. The amount of food and other products used or eaten by people

_____ 8. A species that does not naturally grow in the local area

_____ 9. The abbreviation for National Oceanic and Atmospheric Administration

_____ 10. The abbreviation for National Marine Fisheries Service

EXPLORING

1. Assume you are starting an aquaculture production facility in your community. Identify the regulatory agencies you will need to get permits from before starting production. Obtain an example of each application you will need to complete. (You may want to talk to an aquafarmer in your community or to a local wildlife officer and contact the state Department of Agriculture.)

2. Go to the USDA–Economic Research Service Web site (**www.econ.ag.gov/pubs/**). View a current "Aquaculture Situation and Outlook" report. Prepare a report that summarizes what you observed.

3. Invite a local aquafarmer to serve as a resource person in class. Ask the person to explain production practices, describe facility needs, and tell what it takes to get started in aquaculture.

PART TWO

The Science of Aquaculture

Taxonomy, Habitat, and Genetics

This chapter covers the classification of aquatic species and basic genetic information. It has the following objectives:

1 Describe the taxonomy of aquatic species

2 Classify important aquaculture species

3 Describe general habitat considerations as related to species

4 Discuss genetic potentials in aquaculture

5 Explain the use of genetically improved species

TERMS

allele	gene	Osteichthyes
bivalve mollusk	genetic code	phenotype
breed	genetic engineering	recessive trait
breeding	genetics	selection
chromosome	genotype	strain
cloning	habitat	taxonomic name
crustacean	heredity	taxonomy
decapod	heterozygous	transgenic fish
DNA	homozygous	transgenic organism
DNA sequencing	hybridization	variety
dominant trait	hybrid vigor	zoeae
gastropod	marker-assisted selection	

3–1. A hybrid striped bass in a Delaware pond is being examined for growth and development. (Courtesy, Agricultural Research Service, USDA)

SCIENTISTS have discovered more than 24,000 species of fish. Each year new species are found. In addition, there are thousands of species of crustaceans, mollusks, aquatic plants, and other aquatic organisms. Keeping all these species classified in some way for ease of reference and study requires sophisticated systems of taxonomy.

Besides its use in classification, information about species can be used to improve and develop desired qualities. Newer methods in genetics are being used along with the well-established approaches for improving fish stocks. Today's aquaculturists are benefitting from these advances.

A basic understanding of taxonomy and genetics is important to successful aquaculture. Without this knowledge, scientific names and genetic traits will have little meaning.

53

TAXONOMY OF AQUATIC SPECIES

Whenever a number of items becomes too large to remember easily, people search out some orderly way to classify the items. More than 1.5 million species of living organisms are known to exist. Therefore, scientists have developed a system to classify animals, plants, and other living things.

3–2. A species of flying fish. Note its unique features. (Courtesy, National Oceanic and Atmospheric Administration)

Taxonomy is a system of arranging organisms into groups. It is also known as scientific classification. Taxonomy is based on relationships between living things. Some people refer to taxonomy as systematics. Similarities and differences are factors in taxonomy. Obviously, a pine tree and a catfish have little in common, but what about a catfish and an oyster?

Scientific classification groups living organisms so it is easy to tell what is the same and what is different about them. While the differences are usually noticed first, the similarities show up more than the differences after some study.

People have long tried to classify organisms. Ancient systems have been replaced with modern systems that involve greater insight into the biological makeup of organisms.

3–3. Fiddler crabs (*Uca* spp.) are being raised at the Gulf Specimen Marine Laboratory in Florida.

EARLY SYSTEMS

The early scientific classification systems classified all living organisms as either plants or animals. An organism was placed in either the animal kingdom (Animalia) or the plant kingdom (Plantae). Single-celled organisms, such as bacteria, paramecia, and fungi, were classified into one of these two kingdoms, depending on the scientist doing the work.

MODERN SYSTEMS

Modern scientific classification systems have five kingdoms. A widely accepted classification used today places all organisms with complete cells into these kingdoms: Monera, Protista, Fungi, Plantae, and Animalia. A sixth group contains the viruses. Viruses do not have complete cells as do organisms in the other kingdoms.

Each kingdom is further broken down into six stages, based on differences and similarities. The classification structure is

> Kingdom
> > Phylum or Division
> > > Class
> > > > Order
> > > > > Family
> > > > > > Genus
> > > > > > > Species

Organisms become progressively similar in moving from kingdom to species. The kingdom is the broadest group. The species is the most specific group. Scientists have established additional differences within species to accommodate genetically improved organisms.

Each organism is classified into these seven principal areas. Most classifications are further differentiated by sub or super categories; for example, a subphylum (subordinate to a phylum) would be between a phylum and a class, and a superorder (superior to an order) would be between a class and an order. These classifications may be different, based on the particular system used. For this book, the species are classified into the seven principal areas only.

A *variety* is a group of related organisms within a species with some unique characteristics but whose differences are not great enough to warrant another species. Varieties are often developed to create or improve desired traits within a species. Many times this involves breeding selected individuals with the desired traits. The term *variety* is most often applied to plants, including terrestrial and aquatic plants.

3–4. Four species of trout are shown here (top to bottom): lake trout (*Salvelinus namaycush*), rainbow trout (*Oncorhynchus mykiss*), brown trout (*Salmo trutta*), and coho trout (*Oncorhynchus kisutch*). (Courtesy, Center for Great Lakes and Aquatic Sciences)

A **strain** is a group of organisms developed with similar traits to achieve a desired goal. Members of a strain have a common background and are not taxonomically distinct from other members of a species. However, members of a strain are distinguishable on the basis of productivity, vigor, resistance to disease or environmental problems, or some other characteristics. *Strain* is the term most often applied to fish and other aquatic animals.

A **breed** is a group of animals of the same species with distinct and similar features that are passed on to offspring. Breeds often emerge from careful efforts to develop unique organisms within a species. Breeds are particularly important with agricultural animals, such as hogs and cattle. Increasingly, scientists are working to improve aquatic animals, such as fish, so that particular bloodlines may one day be known as breeds.

KINGDOMS

Each of the five kingdoms has unique characteristics that make it possible to place every known organism into one of the kingdoms. The kingdoms are

- Monera—The Monera kingdom contains very primitive organisms—cells without membranes, such as bacteria and blue-green algae. Organisms in this kingdom are often called monerans. About 5,000 species of monerans have been identified. Members of this kingdom are present all around us. We often cannot see them without magnification. We know that they may cause disease and that they help restore the environment by decomposing organic matter. We also know that they are sometimes factors that cause water to be unfit for aquaculture.

3–5. Algae are being cultured in these tanks for feeding to larval fish. Algae are difficult to classify. Blue-green algae, usually placed in the Monera kingdom, are sometimes considered to be in the Protista kingdom; all others are in the Protista kingdom. (Courtesy, National Oceanic and Atmospheric Administration)

- Protista—The Protista kingdom contains single-celled and very primitive multicelled organisms, such as slime molds, protozoa, and primitive fungi. Some protists form collections of cells that resemble plants and animals. More than 65,000 organisms have been classified as protists. Seaweed (algae) is an aquatic crop valued for food and other uses. Plankton in water has major impacts on the water's use. Some types of plankton make water unsatisfactory for aquaculture. Other types of plankton add oxygen and improve the quality of water for aquaculture.

- Fungi—The Fungi kingdom consists of yeasts, mildews, and mushrooms. Some fungi cause disease, such as infections in fish. Other fungi are floating and suspended in water. Some fungi may be food sources for aquatic organisms.

3–6. Kalo (*Colocasia esculenta*) is a species of wetland taro grown in Hawaii.

- Plantae—The Plantae kingdom is composed of plants that produce their own food through photosynthesis. Several species of plants are important in aquaculture. These are covered in more detail later in the book.

- Animalia—The Animalia kingdom is made up of multicellular animals. Fish and many other aquatic organisms in aquaculture are in the Animalia kingdom. Animals are further classified based on similarities and differences, resulting in phylums, such as Mollusca, Arthropoda, and Chordata. The Chordata are divided into subphylums. Those that are vertebrates (i.e., have backbones) include the common fish species produced in aquaculture. Several chapters in this book are devoted to the production of aquatic animals.

This chapter focuses on the Plantae and Animalia kingdoms, although some organisms in the other kingdoms play important roles in aquaculture. Some single-celled organisms make up the primary food source for aquacrops. Others, most notably blue-green algae, play an important part in oxygenating the water in which aquacrops are grown.

CLASSIFICATION AND TAXONOMIC NAMES

In books and reports, most species are referred to by their common names and their taxonomic (scientific) names. A ***taxonomic name*** is the scientific name of an organism based on its genus and species. Taxonomic names are written in italics or are underlined. Usually only the first letter of the first word of a name is capitalized.

As scientists learn more about plants and animals, taxonomic names sometimes change. A good example of this is the rainbow trout.

In books written 20 years ago, the rainbow trout was classified as *Salmo gairdneri*. This made it a member of the same genus as the brown trout and the Atlantic salmon. Although some classifications of the rainbow trout have kept this designation, most new classifications now have the rainbow trout as part of the same genus as the Pacific salmon. The scientific name for the rainbow trout is now *Oncorhynchus mykiss*.

CLASSIFICATION OF IMPORTANT AQUACULTURE SPECIES

Some of the important species of aquacrops and those deemed to have potential as important species in the future are presented in Figures 3–8, 3–11, 3–13, 3–15, 3–17, 3–19, and 3–29. Those that have the same kingdom, phylum, and order are grouped together. A brief phrase is given to help explain the classification area. When the same genus is referred to consecutively, it is abbreviated by the first letter, as is common scientific practice. For example, two similar species are *Salmo salar* (Atlantic salmon) and *S. trutta* (*Salmo trutta*, or brown trout). The species name is usually lowercase, while the genus and other classifications usually begin with capital letters.

Fish

All the freshwater, saltwater, and brackish-water fish, ornamental fish, and baitfish that are important to aquaculture belong to the class Osteichthyes. Every member of the **Osteichthyes** class has a skeleton with true bones, a skull with sutures, teeth (if present) usually fused to the bones, nasal openings on each side, premaxillae and maxillae, and a swim bladder or a functional lung. The fish in this order are sometimes known as bony fish or finfish.

Catfish

Ictalurus punctatus (channel catfish) is the most important species in the order Siluriformes, which means catfish. Several other species of catfish are cultured for both food and sport and as ornamentals. The channel catfish and its culture are further discussed in Chapter 12.

3–7. A 6-inch channel catfish fingerling shows major identifying characteristics of the species when it is mature.

Scientific Classification of Freshwater Food Fish

Kingdom—Animalia (animals)
Phylum—Chordata (with spinal cord)
Class—Osteichthyes (bony fish)

Channel Catfish:

Order—Siluriformes (catfish)
Family—Ictaluridae (freshwater catfish)
Genus—*Ictalurus* (catfish)
Species—*punctatus* (spotted or channel)

Rainbow Trout:

Order—Salmoniformes (maxilla in gape of mouth)
Family—Salmonidae (salmon)
Genus—*Oncorhynchus*
Species—*mykiss (rainbow trout)*

Brown Trout:

Order—Salmoniformes
Family—Salmonidae
Genus—*Salmo*
Species—*trutta* (brown trout)

Walleye:

Order—Perciformes (very diverse, scaly fish)
Family—Percidae
Genus—*Stizostedion*
Species—*vitreum*

Tilapia:

Order—Perciformes
Family—Cichlidae (cichlids)
Genus—*Tilapia*
Species—*aurea* (blue), *mossambica* (Java)

Hybrid Striped Bass:

Order—Perciformes
Family—Percichthyidae (temperate bass)
Genus—*Morone* (freshwater bass)
Species—*saxatilis* (striped bass, female), *chrysops* (white bass, male)

Bream (sunfish):

Order—Perciformes
Family—Centrarchidae
Genus—*Lepomis* (sunfish)
Species—*microchirus* (bluegill), *cyanellus* (green sunfish), *microlophus* (redear sunfish)

Sturgeon:

Order—Acipenseriformes
Family—Acipenseridae
Genus—Acipenser (sturgeon)
Species—*transmontanus* (white), *medirostris* (green), *fulvescens* (lake), *oxyrhynchus* (Atlantic)

Common Carp:

Order—Cypriniformes
Family—Cyprinidae
Genus—*Cyprinus*
Species—*carpio*

3–8

3–9. Brown trout (left) and rainbow trout (right). (Courtesy, New Hampshire Fish and Game Department)

Salmonids

The order Salmoniformes and the family Salmonidae, which means "salmon-like," contain two important aquaculture species in the *Salmo* genus: *Salmo salar* (Atlantic salmon) and *S. trutta* (brown trout). The various species of Pacific salmon are part of the *Oncorhynchus* genus, included in the same order and family. These species include *Oncorhynchus tshawytscha* (chinook salmon), *O. kisutch* (coho salmon), *O. nerka* (sockeye salmon), *O. keta* (chum salmon), and *O. gorbuscha* (pink salmon). The same genus also includes *O. mykiss* (rainbow trout).

3–10. Female (top left) and male (bottom left) sockeye salmon and female (top right) and male (bottom right) coho salmon. (Courtesy, Richard R. Whitney, Leavenworth, WA)

Cypriniformes

The order Cypriniformes is a large and varied order of freshwater fish. The primary family, Cyprinidae, contains the baitfish, common carp, and some of the ornamental fish. The baitfish species include *Pimephales promelas* (fathead minnows), *Carassius auratus* (goldfish), and *Notemigonus crysoleucas* (golden shiners). Many ornamental species are classified in this family, including the genera *Puntins*, *Barbodes*, and *Capoeta* (barbs); *Brachydanio* (danios); and *Rasbora* (rasboras).

Perciformes

The order Perciformes is the most diverse of all fish orders. It is the dominant order in saltwater and brackish-water fish and, in some tropical areas, is the dominant freshwater fish order as well.

Scientific Classification of Baitfish

Kingdom—Animalia (animals)
Phylum—Chordata (with spinal cord)
Class—Osteichthyes (bony fish)

Fathead Minnow:

Order—Cypriniformes
(protractile, toothless
mouths)
Family—Cyprinidae (minnows
or carp)
Genus—*Pimephales* (North
American minnows)
Species—*promelas* (fatheads)

Goldfish:

Order—Cypriniformes
Family—Cyprinidae
Genus—*Carassius*
Species—*auratus*

Golden Shiner:

Order—Cypriniformes
Family—Cyprinidae
Genus—*Notemigonus*
Species—*crysoleucas*

3–11

3–12. Common baitfish: golden shiner (top), goldfish (center), and fathead minnow (bottom). (Courtesy, New Hampshire Fish and Game Department—golden shiner and goldfish; William N. Roston, Forsyth, MO—fathead minnow)

The major freshwater fish of this order are tilapia, hybrid striped bass, and North American walleye. Of the ornamental fish, gouramis and cichlids are from the order Perciformes.

Of the saltwater and brackish-water fish in the order Perciformes, the most important aquaculture species are *Mugil cephalus* (striped mullets), *Micropogon undulatus* (Atlantic croakers), *Sciaenops ocellata* (red drums, or redfish), and *Trachinotus carolinus* (pompanos).

The ornamental gouramis classified in the order Perciformes include *Trichogaster trichopterus* (three-spot gouramis), *T. leeri* (pearl gouramis), and *Helostoma temmincki* (kissing gouramis). The family Cichlidae includes numerous ornamental species from the genera *Pterophyllum* (angel fish), *Symphysodon* (discus fish), *Nannacara* (dwarf cichlids), *Apistogramma* (also dwarf cichlids), *Pelvichachromis* (kribensis), and *Cichlasoma* (normal cichlids).

Scientific Classification of Ornamental Fish

Kingdom—Animalia (animals)
Phylum—Chordata (with spinal cord)
Class—Osteichthyes (bony fish)

Guppies and Mollies:

Order—Cyprinidontiformes
Family—Cyprinidontidae (killifish or toothcarp)
Genus—*Poecilia*
Species—*reticulata* (guppies), *velifera* (sailfin mollies), *sphenops* (common mollies)

Swordtails and Platy:

Order—Cyprinidontiformes
Family—Cyprinidontidae
Genus—*Xiphophorus*
Species—*helleri* (swordtails), *maculatus* (platy)

Barbs:

Order—Cypriniformes
Family—Cyprinidae
Genera—*Puntins, Barbodes, Capoeta*
Species—(numerous living species)

Danios:

Order—Cypriniformes
Family—Cyprinidae
Genus—*Brachydanio* (danios)
Species—*rerio* (zebra danios), *albolineatus* (pearl danios)

Rasboras:

Order—Cypriniformes
Family—Cyprinidae
Genus—*Rasbora*
Species—*heteromorpha* (harlequin fish), *trilineata* (scissortails), *einthoveni* (brilliant rasboras)

Tetras:

Order—Characiformes (small, extremely colorful)
Family—Characidae (characins)
Genera/Species—*Paracheirodon innesi* (neon tetras), *Cheirodon axelrodi* (cardinal tetras), *Hemigrammus* (several living species)

Cichlids:

Order—Perciformes
Family—Ciclidae
Genus—*Pterophyllum* (angel fish)
Species—*scalare* (angel fish)
Genus—*Symphysodon* (discus fish)
Species—(several living species)
Genus—*Nannacara* (dwarf cichlids)
Species—*anomala* (golden dwarf cichlids)
Genus—*Apistogramma* (dwarf cichlids)
Species—*agassizi* (Agassizi's dwarf cichlids), *rameriz* (butterfly cichlids)
Genus—*Pelvichachromis* (kribensis)
Species—*pulcher* (kribensis), *taeniatus* (striped kribensis)
Genus—*Cichlasoma* ("normal" cichlids)
Species—*meeki* (firemouths), *festivum* (flag cichlids)

Top Minnows:

Order—Cyprinidontiformes
Family—Cyprinidontidae
Genus—*Aphyosemion*
Species—*ahli* (Ahl's lyretails), *australe* (lyretail panchax)
Genus—*Aplocheilichthys*
Species—*lineatus* (striped panchax)
Genus—*Epiplatys*
Species—*dageti* (red-chinned panchax)

Gouramis:

Order—Perciformes
Family—Belontiidae (gouramis)
Genus—*Trichogaster*
Species—*trichopterus* (three-spot gouramis), *leeri* (pearl gouramis)
Family—Helostomatidae
Genus—*Helostoma*
Species—*temmincki* (kissing gouramis)

Tilapia and Other Species

The two primary tilapia species raised in the United States are *Tilapia aurea* (blue) and *T. mossambica* (Java), both from the family Cichlidae. The culture of several other tilapia species and hybrids (e.g., *T. nilotica*) is still experimental.

The hybrid striped bass is a cross of two Perciformes species: usually a female *Morone saxatilis* (striped bass) and a male *M. chrysops* (white bass). The primary walleye is the North American walleye (*Stizostedion vitreum*).

3–14. The koi is a popular ornamental species. This fish is being produced in a recirculating tank system.

Killifish and Toothcarp

Several species of ornamental fish are classified in the order Cyprinidontiformes and family Cyprinidontidae, also called killifish or toothcarp. These species include the guppies and mollies from the genus *Poecilia*, along with the *Xiphophorus helleri* (swordtails), and the *X. maculatus* (platy). Top minnows from the genera *Aphyosemion*, *Aplocheilichthys*, and *Epiplatys* also come from this order and family.

Characidae

The order Characiformes and family Characidae contain several species of tetras. These ornamental species include *Paracheirodon innesi* (neon tetras), *Cheirodon axelrodi* (cardinal tetras), and several species from the genus *Hemigrammus*.

Milkfish

The only important aquaculture species from the Gonorynchiformes order is the *Chanos chanos* (milkfish), a brackish-water food fish cultured widely in Southeast Asia. Little culture of milkfish is currently carried out in the United States, but there is much potential for culture, especially in Hawaii and California.

Scientific Classification of Saltwater and Brackish-Water Fish

Kingdom—Animalia (animals)
Phylum—Chordata (with spinal cord)
Class—Osteichthyes (bony fish)

Striped Mullets:

Order—Perciformes (very diverse, scaly fish)
Family—Mugiladae
Genus—*Mugil*
Species—*cephalus*

Atlantic Salmon:

Order—Salmoniformes
Family—Salmonidae (salmon)
Genus—*Salmo* (trout)
Species—*salar*

Pacific Salmon:

Order—Salmoniformes
Family—Salmonidae (salmon)
Genus—*Oncorhynchus* (Pacific salmon)
Species—*tsawytscha* (chinook salmon)
   kisutch (coho salmon)
   nerka (sockeye salmon)
   keta (chum salmon)
   gorbuscha (pink salmon)

Milkfish:

Order—Gonorynchiformes (swim bladder)
Family—Chanidae (milkfish)
Genus—*Chanos*
Species—*chanos*

Atlantic Croakers:

Order—Perciformes
Family—Sciaenidae (drums, croakers)
Genus—*Micropogon*
Species—*undulatus*

Red Drums:

Order—Perciformes
Family—Sciaenidae (drums)
Genus—*Sciaenops*
Species—*ocellata* (red drums)

Pompanos:

Order—Perciformes
Family—Carangidae (jacks and pompanos)
Genus—*Trachinotus* (pompanos)
Species—*carolinus*

3–15

3–16. Paddlefish. (Courtesy, John McGregor, Woods Hole, MA)

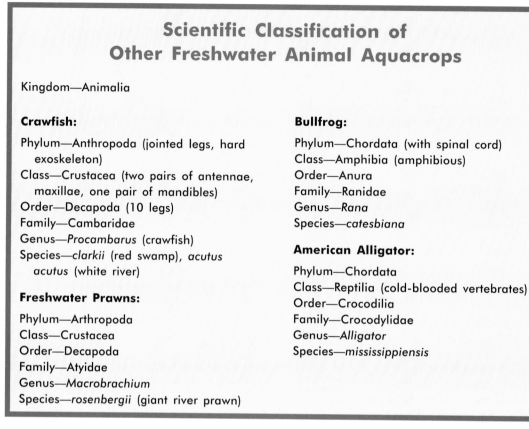

Scientific Classification of Other Freshwater Animal Aquacrops

Kingdom—Animalia

Crawfish:

Phylum—Anthropoda (jointed legs, hard exoskeleton)
Class—Crustacea (two pairs of antennae, maxillae, one pair of mandibles)
Order—Decapoda (10 legs)
Family—Cambaridae
Genus—*Procambarus* (crawfish)
Species—*clarkii* (red swamp), *acutus acutus* (white river)

Freshwater Prawns:

Phylum—Arthropoda
Class—Crustacea
Order—Decapoda
Family—Atyidae
Genus—*Macrobrachium*
Species—*rosenbergii* (giant river prawn)

Bullfrog:

Phylum—Chordata (with spinal cord)
Class—Amphibia (amphibious)
Order—Anura
Family—Ranidae
Genus—*Rana*
Species—*catesbiana*

American Alligator:

Phylum—Chordata
Class—Reptilia (cold-blooded vertebrates)
Order—Crocodilia
Family—Crocodylidae
Genus—*Alligator*
Species—*mississippiensis*

3–17

Sturgeon

The only important aquaculture species from the Acipenseriformes order is the sturgeon (Acipenseridae family), a very old fish in terms of its place on the evolutionary ladder. The most common species are the white sturgeon (*Acipenser transmontanus*), green sturgeon (*A. medirostris*), lake sturgeon (*A. fulvescens*), and Atlantic sturgeon (*A. oxyrhynchus*).

3–18. Green sturgeon. (Courtesy, Dan Gotshall, Sea Challengers, Inc., Monterey, CA)

Scientific Classification of Other Saltwater and Brackish-Water Aquacrops

Kingdom—Animalia (animals)

Oysters:

Phylum—Mollusca (molluscs)
Class—Pelecypoda (bivalve molluss)
Order—Isodontida
Family—Ostreidae
Genus—*Crassostrea*
Species—*virginica* (American oyster) *gigas*
   (Pacific cupped oyster)

Lobsters:

Phylum—Arthropoda (jointed legs, hard
   exoskeleton)
Class—Crustacea
Order—Decapoda
Family—Homaridae
Genus—*Homarus*
Species—*americanus* (Maine lobster)

Shrimp:

Phylum—Arthropoda
Class—Crustacea
Order—Decapoda
Family—Penaeidae
Genus—*Fenneropenaeus*
Species—*aztecus* (brown shrimp)
Genus—*Fartantepenaeus*
Species—*duorarum* (pink shrimp)
Genus—*Litopenaeus*
Species—*vannamei* (Pacific white shrimp)

Blue Crab:

Phylum—Arthropoda
Class—Crustacea
Order—Decapoda
Family—Geryonidae
Genus—*Callinectes*
Species—*sapidus*

Red Abalone:

Phylum—Mollusca
Class—Gastropoda
Order—Archaeogastropoda
Family—Haliotidae (abalone)
Genus—*Haliotis*
Species—*refescens*

3–19

AMPHIBIANS

The only amphibian species with potential for culture in the United States is *Rana catesbiana* (bullfrogs). Bullfrog culture has been tried because of the high value of frog legs as food. Demand also exists for frogs as experimental laboratory animals.

Most experiments in bullfrog culture have found high disease risk and problems with predators. Bullfrogs produce a relatively low amount of meat in relation to the water area required. Bullfrogs also have erratic reproduction cycles, which makes raising them unpre-

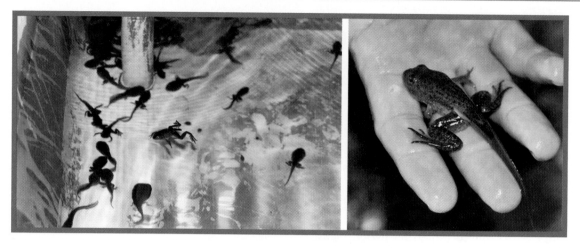

3–20. Immature frogs growing in a tank.

dictable. The best method of culturing the bullfrog seems to be in a polyculture with one or more other aquaculture species.

Reptiles

The only reptile cultured to any significant degree in the United States is the American alligator, *Alligator mississippiensis*. The alligator is cultured in the southeastern states, primarily Louisiana and Florida.

The alligator is cultured for both its meat (from the tail) and its hide. The belly hide is tanned and made into expensive leather items.

3–21. The correct way to carry a small alligator. (Courtesy, James N. Butler, University of Tennessee at Martin)

DECAPODS

Decapod is a shortened form of "decapod crustacean," which is a crustacean that has five pairs of appendages on the thorax. At least one pair is modified as pincers. A **crustacean** is an arthropod with a relatively hard exterior skeleton. Several decapods are important to aquaculture or have potential importance to aquaculture. Examples of cultured decapods are the lobster, the shrimp, the blue crab, the crawfish, and the freshwater prawn.

Homarus americanus (lobsters) and the shrimp species, *Fenneropenaeus aztecus* (brown shrimp), *Litopenaeus vannamei* (white shrimp), and *Farfantepenaeus duorarum* (pink shrimp), are the most important saltwater and brackish-water decapod species. These species are discussed in more detail in later chapters.

Of freshwater crustaceans, only *Procambarus clarkii* (red swamp crawfish) and *P. acutus acutus* (white river crawfish) are cultured widely. Crawfish culture is presented in Chapter 12.

The culture of two decapods, the *Callinectes sapidus* (blue crabs), a brackish-water species, and *Macrobrachium rosenbergii* (freshwater prawns), is now moving beyond experimental stages. Both species show potential. Techniques for producing them continue to need improvement.

3–22. Blue crabs (*Callinectes sapidus*) are cultured in brackish-water areas in the eastern United States.

3–23. A prawn grown in a tank.

MOLLUSKS

Mollusks are animals with soft bodies that are often enclosed in shells. Shells vary in structure, with two being most common: bivalve and univalve. Besides the species of mollusks that are cultured, octopuses and squids and a few other species are harvested wild from the ocean.

3–24. Mussel.

3–25. Oyster.

Bivalve Mollusks

A *bivalve mollusk* has two shell parts hinged together. The organism can open and close the shell. A bivalve mollusk usually has a foot that can be extended from the shell to help in moving around and digging in the mud or sand.

Oysters, mussels, scallops, and clams are the major bivalve mollusks. The *Crassostrea virginica* (American oyster) and the *C. gigas* (Pacific cupped oyster) are the important aquaculture species in the Pelecypoda class of the phylum Mollusca.

The oyster is cultured all over the world and in most coastal waters of the United States. The American oyster is cultured along the eastern coast and the Gulf of Mexico. The Pacific cupped oyster is cultured primarily off the coasts of Washington and Oregon. Oyster culture is further described later in the book.

3–26. Live, iced-down Manila clams in a market. Note the structure of the shells.

Univalve Mollusks

Also known as **gastropods**, univalve mollusks have single coiled shells. Examples include snails and abalone. A few gastropods have no shells at all, such as the slug and the nudibranch.

In California, the *Haliotis rufescens* (red abalone) is cultured, the only gastropod culture in the United States of any consequence. Some snails are grown in Hawaii and other isolated locations. A description of red abalone culture is presented in Chapter 14.

3–27. Some species of snails (gastropods) are popular as food (known as escargot). (This *Helix* snail is being raised in a tank.)

PLANTS AND SEAWEED

Several species of algae, sometimes called seaweed, are cultured around the world, although not very much is done in the United States. Seaweed, which is viewed as a health food, is not expected to become a staple of most American diets.

Algae

The primary types of algae are classified into three divisions:

3–28. A seaweed with the scientific name of *Mastocarpus stellatus*. (Courtesy, M.D. Guiry, National University of Ireland)

- Rhodophyta—All species in the genus *Porphyra* (red algae) are in the division Rhodophyta.

- Chlorophyta—*Monostroma, Enteromorpha,* and *Chlorella* (green algae) are the primary genera in the division Chlorophyta.

- Phaephyta—*Undaria pinnatifida, Macrocystis pyrifera,* and *M. integrifolia* (brown algae, also called kelp) are in the division Phaephyta.

The best-known kelp in the United States is *Macrocystis pyrifera* and *M. integrifolia,* two species of giant kelp.

Scientific Classification of Food Plants and Algae

Kingdom—Protista

Red Algae:

Division—Rhodophyta
Class—Rhodophyceae
Order—Bangiales
Family—Bangiaceae
Genus—*Porphyra*
Species—*angusta, kuniedai, pseudolinearis, tenera, yezoensis*

Green Algae:

Division—Chlorophyta
Class—Chlorophycea
Order—Ulvales
Family—Monostromataceae
Genera—*Monostroma, Enteromorpha, Chlorella*
Species—several

Brown Algae:

Division—Phaephyta
Class—Phaeophyceae
Order—Laminariales (kelp)
Family—Alariaceae (Japanese kelp)
Genus—*Undaria*
Species—*pinnatifida*
Family—Lessoniaceae (giant kelp)
Genus—*Macrocystis*
Species—*pyrifera, integrifolia*

Kingdom—Plantae

Watercress:

Division—Anthophyta
Class—Magnoliopsida
Order—Cruciferales
Family—Cruciferae
Genus—*Nasturtium*
Species—*officinale*

Chinese Waterchestnuts:

Division—Anthophyta
Class—Magnoliopsida
Order—Myrtales
Family—Trapaceae
Genus—*Eleocharis*
Species—*dulcis*

3–29

Freshwater Plants

Two freshwater aquatic plants cultured to some extent in the United States are *Eleocharis dulcis* (Chinese water chestnuts) and *Nasturtium officinale* (watercress). Both are expensive foods for humans, and neither is widely cultured.

BLUE-GREEN ALGAE

Some important species in aquaculture are the blue-green algae. Blue-green algae play a significant role in freshwater ponds by oxygenating the water as they undergo photosynthesis.

Blue-green algae are usually classified in the Monera kingdom and Cyanophyta division. About 1,800 living species of blue-green algae exist. Five of the most common genera are *Gloeocapsa, Microcystis, Oscillatoria, Nostoc,* and *Scytonema.*

GENERAL HABITAT CONSIDERATIONS

Habitat is the environment in which an organism lives and thrives. All species have natural habitats to which they are well suited. Those species that are aquacrops are often removed from their natural habitats. A producer tries to duplicate a species' habitat in a tank, pond, or other growing facility. Knowledge of the natural habitat is essential to enable its duplication in aquaculture.

Each aquacrop has different habitat requirements, such as water temperature, salinity (salt content), and amount of dissolved oxygen. Some aquacrops will tolerate wide ranges in habitat factors. Others will not, because their body structures are designed for particular environments.

3–30. Tilapia (*Tilapia* spp.) require warm water. They will die if the water temperature goes below 55°F (13°C).

FISH

The habitat requirements for fish vary greatly, depending on the species. The general requirements can be grouped into the categories of dissolved oxygen (DO), temperature, water movement, pH, and salinity.

Although catfish are usually found in streams and rivers in the wild, they adapt well to pond culture. They are freshwater fish primarily but can withstand some salinity, maybe even up to 20 parts per thousand (ppt). Catfish will live for a short time in water with a dissolved oxygen content as low as 1 part per million (ppm) but need about 4 ppm to grow. Although they can withstand the cold temperatures of the northern United States, they will grow much faster in warmer water. They often stop feeding when the water temperature gets too cold.

Trout are coldwater fish and perform best in running water, although they can adapt to ponds. They must have running water for spawning. Trout also need a high level of DO to survive, at least 5 ppm.

Tilapia require warm water. Most species of tilapia will die if the water temperature gets below 55°F. Tilapia can survive a DO of 1 ppm. They need water with a fairly high pH.

Hybrid striped bass grow well in a wide range of water-quality variables. They survive in both warm and cold water and can withstand a pH range of 5.5 to 10.0. Like catfish, they can survive a DO level of 1 ppm for a short period, but they need water with a DO of 5 ppm or higher to grow well.

Baitfish are usually found in small, weedy ponds but adapt well to pond and tank culture. Fathead minnows can withstand salinity of up to 10 ppt and wide ranges of pH.

Most saltwater fish have very few specific habitat requirements. They adapt well to the various conditions found at sea. They do not, however, respond well to contact with humans.

Striped mullets require warm water and are usually found in tropical and subtropical areas. Striped mullets usually live in bays, marshes, rivers, or the open sea, but they can be grown in ponds. They are very tolerant of changes in water salinity, surviving in water anywhere from 0 to 38 ppt.

DECAPODS

Crawfish are found naturally in shallow, weedy swamps, ponds, and ditches. They adapt well to polyculture in rice fields. Crawfish are very sensitive to chemicals and prefer hard water.

Blue crabs require salt water or brackish water, but the percentage of salinity varies. Males tend to stay in low-salinity water, while females migrate to higher-salinity areas to hatch their young. The larval crabs, called *zoeae*, cannot survive in water with salinity less than 2 ppt. Freshwater prawns also need some salinity for the larval stages to survive.

Shrimp and lobsters have few habitat considerations. Shrimp do come into brackish water or nearly fresh water to spawn. Both tanks and ponds have been used to produce shrimp. Lobsters are not commonly cultured from hatching to harvest size. Lobsters may reproduce in a hatchery, with the young being raised until they are stocked in ocean water.

OYSTERS

The primary habitat consideration for oysters is that they have at least a small water current flowing through them to provide oxygen and food and to carry away wastes. Water that

3–31. A system of long-line rafts is used to culture oysters in a bay that provides a near ideal environment. (Courtesy, National Oceanic and Atmospheric Administration)

is silty will clog the food transport system and slow the growth and respiration processes. As filter feeders, oysters are very susceptible to pollutants (such as sewage or chemical runoff) in the water.

Oysters also need water that is free of harmful contamination. Certain forms of bacteria in water cause harvested oysters to be hazardous when eaten, especially if raw.

Oysters are cultured where tide movement cleans the area. Low tides carry water away, and high tides bring "new" seawater in. Isolated bays along the Oregon and Washington coast are particularly suited. East Coast and Gulf of Mexico oyster culture is also possible, though the oysters may need to be "cleaned" with fresh water after harvest.

USING GENETICS IN AQUACULTURE

Major advances in aquaculture using genetics and related processes available to researchers are emerging. **Genetics** is the study of the laws and processes of biological inheritance. Parents—animals, plants, and organisms in other kingdoms—have traits that are passed to their offspring. The passing of traits from parents to offspring is **heredity**. Heredity of fish stock is important to producers. Knowing heredity and the reputation of, for example, a fingerling producer helps a fish producer make good choices about the source of fingerlings as related to achieving desired goals.

3–32. Genetically improved USDA 103 fish are being harvested following growth in experimental ponds. (Courtesy, Agricultural Research Service, USDA)

CHROMOSOMES

All organisms are made of cells. A living cell consists of a cell membrane and the cytoplasm, which contains the nucleus. The nucleus has chromosomes. A *chromosome* is a tiny threadlike part in a cell that contains the genetic material. This genetic material is the genome of the organism.

CONNECTION

SEEKING ANSWERS TO IMPORTANT QUESTIONS

Questions often arise about aquaculture. Sometimes the answers are known; other times the answers are not known. More questions are being answered all the time.

Aquaculture research has an important role in the future success of the culture of aquatic organisms. Private industry, research stations, and colleges and universities carry out research. Growers often do research of their own to solve problems they have.

Research is using scientific procedures to answer questions. Scientists have special training in how to go about research procedures. Anyone can do at least some research by following the scientific method. However, specialized facilities, such as those that the scientist is using here, may be needed for more advanced research. (Photo courtesy, U.S. Department of Agriculture)

Chromosomes are the links between parents and offspring. When organisms reproduce sexually, the genome is the combination of the traits from the mother and the father. For every pair of chromosomes, the offspring receives one chromosome from each parent. This gives the offspring pairs of *like* chromosomes. All the cells within the organism are genetically identical. Each cell contains the same number of chromosomes.

Deoxyribonucleic acid (DNA) forms genes that make up chromosomes. Chromosomes make up genetic information for cells. Cells make tissues that form organs. Organs form organ systems. These organ systems make up the organism.

Genes

A **gene** is a segment of a chromosome that contains the hereditary traits of an organism. Since chromosomes come in pairs, genes also come in pairs.

An **allele** is a different form of a gene. Forms of alleles may be similar, or they may be different. An organism having similar alleles is said to be **homozygous** for a particular trait. An organism having different alleles is said to be **heterozygous** for the trait.

Genotype and Phenotype

The genetic makeup of an organism is its **genotype**. All offspring of the mating of a pair of fish have similar genotypes. By selectively mating fish with desired traits, the likelihood of the offspring having these traits is increased.

Phenotype is an organism's physical or outward appearance. Phenotype helps in distinguishing visually between, for example, catfish and trout.

The transmission of traits by parents to offspring is important in breeding to improve aquatic crops. Breeding practices use the concept of alleles to produce various phenotypes or outcomes. Outcrossing is used to develop heterozygous offspring, and inbreeding is used to develop homozygous offspring. The genotype and the environment determine phenotype.

It should be noted that organisms mate within their species. In nature, a male rainbow trout will mate with a female rainbow trout. In some cases, scientists artificially mate organisms of different, but usually quite similar, species.

3–33. Two oysters of the same species can be used to illustrate phenotype. Outward appearance varies with the environment in which they grew.

Dominant and Recessive

Some traits are dominant, while others are recessive. A *dominant trait* is one that covers up or masks the allele for a recessive trait. A *recessive trait* is one that is covered up or masked by the allele for a dominant trait. If an organism has a dominant allele, it will phenotypically show the dominant trait in complete dominance. If the organism receives two recessive alleles, then it will be homozygous recessive and will show the recessive trait.

Aquaculture geneticists are now beginning to unravel much of the mystery of genetics in aquatic organisms. The long history of culture does not exist with aquatic species as it does with traditional farm animals, such as dairy cattle and horses.

Predicting Genotype

By observing the traits of parents, some sort of prediction about the traits of offspring is possible. In genetics, prediction is based on probability. Probability is the likelihood or chance that a trait will occur. It is used by geneticists to predict the outcome of mating. Mating animals that have a particular trait does not guarantee that the trait will be expressed in offspring.

Role of DNA

DNA (deoxyribonucleic acid) is a protein-like nucleic acid on genes that controls inheritance. Each DNA molecule consists of two strands shaped as a double helix or spiral structure. These strands are nucleotides bonded together by pairs of nitrogen bases.

This double helix is similar to a tiny twisted ladder. The supports are made up of sugar molecules held together by phosphates. The rungs consist of four nitrogen materials: adenine (A), cytosine (C), guanine (G), and thymine (T). The rung structure allows DNA segments to be cut out and new ones inserted.

Genetic Code

The *genetic code* is the sequence of nitrogen bases in the DNA molecule. This sequence codes for amino acids and proteins. The unique ability of DNA to replicate itself allows for the molecule to pass genetic information from one cell generation to the next.

When a chromosome divides during mitosis, the two strands unravel and separate. Each strand contains the complementary base and will immediately become a new double strand identical to the original. A gene is structurally a triplet sequence of nitrogen bases A, C, G, and T.

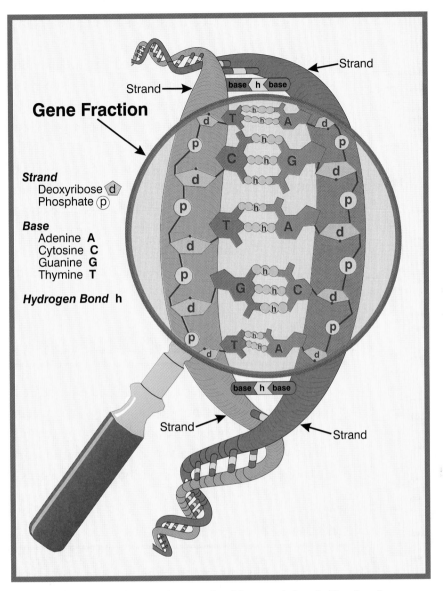

Gene Fraction

Strand
Deoxyribose (d)
Phosphate (p)

Base
Adenine **A**
Cytosine **C**
Guanine **G**
Thymine **T**

Hydrogen Bond h

3–34. DNA structure consists of two nucleotide strands bonded by the nitrogen bases adenine, cytosine, guanine, and thymine.

The genetic code determines the nature of an organism. Hogs have a different genetic code from that of cattle or humans. Research is identifying the genetic code of animals.

DNA Sequencing

A tool being used in biotechnology is DNA sequencing. **DNA sequencing** is determining the order of nucleotides on a DNA fragment. It is being used to unravel the mystery of heredity and allow genetic engineering to be used. A good understanding of the DNA double helix is essential.

DNA sequencing is being used to understand the genetic makeup of animals and other organisms. The genetic information in one organism is huge. Large projects are being used to research the information. These are known as genome projects. Among the best known is the Human Genome Project.

With DNA sequencing information, heredity can be used in animal selection. The information will provide a genetic map of the characteristics of an animal. Methods of genetic engineering can be used to modify the genetic makeup of an organism. The use of DNA sequencing information is now largely limited to scientists. This is because of its complexity and the ethical issues surrounding some uses of biotechnology.

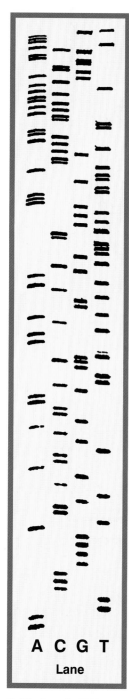

A C G T
Lane

3–35. Sample DNA sequencing ladder obtained with gel electrophoresis.

ROLE OF GENETICS IN SELECTION

Selection involving both genotype and phenotype can be used to promote desired traits in aquatic species. Management practices may focus around the genetic capability of the organisms.

Improvement can be made in organisms without artificially altering their genetic makeup. Various breeding practices may be used.

BREEDING

Breeding is the process of helping organisms reproduce so that the offspring have desired qualities. It is often used to improve quality of the species.

Selection

A common breeding practice is selection. **Selection** is the choosing of a male parent and a female parent for mating because of desired qualities, such as coloring in an ornamental fish species. Through genetics, we know that offspring are more likely to reflect traits of their parents than of members of the species that are not their parents.

New approaches in selection include marker-assisted selection. *Marker-assisted selection* is a process of selecting broodfish using genetic markers that identify specific genes. It relies on the identification of quantitative trait loci (QTLs). QTLs take the guesswork out of evaluating individual fish. DNA sequences are studied to develop linkage maps that associate with specific genes. The goal is to select the best broodstock for producing a new generation of young. Marker-assisted selection is useful only when an association exists between a marker and a gene.

Selection has been a common breeding practice in aquaculture. It has been especially helpful in improving fish quality.

3–36. A pond-raised hybrid bluegill sunfish.

Hybridization

Hybridization is the process of breeding individuals that are distinctly different. With fish, it involves using different species that are closely related. The goal is to gain a superior trait in offspring. This superior trait is known as hybrid vigor. *Hybrid vigor* is a condition in which offspring have greater desired traits than their parents. The hybrid striped bass is an example.

GENETIC ENGINEERING

Genetic engineering is removing genes from DNA, modifying genes, or adding genes to DNA. Genetic engineering using recombinant DNA (gene splicing) along with other reproductive technology has the potential to change aquaculture greatly.

Genetic marker technology is being used to detect the presence of certain genes. This technology, along with cloning, has the potential for further increasing genetic progress.

Some organisms that have been genetically engineered are said to be transgenic. A *transgenic organism* is a genetically engineered organism that can pass the altered gene to its offspring. This means that offspring will possess the desired trait.

Humans have varying views about genetic engineering. Some feel it is unnatural and should not be done. Others feel it is okay when carefully planned and tested before an organism is released into the environment. You should learn as much as you can about the pros and cons of genetic engineering by reading scientific books and articles.

CLONING

Cloning is the production of one or more exact genetic copies of an organism. Only a few cells may be used. There is no sexual union between male and female reproductive cells.

Cloning has been used with plants for many years, with some naturally reproducing so that an offspring is a clone of its parent. An example is cutting a piece from a waterlily and moving it to another pond for growth. Cloning with aquatic animals is expanding and may be widely available soon. Several methods of cloning are used.

CULTURING GENETICALLY IMPROVED SPECIES

Because most of the species used in aquaculture are no different genetically from their counterparts in the wild, the potential for genetic improvement seems almost unlimited. The primary source of this potential is breeding programs that select for traits important to the culture of the different species. Newer methods of genetic engineering look especially promising.

AQUACROP IMPROVEMENTS

The cultured rainbow trout is a good example of the genetic potential of aquacrops. The rainbow trout that is commercially hatched and cultured in raceways has been genetically improved through breeding programs to accept commercially prepared feed better, to respond to handling better, to grow well in intensive production systems, and to reproduce well in captivity.

Other species will probably improve much like the rainbow trout as breeding programs result in genetically superior strains that react better to common production techniques. Also, improved genetics through selective breeding programs may produce species that grow well in polyculture systems. One of the greatest potentials is to produce species genetically that require more or less salinity in the water or that can adjust better to changes in salinity so the potential areas for production can be increased.

Another example of using genetics to improve aquaculture is the hybrid striped bass, a strain of fish produced by breeding bass of two different species. The *Morone saxatilis* female and *M. chrysops* male were crossed. There may be other crosses that will turn out just as well.

Genetic breakthroughs may also help aquafarmers overcome some of the problems that often reduce profits. For example, off-flavor in catfish can cost producers much money. If this problem could be eliminated genetically, one of catfish producers' biggest problems would be overcome.

Geneticists have already developed a system of breeding tilapia so a single sex of offspring can be produced. All the members could be male, for example. This would eliminate the problem of tilapia reproducing before they reach harvest size.

Genetic engineering that reduces the likelihood of disease is also an area where great potential exists. Finding individuals that are

3–37. The hybrid striped bass (top) was developed by crossing a female *Morone saxatilis* (center) and a male *M. chrysops* (bottom).

3–38. A naturally occurring example of a genetic mutation is an albino channel catfish (*Ictalurus punctatus*). (An albino is an organism lacking normal pigmentation.)

resistant to disease and then determining why they are resistant may make many diseases problems of the past.

GENETICS RESEARCH UNIT: CATFISH

The Genetics Research Unit (GRU) at the National Warmwater Aquaculture Center has initiated an aggressive program to investigate fish genetics. The species of primary interest is catfish. (The National Warmwater Aquaculture Center is located in Stoneville, Mississippi.)

The GRU is focusing on four areas of fish genetics research:

• Inheritance of desirable characteristics of fish

• Interaction of genotype and environment for different strains of catfish

• Breeding strategies to gain genetically enhanced species

• Development and release of improved catfish germ seed stock for commercial production

In 2001, the GRU released a genetically enhanced strain of catfish to 35 producers. This strain was known as USDA 103 (also known as NWAC 103). The interest of producers in growing the fish was greater than could be accommodated; therefore, a lottery was used to select the producers. The development of USDA 103 involved a great deal of DNA analysis to determine molecular markers and establish a sequence of genetic code. Research trials with USDA 103 were positive. The improved fish were 20 percent larger than regular channel catfish when on identical feed for the same period. Disease resistance was also improved, with a higher percentage of the USDA 103 fish surviving.

3–39. This seafood marketer is holding a whole fish. How would we know if this fish were transgenic? (Courtesy, U.S. Department of Agriculture)

AQUA BOUNTY FARMS: TRANSGENIC SALMON

Fish with artificially altered genetics are known as *transgenic fish*. A transgenic fish fits into the overall category of genetically modified organism (GMO).

Transgenic salmon with foreign genes that promote growth have been developed by Aqua Bounty Farms, of New Brunswick, Canada. These Atlantic salmon grow to market size twice as fast as natural Atlantic salmon.

Reaction to the possibility of a GMO salmon has been mixed. Federal regulatory agencies, particularly the Food and Drug Administration, must act on marketing such a fish in the United States. Opponents have labeled this fish and other transgenic fish as frankenfish. The state of Maryland passed a law prohibiting transgenic fish anywhere that might allow them to get into a natural waterway. Some producers use only sterile females in food fish production to avoid the possibility of an escaped fish reproducing. In 2002, Washington State became the first state to ban genetically engineered fish permanently. Laws have sometimes failed to recognize that the improved fish reduce production costs and help assure a good food supply for people of the world.

REVIEWING

MAIN IDEAS

Successful aquaculturists need a good foundation in the scientific classification, natural habitats, and genetics of the species they are producing.

Taxonomy is a way of arranging organisms in groups based on similarities and differences. It is also known as scientific classification. The modern classification system has seven divisions. The kingdom is the broadest grouping. There are five kingdoms: Monera, Protista, Fungi, Plantae, and Animalia. Each kingdom is broken down into six groups that become increasingly specific. The groups are phylum or division, class, order, family, genus, and species. Some of these have sub or super groupings to better accommodate the species being classified. Some species are further classified as varieties, strains, and breeds.

Scientific names involve using the genus and species of an organism. Scientific names are written in italics or are underlined. Usually only the first letter of the first word is capitalized.

Scientific classification of common aquaculture species includes fish (Osteichthyes), amphibians, reptiles, decapods, mollusks, plants and seaweed, and blue-green algae.

Each species has habitat needs. Habitat is the environment in which a species lives and thrives. With aquaculture, this is an aquatic environment.

Genetics is the study of the laws and processes of biological inheritance. Heredity is the passing of traits from parents to offspring. Understanding genetics helps aquaculture producers gain advantages in aquacrop production. It also helps improve aquaculture species for efficiency, disease resistance, or some other reason. Genetic code information and newer methods of DNA analysis are helping to develop improved strains of aquacrops. Traditional methods of selection and hybridization are also useful.

QUESTIONS

Answer the following questions, using complete sentences and correct spelling.

1. What is the basis for modern classification?

2. What are the five kingdoms? Briefly describe each.

3. What are the typical divisions within each kingdom?

4. What is a strain? Why are strains useful?

5. What is a taxonomic name?

6. How are taxonomic names written?

7. What are the characteristics of organisms that are Osteichthyes?

8. What are the general characteristics of decapod crustaceans?

9. What are the distinguishing characteristics of mollusks?

10. Compare and contrast bivalve mollusks with gastropods.

11. What is habitat? Why should producers know the natural habitat of a cultured species?

12. Why is knowing the heredity of aquatic organisms important?

13. What is a chromosome?

14. What is genotype? Phenotype?

15. What is genetic code?

16. What is breeding? How does it relate to selection and hybridization?

17. What is a transgenic organism?

18. What is an example of a genetic improvement in aquaculture? Why is this improvement useful?

EVALUATING

Match the term with the correct definition. Write the letter of the term on the line provided.

a. strain
b. taxonomic name
c. decapod
d. gastropod

e. bivalve mollusk
f. zoeae
g. genetics
h. heredity

i. phenotype
j. hybrid vigor

_____1. A condition in which offspring have one or more desired traits superior to those of their parents

_____2. The scientific name of an organism that consists of genus and species

_____3. A group of organisms developed with similar traits to achieve a desired goal

_____4. A species with an exterior skeleton

_____5. A species with a single coiled shell

_____6. The passing of traits from parents to offspring

_____7. An organism's physical or outward appearance

_____8. An organism with a two-part hard shell that is hinged

_____9. Larval crabs

_____10. The laws and processes of biological inheritance

EXPLORING

1. Take a field trip to a local supermarket. Study the products of the fresh seafood department. Prepare a list of the species sold. Note how they have been processed and packaged. Elsewhere in the store observe canned and frozen fish and seafood products. Prepare a written report on your findings.

2. Set up an aquarium. Select the species to be kept. Determine the environment needed. Select equipment to duplicate that environment in the aquarium. Prepare the aquarium and stock it with two or more organisms. Regularly tend the fish. Keep a diary of your experiences.

3. Survey the production and/or use of aquaculture in the area where you live. What species are raised? What practices are followed in raising them? Prepare a report on your findings.

Aquatic Biology

This chapter focuses on those biological principles that will help in producing a vigorous, attractive aquacrop that will bring a suitable price. It has the following objectives:

1 List and explain life processes of aquatic organisms

2 Define morphology and physiology, and discuss relationships to aquatic organisms

3 Explain the morphology and physiology of common finfish

4 Explain the morphology and physiology of common crustaceans

5 Explain the morphology and physiology of common mollusks

6 Describe reproductive processes with aquatic species

TERMS

anadromous
anatomy
arteries
asexual reproduction
bilaterally symmetrical
catadromous
cell
cell specialization
cell structure
conchiolin
division

exoskeleton
filter feeder
ganglia
gills
haploid cell
life cycle
life process
life span
locomotion
meiosis
mitosis

molting
morphology
multicellular organism
organ
organ system
physiology
reproduction
sexual reproduction
tissue
veins

4–1. The desired result from aquaculture is a quality product that has appeal to consumers. (Courtesy, U.S. Department of Agriculture)

AQUACROPS have basic life processes. Understanding these processes is a key to rearing aquacrops successfully. A close relationship exists between maintaining healthy aquacrops and making a profit from their production.

Life processes vary among the species. Some require salt water, others fresh water. Some require cold water, others warm water. Many other differences exist, such as how they get food and reproduce.

Each aquaculture species has its own biological makeup, which determines how it is fed, cared for, reproduced, harvested, and marketed. When aquafarmers understand the biological makeup of their aquacrops, they are well on their way to having successful aquaculture operations.

LIFE SPAN AND PROCESSES

All organisms are living things until death. Aquatic organisms are no exceptions. To be in the living condition, they must carry out life processes. The nature of these processes tends to vary, but all organisms must carry them out.

LIFE SPAN

Life span is the length of an organism's life. Some life spans are long; others are short. Every species has a normal life span. Events in an organism's environment influence the length and quality of a life span.

4–2. Most aquatic animals reproduce by laying eggs. This shows eyed salmon eggs that will soon hatch.

Span Stages

All organisms typically go through five life-span stages:

1. Beginning—Every organism has a beginning point. The beginning varies by species, depending on how the species reproduces.

2. Growth—Growth occurs most rapidly in young organisms. It declines as maturity nears. Young organisms often need special nutrients to meet their needs for creating new cells and growing rapidly.

3. Maturity—This is the stage at which an organism is said to be fully developed. Growth has stopped except for the repair of worn or damaged cells. This is also the stage at which reproduction normally occurs.

4. Decline—As an organism ages, it passes through maturity into a time of deterioration. Animals may not be as active, and their flesh may not be as appealing for food. Plants may become dry and turn brown. Decline is a part of increasing age.

4–3. A mature male coho salmon at a fish hatchery in Washington.

5. Death—Death occurs when life processes stop. An organism is no longer capable of replenishing itself. Sometimes hazards in the environment (e.g., lack of oxygen in water), accidents, or other events (e.g., harvesting) cause death before an organism has passed through all the life-span stages. No aquaculture producer wants desired animals or plants to die. The goal is to promote life processes to achieve a desired product.

Life Cycle

Life cycle is the changes that an organism goes through from a given stage until the same stage recurs in the next generation. Life cycles vary by species. Life cycle is often viewed as the stages involved from the time an organism reproduces until the next generation of organisms reproduces.

LIFE PROCESSES

A **life process** is an essential activity for an organism to remain in the living condition and perpetuate its species. Without activities of this type, organisms are threatened. The life of an individual would end if some of the processes were not carried out.

The eight life processes are briefly covered here.

Getting and Using Food

Food provides the energy and other nutrients needed for growth and activity. The need for food is continuous in the life of an organism. How organisms acquire food and the kinds of materials used for food vary. This is also true for aquatic animals and plants.

Animals ingest (eat or consume) their food. The food is digested to break the materials into simpler forms that can be used by the body. Absorption is the process of food nutrients entering the bloodstream and occurs in the small intestines. This process produces wastes. Elimination is the process of expelling wastes from the body. Aquatic animal producers must understand the processes of the species they are producing and provide needed food materials.

4–4. Underwater view of an abalone showing it feeding on plants, algae, and other materials scraped from rocks in the water. (The abalone is a species of marine snail found along the West Coast of the United States.)

Plants take in nutrients (primarily through their roots) and convert them to food through photosynthesis. An aquatic plant producer must understand the nutrients needed and how nutrients are acquired and used. This will vary somewhat between species.

Wild aquatic organisms obtain food from their habitats. Cultured aquatic organisms rarely obtain sufficient natural food. A producer promotes growth by assuring sufficient food and/or nutrients for food making. Later sections of this chapter, along with other chapters, have content related to food.

Movement

Movement is of two kinds: internal and external. Internal movement is needed to carry out life processes. *Locomotion* is the process of moving from one location to another. It is a kind of external movement.

In an animal, a heart moves blood through vessels to provide oxygen and nutrients to cells and to remove wastes. Movement also includes motions of the lungs or gills, eyes, and other organs. Most animals are also capable of locomotion, such as a fish moving about by swimming in the water. Some aquatic organisms move very little, such as oysters that attach themselves to objects in the water.

Movement in plants is to circulate food substances and adjust to changes in light, such as when leaves of a plant turn toward sunlight. Movement also includes opening of flower buds, dispersal of fruit or seed, and other motions, depending on the species.

Circulation

Circulation is closely related to internal movement. Food nutrients, digested food, and other materials move within an organism.

An animal has a circulatory system. The heart uses a squeezing motion to move blood through vessels to organs and tissues throughout the body. If circulation fails, the animal will not survive.

In a plant, circulation is primarily in a vascular system. Xylem is the part of the vascular system that moves water and nutrients. Phloem is the part that moves food from its point of manufacture to other parts where it is needed.

4–5. Crawfish have several appendages that help with locomotion. Greatest speed is backward when a crawfish uses the large telson to propel away from danger.

Respiration

Respiration is the process an organism uses to provide its cells with oxygen. The oxygen is used to release the energy from food nutrients. Respiration is a continuous process in all living cells.

In animals, various respiratory structures acquire oxygen and release carbon dioxide. Fish have a gill system for this process. Mammals, amphibians, and others have lungs or similar structures. The blood carries nutrients, oxygen, and other substances throughout the body. Chemical energy and carbon dioxide are produced by oxidation as the energy is used by an organism. Conditions must be provided so that animals have sufficient oxygen. Water aeration is often used to provide sufficient oxygen for fish and other aquatic species.

With a plant, respiration occurs both night and day. Oxygen and carbon dioxide are absorbed through stomata in leaves and stems. The vascular system moves the oxygen and carbon dioxide throughout the plant. Wastes are released through stomata.

Growth and Repair

Growth and repair occur throughout the life of an organism. Young, immature organisms add cells to increase in size. One goal of an aquaculture producer is to promote the rapid addition of

4–6. External secretions make a fish hard to hold.

cells and overall growth by providing nutrients and a good environment. Mature organisms may not increase in size but use growth processes to repair and replace damaged cells.

Secretion

Secretions are juicy or watery substances in and on organisms. A good example is the slippery secretion fish produce to cover their bodies, making themselves hard to hold onto. Several body fluids are secreted internally by animals and plants. In animals, these promote digestion and respiration. In plants, secretions may be observed as sap or juice inside roots, stems, and leaves.

Sensation

Sensation is the ability of an organism to receive information and respond to it. Fish, for example, may sense something dangerous near them and quickly swim away. Plants may turn toward a light source or droop when temperatures are below normal conditions needed for growth.

4–7. A mass of fertile fish eggs will soon hatch under ideal conditions.

Reproduction

Reproduction is the process by which new individuals of a species are created. Processes vary between plants and animals and between species of each. Some plants form seed. Others have parts that break away, such as a water hyacinth leaf, to form new plants.

Animals may lay eggs or give birth to live young. Some organisms, such as bacteria, reproduce by cell division.

Reproduction is not needed for an organism to live. It is, however, needed for a species to continue to exist. Without reproduction, a species would become extinct when the last survivor ceases to live.

MORPHOLOGY AND PHYSIOLOGY OF AQUATIC ORGANISMS IN GENERAL

Aquatic species have body structures and systems that make life possible. Morphology and physiology help in understanding structures and processes. Knowledge gained from these branches of biology promotes better care by producers, including increased understanding of the needs and problems associated with aquatic species.

Morphology deals with the form and structure of organisms, including animals and plants. Morphology includes the study of cells, or cytology. Cells are the basic building blocks of organisms. Morphology does not include the functions of the forms and structures.

4–8. A fish has been surgically opened to reveal its internal structure.

Anatomy is included in morphology. *Anatomy* deals with the structure of whole organisms, including form, shape, and appearance. Both internal and external structures are studied in anatomy. Experienced people can look at an organism and instantly identify its species. That is because they know the appearance of members of that species. You can probably tell a rainbow trout by its color, spots, body shape, and arrangement of fins.

Physiology deals with the functions of cells, tissues, organs, and systems of an organism. Specialized body structures perform important physiological functions, such as ovaries, which produce eggs, and gills, which absorb oxygen.

Producers can more efficiently culture aquacrops by knowing the morphology and physiology fundamentals of the species they are culturing.

BUILDING BLOCKS

Organisms are made of many cells. A *cell* is the basic unit of a living thing. Cells contain substances that promote life processes. Most cells are very small and must be viewed with a microscope. Some cells, however, are large, such as eggs. (The information in this chapter primarily focuses on organisms that are multicellular—i.e., made of many cells.)

Cell Structures

Cells appear to be similar in plants, animals, and other organisms, but close examination reveals differences. A microscope is used to see the differences in structure. *Cell structure* is the general pattern of organization and relationship in a cell.

Cells have three major structural parts: cell membrane, nucleus, and cytoplasm. Each has specific functions.

The cell membrane surrounds the cell and controls the movement of materials into and out of the cell. The membrane consists of several types of substances. Its arrangement varies in plants and animals.

In a plant cell, a wall outside the cell membrane provides rigidity and protects the cell. The cell wall contains materials that make aquatic plant foods appealing and tasty.

4–9. Each egg is one cell. (These turtle eggs are ready for delivery to a turtle farm.) (Courtesy, National Oceanic and Atmospheric Administration)

Animal cells, as in fish and shrimp, do not have walls. To provide body structure, many animals have skeletons. Skeletons give rigidity and body shape. Since their cell membranes are soft and pliable, animals can move about more easily than plants.

The nucleus contains genetic information. It is usually near the center of a cell. This organelle (little organ) is made up of several materials, including a type of protoplasm known as nucleoplasm and fine strands of chromatin. Chromatin is the substance that forms chromosomes, which are the structures in cells that carry the material that determines gender (male or female) and other characteristics. A chromosome is made up of proteins and nucleic acid. Chromosomes have the DNA and genes.

Cytoplasm is a thick, semifluid material that surrounds the nucleus. It contains the rest of the organelles.

The remaining organelles in a cell are the endoplasmic reticulum, mitochondria, lysosomes, Golgi apparatus, plastids, and vacuoles. Each has specific functions. (Refer to an agriscience or biology book for more details.)

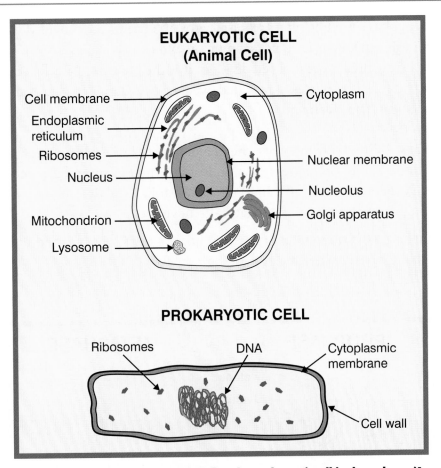

4–10. A comparison of a eukaryotic cell and a prokaryotic cell is shown here. (A eukaryotic cell has at least one membrane that encloses the nucleus. A prokaryotic cell does not have a separate membrane enclosing the DNA or other internal parts. Plants and animals have eukaryotic cells; bacteria are prokaryotic cells.)

Cell Processes

Cells perform a number of processes in an organism: using food materials, sensing and responding to stimuli, and growth. Most likely, growth is most important in aquaculture production.

Organisms grow through division. **Division** is the duplication process in which one cell splits into two cells. The original cell is the parent cell. The new cells are daughter cells. The two kinds of division are mitosis and meiosis.

Mitosis. *Mitosis* is cell division for growth and repair. Each parent cell produces two daughter cells with identical genetic material. The number of cells in an organism increases by mitosis, with the outcome being a larger organism or the replacement of damaged cells. In aquaculture, emphasis is on helping organisms grow. Nutrients are provided to plants and animals so mitosis can take place quickly and more often.

Mitosis is a sequential process of cell division. It is the phase of the cell cycle when one cell becomes two cells. The process is repeated over and over during the life of an organism.

Mitosis occurs in four steps:

1. Prophase—Prophase involves the development of chromosomes. (DNA has replicated before prophase at the end of interphase. Interphase occupies more than 90 percent of a cell's life.) Prophase follows a time of rest for the cell, although some scientists say that cells never rest.

2. Metaphase—During metaphase, the chromosomes move to the middle of the cell along an invisible line called the equator.

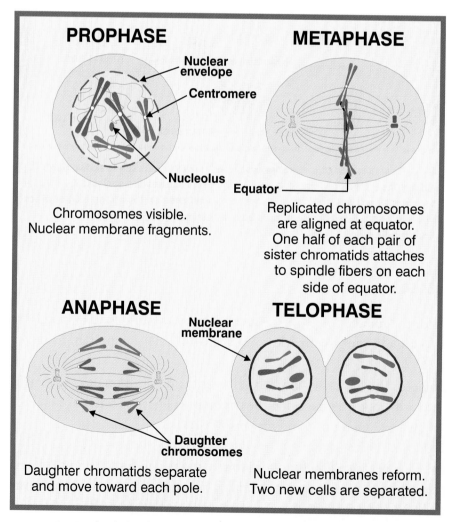

4–11. Mitosis is a four-step process of one cell becoming two cells.

3. Anaphase—In this step, the chromosomes separate and, pulled by shortening spindle fibers, move to opposite sides of the cell.

4. Telophase—In telophase, the chromosomes undergo additional maturity, the nucleus reforms, and a membrane appears between the two masses of chromosomes and divides the cytoplasm. The two separate cells can repeat the process.

Meiosis. *Meiosis* is cell division in the sexual reproduction of organisms. Each parent cell produces four daughter cells. Each daughter cell has half the number of chromosomes of the parent cell. Fertilization restores the number of chromosomes.

The cells produced by meiosis are called gametes. With animals, male gametes are known as spermatozoa (sperm) or microgametes. Female gametes are known as ova or macrogametes. Sperm are produced in the testicles of males, and ova are produced in the ovaries of females.

A cell produced by meiosis is a *haploid cell*. It has single chromosomes rather than homologous (matching) pairs. When a sperm unites with an ovum, they form a new individual having diploid cells. Diploid cells have similar complements of chromosomes.

Meiosis I:

1. Prophase I—DNA is replicated at the end of interphase I before prophase I begins. The formation of threadlike spindle fibers that will attach to the chromosomes begins. The homologous chromosome pairs (the ones that are alike) are located together. Synapse or crossing over of the chromosomes can occur in this phase, giving a different combination of genes. The nuclear membrane and the nucleolus will be dismantled by the end of this phase.

2. Metaphase I—The tetrads (groups of four chromosomes that are alike) align at the equator, with spindle fibers attached from each centromere to the poles. The centromere is the point of attachment between the two chromatids.

3. Anaphase I—The centromere does not duplicate. The paired chromosomes are pulled to the poles by the shortening spindle fibers. This halves the chromosome number.

4. Telophase I—Chromosomes are still joined, with half the original chromosome number (haploid number). The nucleolus and the nuclear membrane reform. Two daughter cells are produced with one half the original chromosome number.

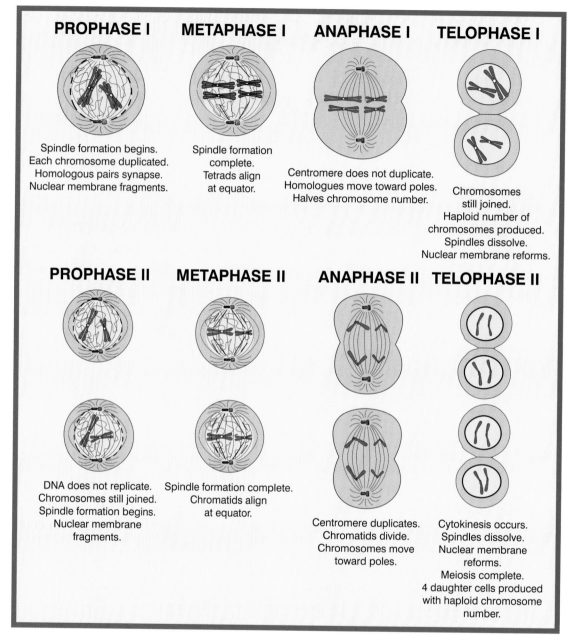

4–12. Divisions and phases of meiosis.

Meiosis II:

1. Prophase II—DNA does not replicate before the phase begins. Spindle formation begins.

2. Metaphase II—The chromatids align at the equator of the cell, with spindle fibers attached from the centromere to the poles.

3. Anaphase II—The centromere duplicates, which divides the chromosomes, with each half pulled by the spindle fibers to the poles.

4. Telophase II—A cell membrane forms between the two developing nuclei. The nucleolus and the nuclear membrane reform. Cytokinesis occurs. Four daughter cells are produced, containing the haploid number of chromosomes.

Multicellular Organisms

Organisms may consist of one or more cells. Many aquatic organisms, such as oysters, clams, fish, and shrimp, are *multicellular organisms* (i.e., have many cells). The cells are organized to form other structures, known as tissues, organs, and organ systems.

Cell specialization is the development of cells for a particular purpose or function. The grouping of specialized cells forms unique organisms. If all cells were alike, organisms would not exist as we know them. Clusters of specialized cells form tissues.

4–13. A fish has millions of cells specialized into organs that perform specific functions. What cell specialization do you see in this fish?

Tissues

A *tissue* is a group of cells that are alike in structure and activity. The cells in tissues are specialized. This means that the cells are suited to specific kinds of activities. In animals, tissues include muscles, nerves, and bones.

Tissues have specific jobs to do in an organism. For example, the cells in muscle tissues provide motion. These specialized cells do not perform other jobs.

Organs

An *organ* is a collection of tissues that work together to perform a specific function, such as the gills of a fish. Although, the tissues may differ in the jobs they do, each contributes to the overall function of an organ. Examples of organs in animals are the skin, heart, lungs, stomach, and liver. In plants, organs include roots, leaves, and stems.

Organ Systems

An *organ system* is the association of several organs that work together to perform an activity. These are the major systems of the bodies of many animals. For example, the digestive system is made up of several organs: mouth, stomach, small intestine, large intestine, and others. Organ systems are typically found in complex animal organisms. An example of an organ system in a plant is the vascular system.

MORPHOLOGY AND PHYSIOLOGY OF FINFISH

Morphology and physiology are important in providing the cultural practices needed for success in finfish aquaculture. A finfish is any fish that has fins. This encompasses a large number of fish species.

BILATERAL SYMMETRY

Most fish are *bilaterally symmetrical*; that is, they could be divided into two mirror-identical halves. Anterior refers to the front of a fish (the end with the mouth and head). Posterior refers to the tail end of a fish. The belly plane of a fish is ventral. The back plane, or the opposite of ventral, is dorsal. The side of a fish is lateral.

Fish producers need to understand the meaning of anterior, posterior, ventral, dorsal, and lateral as related to the species they produce.

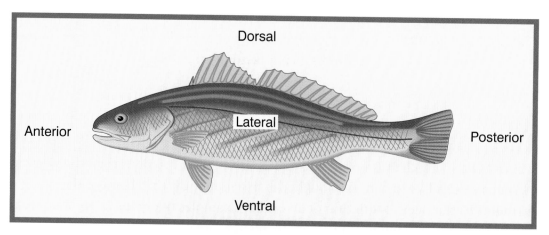

4–14. Locations of the common sides of a fish.

EXTERNAL FEATURES

The body of a fish can be divided into three parts: head, trunk, and tail. The head begins at the nose and ends at the posterior end of the operculum (gill cover). The snout is located between the anterior end of the premaxillary (outer jaw bone) and the eye. The nares, or nostrils, are located on the snout, usually one on each side. The dorsal part of the head is called the nape. The ventral part is called the thorax.

The trunk begins at the posterior end of the operculum and extends to the anus. The humeral area is the side of the trunk. The trunk contains the dorsal fin, a pair of pectoral fins, and a pair of pelvic fins. The length of the trunk varies widely among different fish. The trunk of the channel catfish is very short when compared with that of the rainbow trout, for example.

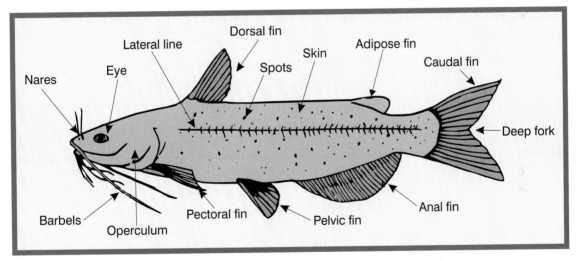

4–15. External parts of channel catfish (*Ictalurus punctatus*).

The tail extends from the anus to the posterior tip of the caudal fin. The tail contains another fin, the anal fin, which is located just posterior to the anus. The tail may also have an adipose fin, a fleshy fin found on salmon, trout, and catfish.

The fins on a fish are supported by soft rays and sometimes by spines. The spines, if present, will be located anterior to the soft rays of a fin. The shapes and number of rays in fins are often used as the basis for identification.

The lateral line, visible on the trunk and tail, is a series of pores on a linear series of scales. On a fish without scales, the lateral line shows up as a small crease or indention running the length of the trunk and tail. The lateral line is part of the sensory system of the fish.

SYSTEMS

Fish have several body systems. Each system has specific duties to perform. Good health is needed to assure that the systems perform as they should. Disease sometimes damages systems so that they fail. A producer needs to understand systems and take steps to promote good health.

Nervous System

The nervous system of a fish has two major parts: the central nervous system and the peripheral nervous system. The central nervous system contains the brain and the spinal cord. The peripheral nervous system contains two types of paired nerves. Nerves that branch from the spinal cord are called spinal nerves, and nerves that branch from the brain are called cranial nerves.

Sensation is associated with the nervous system. Stimuli are detected by sensation, and the fish responds in a particular way. If the sensation is hazardous, the fish tries to escape. If the sensation is pleasant, such as the appearance of food, the fish moves to continue the sensation, such as by consuming the food materials.

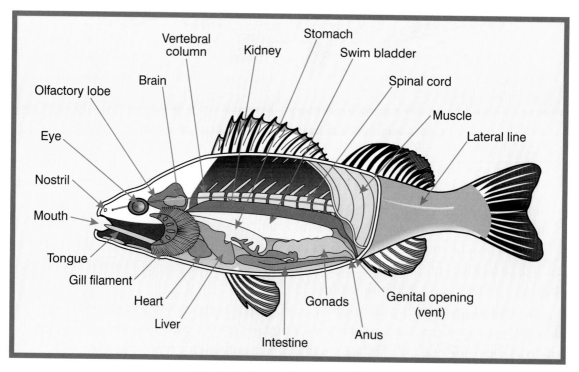

4–16. Major internal parts of a finfish.

Sensory System

The sensory system of fish consists of the eyes, the ears, the nares (with olfactory sacs), and the skin (and its appendages). The eyes will vary, depending on the type of fish. Fish that must see their food, such as trout, have larger eyes. Fish that find food by their sense of smell, such as catfish, have smaller eyes. Most fish do not have external ears but sense vibrations through the ear bones in their heads. The sense of smell is accomplished through the olfactory sacs, which open through the nares, usually located between the eyes and the snout.

The skin and its appendages, such as barbells and cirri, give fish a sense of touch. The skin secretes a substance that makes fish slimy, or slippery. Also, on some fish, the scales are developed from the embryonic cells of the dermis, the inner layer of the skin. The outer layer of the skin is called the epidermis.

Circulatory System

A fish has a heart and various blood vessels similar to other higher animals. Both white and red blood cells are present in the circulatory system. *Arteries* carry blood from the heart. The primary arteries in fish are the dorsal aorta, the ventral aorta, the carotid artery, and the coelicomesenteric artery. *Veins* carry blood to the heart. The portal system transports blood to the liver, from where it is then transported to the heart through the hepatic vein. Other primary veins are the portal vein, the caudal vein, and the anterior cardinals.

CONNECTION

GRASS CARP TESTING

Grass carp are sometimes used in fish ponds to control unwanted vegetation. Occasionally, these carp escape into nearby natural streams and lakes, where they reproduce rapidly. They will consume and destroy natural habitat for wild fish. The result is that the native fish will not thrive and the streams and lakes will no longer have native fish.

To prevent a takeover by escaping grass carp, carp eggs are treated at spawning, making the resulting fish functionally sterile. This means that they do not reproduce. These fish are known as triploid grass carp because of the genetic alteration caused by the treatment chemical. The cells of the fish have three sets of homologous chromosomes rather than the usual two sets.

Here a fish producer is determining triploidy of a fish. The equipment being used is a coulter counter with monitor. It uses a tiny amount of blood to test quickly for size of blood cell. Small blood cells indicate that the fish is diploid and capable of reproduction. Large blood cells indicate that the fish is triploid and therefore sterile. Only triploid grass carp are released into fish ponds for vegetation control.

Skeletal System

The skeletal system of a fish consists of two major parts: the axial skeleton and the appendicular skeleton. The axial skeleton contains the skull (the cranium, which protects the brain) and the visceral skeleton, which is made up of the jaws and gill arches. The remainder of the axial skeleton is composed of the vertebrae and ribs.

The appendicular skeleton consists of the girdles of the paired fins and the bones supporting the fins.

Muscular System

Fish move through the water by undulating their bodies. The muscular system is composed of a series of myotomes, or muscle segments, arranged in the shape of a "W" lying on its side. The myotomes are separated by connective tissues called myosepta.

The muscle tissue of fish is the desired food product. Growers consider the quantity and quality of muscle tissue when selecting a species to culture. Of course, other factors are also important, such as adaptability to the climate.

Respiratory System

In fish, the primary organs that oxygenate the blood and exchange carbon dioxide are the *gills*. Gills are blood-filled membranes located under the operculum. The lamellae have spaces through which blood moves rapidly. The afferent artery carries blood to the gills, and the efferent artery carries oxygenated blood back to the heart.

As the fish swims, water is forced through the mouth and passes over the gills, where the oxygen–carbon dioxide transfer occurs. The oxygenated blood is then transported to the heart and the rest of the body to continue the cycle.

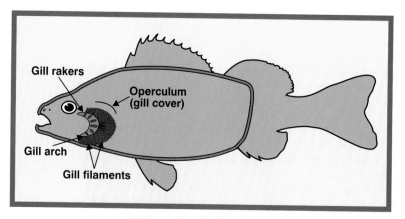

4–17. Location of gills on a fish.

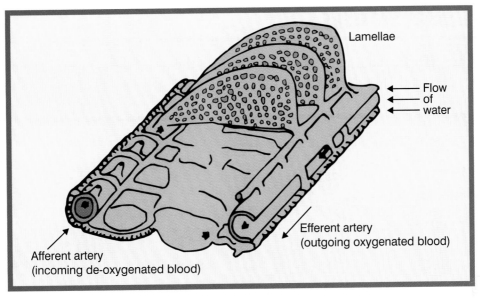

4–18. Parts of a gill filament.

Digestive System

The digestive system of a fish is composed of the mouth, the esophagus, the stomach, the intestine, and the anus. The food moves through the mouth and the esophagus to the stomach, where most of the digestion occurs. The digestive process is completed in the intestine, and wastes are excreted by the anus.

The size and shape of the parts vary according to the type of fish and its natural diet. For example, the catfish, a bottom feeder in its natural habitat, has an inferior mouth, while the rainbow trout has a terminal, or normal, mouth. A fish that is strictly a surface feeder usually has a superior mouth. A fish that feeds on algae and microorganisms will have a small stomach and a long intestine. A carnivorous fish (one that eats other animals) will have a large stomach and a short intestine.

MORPHOLOGY AND PHYSIOLOGY OF DECAPOD CRUSTACEANS

Shrimp, crawfish, and lobster are three important decapod crustaceans. They are sometimes referred to as decapods. They are part of the same order as insects, and their body parts may be observed in much the same way.

EXTERNAL FEATURES

The three primary body parts of a crustacean are the head, the carapace (similar to the thorax in an insect), and the abdomen.

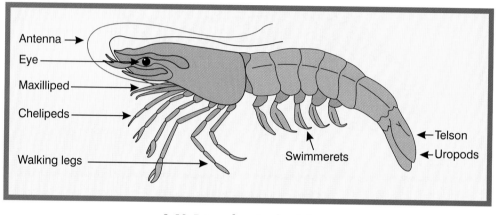

4–19. External parts of a shrimp.

The head of a decapod contains the antenna, the eyes, and the maxilliped. These parts may look quite different, depending on the species.

The carapace consists of the chelipeds (clawed appendages) and the walking legs.

The abdomen is the body part that has most of the "meat" of a crustacean. The swimmerets (short legs that help in swimming) are part of the abdomen. The "tail" of a decapod is made up of the uropods and the telson.

Nervous System

The decapod's nervous system is similar to that of vertebrates but not nearly so complex. A decapod has a central nervous system with a brain (or at least a ganglionic mass) and a ventral nerve cord. Several *ganglia* (masses of nerves) branch from the ventral nerve cord to serve the major appendages.

Sensory System

Decapods are very responsive to light and to movement. The primary sense organs include the eyes, the antennae, and the tactile hairs. The antennae and the tactile hairs are responsive to the tactile stimuli of contact with other organisms or movement of water. Lobsters and crabs have very good vision, which helps them find prey.

Circulatory System

A decapod has an open circulatory system with a single-chambered heart. The blood, or hemolymph, flows freely through the hemocoelic cavity. The heart pumps the blood, but circulation also occurs as the result of movement and gut contractions. The decapod has arteries to carry blood away from the heart, but it lacks veins. Blood returns to the hemocoelic cavity through passages called sinuses.

Skeletal System

Every decapod has an **exoskeleton**, which means that the skeleton is outside the body. The exoskeleton is made of a chitin-protein material secreted by the epidermis. The epidermis is a single layer of skin cells.

Decapods, such as the lobster, blue crab, shrimp, freshwater prawn, and crawfish, all grow by the process of molting. **Molting** refers to an animal's shedding its outer shell (exoskeleton) and increasing in size as it develops a new one. A blue crab, for example, increases about one third in size at each molt. Molting stops when an organism is mature.

Molting is an important phase in the production of some species. The softshell crab, for example, is a crab harvested during molting. The crab has lost its exoskeleton and has not developed another.

4–20. The crawfish is an example of a decapod crustacean. Note the hard outer skeleton called the exoskeleton. (Courtesy, National Oceanic & Atmospheric Administration)

Muscular System

Crustaceans have a well-developed system of muscles for various types of locomotion. Decapods have evolved so that those special appendages, all the same on lower crustaceans, have specialized functions and muscles to control those functions. The cheliped, the large claw on a lobster, for example, is used for protection and for tearing some foods.

The appendages on the abdomen, the swimmerets, are obviously used for swimming. Between these, the walking legs have developed for terrestrial (land) movement.

Respiratory System

When in water, decapods breathe through their gills. The water may be moving from front to back or from back to front. The decapods have appropriate openings for either case. In shrimp, the carapace moves, creating a negative pressure to draw the water in. Respiration also occurs through cell diffusion in the exoskeleton.

Digestive System

The basic digestive system of decapods consists of a foregut, a midgut, and a hindgut. The foregut varies, depending on the diet of the particular species. It may be a simple esophagus or a series of straining or filtering mechanisms. The midgut normally contains various outpockets, referred to as ceca, midgut glands, and diverticula. The hindgut is usually very short and similar to an intestine. It ends at the anus.

MORPHOLOGY AND PHYSIOLOGY OF COMMON MOLLUSKS

Oysters, clams, and mussels are common mollusks that may be cultivated. Snails, scallops, and other species are also cultivated. Some species are freshwater; most are saltwater.

EXTERNAL FEATURES

Although clams and mussels are cultured in some areas, the most important mollusks to aquaculture are the oysters *Crassostrea virginica* and *C. gigas.* The oyster is a bivalve mollusk. This means it has two sides of a shell hinged together by a ligament. The ligament is located at the pointed end of the shell, called the beak or anterior region. The rounded posterior end of the shell has an oval-shaped, pigmented (colored) area called the muscle scar. The muscle scar is from the adductor muscle. The oyster uses the adductor muscle to pull the shell closed when it senses danger.

The adductor muscle must be cut before the shell can be opened to expose the inner parts of the oyster. This is usually done with a specialized oyster knife. Cutting muscle and opening the shell is known as shucking.

With the shell opened, the oyster will look like a mass of flesh. Closer inspection, however, will reveal the gill, mouth, stomach, intestine, gonad, and anus.

Skeletal System

The shell is created by the mantle, a double fold of the body wall that lines the surfaces of the valves. While using elements from the water to create the shell, the mantle also protects the inner organs.

The shell consists of three layers: the periostracum, the prismatic layer, and the nacreous layer. The periostracum is made of an organic material called **conchiolin**. The periostracum protects the rest of the shell from erosion caused by sand and water. Other organisms are often found attached to this outer layer.

The middle layer, or prismatic layer, is made of alternating layers of calcium carbonate and conchiolin.

4–21. The bivalve mollusk shell on the left (mussel shell) is open, and the one on the right (clam shell) is closed.

4–22. An opened oyster on half of its shell.

The inner layer, or nacreous layer, is commonly known as mother-of-pearl. It is composed of plates of calcium carbonate. A pearl is formed when the oyster secretes several layers of nacre around a foreign object, such as a grain of sand. The oyster's purpose in creating a pearl is to prevent the soft inner parts from becoming irritated. The *Crassostrea virginica* produces poor-quality pearls and thus is not usually cultivated for this purpose. Asian oysters produce most of the pearls that have value as jewelry.

Nervous System

An oyster does not have a true brain. Instead, it has two masses of nerves called ganglia. Small nerves radiate from the ganglia to all parts of the oyster.

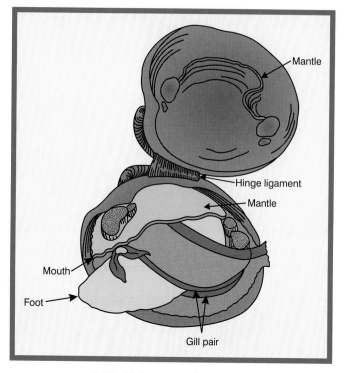

4–23. Major parts of an oyster.

Sensory System

Oysters do not need eyes or ears since they do not move around. They can detect changes in light, however, and will close their shells when a shadow falls over them. The most notable evidence of senses in an oyster is the formation of a pearl when a foreign substance enters the shell.

Circulatory System

An oyster has a three-chambered heart located just above the adductor muscle. Blood is forced out the ventricle to the gills for oxygenation. Some blood returns to the heart from the mantle, while the rest is purified in the very small kidney before returning to the heart. Oyster blood has a bluish tint because of the copper content.

Muscular System

Oysters do not have a complex muscular system. Because oysters are sessile animals (they do not move around in search of food), they have no need for a well-developed muscular system. The primary muscle of the oyster is the adductor muscle, which, as mentioned earlier, keeps the shell closed when necessary.

Respiratory System

The gills accomplish respiration in oysters, just as in fish. Oxygen (O_2) diffuses from the water, flowing across the gills into the bloodstream, to be carried to the rest of the body. At the same time, carbon dioxide (CO_2) is released into the environment. Some oxygen–carbon dioxide transfer occurs in the mantle, which is a tissue covering the internal organs of the oyster.

Digestive System

Oysters, clams, and other mollusk species are filter feeders. A *filter feeder* is an organism that filters small particles of food materials from the water. The mantle filters out the larger particles and allows microorganisms to pass through. The organisms, usually single celled, are often collectively referred to as plankton. The plankton particles are trapped in mucus from the gills and moved to the mouth of the mollusk.

The mouth accepts the food unless there is too much or the particles are too large. Then, the excess is rejected to a cavity that is emptied when the shell closes.

The food particles move from the mouth through a short esophagus to the stomach, where nutrients are absorbed. The fecal material moves through the intestine and out the anus. The anus empties into the cavity where excess food is rejected by the mouth.

REPRODUCTIVE PROCESSES

Reproduction is either sexual or asexual. ***Sexual reproduction*** is the production of a new individual from the union of a male sex cell and a female sex cell. The specific processes vary somewhat among the aquatic species, but the general process is constant. Hatchery operators are well aware of the processes in sexual reproduction.

Asexual reproduction is the production of a new individual without the union of a male sex cell and a female sex cell. It is the same as cloning. Asexual reproduction occurs naturally with some organisms, such as many kinds of water plants. A water hyacinth, for example, may send out growth structures that develop roots and separate from the parent plant.

FISH

All the important aquaculture fish reproduce by spawning. In nature, the female lays her eggs, and the male deposits sperm over the eggs. After fertilization, one of them usually guards the eggs until they hatch. This is not always the female. In catfish, for example, the male guards the eggs. In some species of tilapia, the female holds the fertilized eggs in her mouth until they are hatched.

Fish vary widely in their preferred place of spawning. Some spawn on the bottom of a pond. Others, such as trout, require running water to spawn. Catfish need a cover and, in the wild, usually spawn in submerged hollow logs. In ponds, the catfish used for reproduction usually spawn in human-made barrels or boxes. If the preferred method of spawning is not available, many fish simply will not spawn.

4–24. One benefit of aquaculture is the control of spawning and hatching. Here rainbow trout eggs are being placed in a jar for hatching.

4–25. Salmon spawning in fresh water. (Courtesy, National Oceanic & Atmospheric Administration)

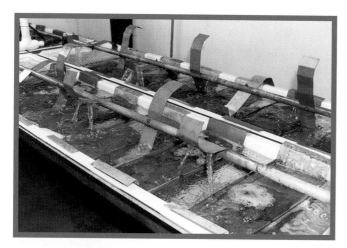

4–26. Egg masses in a catfish hatchery.

The tilapia is an example of a tremendously reproductive species. This causes some problems in that tilapia can reproduce before they reach harvesting size. As a result, the tilapia use too much energy for reproduction and not enough for growth. One way to reduce this problem when culturing the bottom-spawning species is to place a net that keeps tilapia from the bottom so they cannot spawn. Another remedy is to raise only fish of the same sex, usually males. This procedure is discussed in more detail in Chapter 12.

Some fish, such as salmon, live most of their lives in salt water but return to fresh water to spawn. These fish are called **anadromous**. Fish that spend most of their lives in fresh water but spawn in salt water are called **catadromous**.

Many cultured fish are reproduced in hatcheries. With catfish, the fertilized egg mass is removed from the tank or barrel and placed in the hatchery. In some species, the eggs are removed from the female and the sperm are removed from the male, with the fertilization being done artificially. Trout used in aquaculture are usually spawned this way.

DECAPODS

The female decapod secretes a substance (sex pheromone) that alerts the male that she is receptive to breeding. Immediately after a molt at maturity, breeding occurs. Most decapods breed by copulation. The male places the sperm in or near the female's seminal receptacle. Depending on the species, the male sometimes remains a few days to protect the female from predators and other males. The female holds the fertilized eggs until they hatch.

Most decapods must reach certain sizes before they become sexually mature. A male lobster, for example, must have a carapace of about 40 to 45 millimeters long before he can produce sperm, but he may not be able to mate with a mature female until he is about 70 millimeters in carapace length.

Mollusks

Reproduction among clams, mussels, scallops, and other mollusks tends to be similar to that of oysters.

The oyster species of *Crassostrea virginica* and *C. gigas* are protandrous hermaphrodites. This means that the same oyster may be male or female at different times. Although not always, the oyster is usually male, producing sperm its first spawning season or two. After this period, the oyster will usually become female and produce eggs for the rest of its life. Although very uncommon in these two species, some oysters produce both sperm and egg cells at the same time.

Sperm produced by a male and eggs produced by a female are released into the mantle cavity, where the combination of water movement and cilia action moves them out into the water. Because fertilization and development of the offspring take place in the water, *Crassostrea virginica* and *C. gigas* are called nonincubatory oysters. In incubatory oysters, the females hold the eggs in their mantle cavities until sperm enter to fertilize them.

Each oyster produces millions of sperm or eggs, but the survival rate is low. During the spawn, the gonad becomes so enlarged that the rest of the inner parts of the oyster are extremely small. After the spawn, the oyster increases the energy spent in digestion to build its energy reserves.

REVIEWING

MAIN IDEAS

Every organism has a life span, which is the length of the organism's life. Typically, all organisms go through five life-span stages: beginning, growth, maturity, decline, and death.

Life processes are the essential activities for an organism to remain in the living condition. These include getting and using food, movement, circulation, respiration, growth and repair, secretion, sensation, and reproduction. Reproduction is not needed for an organism to live, but it is essential for a species to perpetuate itself.

Morphology and physiology deal with the structures and functions of organisms. Cells are the basic structures and carry out specific roles. Cells increase by division, or mitosis, and this is how growth occurs. Some cells are involved in reproduction. They divide by meiosis. Cells form tissues,

tissues form organs, and organs form systems. An organ system is a collection of organs that work together to carry out important life processes.

Finfish, decapod crustaceans, and mollusks are characterized by specific morphology and physiology. External and internal features promote life. Internal systems perform important processes. These systems include nervous, sensory, circulatory, skeletal, muscular, respiratory, digestive, and reproductive. Some species have internal skeletons; others have exoskeletons.

Reproduction may be through sexual or asexual processes. Most animals reproduce sexually, which involves the union of a male sex cell and a female sex cell. Plants and other species also reproduce sexually, though some reproduce asexually. Asexual reproduction is a natural cloning process.

When an aquaculture producer selects a type of aquacrop to produce, the biology of the particular species often plays an important role. For an aquafarm to be productive, it must be adapted to the different biological requirements of the species being cultured.

QUESTIONS

Answer the following questions, using complete sentences and correct spelling.

1. What is life span? What are the five stages in life span?

2. Organisms typically have eight life processes. List them and briefly explain each.

3. What is anatomy? How is it related to morphology?

4. What is the role of mitosis? Meiosis?

5. Draw a fish and label the following sides: dorsal, ventral, anterior, posterior, and lateral.

6. What are the three major body parts of a fish?

7. What are the three major body parts of a decapod?

8. Explain how an oyster makes a pearl.

9. In most aquatic animals, what purpose do the gills serve? How do they accomplish this purpose?

10. What does filter feeder mean?

11. What often determines the shape of a fish's mouth?

12. What is the most important habitat consideration of oysters? Why is this so important?

13. What happens to catfish and many other warmwater fish when the water temperature gets too cold? What happens to tilapia?

14. Why does an aquaculture producer need a knowledge of aquatic biology?

EVALUATING

Match the term with the correct definition. Write the letter of the term on the line provided.

a. anadromous
b. arteries
c. bilaterally symmetrical
d. exoskeleton

e. gills
f. life span
g. molting
h. life cycle

i. morphology
j. physiology
k. veins
l. organ system

_____ 1. Blood vessels that carry blood away from the heart

_____ 2. Form and structure of an organism

_____ 3. Functions of cells, tissues, organs, and systems of an organism

_____ 4. Length of life of an organism

_____ 5. Hard, outer skeleton

_____ 6. An animal's losing its shell

_____ 7. Changes in form of an organism as it goes through life

_____ 8. Living in salt water, spawning in fresh water

_____ 9. Blood vessels that carry blood to the heart

_____ 10. Several organs working together

_____ 11. Blood-filled membrane that fish use for oxygenating blood

_____ 12. Having two identical sides

EXPLORING

1. Dissect the following: one fish, one oyster, one decapod, and one frog. Compare and contrast the body parts in a written report.

2. Set up an experiment with four of the same species of filter feeders, such as clams, mussels, or oysters. Place two in clear water. Place the other two in water with food coloring. After one day, take one of the filter feeders from the colored water and dissect it. Dissect one from the clear water and compare. Remove the other one from the colored water and place it with the one remaining in clear water. After another day, dissect them both and compare. Write a report of your observations and conclusions.

3. Download some pictures of aquaculture species from the World Wide Web. Create a slide show of species that are important in your community. (Hint: Go to the AquaNIC homepage at **http://aquanic.org**.) Note: Be careful not to use material that is copyrighted in a way that would violate copyright laws. Your teacher can explain this to you.

Nutrients and Feeding

OBJECTIVES

This chapter covers the basic nutrient needs of aquaculture species, with emphasis on aquatic animals. It has the following objectives:

1 Explain how animals and plants vary in the acquisition of nutrients

2 Discuss the nutrient requirements of aquaculture species

3 Explain how nutrient requirements are met during culture

4 Describe kinds and sources of feed

5 Identify and evaluate approaches in feeding

6 Discuss buying and storing feed

TERMS

additive	free-access feeding	pellet
buoyancy	handling	proteins
carbohydrates	ingest	ration
diet	meal	scheduled feeding
fats	minerals	storing
food	nutrient	vitamins

AQUACROPS need nutrients to live and grow. When nutrient needs are not properly met, aquacrops fail to thrive and produce marketable crops. Fortunately, the producer can take steps to assure that nutrient needs are met.

In the wild, aquatic organisms obtain nutrients from their habitat. Fish, for example, ingest food materials, such as smaller fish and insects. Each species tends naturally to consume certain kinds of food materials that are available in its habitat. If these become low, the fish population may be lost.

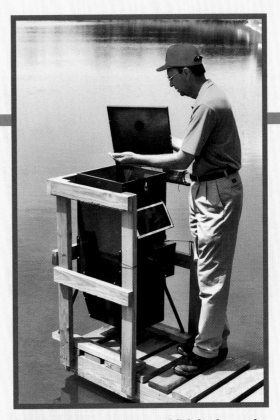

5–1. Checking a solar-powered fish feeder used in pond culture.

The first aquaculturists observed the natural food behavior of fish and other organisms. They tried to provide these same food materials in culturing aquatic organisms. Today, scientists have researched many species and know how to meet nutrient needs and promote growth more efficiently. But, the research continues. As more becomes known, more needs to be studied!

NUTRIENTS FOR ANIMALS AND PLANTS

Aquatic organisms require nutrients. A *nutrient* is a substance used by organisms to live and grow. Proper kinds and amounts of nutrients are essential for rapid growth and efficient production. Aquaculture producers must be well aware of needed nutrients.

Animals and plants vary in how they get nutrients. In some cases, plants can obtain nutrients by cleaning water fouled by fish or other uses. Algae and some other organisms may act similar to plants.

5–2. Hand feeding fish in a recirculating tank.

ANIMALS

Animals obtain nutrients by ingesting food. *Ingest* means that the animals consume or eat food. *Food* is any material eaten that contains nutrients needed by animals.

Food materials eaten vary with the nature of the species. Some species, such as sharks, are predators and carnivores; that is, they prey upon and eat other animals. Some species, such as grass carp, are herbivores and eat only plant materials. Others, such as catfish, are omni-

5–3. Fish are ingesting floating feed thrown on the water.

vores and consume food materials of both plant and animal origin. Some species ingest only living materials; others eat dead materials.

Once ingested, food goes through the process of digestion. Digestion breaks food materials down and into substances that can be used by the body. Undigested food materials are eliminated from the body as waste. (The digestive system was discussed in Chapter 4.)

Research has found that some feeding practices promote improved growth and profitability. For example, as channel catfish grow, their food intake as a percent of body weight decreases. The amount of feed needed for gain, however, increases. Water temperatures and other conditions also affect feed use and efficiency.

Rations

A *ration* is the feed given an animal each day to meet its nutrient needs. Good rations have variety and are balanced, palatable, economical, and suitable. Palatability refers to how well an animal likes the food material when it is being ingested. A balanced ration meets the needs of an animal in terms of growth, activity, and production.

5–4. Manufactured pellets are the usual diets of cultured aquacrops. (This scoop contains floating feed.)

Diets

A *diet* is the type and amount of feed in a ration. Diets are based on the nutrient needs of animals. Young animals, such as fry, need diets different from those of older animals, such as broodfish. Diet may also be used to regulate growth, assuring that a crop is ready for harvest at a particular time. Diets can be formulated to speed up or slow down rate of growth.

PLANTS

Plants make their food by a process known as photosynthesis. Photosynthesis occurs in the presence of light (usually sunlight) on the leaves of plants. The process involves using carbon dioxide and water to make simple sugars, which the plants use as food. Also, minerals, such as iron, magnesium, and potassium, are needed for plant growth. The notion that plants obtain food is incorrect; plants take in substances from their environment and then manufacture their food.

The most important nutrients are often referred to as chemical elements. The most needed elements for plant growth are oxygen (O), hydrogen (H), carbon (C), nitrogen (N),

5–5. The broad leaves of these watercress plants are very effective in using sunlight for photosynthesis.

phosphorus (P), and potassium (K). The first three are usually readily available in the environment. The last three may be added as fertilizer. Mixed fertilizers are often known by numbers. An example is 10-20-10. This means the fertilizer contains 10 percent nitrogen, 20 percent phosphate (a compound containing phosphorus), and 10 percent potash (a compound containing potassium).

Rate and time of fertilizer application must be understood for each crop. Excessive fertilizer application damages plants and wastes the money invested in the excess. The time of application is just before the plants most need the added nutrients, such as in the spring when growth begins.

Very little research information is available on fertilizing aquatic plants. It is best to talk with a specialist at a university or to another producer.

GENERAL NUTRIENT REQUIREMENTS

Scientists have studied the nutrient requirements of several aquatic animal species. In other cases, producers have found what works best by trial and error.

FISH

Many companies manufacture feeds suitable for the various species of fish discussed in this chapter. For the most important freshwater species, catfish and trout, several companies produce feeds mixed specifically for each. Some of the requirements for fish diets are discussed here.

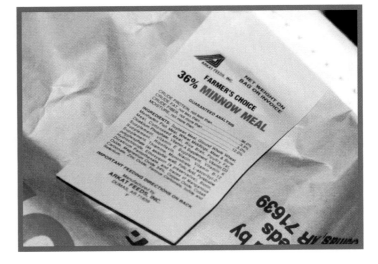

5–6. When an aquacrop becomes established, companies will manufacture feed designed specifically for it. (This shows the label on minnow feed containing 36 percent protein.)

Proteins

Proteins are substances formed by simple organic compounds called amino acids. Proteins are broken down by the digestive process so the fish can use them to form new tissue and to repair damaged tissue. Ten amino acids have been identified as essential amino acids; because fish cannot produce these amino acids, they must be included in their diet. Table 5–1 shows these essential amino acids.

Protein is by far the most critical ingredient in a fish feed. Common prepared feeds range from 25 to 40 percent protein.

Proteins in prepared rations usually come from fish meal, but they may also come from other animal waste products, such as blood meal or meat scraps. Some of the proteins may come from plant sources, such as soybean meal. Fish that are natural carnivores require a feed that derives at least 50 percent of its protein from animal products. Fish that are naturally herbivores or omnivores can get by on less but still may need around 30 percent to come from animal products.

Table 5–1. Amino Acids Essential to Fish and the Minimum Percentage Required for Rainbow Trout

Amino Acid	Percentage Required
Arginine	2.5
Lysine	2.1
Isoleucine	1.5
Valine	1.5
Cystine	1.0
Leucine	1.0
Threonine	0.8
Histidine	0.7
Methionine	0.5
Tryptophan	0.2

Source: W. O. McLarney, *The Freshwater Aquaculture Book.* Point Roberts, WA: Hartley & Marks, Inc., 1987.

5–7. Fingerlings, because they are growing rapidly, need feed with a higher percentage of protein than fish nearing maturity.

Fats

Fats are substances composed of fatty acids. In fish rations, fats usually come from animal wastes. Fish require fats to maintain proper health and growth. Any artificial feed ration for fish should contain supplemental fats.

The amount of fat in a diet usually depends on the temperature of the water in which the fish are cultured. This is because the melting point of the fat must be below the water temperature if the fat is to be digested completely. For this reason, feeds prepared for coldwater fish, such as trout, usually contain unsaturated fats from vegetable oils. Feeds for warmwater fish, such as catfish and tilapia, usually contain saturated animal fats.

The total amount of fat in the diet is usually between 4 and 15 percent.

Carbohydrates

Carbohydrates are substances that come from sugars, starches, and celluloses. Carbohydrates provide fish with energy. Fish vary greatly in their ability to digest carbohydrates. Fish that eat mostly plants, such as carp, can digest more carbohydrates because their bodies produce the enzyme amylase, which breaks down the carbohydrates. Fish that eat mostly animals, such as catfish and trout, usually need less than 10 percent carbohydrates in their diets.

Minerals

Minerals are inorganic earth materials. Several minerals are important to the health and growth of fish. Because many minerals are necessary only in very small amounts, they are often called trace elements. (Large amounts of some of these minerals could be fatal.)

The following minerals have been identified as necessary for fish: calcium, phosphorus, iron, silicon, manganese, magnesium, boron, cobalt, copper, iodine, molybdenum, selenium, zinc, and sodium.

A knowledge of the characteristics of the water in which the fish are being grown is necessary to determine which minerals are deficient. A choice must usually be made between adding the minerals to the water as part of a fertilization program and adding them to the feed as a supplement. Adding the minerals to the water is usually easier, but in raceways and other moving water systems, adding the minerals as a feed supplement may be better. Some commercially prepared feeds already contain sufficient quantities of some minerals.

Vitamins

Vitamins are organic substances necessary for proper nutrition. Vitamin deficiencies can be very serious, causing poor growth, anemia, skin lesions, clubbed gills, and many other problems. Fortunately, most commercial feeds contain vitamin supplements.

5–8. Bags of premix await being added to feed during manufacture to increase vitamin content. Very small amounts produce good results with aquatic species.

The two types of vitamins important to fish are water-soluble vitamins and fat-soluble vitamins. Water-soluble vitamins are taken into the body and used; then, any excess is excreted. Fat-soluble vitamins are stored in the body. Therefore, an excess of fat-soluble vitamins in the diet may cause problems, just as a deficiency might. Table 5–2 lists the vitamins important to fish.

Table 5–2. Vitamins Essential to Fish and Minimum Daily Requirement (MDR) for Rainbow Trout

Vitamin	MDR
Water-Soluble Vitamins:	
Thiamine (B₁)	0.15–0.2 mg/kg of fish
Folacin or folic acid	0.10–0.15
Riboflavin (B₂)	0.5–1.0
Cyanocobalamin (B₁₂)	0.0002–0.0003
Pyridoxine (B₆)	0.25–0.5
Ascorbic acid (C)	450–500
Pantothenic acid	1.0–2.0
Inositol	18–20
Niacin or nicotinic acid	4.0–7.0
Choline	50–60
Biotin (H)	0.04–0.08
Fat-Soluble Vitamins:	
K₃	15–20 mg/kg of fish
A	8,000–10,000
E	125 IU/kg of feed
D	1,000

Source: W. O. McLarney, *The Freshwater Aquaculture Book.* Point Roberts, WA: Hartley & Marks, Inc., 1987.

Additives

An *additive* is a substance placed with the feed ingredients during manufacture. Additives are considered nonnutritive ingredients. Additives are used to facilitate feed manufacture, prevent deterioration, improve health of the aquacrop, and ensure a quality manufactured feed product. Antibiotics are additives in some feeds.

Caution must be followed, as some additives cannot be fed to aquacrops that will be used for food. In some cases, no feeding of feeds with certain additives is allowed. In other cases, a minimum number of days must elapse between time of feeding and harvest.

DECAPOD CRUSTACEANS

The nutrient requirements of decapods vary greatly. All species require a source of phytoplankton or zooplankton as larvae. Adult crawfish are omnivorous but usually require some type of forage supplement, such as wastes from a rice field or a commercially prepared feed, when they are cultured.

Shrimp are usually fed by fertilization of the pond, but commercially prepared chicken feed or shrimp feed is sometimes used as a supplement. Freshwater shrimp in tanks or ponds are fed a commercial feed.

Crab are natural scavengers that remove food materials from water. They will eat other small animals, decaying organic material, and material that floats in the water. Crabs prey on oysters, hard clams, and some fish. They will eat dead fish and other dead aquatic animals. Juvenile crab and zoeae eat algae, plankton, and small particles of dead organisms.

MOLLUSKS

Mollusk species appear quite similar in nutrient needs. Scientists are continuing to investigate the needs of various species, such as clams and mussels. Discussion in this chapter is based on the oyster.

Because they are filter feeders, oysters are not fed when cultured except in a hatchery or research situation. Very little is known about their nutritional requirements. The primary concern with oysters is that they have plenty of phytoplankton and that the water in which they are cultured be free of pollutants. Oysters are extremely susceptible to pollution; their bodies absorb the pollutants just as they absorb nutrients. Thus, water pollutants are a primary concern to aquafarmers who produce oysters.

5–9. Species produced in tanks and other facilities do not have access to natural foods. Feed must be provided. An example is this flow-through hanging basket system being used to produce clams. (Courtesy, National Oceanic and Atmospheric Administration)

MEETING NUTRIENT NEEDS

Organisms get nutrients to meet their needs from the environment in which they live. How the nutrients are obtained and what nutrients are needed vary with the species. Wild fish, for example, consume food materials found in the water that is their habitat.

PROMOTE NATURAL FOOD GROWTH

Ponds, streams, lakes, and other bodies of water contain algae, plants, and animals that serve as food for aquatic species. Steps can be taken to promote the growth of these organisms.

Fertilizer can be applied to a pond to increase the growth of certain food materials, especially zooplankton and phytoplankton. This approach is used with low rates of stocking, with the rearing of young, and with ponds used for recreation, livestock watering, and similar purposes.

Even when fertilizer is used, the increased growth of natural food materials is inadequate to meet the nutrient needs of fish stocked at a typical commercial fish farm rate. Most unfertilized ponds in which feed is not added will produce 50 to 100 pounds of fish a year per acre of water. When fertilizer is used, that amount is increased to 200 to 400 pounds of fish per acre. Fertilizing a pond is most common for bass and sunfish production.

Pond water should be analyzed for alkalinity, total hardness, and calcium hardness before fertilization. Ponds with low alkalinity (20 ppm or below) will need liming before being fertilized. Liming rates are typically 1.5 to 2.5 tons of dolomitic lime per acre. Common kinds of

5–10. Agricultural fertilizer may be used in aquaculture ponds to promote the growth of natural foods. Phosphorus is usually the most needed nutrient.

complete fertilizers as used in agronomic crop production are often used, such as 10-20-10. Nitrogen is needed more in new ponds and may create excessive plankton growth in established ponds. Phosphorus is likely the most important nutrient in fertilizing a pond. Potassium is less likely to produce improved results. Fertilizer can be applied in liquid, powder, and granular forms. Time-release or slow-release fertilizer materials may also be used.

The amount of fertilizer to apply varies with water chemistry and fertilizer analysis. High-phosphorus fertilizer blends are used. Some fertilizers that add only phosphorus, such as superphosphate, are also common. Water with low hardness can be made more productive by applying 4 to 8 pounds of fertilizer per acre. Water with high hardness will need 20 pounds of fertilizer per acre.

Organic fertilizer may also be used in ponds. Cotton seed meal is likely the most widely used organic fertilizer.

Fertilizer materials must be distributed around a pond and become suspended in the water. Granular fertilizers are broadcast over the surface of a pond. Liquid materials are the easiest to apply. Water temperature should be above 60°F for fertilizer application.

Using fertilizer on ponds has greater potential in culturing fry and fingerlings. These organisms feed on plankton and require less overall plankton growth to help meet nutritional needs.

Always use care in applying fertilizer to a pond. Too much fertilizer can result in excessive plankton growth and a deficiency of oxygen.

CONNECTION

DIETS MIMIC NATURAL FOODS

The diets of cultured species are developed after studying the natural food sources of aquatic species. Feeds are chosen or formulated that mimic what the species consume in the wild. Careful observation of the habits of wild species is essential.

The Fish Technology Centers of the National Fish Hatchery System of the U.S. Fish and Wildlife Service conduct research into wild fish feeding habits. The findings are used to develop feed materials and approaches appropriate for the species being cultured.

This shows a fishery biologist feeding fish being kept in raceways. The research helps develop feed that improves the health and quality of fish reared in captivity. (Photo courtesy, U.S. Fish and Wildlife Service)

CULTURE FOOD MATERIALS

Some species, particularly newly hatched and juvenile organisms, feed on plankton, shrimp, and other immature organisms. The plankton can be cultured in laboratory situations and provided as feed to the aquatic organisms. Tanks and other facilities are used to grow organisms used as food.

A species of brine shrimp in the genus *Artemia* is an important food source for larval shrimp and marine finfish. Scientists have improved selected strains of *Artemia,* with about 60 strains found today.

More details on plankton production are given elsewhere in the book.

CAPTURE FOOD MATERIALS

Food materials for cultured species are sometimes captured from wild sources. Copepods, minnows, and similar small aquatic animals may be captured and used in feeding cultured aquacrops. Care must be used to prevent the introduction of disease and unwanted wild species into the culture system.

Copepods are captured from freshwater and saltwater sources to use in feeding juvenile forms of aquacrops, such as cobia. A copepod is a very small crustacean. Copepods are part of the plankton mass often found swimming near the surface of the water. Scientists have identified more than 7,500 species of copepods. Copepods are in the phylum Arthropoda, subphylum Crustacea, and class Copepoda. Various devices may be placed in the water to capture copepods.

5–11. A collector for capturing marine copepods that will be fed to juvenile cobia. (Courtesy, National Oceanic and Atmospheric Administration)

PROVIDE MANUFACTURED FEED

In commercial aquaculture, the most common way of providing nutrients to a growing fish crop is to use manufactured feed. Such feed is specially formulated to meet the needs of organisms of specific species and ages.

Using manufactured feed has several benefits. An important one is the ability to use ingredients that assure proper nutrition. The feed materials are also manufactured in forms that promote good management. An

5–12. A large feed mill showing storage elevators and rail cars for transporting grains used in manufacturing the feed.

example is floating feed that requires fish to come to the surface, making it possible to observe feeding behavior. Additives can be used to enhance nutrition or meet the needs of a crop at a particular time. Another benefit is that the cultured crop, such as fish, does not eat foods that are contaminated. Feeds are manufactured with clean, wholesome ingredients. This helps assure a quality food product in the supermarket.

5–13. Inside structures of a modern feed mill move raw materials and manufactured feed through the grinding, mixing, and forming processes.

FORMS OF FEED

Manufactured feed is prepared in a number of ways. These relate to the size of the feed particle and how the particle responds when it gets into the water.

MANUFACTURING

Manufacturing involves grinding, mixing, and otherwise preparing feed. Feed ingredients such as corn are ground so that they can be mixed and formed into particles that contain nearly equal amounts of nutrients. Mixing must be complete so that all particles provide essential nutrients. Heat is often used in manufacturing or is produced by manufacturing processes. Care is needed to assure that the heat does not lead to deterioration of the nutrients in the feed. Some feed ingredients are cooked as part of manufacturing.

Feed particles vary in size depending on the size of the organism to be fed. Small fish, for example, need small particles of food materials.

Feed manufacturing facilities receive and store feed ingredients. Proper storage is essential to prevent contamination and assure that the feed ingredients do not get wet or get damaged by pests before use.

Ingredients

Ingredients are the materials used in manufacturing feed. Feed ingredients vary with the intended species to receive the feed and the life stage of the organism. Corn, soybean meal, canola meal, meat and bone meal, blood meal, fish meal, and vitamin premixes are often used in manufacturing feed for fish. Each of these ingredients provides nutrients needed for growth and maintenance.

Besides the major ingredients, feed may also have additives. Additives are ingredients that typically do not contain nutrients. They are used to gain a desired quality in the feed or promote the well-being of organisms that consume the feed. Binders are materials added to feed to help the feed particles stick together. Antioxidants are added to prevent oxidation spoilage. Antimicrobial additives may be used to prevent action by microbes that causes

5–14. Yellow corn is a key ingredient in many feeds for growing food fish.

spoilage. Additives may also include enzymes, hormones, pigments, and other materials that promote production of a quality aquacrop.

After manufacturing, feeds are prepared for sale to producers. Some feeds may be bagged. Bags are most widely used for feeds sold to small growers or for specialty feeds used only in small amounts, often in hatcheries. Feed for large grow-out farms is delivered in bulk by large trucks. It is emptied from the trucks into feed bins. These bins are elevated so that feed can be easily removed and placed in feeding equipment.

Life-Stage Feeds

Feeds are typically manufactured to meet the life-stage needs of fish and other aquacrops. Feed is typically of four types: larval, starter, grower, and broodstock. The types are formulated to meet the nutritional needs. Larval and starter feeds have high protein content. Grower and broodstock feeds have lower protein content.

Particle size also varies with life stage. Larval feeds are prepared in very small particle sizes—almost a dust. An

5–15. Careful laboratory testing is used to assure feed quality.

example is partial replacement of artemia feed for larval shrimp that is 100 to 450 microns in diameter. Starter feeds are somewhat larger. Grower and broodstock feeds are still larger in particle size.

Buoyancy

Buoyancy is the characteristics of food particles in water as related to position. Feed particles may be manufactured to sink, float, or remain suspended in a relatively constant position in water.

Floating feed tends to remain on the surface of the water for a while. The feed floats because of the lower density of the pellets. Floating pellets may contain more air than those that sink. Fish rise to the surface to eat floating pellets. This allows the producer to observe the fish as related to food intake. Fish that don't eat are experiencing a problem often related to water quality or disease. Floating feed makes it easy to regulate the amount to feed. No more should be fed than will be consumed in a few minutes. Excess, uneaten feed causes water problems.

Feed that quickly sinks to the bottom of the water does not allow observation of feeding behavior. In some cases, neutral buoyancy feeds are used. They neither float nor sink but tend to remain suspended in water for a time.

Buoyancy also varies with the species of fish. Catfish, though bottom feeders, are fed floating feed. Salmon and sea bass are fed feed that slowly sinks.

PARTICLE PREPARATION

Common feed particles used in food fish production are meals and pellets. Flakes, food sticks, crumbles, and granules are other forms of preparation primarily used with ornamental fish, such as koi.

A *meal* is a coarsely ground feed. It has not been shaped and compressed into particles, such as pellets. Meals are often used as starter feeds for young fish. Most are too large for larval forms of shrimp and mollusks.

A *pellet* is a mixture of ground feed materials that has been compressed to form a feed particle of appropriate size. Pellets are manufactured using heating and extruding processes. Pellet sizes vary depending on the size and species of fish to be fed. Pellet sizes are often stated in metric measurements, such as 3 millimeters or 8 millimeters in diameter. In U.S. aquaculture, pellet sizes are stated in inches. An example is a 3/16-inch-diameter pellet, which is common in feeding catfish.

Water stability is a characteristic desired in pellets. This means that the food materials stay in pellet form for a time in the water—they do not readily disintegrate upon coming into contact with the water. If the pellets disintegrated, the fish might not be able to ingest the nutrients contained in the feed.

5–16. Several different types of feed may be used, depending on the size and type of fish. The smaller granules are for fry, with feed sizes increasing as the fish get larger. (Courtesy, Louisiana Agricultural Experiment Station—Louisiana Cooperative Extension Service, Louisiana State University Agricultural Center)

APPROACHES IN FEEDING

Aquatic animals may be fed in different ways. Each has benefits, but the benefits depend on the species produced and the methods of production. Whatever the approach used, proper nutrition is essential for growth and profit.

Two major approaches are used in feeding: scheduled and free access.

SCHEDULED FEEDING

Scheduled feeding is providing feed each day at specific times. Schedules are established based on the needs of the aquacrop and the producer.

5–17. Scheduled feeding is used with koi in this ornamental water pond.

Young organisms are fed more frequently than older animals. Larval, fry, and juvenile forms receive feed several times a day, with some being fed each hour, 24 hours a day, for their first few days of life. The organisms are very small. Because of their tiny stomachs, they are unable to ingest and store much at a time.

Older fish, such as food fish nearing market size and broodfish, may be fed only once a day. In cold weather, they may be fed less frequently because their metabolisms have slowed.

5–18. A blower feeder behind a tractor is being used to feed fish in a large pond.

The time of feeding should be approximately the same each day. Fish tend to develop a routine and may be more efficient if the same schedule is followed.

Scheduled feeding involves using equipment that blows or throws feed into the water. With a small pond or tank, hand feeding may be appropriate. A large pond requires the use of a pull-behind feeder attached to a tractor PTO. This uses air generated by a fan to blow the feed out into the water. A stationary feeder operated automatically with a timer may also be used for scheduled feeding.

A major benefit of scheduled feeding is that the person doing the feeding gets to observe the eating behavior of the fish. When the fish fail to eat, there is usually a problem, such as oxygen depletion or disease. This allows the producer to take corrective action before the fish die.

FREE-ACCESS FEEDING

Free-access feeding is making feed available all the time so that fish or other animals may eat when they wish. The feed is available on a free-choice basis.

Free-access feeding requires feeding equipment that is designed for the fish or other animal to activate. The activation may involve bumping an object suspended in the water to release feed. Specially prepared feeds may be compressed and placed in the water so that fish can nibble small amounts whenever they choose. A feed of this type is often used in an aquarium when the keeper is not available to feed the fish on a schedule.

The way wild fish, mollusks, and crustaceans ingest their food in nature is much like a free-access approach. In some cases, food materials may not be available all the time.

BUYING AND STORING FEED

Aquaculture producers typically buy feed from a manufacturer and store it for a while in their facilities or on their farms. Both buying and storing should be carefully done to avoid overspending and damage to a valuable feed product.

BUYING

Where and how feed is bought depends somewhat on the kind and life stage of the aquacrop and on the size of the production enterprise. Always buy feed that is appropriate for the kind and life stage of the aquacrop that will receive it.

Small Producers

A producer with a small aquaculture enterprise should buy small quantities of feed appropriate to the enterprise. Buying in large amounts when only small amounts are needed results in more being spent for feed and in problems with storage.

A producer with a few aquariums of ornamental fish should buy small containers of appropriate feed. The likely source would be an aquarium supply company, a pet supplies store, or an Internet site.

A producer with a hatchery or larval facility should buy smaller quantities by volume than a large food fish producer. The food materials may be purchased from an aquaculture feed provider, a farm supplies store, a scientific supply house, or an Internet site.

A producer with one or two small ponds might buy several hundred pounds of feed at a time from a local seed and feed store, a discount store, or an Internet site. Large amounts of feed would not be needed. Buying large amounts and storing them would likely result in a decline in the nutrients in the feed. Mold might grow, vitamins might deteriorate, and the feed might otherwise lose its desirable qualities.

5–19. Feed may be bought in 50-pound bags.

Large Producers

A producer with several acres or more in food fish production would need several tons of feed over a growing season. Most likely, the feed would be bought in bulk and delivered to a

5–20. A large producer may deal directly with a feed mill to obtain the desired nutrients in feed. This feed mill operator is discussing materials flow in the manufacturing process.

feed bin. Bulk feed is more economical because no bags are involved. Bagging feed adds cost to production and requires removing feed from bags when it is used.

A large producer may have a contract with a feed manufacturer for timely delivery of the feed to the farm. Feed should be ordered based on use. Always order a few days ahead of running out to allow time for the feed to be manufactured and delivered. Running out of feed means that the aquacrop is not fed. This delays growth and may create other health-related problems.

HANDLING AND STORING

Feed and the ingredients used to manufacture it are perishable. This means that feed must be handled and stored so that it maintains the high quality it had upon manufacture. Regardless of the care given, some loss in quality will occur during handling and storage.

Handling

Handling refers to moving feed. Moving may be in bags or bulk. Some damage occurs any time feed particles bump together or against other solid objects. Bags are moved about and may occasionally burst, spilling the feed. Moving bags may cause the pellets inside to break into small particles that become waste.

Augers and conveyor belts cause feed materials to break apart. Augers create more damage than other kinds of material-handling equipment. Conveyor belts, bucket elevators, and other equipment cause some damage.

Loading feed into a truck or bin should be done in a way that minimizes damage. Dropping pellets several feet causes them to bump against the container and each other, with some breakage resulting. The dust and fine particles that develop will likely not be consumed by aquacrops.

Storing

Storing is holding or keeping feed in a warehouse or bin until it is fed. The feed is placed there for later use. How it is stored has a big impact on maintaining its quality.

Feed quality is damaged by the following in storage:

- Insect pest infestation
- Rodent damage and contamination
- Growth of mold

- Development of rancidity

- Loss of vitamin potency

- Contact with water

- Contamination with chemicals

Bags of feed are kept in a warehouse. Never place bags directly on a concrete floor. Put bags on a pallet or raised floor area. This keeps bags from absorbing moisture and helps prevent damage by rodents. The warehouse should have a good roof and rodent-proof walls and floors. Some sort of temperature control is needed so that the feed does not get too warm and lose nutrients. Keeping humidity low is also important in protecting the quality of the feed.

Bulk feed is stored in a bin. A bin should be tight to keep out insect pests and rodents. A good cover is needed to keep out moisture.

Researchers at Kentucky State University recommend storing feed no longer than 60 to 90 days following manufacture. Feed quality deteriorates. Fish derive less nutritive value from feed stored for a longer time. (For more details, refer to "Review of Feeding Practices for Channel Catfish Production" in *The Aquaculture News*, September 2001.)

5–21. This bag of feed is warehoused on a pallet to reduce the chance of damage by contact with a concrete floor.

5–22. The label on this feed bag gives information on analysis, ingredients, and how to feed.

REVIEWING

MAIN IDEAS

All aquatic organisms—animals, plants, and others—need nutrients to live and grow. A nutrient is a substance used by organisms to carry out life processes. Insufficient nutrients result in failure to grow, susceptibility to disease, and an unprofitable aquaculture enterprise. Aquatic animals ingest food, which is digested to obtain nutrients. Plants use nutrients to make their food through photosynthesis.

The general nutrient requirements of animals are appropriate amounts of proteins, fats, carbohydrates, minerals, and vitamins. Manufactured feed may also contain additives, which are substances intended to benefit the feed or the animal.

The natural habitats of aquatic animals provide needed nutrients through available food materials. Small fish, algae, decaying organic matter, and other materials in the water are used as food, depending on the species. Producers with low intensity of stocking can promote the growth of natural food materials by using fertilizer. High-intensity culture requires the use of feed. Most commercial producers use manufactured feed.

Manufactured feed is prepared in a range of forms to meet the needs of specific species and life stages. Some species prefer floating feed; others prefer sinking feed. Some need very small particles of feed; others can use larger particles, such as pellets 3/16-inch in diameter. Pellets are mixtures of feed ingredients pressed together to facilitate feeding and ingestion.

Fish and other aquatic animals can be fed on a schedule or provided free access to feed. A schedule may be several times a day, twice a day, once a day, or less frequently, depending on the needs of the crop.

Manufactured feed is bought and stored. Purchase feed that meets the life stage of the crop. Small producers may buy small containers or bags of feed. Larger producers may buy semitrailer loads delivered in bulk. Feed should be stored to prevent deterioration and loss. Never buy more feed than can be used in 60 to 90 days.

QUESTIONS

Answer the following questions, using complete sentences and correct spelling.

1. Contrast how plants and animals get the nutrients they need to live and grow.

2. What role do the leaves of a plant have in nutrition for the plant?

3. What are the five nutrients required by fish? Briefly explain the role of each.

4. What are feed additives? Why are they used?

5. What is meant by mollusks being "filter feeders"?

6. Why is fertilizer sometimes used in ponds?

7. What are artemia?

8. What is meant by "life-stage feed"? What are the four types of feed based on life stage?

9. What is buoyancy? How is it important in manufactured feed?

10. What are the two major approaches in feeding? Briefly describe each.

11. Why is proper storage important with feed?

12. How do the feed purchasing approaches vary by size of the aquaculture producer?

EVALUATING

Match the term with the correct definition. Write the letter of the term on the line provided.

a. nutrient   e. pellet   i. protein
b. food   f. scheduled feeding   j. meal
c. diet   g. storing
d. buoyancy   h. ingest

_____1. A compressed form of feed

_____2. The characteristics of feed in water as related to position

_____3. A coarsely ground feed

_____4. A substance used by organisms to live and grow

_____5. The type and amount of feed in a ration

_____6. To take something into the body

_____7. Any material ingested for the nutrients it contains

_____8. Providing feed at specific times

_____9. Holding feed until it is needed

_____10. The most critical nutrient needed for growth

EXPLORING

1. Obtain the label from a fish feed container. Study the label to determine feed ingredients, percent protein and other nutrients, and the name of the manufacturer. Write a short report on your observations.

2. Observe an aquarium to determine if the fish are fed on a schedule or if food is available free access. Investigate the kind of feed used. Prepare a short oral report on your findings.

3. Take a field trip to a fish farm. Determine how and what the aquacrops are fed. Prepare a report on your findings.

Disease and Pest Management

TERMS

abscess	indefinite treatment	predator
bacterial disease	indirect loss	prevention
bathing	infectious disease	prophylactic treatment
chemical disease	injection	quarantine
diagnostic laboratory	internal parasite	sanitation
dipping	lesion	symptom
direct loss	noninfectious disease	trash fish
disease	nutritional disease	treatment
environmental disease	parasite	ulcer
external parasite	pest	vigor
fungal disease	physiological disease	viral disease

6–1. Observing fish provides information about health. This fishery technician is examining a sample of USDA 103 line catfish to measure growth and assess health. (Courtesy, Agricultural Research Service, USDA)

AQUACROPS have diseases and pests, just as do livestock, poultry, and grain and fiber crops. Knowing what is involved can help reduce losses. Good managers are always on the alert for problems. Of course, the key is to prevent problems. Preventing disease and pest problems is much easier than eradicating them after an outbreak.

Many factors are involved in disease and pest control. These include getting only problem-free stock, using quality water, and following good cultural practices. Sometimes, visitors carry diseases and pests from one place to another on their shoes. Therefore, in some cases, visitors may not be allowed. Quarantine and sanitation are also an important part of disease and pest control.

AQUACULTURE DISEASES AND PESTS

All aquacrops are susceptible to damage or loss from diseases and pests. Through good management, most disease and pest problems can be kept to a minimum.

Maintaining a good environment is essential for efficient production. Disease and pest problems will be reduced or eliminated.

6–2. A healthy, rapidly growing crawfish.

Healthy Environment

The environment of aquacrops should promote good health. This means that the organisms are free of disease and of damage by pests.

A *disease* is a condition that develops in an organism and then damages it in some way. The condition of the fish or other species deviates from normal. A diseased organism is unhealthy. The goal is to keep aquatic organisms in good health so that they will grow and be productive.

A *pest* is a plant, animal, or other organism that is detrimental to a species. This means that a pest in some way interferes with production. Pests may be large organisms or one-celled organisms. They may compete for nutrients, consume the aquacrop, or attack the crop so normal life functions are changed. Some pests attack the water structure in which a crop is being grown.

All aquacrops are susceptible to damage by diseases and pests. Plants may be damaged by diseases, insects, large animals, and other pests. Animals may be damaged by diseases, parasites, water birds, and other water animals.

6–3. Regularly assessing water quality helps assure a healthy environment for aquacrops.

6–4. An aquarium may provide a good environment for fish as well as disease organisms. (This shows healthy, hybrid striped bass.)

ENVIRONMENT HARBORS DISEASES AND PESTS

The environment in which aquacrops grow tends to be a good place for diseases and pests. Water with high crop populations has many potential problems. Reasons for this include the following.

- High concentrations of aquacrops allow for more rapid transfer of diseases and pests from one individual to another.

- Handling (such as hauling) causes stress, and stress, in turn, reduces resistance to some diseases and pests.

- High populations in ponds, open tanks, and raceways are easy for predators to catch.

6–5. Variations in diet and other health conditions resulted in different rates of growth for these steelhead trout that are the same age. (Courtesy, Maine Agricultural Experiment Station)

- Uneaten feed, fish excrement, and excess fertilizer provide nutrients for the growth of weeds.

- Soft earth near water and uneaten feed attracts animals that burrow into levees and dams.

Knowing the environmental conditions that lead to problems allows the use of management practices that reduce or remove disease or pest problems.

KINDS OF LOSSES

Diseases and pests are of concern because of the losses they can cause. In some cases, the losses are small. In other cases, entire crops may be affected or lost. Any losses lower the profit that can be made.

Disease and pest damage may occur in two major ways: direct and indirect. Sometimes, the aquacrop is attacked directly, as when a disease causes the death of fish. At other times, pests compete for nutrients, oxygen, and other essentials for life. This indirect damage causes the crop to grow more slowly. Farmers' investments may be lost to pests, such as when trash fish eat feed intended for a crop of fish.

Direct Losses

Direct losses occur when the aquacrop is attacked or injured. Here are a few examples:

- Water birds and other predators—Catch and eat or injure fish.

- Diseases—Impair the body functions of fish, resulting in reduced growth rate or death.

- Parasites—Take nourishment from fish, reducing growth; make fish (the hosts) more susceptible to diseases.

- Poaching—Theft of aquacrops by humans. (Yes, humans are pests when they steal fish!)

Indirect Losses

Indirect losses result when the environment in which an aquacrop is living is less than ideal. Here are a few examples:

6–6. This bear has caused a direct loss of fish.

- Weeds—Grow in water, tying up nutrients and making harvest difficult.

- Trash fish (undesirable stray fish)—Consume feed intended for the fish crop; also, compete for oxygen and can introduce diseases and parasites.

- Rodents and other burrowing animals—Burrow into earthen levees, possibly causing water leaks or weakening them so they collapse.

SIGNS OF DISEASE IN FISH

Diseased fish or other aquacrops may be unable to carry out normal body functions. Diseases may cause fish to fail to grow or may cause them to grow at a reduced rate. Sometimes, the fish may die. Diseased fish are unfit for human consumption. Processing plants will reject them. In any case, the owner of the fish loses money when disease outbreaks occur.

Fish that are healthy show a certain behavior and have a certain appearance. They are alert and active. When they become diseased, their behavior changes. Fish and other species must be regularly observed for changes, or symptoms.

A *symptom* (or a sign) is evidence that a disease exists. Occasionally, more than one symptom may be apparent. Symptoms are not causes of disease. Causes result in or bring about the symptoms. Causes may require laboratory analysis for identification. For example, many diseases are caused by germs. These germs are tiny bacteria, viruses, or fungi. A microscope is needed to see them.

The most common ways fish show disease are by not eating, developing sores

6–7. These grass carp have Ich disease, caused by the protozoan *Ichthyophthirius multifiliis*. (Grass carp are also known as white amur.) (Courtesy, Fish Farming Experimental Station, Stuttgart, AR)

6–8. Skin deterioration and bloody areas are signs of disease on this fish.

6–9. The ulcer on this diseased fish was caused by *Flexibacter columnaris* disease. (Courtesy, Mississippi Cooperative Extension Service)

(lesions), lacking vigor, developing abnormal body shapes, changing their behavior, and dying.

Not Eating (Going Off Feed)

Healthy fish have a distinct eating behavior. Fish that are not healthy will not eat when they are fed. The alert fish farmer pays careful attention at feeding time.

Healthy fish normally eat a few minutes after feed is put in the water. If the fish do not eat, the cause should be quickly determined. Sometimes the failure to eat may not be due to a disease but to a water problem. For example, fish may stop eating when the oxygen is low. Using feed that floats on the water is a good management tool in that the fish must come to the surface to eat. Some fish, however, are bottom feeders and do not respond well to floating feed.

6–10. Channel catfish with ESC—enteric septicemia of catfish. (Redness in the fins is a sign of bleeding or hemorrhaging.) (Courtesy, Fish Farming Experimental Station, Stuttgart, AR)

Skin Abnormalities

Diseases may show up as ulcers, lesions, abscesses, or cysts on the skin or gills or as discoloration.

An **ulcer** is an open sore on the skin that festers and contains pus. Ulcers are different from lesions.

A *lesion* is a change in a tissue as a result of injury or disease. Rough handling in hauling can scrape the sides of fish. Attacks from predators can also leave lesions.

An *abscess* is a swollen area in the tissue of the body. Pus usually gathers at abscesses.

Cysts are abnormal pockets (sac-like structures) filled with fluid or diseased flesh.

The experienced fish farmer knows the normal color of fish. For example, gills that are pale show that the fish has a problem. When color changes, a disease may be present. Certainly, sores on a fish show that something is wrong.

6–11. The pinpoint ulcers on the skin of this fish are caused by bacteria. (Courtesy, Eddie Harris and Pete Taylor, Mississippi Cooperative Extension Service)

6–12. The lesions on this paddlefish are signs that it has had a sea lamprey parasite attached by its teeth. Sea lampreys are eels that can grow to 6 feet or longer. Though adapted to seawater, they can migrate hundreds of miles into freshwater streams. Sometimes they become landlocked and adapt to fresh water.

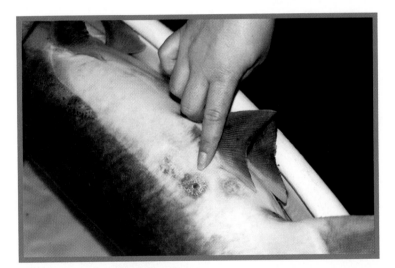

LACK OF VIGOR

Vigor is the lively movement of fish in water. Some fish can move vigorously through the water. When they stop doing so, we say that they show reduced vigor. This may be the sign of a disease.

Fish quickly swim away from apparent danger. To them, a splash in the water may indicate danger. Fish are not always moving vigorously, as they are sometimes in a resting state. Fish that appear sluggish, lose their balance, and have drooping or folded fins lack vigor.

Knowing the normal vigor of a fish is very beneficial in sensing changes that are due to disease.

6–13. Popeye, also known as exopthalmia, in this bass is caused by parasites, bacteria, or viruses. (Courtesy, Eddie Harris and Pete Taylor, Mississippi Cooperative Extension Service)

ABNORMAL BODY SHAPE

Most aquatic species have body features or shapes within a range that definitely characterizes a healthy member of the species. Abnormal body shape may suggest that a fish is diseased.

Growths on the body, particularly around the mouth and fins, may result from disease. Swollen bellies and protruding eyes are symptoms of disease. Sometimes, water pollution can result in abnormalities. At other times, abnormalities may be the result of genetic variations.

6–14. The absence of an eye on this fish's left side and an extended lower jaw are signs of mutation. A mutation is the by-chance and nonpredictable occurrence of an abnormality that distinguishes an organism from other members of its species.

BEHAVIORAL CHANGE

Any time fish change behavior, a problem should be suspected. Knowing normal behavior is important. This can be learned through watching fish. When fish gather near incoming water, scratch their bodies on vegetation or rocks, go into shallow water, or gulp at the surface of the water for air (sometimes called piping), they are showing that a problem may exist. The alert fish farmer will check out the situation.

DEAD FISH

When fish die, they usually float on the water for a while. Any time dead fish appear, some concern is justified. The cause of death should be determined as quickly as possible. This may require a laboratory analysis. Determine if there is plenty of oxygen in the water and then look at the remaining fish to see if they appear normal.

All dead fish should be immediately removed from the water. Occasionally, a fish will die when there is no disease problem, and this should not be cause for alarm.

6–15. A bloated, dead fish floating belly up in water is a sign of disease.

DISEASES AND THEIR CONTROL

Good management can prevent most disease problems. Knowing the nature of disease and how diseases are controlled is essential.

KINDS OF DISEASES

Diseases can be classified in several ways. Two broad categories of fish diseases are infectious and noninfectious.

Infectious Diseases

An *infectious disease* is caused by germs or pathogens (disease-causing organisms) that may be transferred from one fish to another. The germs or pathogens are

Table 6–1. Examples of Diseases in Aquaculture Species*

Bacterial Diseases:

Name: ESC (Enteric Septicemia of Catfish)

Signs: Lesion between eyes, pimple-size lesions over body, reddish areas on body, listlessness, failure to eat, erratic swimming in circles

Cause: *Edwardsiella ictaluri*

Prevention: Maintain good water quality with DO level above 4.0; use feed high in vitamin C; avoid broodfish that may be carriers.

Treatment: Antibiotics in feed may produce results but may not be approved for food fish.

Species affected: Channel catfish

Name: Columnaris

Signs: Discolored patches on body, mouth and fin erosion, tail loss, gill deterioration (can also be internal)

Cause: *Flexibacter columnaris*

Prevention: Use care in moving and handling fish to prevent superficial injuries to exterior; do not crowd; maintain good water quality; feed complete feed high in vitamin C.

Treatment: Add potassium permanganate to water; use feed with Terramycin.

Species affected: All species

Name: Hemorrhagic Septicemia

Signs: Reduced feed consumption, listlessness, enlarged bellies due to fluid, red streaks on fins, ulcers on sides, popeyes

Cause: *Aeromonas hydrophila* or *Pseudomonas fluorescens*

Prevention: Do not overcrowd or handle roughly; keep good water quality; feed complete feed with vitamin C.

Treatment: Add Terramycin to feed.

Species affected: All species

Viral Diseases:

Name: Infectious Hematopoietic Necrosis

Signs: Pale gills, dark coloration, abdominal swelling, hemorrhages at the base of fins

Cause: Virus

Prevention: Avoid stocking infected species, including eggs, and use food materials free of disease; resistance appears to increase in older fish.

Treatment: None; destroy infected fish.

Species affected: Many species, with rainbow trout particularly affected

Name: Channel Catfish Virus (CCV)

Signs: Swelling of abdomen, with yellow fluid in body cavity; popeyes; hemorrhaging at base of fins and other skin sites; erratic swimming

Cause: Virus; low DO in water, high ammonia, and warm water contribute to development of CCV.

Prevention: Maintain good water quality, with DO of 4.0 ppm or higher; feed properly; avoid overcrowding; disinfect equipment used in handling fish.

Treatment: No effective treatment available; destroy affected fish.

Species affected: Primarily channel catfish

(Continued)

Table 6-1 (Continued)

Fungal Diseases:

Name: All fungal diseases

Signs: Fuzzy or fur-like appearance to skin, discoloration, lesions

Cause: Several fungi, including those in the genera of *Achlya* and *Saprolegnia*; unhealthy fish and those with injuries are more susceptible.

Prevention: Maintain good water quality and DO levels; avoid stressing fish; handle fish carefully when they must be moved; feed a balanced diet.

Treatment: Potassium permanganate and copper sulfate in water can be used.

Species affected: All freshwater fish

*Note: This table presents common examples of diseases. Professional assistance is needed for the proper identification and management of diseased fish.

living organisms that attack the tissues of fish. They produce poisons that may kill the fish. The four kinds of infectious diseases are bacterial, fungal, viral, and parasitic.

Bacterial Diseases. A *bacterial disease* is caused by bacteria. Most bacterial diseases are internal, though a few may cause problems on the skin and gills. Laboratory analysis is needed to confirm a bacterial disease. Bacteria are microscopic and are about 3/25,000 of an inch long. An example of a bacterial disease is ESC, which is caused by the bacterium *Edwardsiella ictaluri*.

Fungal Diseases. A *fungal disease* is caused by tiny organisms known as fungi. Since fungi grow on dead flesh, fungal diseases usually indicate that fish have other problems. A fish injured in some way is particularly vulnerable to fungal diseases.

Viral Diseases. A *viral disease* is caused by a virus. Viruses are often so small that they cannot be seen with an ordinary microscope. They are difficult to treat with drugs and chemicals.

Parasitic Diseases. Parasitic diseases are caused by parasites. A *parasite* is a plant or animal that lives in or on another plant or animal, known as the host. A parasite causes harm by chewing or sucking fluids from the host or by taking nutrients from the food in the digestive tract of the host.

Noninfectious Diseases

A *noninfectious disease* may be due to improper diet, poor environment, chemicals, and/or physiological changes. Noninfectious diseases are not caused by pathogens and are not transferred from one fish to another.

Nutritional Diseases. A *nutritional disease* results from an inadequate diet. Usually, the fish do not receive enough food with the proper nutrients. Sometimes, too much feed can cause problems. Providing the appropriate amount and kind of feed will virtually eliminate nutritional diseases. Deficiencies of vitamins, minerals, protein, and other essential nutrients may result in nutritional diseases.

6–16. The abnormal body shape of these catfish is due to a nutritional disease caused by a deficiency of vitamin C. (Courtesy, Fish Farming Experimental Station, Stuttgart, AR)

Environmental Diseases. The water environment in which fish and other aquacrops grow may cause a type of disease known as *environmental disease*. Gases in the water may cause gas bubble disease. Other substances, such as heavy metals and pesticides, can result in fish that lack vigor, develop secondary problems, or die.

Chemical Diseases. A range of toxic substances may get into water. Pesticides from agricultural crops may drift into fish ponds or water supplies. Fish may become stunted or die of chemical toxicity. A *chemical disease* results when the amount of a chemical in the water injures or kills the fish.

Physiological Diseases. Malfunctions of organs or other life processes result in *physiological disease*. Sometimes, the blood may have a sudden change in pH. Feeding too near the time of harvest can cause problems.

DISEASE CONTROL

The best approach to disease control is prevention. Good management of the aquacrop and its environment is important. Poor management may allow disease problems to occur that could have been avoided. After a disease occurs, some kind of treatment is necessary. Very few treatments are approved for use on fish for human consumption. Those that are available tend to be expensive and sometimes difficult to administer.

Prevention

Prevention is the practice of keeping fish and other aquacrops healthy and free of disease. Following good management practices can prevent most disease problems. Proper nutrition can help fish to be more resistant to diseases. Stress reduces the resistance of fish to disease. Stress often occurs when fish are hauled and handled. Being careful not to inflict injury can go a long way in controlling stress. Fish are stressed when their environment is suddenly changed. High water temperature, low oxygen level, crowding, pollution getting into the water, and excessive accumulation of wastes can also trigger stress.

Two procedures routinely used in prevention are sanitation and quarantine.

Sanitation is the practice of keeping water and facilities clean. Properly washing tanks after use can remove any disease agents that may remain in the tanks. Water from tanks should not be dumped into growing facilities.

People can transfer disease from one pond or farm to another on their feet. Farms with disease problems should inform people who visit there or who may buy fish. Visitors should disinfect footwear upon arrival or departure. Farms that are disease free may require visitors to dip their footwear into a disinfectant solution, such as iodine. Some fish farms do not allow visitors.

Quarantine is the isolation of fish from each other. Isolation is used when new fish are brought onto a farm. It involves keeping them in separate facilities for a while (normally two weeks) to see if any diseases develop. Fish that develop disease should be kept separately. Whole farms may be quarantined when a disease outbreak occurs. Quarantine is needed even if the fish are being treated for the disease.

Several important management considerations in preventing disease are

- Use plenty of disease-free water.

- Stock only healthy fish.

- Quarantine new fish two weeks before adding to other fish.

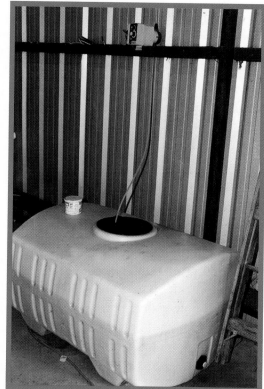

6–17. Quarantined area where people must dip their footwear in a disinfecting chemical solution before entering the facility.

6–18. A metering system for adding calcium to water in a facility for raising fry is shown here. (Tiny fry get calcium from the water they are in. If the water has low hardness—low calcium— additional calcium is needed. Fry need about 10 ppm of calcium in water for good health.)

- Use prophylactic treatments when fish are being hauled. (**Prophylactic treatments** are practices used to prevent disease. Small-haul tanks make it easy and economical to apply treatments.)

- Feed fish properly.

- Control aquatic weeds.

- Disinfect equipment when it is moved to prevent the spread of disease from one site to another.

- Properly treat empty tanks and ponds. Allowing tanks and ponds to dry thoroughly between uses destroys some organisms that may cause disease.

- Restrict visitors and provide for sanitation of footwear (as with dipping shoe soles in an iodine solution).

Treatments

Treatment is the use of therapeutic or management practices to help fish and other aquacrops overcome disease. The kind of treatment to use depends on the disease. This means that having an accurate diagnosis of the disease before beginning treatment is very important. Very few treatments have been approved by the U.S. Food and Drug Administration for use on food fish. Specific drugs to use should be determined as the need arises. Contact your local agriculture teacher, county extension agent, or land-grant university for recommendations.

Several methods of treating fish are available. Some are practical only under certain situations. A few treatment methods are described here.

Dipping. *Dipping* is immersing fish into a concentrated solution for a few seconds (usually 15 to 45 seconds). Dipping can be used with a small number of fish, such as with broodfish or fingerlings. Trying to dip many fish, such as all those in a pond, is impractical. Formalin and salt are common materials used in preparing solutions used for dipping.

Feeding. Some medications may be added to feed. A medication should be thoroughly mixed in the feed so all fish get the treatment. Large quantities of fish can be treated in this way. When a few large fish are involved (such as broodstock), capsules with medication can be placed in the stomachs of the fish with a balling gun.

Bathing. Similar to dipping, *bathing* involves adding chemicals to the water where fish are being kept or placing the fish in chemically treated water. In either case, the fish are exposed to the chemicals for a longer time than with dipping. For example, chemicals may be added to the water in tanks or vats for an hour or so. Correctly calculating the amount to use and the length of time the bath should last is essential.

A large quantity of fresh water is added to flush out the chemicals after the treatment. Disposal of water containing the chemicals may be a problem.

Injecting. Some drugs can be administered to small numbers of fish with a hypodermic needle and a syringe. Known as *injection*, this method is appropriate only with fish large enough to hold. Medications act more rapidly when given by injection than when put in feed or baths.

Treating indefinitely. *Indefinite treatment* (also known as prolonged treatment) involves treating fish for long periods by adding low concentrations of therapeutants (chemicals) to the water. This method can be used with both ponds and tanks. The chemi-

6–19. Treating fish is easier in vats than in ponds.

cals must be evenly mixed in the water. Such treatments are useful only with chemicals that break up and disappear with the passage of time.

PARASITES AND THEIR CONTROL

Normally parasites cause harm by chewing on the host, sucking fluids from it, or taking nutrients from the food in the digestive tract. Parasites are often considered a form of infectious disease.

External parasites attach themselves to the outside of a fish's body. They may be found on the skin, gills, and/or fins. They get food by eating or sucking on the fish. Fish with external parasites frequently try to scratch themselves on vegetation or rocks to remove the parasites.

Internal parasites live in the organs or digestive tracts of fish. They cause damage to the organs and make the fish susceptible to other diseases by weakening them. In a fish's digestive tract, they live on the nutrients in the feed that the fish has eaten.

KINDS OF PARASITES

Fish may have several kinds of parasites. Some are very small and visible only with a microscope; others are large and visible to the eye. The most common parasites are briefly described here.

Worms

Fish may be attacked by several kinds of worm parasites. Tapeworms, roundworms, leeches, and flukes are common examples. All are usually internal, except leeches, which attach themselves to the outside of fish and suck blood.

Worm parasites can cause serious damage to fish. Tapeworms and roundworms compete in the intestines for the nutrients in the food a fish has eaten. Some forms of flukes may live as external parasites, particularly on the gills of fish.

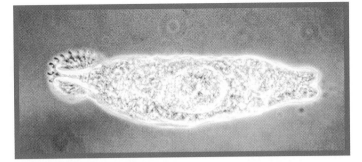

6–20. Flatworms may infect fish and reduce growth efficiency. This is a photograph of a monogenetic trematode (flatworm that lives on one host) in the *Gyrodactylus* sp. This external parasite attacks the skin, fins, and gills of fish. It is controlled in ponds with 25 ppm of formalin or in vats with 200 ppm of formalin for one hour. (Courtesy, Fish Farming Experimental Station, Stuttgart, AR)

Crustaceans

Parasitic crustaceans, sometimes known as anchor parasites, may resemble insects and have hard outer shells. One kind attaches itself to the gills of fish. These parasites burrow into the skin or gills and can usually be seen with the naked eye. Parasitic crustaceans can transmit infectious diseases among fish. These parasites can be transferred by birds and other animals from one pond to another.

Protozoa

Protozoan parasites are one-celled parasites that live in water. They may become a problem when fish are stressed, as when fish have inadequate nutrition or when the water quality is poor. Symptoms of protozoan parasites include small, bloody spots on the fins, ragged fins, and loss of appetite.

Some kinds of protozoa (known as sporozoa) form cysts in the organs or skin of fish. These cysts may break open, releasing many spores. An example of a protozoan parasite is Ich, or white spot.

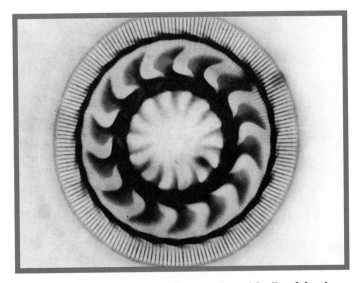

6–21. Enlarged photograph of the parasite *Trichodina fultoni*. (Courtesy, Fish Farming Experimental Station, Stuttgart, AR)

Table 6–2. Examples of Parasites in Aquaculture Species*

Internal Parasites:

Name: Tapeworms

Signs: Loss of weight and listlessness. (May not be evident until infestation is advanced.)

Types: Several species of tapeworms, including *Corallobothrium fimbriatum, Ligula intestinalis, Proteocephalus ambloplitis,* and *Bothriocephalus opsarichthydis*

Prevention: Avoid stocking contaminated fish; keep birds away (birds can carry parasites).

Treatment: None; disinfect ponds and other water facilities between fish crops.

Species affected: All species

Name: Fish Grubs (Larval Internal Parasites)

Signs: Black, white, or cream-colored nodules or spots in flesh. (Color is related to the species of the larvae.)

Types: Genera are *Crassiphiala* (black), *Posthodiplostomum* (white), and *Clinostomum* (yellow or cream).

Prevention: Stock clean fish; keep birds away (intermediate hosts); clean ponds.

Treatment: Rely on prevention.

Species affected: Minnows, sunfish, bass, and others

External Parasites:

Name: Ich

Signs: Small, raised white spots on skin; infected fish gather at a water inlet or outlet; fish in tanks "flash" on bottom or sides.

Type: Protozoan *Ichthyophthirius multifiliis*

Prevention: Maintain quality water; use only disease-free stocker fish; sanitize equipment between batches of fish.

Treatment: Formalin, copper sulfate, potassium permanganate, table salt

Species affected: All freshwater fish; particularly a problem in catfish culture.

Name: Parasitic Crustaceans (also known as anchor parasites)

Signs: Rubbing against objects; small reddish lesions on the surface, with small shaft-like barbs protruding; fungus may grow around the lesions.

Type: *Lernaea cyprinacea* (a small copepod)

Prevention: Avoid infected fish.

Treatment: Masoten, used as directed

Species affected: All freshwater fish

Name: Flukes (monogenetic)

Signs: Fish rub or scratch against objects, followed by listlessness; gills may flare; secondary infections and death may result.

Types: Several genera, including *Cleidodiscus* and *Dactylogyrus*

Prevention: Provide proper diet; maintain water quality; avoid overcrowding.

Treatment: Formalin and potassium permanganate in water

Species affected: Warmwater fish

Name: Lice

Signs: Rubbing against objects and "flashing" in water; listlessness; red spots on exterior; heavy infections may lead to death.

Types: Members of the *Angulus* genus

Prevention: Stock parasite-free fish.

Treatment: Masoten

Species affected: All freshwater fish

*Note: This table presents common examples of parasites. Professional assistance is needed for the proper identification and management of parasite-infested fish.

Lice

Fish lice attach themselves to the body, gills, fins, and mouth areas of fish. These parasites transfer disease, weaken hosts, and can lead to death. Fish lice suck blood from their hosts. Handlers of fish should exercise caution in that some infections have been transferred to humans, with the eyes of humans being especially vulnerable to injury by fish lice.

PARASITE CONTROL

As with diseases, prevention is the best method of control. Several ways of controlling parasites are included here.

- Quarantine—This involves isolating any new fish from existing fish. If parasites are observed, some form of chemical treatment might be appropriate. A quarantine period of two weeks is usually considered adequate.

- Treatment of facilities—Some parasites can be controlled by drying and disking pond bottoms between fish crops. Calcium hypochlorite can be applied to pond bottoms to sterilize them. Tanks and vats can be thoroughly dried and treated with a disinfectant.

- Dipping—External parasites are treated by dipping the fish into a chemical solution. For example, fish with leeches can be dipped for a short while in a 3 percent solution of salt (NaCl). The fish should be removed from the solution when they begin to show signs of stress. (Dipping in salt water causes the leeches to turn loose of the fish and drop to the bottom of the container.) Other parasites may require that fish be dipped for one hour in a 200-ppm solution of formalin.

- Elimination of birds—Birds often transfer parasites from one pond to another. Sometimes, a part of the life cycle of a parasite is spent inside a bird. Controlling the birds and removing roosts where the birds light is helpful. Screens are often put over fish facilities to keep birds away. Some species of birds are protected by law and, therefore, cannot be killed without a permit.

- Indefinite treatment—To control some parasites, large quantities of fish may be treated in ponds at a low level of chemical concentration for an indefinite period. For example, fish with Ich may be treated with formalin at the rate of 25 ppm on alternate days for two weeks. Care should be used with such treatment. Chemicals react differently, depending on the water chemistry. Also, food fish should be treated only according to the regulations of the Food and Drug Administration.

6–22. Small ponds have been covered with a protective netting to keep water birds out of the water.

- Feed additives—Feed additives may be used to treat fish infected with certain internal parasites, particularly tapeworms, roundworms, and flukes. These additives should be used carefully and only as approved.

6–23. Emptying tanks, allowing them to dry, and disinfecting them will control some parasites. Replacing the liner, as shown here, is also a good step. (Courtesy, National Oceanic & Atmospheric Administration)

PREDATORS AND THEIR CONTROL

A *predator* is an animal that attacks and feeds on other animals. The predator is usually larger and stronger than its prey (the animal it attacks).

Fish being raised in captivity are particularly prone to attack. Fish producers can have big losses to predators. Just consider the value lost to a bird that eats 1 pound of fish a day for three months!

Common predators are birds, other fish, snakes, insects, turtles, alligators, and bullfrogs.

Birds

Several species of birds prey on fish. These can cause large losses over a growing season. Cormorants, kingfishers, herons, grebes, and mergansers are some examples.

The double-crested cormorant has been a particular pest. This bird can eat 1 to 2 pounds of fish a day. Over a growing season, the cormorant could consume 200 or more pounds of fish. If several were present, the losses could quickly add up to thousands of pounds of fish.

Some species of birds are protected by law and cannot be killed without a permit. Control measures include placing a screen or net over the fish facilities, using loud exploding cannons, and frightening the birds away with scarecrow-type devices. Constructing ponds with a minimum of shallow water so there are no places for birds to stand can be helpful. However, controlling water depth will not deter birds that swim and dive to catch fish.

6–24. The double-crested cormorant is a major predator in some fish-growing areas. (Courtesy, U.S. Fish and Wildlife Service)

6–25. Netting will protect the fish in this facility from birds. (Courtesy, National Oceanic & Atmospheric Administration)

FISH

Some species of fish prey on other fish; others prey on the eggs or the young of their own species. Knowing something about the nature of fish will help in understanding how to respond in managing them. Various techniques are available to separate fish.

Sometimes, undesirable trash fish get into a pond and become predators. Using water from a good source is the best way to control this problem. After harvest, the water should be cleaned to remove predatory trash fish before the next crop is stocked.

SNAKES

Besides preying on fish, snakes pose hazards to people who work around ponds. Many fish farmers do not feel that snakes eat a large amount of fish. Mowing levees closely to prevent the growth of tall weeds and grass and removing places where snakes can hide will help control them. Killing them when they are accessible is another means of control. Sometimes, the presence of snakes might deter poaching, or the theft of fish crops.

INSECTS

Water insects are a minor problem in most fish farm operations. Some insects may eat or destroy eggs or fry in ponds or hatcheries. Spraying with insecticides is sometimes done but is usually not recommended. Insecticides are poisonous and can make fish unfit for human consumption.

TURTLES

Turtles cause problems in several ways. Some species prey on fish. All species compete with fish for feed and space in the growing facility. Turtles are particularly objectionable at harvest time, as they must be removed from the fish crop. Hand removing can be hazardous because some turtles bite. Trapping or shooting with a rifle (dangerous!) is one means of control. However, some species of turtles are protected by law; thus, a game warden or conservation officer should be consulted about the regulations.

ALLIGATORS

Rarely do alligators cause problems as predators, but they have been observed with fish in their mouths. The greatest danger may be to people who work around fish-growing facilities in areas where alligators grow. The alligators should be trapped and then moved away from the fish farm.

Bullfrogs

Bullfrogs cause losses by killing fry and fingerlings. They also compete with the aquacrop for space and food, particularly while in the tadpole stage. Control is limited to placing a poison (copper sulfate) on the egg masses and trapping, catching, or gigging.

Other Pests

Aquafarms are sometimes damaged by other pests, such as muskrats and beavers, crawfish, and livestock. Muskrats and beavers primarily cause problems by burrowing into levees, thus causing water leaks and weakening water structures so they might break. Crawfish also cause damage by burrowing.

Closely mowing areas around ponds will control burrowing animals. Using rock riprap on levees at the water line may be helpful; however, the rocks may be a problem

6–26. Alligators, sometimes cultured themselves, are occasionally predators on fish farms.

6–27. Tiny snails have become pests in tanks and ponds used for aquaculture. These small animals compete for oxygen, food, and space as well as spread disease.

at the time of fish harvest. Traps can be used to catch some burrowing animals. Sometimes, other methods that are legal and approved by the local game authorities can be used to eradicate the animals.

Livestock should be kept out of aquaculture facilities. Not only do they muddy the water, but they may also damage levees and create deep paths that make the area around a pond rough. Fences will keep livestock out.

It is interesting that some pests are valuable for their own worth. Beavers produce quality fur. Crawfish are grown in some areas as a valuable aquacrop. Livestock are important sources of food. Some pests are animals "out of place," much as weeds are plants growing where they are not wanted.

6–28. Starfish removed from cultured oysters in a processing plant in Washington.

TRASH FISH AND THEIR CONTROL

Undesirable fish that are present in a crop of fish are known as *trash fish*. An example is tilapia in a catfish pond. Sometimes, trash fish are called wild fish. Trash fish can cause losses in several ways:

- They eat the feed provided for the desired fish crop.
- They compete for oxygen and nutrients.
- The fish crop grows more slowly because of the competition.
- Labor requirements at harvest are greater because the trash fish have to be separated from the fish crop.

- They may bring diseases and parasites to a fish farm.

- Some may also be predators and consume the fish crop.

Trash fish reduce the profit from a fish crop. More feed and labor and more energy to oxygenate the water are required. The costs for controlling diseases and parasites are also greater. Trash fish also have to be removed from fish crops before the crops can be processed.

Sources of Trash Fish

Trash fish get into a fish facility in several ways. Through good management, they can usually be kept out.

Only good-quality water should be used. Water from wells is free of trash fish. Water from streams, lakes, and other surface runoff may be contaminated with trash fish.

The construction site for a pond may contain wild trash fish. A pond built across a creek may get trash fish from the water in the creek. Puddles of water in a construction site may be a source of trash fish. Rivers may overflow their banks and take trash fish into fish farms during the rainy season.

Fish stock may contain trash fish. Fingerlings may have undesirable fish growing with them. Buying stocker fish only from reputable dealers will help reduce the problem.

Occasionally, a fish-eating bird will transport a trash fish to a fish farm. The bird may catch the fish in a nearby creek or lake and fly to the fish farm, where the fish escapes uneaten from the bird's beak.

Control of Trash Fish

Control involves keeping trash fish from entering the fish farming facility. Water from streams or lakes needs to be filtered before it is pumped into the aquaculture facility. Sock-type filters may be placed over the ends of pipes. Occasionally, box filters constructed of wooden frames with screens are used. Both types of filters should be cleaned regularly to remove the screened-out trash fish. If this is not done, the screen could get overloaded and break, thus releasing the trash fish into the growing facility.

After harvesting, fish ponds can be emptied to remove the trash fish. Refilling the ponds can be a costly, time-consuming operation.

After the fish have been harvested, some farmers treat the water in ponds with a chemical to kill unwanted fish. Rotenone has been used for this purpose. When used at the rate of 0.005 to 0.25 ppm, it will kill most trash fish. Rotenone and other chemicals should be used only as approved by regulatory agencies.

Biological control is sometimes used, but it is not always practical. For example, when some farmers stock their ponds, they stock a species of fish that preys on the trash fish but not on the fish crop. However, this requires sorting at harvest time and can result in other problems caused by the predator fish themselves.

WHAT TO DO IF FISH APPEAR SICK

How does a producer know when fish are unhealthy? The behavior of the fish changes from what is normal for them. Knowing the normal behavior of the species that is being raised is important.

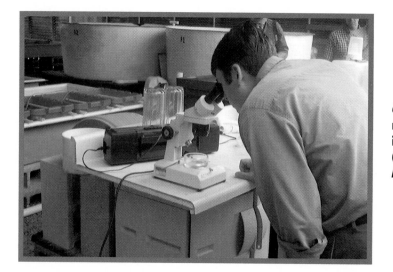

6–29. Microscopic examination may be needed to properly identify the cause of a disease. (Courtesy, National Oceanic & Atmospheric Administration)

RESPONDING TO SIGNS OF UNHEALTHY FISH

If fish begin to show signs of being sick, quick action is needed. Accurate diagnosis of the situation is essential. Delay can result in the loss of an entire fish crop. Here is a list of ten things to do:

1. Stop selling fish to farmers, processors, and others until the problem is solved.

2. Follow quarantine and sanitation procedures to reduce the chance of the problem spreading.

3. Get the advice of a local aquaculture specialist. (The local agriculture teacher or extension agent may help in this.)

4. Contact another fish farmer in the area about the problem.

5. Contact a local supplier of feed or chemicals or a local processing plant.

6. Contact fishery specialists at the state land-grant university.

7. Contact the nearest fish disease diagnostic laboratory to arrange to have a sample of the fish examined.

8. Send or deliver a sample of diseased fish to a diagnostic laboratory. Be sure to follow proper procedures with the sample.

9. Follow the necessary procedures to solve the problem. (Always read and follow the instructions on any chemicals that may be used.)

10. If the crop is insured, contact the insurance agent.

Some farmers set up small diagnostic laboratories on their farms. A few analyses can be made with microscopes and rather simple procedures. Training in how to make analyses is essential.

Once a diagnosis has been made, treatments require consideration of a number of factors. The effectiveness of all treatments depends on water chemistry, temperature, accurate and uniform application, and dosage level.

CONNECTION

A FISH OUT OF WATER HAS . . .

Most fish are easily stressed when taken out of the water. Handling even the smallest fry must be done as quickly as possible to prevent injury.

These fry are being taken from a trough. They are carefully dipped, measured, and moved to a special hauling tank within a matter of seconds. If kept out of the water more than a few seconds, they are stressed. Stressed fry may get diseases, grow slowly, or die.

A fish out of water has . . . a short life!

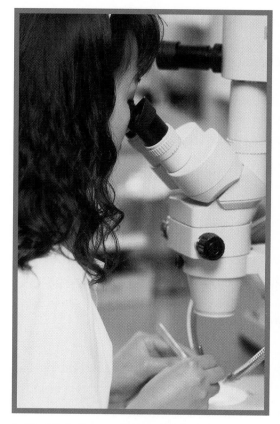

6–30. A fish disease diagnostic laboratory technician carefully examines specimens to diagnose the disease accurately.

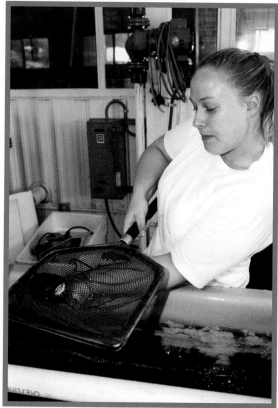

6–31. A sample must typify the disease problem for accurate laboratory diagnosis.

SELECTING AND SHIPPING DISEASED FISH SAMPLES

Samples of diseased fish must often be carefully examined in a laboratory. These fish are identified by the symptoms they exhibit. A *diagnostic laboratory* is a place specially equipped to examine both live and dead fish. It is extremely important that the sample examined typify the problem among the fish.

Selecting a Sample

Live fish provide the best samples. Though they may show symptoms, they may be hard to catch. Only fish that have the symptoms should be sent to a laboratory. Such fish can be caught with a net or seine, but a little patience will be needed—catching them will not be easy. Fish taken at random from a seine may not have the disease. Fish caught by hook and line from different areas of a water facility are poor samples.

Dead fish are not as good for laboratory analysis. The probability of an accurate diagnosis is reduced. Dead fish that have red gills and somewhat normal color and mucus might be okay. Dead fish that have lost body color, have no mucus, and have white gills are of no value and should not be sent. Of course, collecting a sample of dead fish is much easier!

Water samples are unusable with most diseases. Sometimes, however, when fish become ill or die, water samples are analyzed to learn whether a water problem exists. Also, because treatment procedures are often based on the chemistry of the water, an analysis of the water can help provide needed information for administering treatments.

Shipping Fish Samples

Fish samples must arrive at the diagnostic laboratory in a suitable form for analysis.

Live fish can be placed in a sealed plastic bag. The bag can be put in an ice chest with crushed ice. If the fish will be hauled only a short distance, they can be placed in a container with well-oxygenated water and a little ice to keep the water cool.

Sometimes, fish are frozen for shipping. Frozen samples are very difficult to work with in a laboratory, but they are satisfactory for pesticide analysis.

Dead fish samples should be iced down immediately to retard further tissue breakdown. Analyzing dead fish that have deteriorated is impossible. Thus, only dead fish that are still in good condition should be sent. Dead fish should be shipped in an ice chest with plenty of crushed ice.

6–32. This partially decayed fish with *Pseudomonas* lesions has almost passed the stage of usefulness in laboratory analysis. Samples of diseased fish should be good enough to allow accurate diagnosis. (Courtesy, Fish Farming Experimental Station, Stuttgart, AR)

REGULATIONS IN DISEASE AND PEST CONTROL

Diseases and pests cannot be controlled in just any way. Established regulations must be followed. These regulations are intended to protect the environment, the consumer, and the species of animals that may be endangered.

REGULATIONS THAT MAY APPLY

Several areas of regulations in disease and pest control are briefly described here.

Food Safety

Fish crops that are to be used for human food must be protected from contamination with hazardous chemicals. Only a few chemicals have been approved by the Food and Drug Administration for use on fish crops. Those that are approved must be used according to the instructions!

Processing plants will condemn contaminated fish without processing them. All regulations of the Food and Drug Administration, the U.S. Department of Agriculture, and other regulatory agencies must be followed.

Feed Safety

Just as human food should be free of harmful contamination, feed for animals should be also. Often fish by-products are used in manufacturing feed for fish. If the by-products contain hazardous substances, the feed will be unfit for use with fish. If the feed is eaten, the fish crop will be contaminated.

Some by-products from processing are used in manufacturing pet food. Care is needed in processing to avoid making pet food that might damage the animal that eats the food.

Water Pollution

Water treated with certain chemicals is polluted and cannot be released into streams and lakes. A system for holding and cleaning up the water must be in place. Normally, the water cannot be run into a municipal sewage system for disposal.

Protected Animals

Some pests in aquaculture are protected animals, such as cormorants. Individuals are restricted in what they can do to control them. Protected animals cannot be killed without a permit, and some permits are difficult to get. An alternative is to use loud noises, sound waves, bright flashes, or other means to frighten the animals away. Another alternative is to catch the animals and move them to another location. Permits may be required to scare or capture animals. Endangered species may not be harassed.

Worker Safety

Some chemicals are hazardous to those who use them. They must be handled safely. Every precaution should be taken. Protective clothing must be worn. Exposure to these materials might be harmful to the user. If exposed, the individual should immediately take the necessary steps, such as promptly washing exposed skin. Safety information should be on the label of every chemical.

Chemical and Fuel Storage

Specific storage instructions apply to some chemicals. These instructions should be carefully followed. Steps should be taken to prevent pollution in case containers break open and leak.

Fuels should also be stored properly. Leaks from faulty tanks can contaminate the water. Used engine oil should be properly disposed of to prevent it from getting into the water.

Container Disposal

Containers in which chemicals have been held must be properly disposed of. Empty cans should not be thrown into creeks, into ponds, or behind buildings to be ignored. The approved procedures for disposing of pesticide containers should be followed. *Reading the labels for details is important!*

Cleaning Tanks

Vats and tanks in which fish have been treated must be cleaned. The water should be properly handled and not run into streams or lakes. People should be careful to avoid getting the water on their skin.

The runoff water from washing tanks should not be used as drinking water for livestock or pets. The water should not be allowed to run into fish-growing facilities. Haul tanks can be sources of disease, parasites, and trash fish. Thus, water from these tanks should never be emptied into aquaculture facilities.

Release of Illegal Species

States may have laws banning certain fish. Sometimes, these fish may be trash fish or exotic pet-type fish. They cannot be dumped into streams for disposal. For example, striped-bass farmers view tilapia mixed in their crop as trash fish. Some states may have laws against the release of tilapia; therefore, a farmer cannot dispose of them in a nearby creek.

SOURCES OF INFORMATION

Information on legal regulations is available from several sources. Begin searching for information by using the AquaNIC Web site at **http://aquanic.org**. The local agriculture teacher or county extension agent is also a primary source. All states have land-grant universities with staff qualified to help. Most states have state regulatory agencies that can provide assistance. Some areas have private consulting laboratories that can help with problems. Regardless, many sources can give the needed assistance on regulations. Ignorance of the law is not an excuse!

Handling fish in a way that provides for their well-being is essential. This means that they are never abused and that they are provided a proper environment for growth. The U.S. Department of Agriculture has established an Animal Welfare Information Center that includes aquaculture animals. The Web site for the Animal Welfare Information Center is **www.nal.usda.gov/awic/**.

REVIEWING

MAIN IDEAS

Most aquacrops are subject to damage by diseases and pests. The water environment that promotes the growth of aquacrops is also a good place for diseases and pests. Stressed or weakened aquacrops are especially susceptible to damage. Direct and indirect losses can result. Diseases, parasites, and predators directly attack aquacrops. Weeds and trash fish, rodents, and other animals cause indirect losses by competing with the aquacrops.

Fish may be exhibiting signs of problems when they go off feed, develop skin abnormalities, lose vigor, develop abnormal body shapes, change behavior, and/or die. Knowing normal fish behavior, particularly observing it at feeding time, is very important.

Prevention of disease and pest problems is best. Quarantine of new fish and sanitation are important in prevention. Treating problems is more difficult. Treatments may be administered by dipping or bathing the fish in a chemical solution, adding medications to feed, injecting medications, or exposing fish to low concentrations of therapeutants on a long-term basis.

Predators, such as birds, other fish, snakes, insects, turtles, alligators, and bullfrogs, may also cause problems. Good management practices can help to prevent losses from predators.

Diseases and parasites must be properly diagnosed for treatments to be given. Samples of fish should be carefully selected and sent to a diagnostic laboratory. Regulations for using chemicals on aquacrops should always be followed.

QUESTIONS

Answer the following questions, using complete sentences and correct spelling.

1. What is a pest? Why are aquacrops subject to pests?

2. How do diseases and pests cause losses?

3. How do fish show that they are diseased? What are the symptoms?

4. What kinds of diseases may attack fish? Briefly describe each.

5. How are diseases prevented?

6. What treatments are used with fish? Briefly explain each.

7. What is a parasite? What are the differences between internal and external parasites?

8. What are the common kinds of parasites?

9. What are the methods of parasite control? Briefly explain each.

10. What are predators? What kinds cause problems in fish?

11. What are trash fish? How are they controlled?

12. What steps should be taken if fish are observed to be sick?

13. How are samples of diseased fish selected, and how are they shipped to a diagnostic laboratory?

14. What regulations should be observed in controlling diseases and pests in aquaculture?

EVALUATING

Match the term with the correct definition. Write the letter of the term on the line provided.

a. predator
b. parasite
c. pest
d. symptom

e. lesion
f. vigor
g. sanitation
h. quarantine

i. trash fish
j. diagnostic laboratory

_____ 1. Undesirable fish in an aquacrop

_____ 2. A plant or an animal detrimental to an aquacrop

_____ 3. Evidence that a disease exists

_____ 4. A change in a tissue as a result of injury or disease

_____ 5. The practice of keeping water and facilities clean

_____ 6. The lively movement of a fish in water

_____ 7. The isolation of aquacrops

_____ 8. An animal that attacks and feeds on other animals

_____ 9. A place specially equipped to examine fish for disease

_____ 10. A plant or animal that lives in or on another plant or animal

EXPLORING

1. Tour an aquaculture diagnostic laboratory. Determine the nature of the work in the laboratory. Observe the examination of a diseased specimen to determine health problems. Prepare a written report on your observations. Give an oral report in class.

2. Observe fish in an aquarium for signs of disease. Use other chapters in this book and references on fish diseases to try to determine the disease. Identify the appropriate treatment for the disease. If possible, confirm your findings with an aquaculture specialist or fish disease diagnostic laboratory technician. Prepare a written report on your procedures.

3. Prepare a bulletin board or poster that depicts the methods of treating diseases in aquacrops. Cut pictures from magazines and brochures to illustrate the different methods.

4. Shadow a fish disease diagnostic laboratory technician or other specialist for a day. Learn the nature of the person's work. Draw a diagram of the office and laboratory areas. Write a report on your observations.

PART THREE

Aquatic Environments

CHAPTER 7

Water Environments

OBJECTIVES

This chapter covers the general role of water in aquaculture, with emphasis on fresh water. It has the following objectives:

1. Explain the importance of water in aquaculture
2. Describe the kinds of water facilities
3. Explain how to select an aquaculture facility
4. Identify water sources
5. Explain how to assess the suitability of water sources

TERMS

aquarium
aquifer
artesian well
cage
closed raceway
dissolved oxygen
ectothermic animal
gallons per minute
hardness
impoundment
industrial effluent
open raceway
pen
pollutant
pond
spring
stream
surface runoff
vat
water cycle
water pH
water quality
well

AQUACROPS live and grow in water. How well they grow depends on the quality of the water. The importance of good water to aquacrops is much like the importance of good air to people. We cannot live healthy lives in bad air!

An abundance of quality water is required for aquaculture. Decisions about aquaculture should involve information about the amount of water that is both needed and available.

Aquacrops have preferences for certain kinds of water. Those that grow well in warm water will do poorly in cold water, and vice versa. Likewise, saltwater crops

7–1. Maintaining a good water environment usually involves assessing water quality. This shows a DO meter being used to determine the level of dissolved oxygen in the water of a tank.

will do poorly in fresh water, and vice versa. Even if the "right" water is available, the aquafarmer must know how to manage it. Getting, using, and disposing of water requires knowing what is involved.

WATER IN AQUACULTURE

Water is the environment in which aquacrops grow. Crops have different water requirements. The "right" water must be available for the crops to thrive. To the beginner, it often appears that the earth has an abundance of good water. A little investigation shows that this is not so!

7–2. Raceway production requires large amounts of water, as on this Wyoming trout farm. (Courtesy, Vernie Thomas, Danville, IL)

WATER SUPPLY

Nearly three fourths of the earth's surface is covered with water. Of this, some 97 percent is salty and suitable only for those aquacrops that thrive in the oceans and in saltwater lakes.

Only about 3 percent of the earth's water is considered fresh. Two thirds of that is frozen in glaciers and ice caps. This leaves only about 1 percent of the earth's water available for use in many ways that support human and other life. Water for aquaculture, homes, industries, irrigation of crops, operation of power plants, and other uses comes from this 1 percent!

Large amounts of water are needed for aquaculture. Terrestrial crop farms, livestock, and humans compete with aquaculture for the available water. Freshwater aquaculture in some locations is now using water from large aquifers. An *aquifer* is an underground formation of sand, gravel, or rock that contains

7–3. Aquaculture uses large amounts of water.

water. Wells may be drilled several hundred feet or meters into the earth to reach the water in an aquifer. In areas where aquaculture has been underway for several years, the supply of available water from aquifers is declining.

Underground supplies once thought to be endless are beginning to dry up. Conservation is needed to try to maintain enough fresh water. Of course, aquacrops are not the only crops that use water. Rice and other terrestrial crops that are irrigated use large amounts of water. Research shows that rice uses about twice as much water as do pond-raised fish!

WATER CYCLE

The amount of water on the earth does not vary. Where it is found and the form it is in may vary. Sometimes, the water may become polluted and not suitable for aquaculture.

The *water cycle* is the never-ending circulation of the earth's water. The cycle includes evaporation, precipitation, percolation through the earth, and other steps in the process. Along the way, impurities are removed. Used water is made ready to be used again.

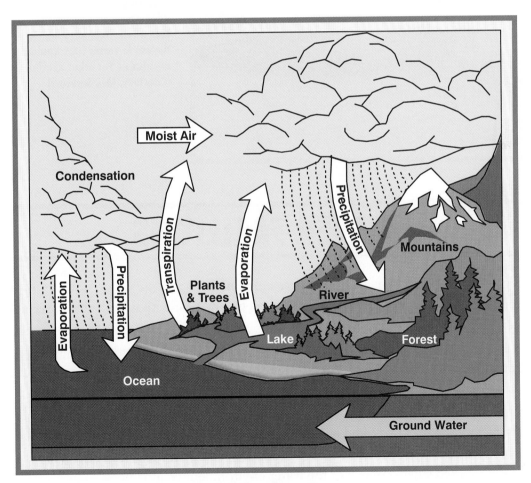

7–4. The water cycle.

WATER AND SPECIES

A challenge is to match the available water supply with the proposed aquacrop and system used to produce the crop. Each species has unique water environment requirements. Success depends on selecting a species that will thrive in the water that is readily available. Careful analysis of water is needed before trying to produce aquacrops. Making big changes in water is costly and impractical on a large scale.

Most aquaculture in the United States has been crops that use fresh water. Since there is a huge supply of salt water, more attention should be given to saltwater species. Growing crops in salt water would cause less stress on the supply of essential fresh water.

7–5. Alligator farming requires adequate water of the right kind. This adult "mama" alligator thrives in water that would be unsuitable for other species. (Courtesy, MFC Services)

WATER FACILITIES

Water facilities are the structures that contain the water in which aquacrops grow. Sometimes these are called growing facilities. The enclosures that hold the water and/or aquacrops are *impoundments*.

Water impoundments allow manipulation of the water environment of the aquacrops so that efficient growth occurs. A knowledge of water facilities helps in making good decisions about the kind of system to be used and the aquacrop to be produced.

Impoundments are often constructed specifically for aquaculture. Common kinds are ponds, raceways, tanks, vats, and aquariums. In each of these, various features of the water environment can be controlled. Control varies depending on the system. Sometimes cages and pens are used where control of the water environment is difficult.

Ponds

A **pond** is an artificial impoundment, usually made of earth. Heavy bulldozers and other equipment construct earthen dams or levees that hold the water. The size may range from less than an acre to 50 or more acres. Research has found that ponds in the 10- to 20-acre size range may be best for commercial food fish production. This size is large enough to reduce construction costs and small enough to be easily harvested.

The amount of water required depends on the pond size (both depth and surface acreage), soil type, and production system used (whether the water is exchanged). Careful attention to site selection is needed to have a soil high in clay. Clay soil has less water loss by seepage.

Ponds are primarily used with freshwater species. The vast majority of fish are produced in ponds. Some producers feel that a pond is the only large-scale water impoundment that is economical and results in a profit to the grower.

Raceways

Raceways are typically long, narrow structures with flowing water. In some cases, water may flow from one to another. Raceways built on hillsides are often in series and allow water to flow naturally. Those built on land that is almost flat require pumps to move the water.

Raceways may be made of concrete, earth, or other materials. Many earthen raceways are lined with plastic to prevent erosion and keep mud from getting into the water.

7–6. Pond arrangement is important in ease of aquacrop production.

7–7. An all-weather road has been installed on this newly constructed pond levee.

7–8. An earthen raceway. (Courtesy, Gary Fornshell, University of Idaho)

Raceways vary in the rate of water flow and the way the water is handled at the end. Greater rates of flow require more water and allow more intensive (higher concentration) production of aquacrops. Raceways with very little water flow are sometimes known as semi-raceways.

7–9. A concrete raceway. (Courtesy, Gary Fornshell, University of Idaho)

Raceways may be closed or open. A *closed raceway* is one in which the water is recycled. Filtering and other treatment of the water may be required. With an *open raceway*, the water is used once and disposed of. Disposal may require treatment of the water before it is released into streams or lakes.

Overall, raceways require more water than ponds. An advantage is that aquacrops may be grown at a higher stocking rate than in ponds. Hilly land may be better suited to raceways than to ponds.

7–10. Raceway lined with black plastic and used for spirulina production. (Spirulina is a blue-green algae used as a food additive. This farm is in Hawaii.)

TANKS

Tanks are water impoundments made of concrete, metal, fiberglass, or other materials. They are usually round or rectangular. Tanks constructed of light materials may be portable. Aeration of the water is essential for the aquacrop to survive.

Round tanks range in size from 6 to 30 feet in diameter and from 2 to 6 feet in depth. The water is run into a round tank at an angle on one side so that it flows in a circular pattern. The water is often removed in the middle, where the flow is lessened and the sludge (solid material consisting mostly of feces and uneaten feed) settles.

Aquacrops are usually stocked at a heavy density in tanks. Properly disposing of the used water is essential. Environmental regulations do not allow dumping used water into streams if the water would cause pollution.

Rectangular tanks range from a few feet to around 25 feet long. They are often 3 feet

7–11. Round tanks used in fish production. The water flows in a circular direction. (Courtesy, National Oceanic & Atmospheric Administration)

7–12. Round tanks used inside a building in North Carolina.

7–13. A round-tank system inside a greenhouse used for freshwater prawn production.

7–14. A large rectangular tank has been partitioned for raising tilapia. Note the hydroponics production in the background, with wastewater from the tanks being used to grow the plants.

wide and 30 inches deep. Water enters at one end and is removed at the other. Aquacrops are stocked at a high density. Used water must be properly handled.

7–15. Concrete vats used for aquaculture. (Courtesy, National Oceanic & Atmospheric Administration)

Vats

Vats are much like tanks but are usually constructed of concrete or concrete blocks. Therefore, they are not portable. Vats are often long, rectangular structures. Water normally flows continuously into a vat at one location and is removed at another. The used water must be disposed of properly. Some aeration of the water is needed.

Vats are most often used for temporarily holding fish and other aquacrops. Occasionally vats are used for raising aquacrops. Retail baitfish stores use vats for minnows and other bait. Small retail food fish markets may store live fish in vats until the fish are sold. Large processing plants use vats to hold fish delivered from farms until the fish go into the plants for processing.

Aquariums

An *aquarium* is similar to a tank and has limited use in most aspects of aquafarming. Certain pet fish may be grown in aquariums. Researchers may use aquariums in the produc-

7–16. An aquarium used for keeping ornamental fish.

tion and observation of small populations of aquacrops. Aquariums are typically made of glass and have capacities of from 5 to 50 gallons or more of water. The water may be flowing or aerated, depending on the system used.

CAGES AND PENS

Cages and pens confine aquacrops for specific purposes. They allow some control over the growing environment that would not otherwise be possible. For example, pairs of broodfish may be held in pens for spawning. Cages and pens are similar in the confinement of aquacrops but vary in how they are positioned in the water.

A *cage* is a container for aquacrops that floats in the water. Most cages are used in deep, unmanageable water areas. For example, cages are used in salmon culture in ocean water. Typical construction involves a frame of wood, plastic, or metal covered with a mesh wire or other fabric. Floats are placed at the top of a cage to keep it at the surface of the water.

A *pen* is a container for aquacrops attached to the earth at the bottom of a water impoundment. Construc-

7–17. A new cage not yet installed in a pond. Note that the large PVC pipe around the top provides buoyancy to float the cage.

tion is similar to that of a cage except that no floats are needed. The frame of a pen may go into the earth under the water. Pens allow some control over aquatic species that would not be possible otherwise.

7–18. Square net pen being used in salmon culture in Wilapa Bay, Washington.

Cages and pens may be used in streams, large lakes, and oceans where controlling the aquacrop and water is impossible. Abandoned quarries where stone or minerals have been mined may also be suitable for cage or pen aquaculture. Without cages or pens, the aquacrops would move throughout the quarries and be next to impossible to harvest and otherwise manage.

7–19. Spawning pens are idle after spawning season. Note the presence of a spawning container in each pen.

SELECTING A WATER FACILITY

Selecting the kind of facility to use is important in going into aquaculture production. Factors to consider are supply of available water, disposal of water, characteristics of the water, and species to be grown.

SUPPLY OF AVAILABLE WATER

If a large supply of good water is economically available, facilities that require large quantities, such as ponds and open raceways, can be used. When water is scarce, smaller systems will likely be better. Recirculated water in tanks and vats may be used. Aquacrops are more intensively managed when the water supply is limited.

Besides water supply, the cost of getting and preparing the water for use is also an important consideration. Expensive deep wells and pumps may be required. Elaborate treatment, such as heating cold water before it is used, adds to the cost.

Permits from appropriate government agencies may be needed before a water supply can be used in aquaculture. Gaining approval may require considerable time.

7–20. Water filtration and oxygenation facilities are used to prepare water from a factory for use in aquaculture.

DISPOSAL OF WATER

Some aquafarms use water and dispose of it without recycling. An approved way of disposing of the used water must be available. Since water from aquaculture contains feces, uneaten feed, and other materials, it cannot usually be run directly into a natural stream or lake.

Selecting a water facility requires attention to how water will be treated before disposal. Some aquafarmers use culture systems that produce very little or no water for disposal. For

7–21. Water discharging from raceways. (Courtesy, U.S. Department of Agriculture)

example, fish ponds usually have no water disposal unless the ponds are drained. On the other hand, raceway and tank systems may produce large amounts of water that require disposal.

CHARACTERISTICS OF THE WATER

Available water should be carefully studied. Some sites have cold water, while others have warm water. Thermal well water (water that is naturally heated by the earth) can be used to produce fish that require warm water. If it is not available, consider an alternative. The kind of crop that is possible has considerable bearing on the kind of water facility to be constructed.

SPECIES TO BE GROWN

Aquacrops have varying water requirements. Species must be carefully studied to be sure that the one chosen will be well suited. A good procedure is to find out what other producers in the area are growing. Of course, many aquacrops are new, and few farms are growing them. Also, farm sites within a geographic area have different features. Neighboring farms may have different possibilities.

SOURCES OF WATER

Sources of water include wells, streams, lakes and oceans, springs, industrial effluent, municipal water systems, recycled wastewater, and surface runoff. Selecting a source is an important decision. Not only must the water be of good quality, but it must also be available at a reasonable cost. Suitable water is likely available from each source, though its use may be impractical in some situations.

WELLS

A *well* is an opening made into a water table of the earth to obtain water. The opening may be made by boring (drilling), by driving a well point, or in other ways.

Boring is used with a deeper well, while a well point on the end of a pipe may be driven from the surface for a shallow well. A pipe is placed in the boring to direct the flow of water. A pump is attached to the pipe to move the water. Often, aquaculture wells are bored 100 feet (30 m) or more to reach suitable supplies of ground water. Some are bored into deep aquifers to get fresh water that is free of pollution.

Wells usually provide the best water for freshwater aquaculture. The water is typically free of pollution from chemicals, parasites, disease organisms, and trash fish. Shallow wells, however, may have traces of pesticide residues or other hazardous compounds. Well water may sometimes contain undesirable gases and minerals. It may also be low in oxygen; thus, some way of adding oxygen will be needed.

Water from wells cannot always be pumped directly into the aquaculture facility. If it is cold, it may need to be pumped into a holding pond for solar warming before being used in aquaculture. This is also a good time to add oxygen. Some wells produce warm (thermal) water. This is particularly advantageous for warmwater crops. For example, tilapia thrive in water that is about 85°F (29°C). The tilapia farm with a year-round supply of appropriate warm well water is fortunate!

The capacity of a well to produce water is measured in **gallons per minute** (gpm). How rapidly a well produces depends on the size of the pipe in the earth and the size, speed, and power of the pump. Pumping rates may range from less than 100 gpm to 2,000 gpm. The time required to fill a vat, a pond, or other facility depends on gpm. For example, it will take a 1,000-gpm pump 16.2 hours to put 3 feet (1 m) of water in a 1-acre pond.

Well depths may range from relatively shallow to deep. Shallow wells are around 30 feet deep. Other wells may be hundreds of feet deep. Depth depends on the distance to the aquifer (the layer or stratum of rock, sand, or gravel that holds water beneath the earth's crust).

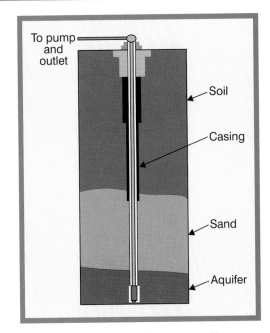

7–22. Structure of a water well.

7–23. This pump can provide a large amount of water.

The cost of drilling and of pumps and energy to operate wells is important in setting up an aquafarm. Commercial well drillers can be hired to bore wells. Well cost is normally based on a per-foot rate plus other items, such as the pump and the motor. A well occasionally needs to be replaced. Sometimes the water level may drop below the pipe that goes into the earth, or the well casing (the pipe used to enclose a well) may rust out or break. In either case, getting water from the well is no longer possible.

To bore (drill) wells, permits are needed and can usually be obtained from local government agencies. A few years ago, permits were not required. As more wells were drilled, the ground water level began to decline. Consequently, regulations were developed to help conserve valuable water. Some abuse of ground water has also occurred. Unfortunately, chemicals have sometimes entered the water through wells when individuals have pumped hazardous chemicals into wells to dispose of them.

In a few sites, artesian wells provide good aquaculture water. An **artesian well** is a well in which natural pressures in the earth cause the water to flow like a fountain. Therefore, a pump is not needed. An artesian well is drilled like any other well and is usually deep. If the water is of good quality, artesian wells can save money on pumps and electricity.

STREAMS

Rivers and creeks are sometimes near aquafarms. These may provide good water for freshwater aquaculture. Careful assessment of the water is needed to decide whether it is suitable for aquafarming.

A **stream** is a flowing body of water. The water is from several sources: springs, runoff from rain or melted snow, industrial effluent, municipal sewage systems, and overflow from farm irrigation, such as runoff from rice farms. Water that comes from springs and the runoff from land that does not have chemical residues is more likely to be suitable. Water from municipal sewage plants, livestock feeding operations, and certain industrial uses is unsuitable for aquaculture.

Water from streams may be seasonal. During summer and fall, a stream may dry up, leaving no water supply. A backup well or another source is needed. The quantity of water that can be removed from a stream is regulated. The general rule is that the removal of water from a stream cannot noticeably reduce its flow. Regulations must be followed in getting water from streams.

Stream water may need to be treated in some way. Water taken from streams may introduce diseases and trash fish to the aquafarm. The water can be filtered to remove objectionable items. A mesh screen may be put over the end of intake pipes, or a filtration system can be installed. Filtering costs money and reduces the profit of an aquafarm.

7–24. Streams have limited capacity to provide water for aquaculture.

Pumps, canals, piping systems, and other facilities may need to be constructed to get the water from streams to where it will be used. Energy is required to operate the pumps. Regular inspection of the facilities is needed to ensure that they are working properly.

Overall, water from streams is considered less desirable than water from wells. Sometimes, it is unfit for aquafarming.

LAKES AND OCEANS

Water in natural lakes and oceans may sometimes be used for aquafarming. Some lakes contain fresh water; others have salt water. All oceans and seas are salty. Hydroelectric or flood-control reservoirs constructed across streams are similar to freshwater lakes.

As with streams, water from lakes and oceans may contain chemical residues, parasites, diseases, and trash fish or weeds. A filtering and treatment system may be needed.

An alternative to pumping water from lakes and oceans is growing aquacrops in cages or other structures in these bodies of water. Cages typically float in the water. They are normally anchored in some way to prevent drifting away. Stationary water structures may be attached to the bottom of a lake or an ocean if the water is shallow. Cages also can be used in deep water.

7–25. The Pacific Ocean has limited potential for aquaculture except with cages, pens, and other structures.

7–26. This spring in Hot Springs, Arkansas, produces thermal water with limited potential use in aquaculture.

Using water from lakes and oceans requires careful analysis of the water and knowledge of the water environment needed by the proposed aquacrop. Regulations must be followed in removing any water from a lake or an ocean. Obtaining the needed permits can be a lengthy process.

Springs

A *spring* is a natural opening in the earth that produces water. The water is often similar to well water. It may be cold or thermal, depending on the spring. Spring water is frequently low in oxygen. It may be high in certain minerals. Of course, the use of spring water in aquaculture is limited to areas where springs are found.

Careful assessment of how much water is produced by a spring is important. Some springs tend to dry up in drier weather. Aquafarming usually requires a year-round, dependable supply of water.

Springs often flow into streams or reservoirs. The water must be caught in some way for use in aquafarming. It is possible that trash fish, pollution, and other foreign matter can enter spring water shortly after it flows from the earth.

Industrial Effluent

Industrial effluent is the water released by manufacturing plants. Some of this water is excellent for aquaculture. For example, power plants use water for cooling and do not alter it otherwise. This water may be warmed in the cooling process. As warm water, it can be very beneficial to certain crops. On the other hand, water released from chemical or other industries may be unfit for aquaculture.

7–27. The effluent from this small electric generating plant in Alaska is appropriate for aquaculture. (In fact, a salmon hatchery is downstream a short distance.)

Only locations near industries that use and release large amounts of water should be considered for aquaculture that uses industrial effluent. The quality of the water must be determined. Often, this requires extensive laboratory analysis. The quantity of water released is also a consideration. Sufficient water must be available for the crop.

All regulations about the use of the wastewater must be followed. The owners of the industries must agree to allow the use of the water. In a few cases, industries have initiated aquaculture.

7–28. Wastewater flowing from this fertilizer plant may be too polluted for aquaculture.

MUNICIPAL WATER SYSTEMS

Municipal and rural community water systems provide water for household and business use. The water may be taken from streams, lakes, and reservoirs or from wells. It is treated with various chemicals to make it suitable for human consumption. Chlorine and fluorine may be added. Both may be harmful to aquacrops!

As a source of water for aquaculture, municipal and rural systems are usually too expensive for large-scale operations. Small

7–29. A two-tank system would not likely be too large for a municipal water system.

aquafarms that use only a few gallons may find them suitable. However, the water must be dechlorinated. This is done by letting it stand in an open container for at least 24 hours, adding sodium thiosulfate, or filtering it through charcoal. Some aquafarms that primarily use other sources for water rely on municipal systems in case the other sources fail.

Small quantities of ornamental fish can be produced using municipal water. Homeowners with aquariums of pet fish almost exclusively use municipal water. They run the water a day or so before using it and allow it to stand in large tubs. While standing, the water loses its chlorine and warms up. Of course, a small amount of water is lost through evaporation while it is standing.

RECYCLED WASTEWATER

Wastewater is water that has been used and discarded. It often contains particles of solid materials. Some may have human wastes. After proper recycling, wastewater might be suitable for aquaculture. This source of water should be used only after careful analysis to be sure that using it is safe. Aquaculture facilities may recondition and use their own wastewater.

SURFACE RUNOFF

Rain, melted snow, and other types of precipitation form *surface runoff*, which may be collected in reservoirs for use in aquaculture. Much of the water in streams is from surface runoff.

The typical use of surface runoff is for the small watershed pond. This kind of pond is built to be filled by surface runoff from hillsides surrounding the pond. Several acres of watershed may be needed to fill a pond. This approach to water supply is not well suited to commercial aquaculture operations. It is best for the hobby farmer or recreational lake operator.

7–30. Pond filled with surface runoff. (Note that the design of the pond makes harvesting difficult. Cattle wading in it make the pond unacceptable for aquaculture.)

Runoff tends to reflect the qualities of the area from which it comes. Runoff from pasture land may be relatively free of residues except for animal feces, vegetative matter, and any chemicals applied to the land. Runoff from cropland may contain eroded soil, pesticide residues, and other undesirable material. Sometimes runoff is collected from roads, residential areas, and business parking lots. However, such runoff is largely unfit for aquaculture.

Before runoff can be used in aquaculture, it must be carefully tested for residues that could be harmful to the aquacrop or the consumer of the crop. Laboratory analysis of a runoff sample is usually required.

SUITABILITY OF WATER

Some water is of good quality for aquaculture; other water is not. All water being considered for potential use in aquaculture should be analyzed to determine its suitability. This involves comparing the qualities of the water with the preferences of the proposed aquacrop. Of course, some water is unfit for any type of aquaculture!

Water quality is the suitability of water for a particular use. Water that is suitable for one purpose might not be suitable for another. Water quality is determined in various ways. Laboratory testing may be required. Farmers may purchase small, portable kits for testing water. Observing how aquatic life responds in the water is a good clue to its quality.

Several things to look for in determining the suitability of water are dissolved oxygen; temperature; acidity, alkalinity, and hardness; pollutants; nitrogen compounds; and carbon dioxide.

7–31. Water being tested in a laboratory.

DISSOLVED OXYGEN

Oxygen is required for animal aquacrops to carry on body functions and to remain alive. Water must contain **dissolved oxygen** (DO). DO is the oxygen that is in water and available to aquatic organisms. DO does not include the oxygen combined with hydrogen to form water molecules. For example, fish draw water into their mouths and force it out over their gills. The gills remove the oxygen by diffusion and pass it into the bloodstream. Without

7–32. Using a meter to measure DO in a pond with aerators present. (Courtesy, Agricultural Research Service, USDA)

enough dissolved oxygen, the fish become sick or die. They may be seen gasping at the surface of the water or dead with their bellies turned up.

Dissolved oxygen in water is stated as parts per million (ppm). For example, 1 pound in a million pounds would be 1 ppm. Tests can be run to detect the amount that is in water. Cold water holds more oxygen than warm water. This means that the highest amount of oxygen is at 32°F (0°C). At 60°F (16°C), water holds up to 9 ppm dissolved oxygen, while at 90°F (32°C), it holds up to 7 ppm.

For animal aquacrops, an oxygen level of 5 ppm or above is preferable. Most will survive at the 1 to 5 ppm level, but growth will be slow, and disease outbreaks are more likely. Low oxygen causes the fish crop to be stressed. Below 1 ppm, the aquacrops are likely to die if exposure is for more than a short time. Required oxygen levels vary among different species. Small fish tend to be more tolerant of low oxygen. For example, the fathead minnow will survive if the level stays at 1 ppm or above. Channel catfish, however, may die if it goes

7–33. Using an oxygen meter to determine DO in a natural lake.

below 2 ppm, except that the small fish of the species may survive at a lower level. Rainbow trout may die when the level reaches 3 ppm or below.

Sometimes water can be supersaturated. This means that it contains more oxygen than it will normally hold. Water is not likely to be supersaturated in ponds. If it is, running normal aeration equipment will cause a reduction in oxygen rather than an increase in it.

Fortunately, dissolved oxygen can be added to water if the water is low in it. This is a management tool available to aquafarmers. Water from wells and springs should usually be aerated before it is used. Close observation must be made of oxygen levels to prevent the loss of aquacrops.

TEMPERATURE

Water temperature is important with many aquacrops. Fish are *ectothermic animals*. An ectothermic animal is one whose body temperature adjusts to that of its environment. Sudden changes in water temperature can cause the death of fish. Different aquacrops require different temperatures for growth.

Temperature influences feeding, metabolism, growth, and reproduction. When water is below the best temperature for a particular aquacrop, the fish will stop eating. This is a result of a slowdown in their metabolism. Metabolism is all the growth and maintenance processes that occur in the body of an animal. Changes in water temperature cause certain aquacrops to reproduce. For example, in the spring, most fish spawn naturally as the water begins to warm.

Because of the expense, trying to control the temperature of water on a large scale is impractical. Exceptions involve hatcheries and the water environments of high-value

CONNECTION

ABUNDANT HARVEST

Most aquaculture crops are not easy to see until harvest time. Water in a pond might have an abundant crop or a small crop. Producers are often surprised by what they see at harvest. Fortunately, steps can be taken to help in having a good harvest every time.

The size and quality of an aquacrop are related to the water environment in which the crop grows. In a good environment, a crop does well. In a poor environment, it does not. After going into aquaculture, it costs no more to manage water environments well than it does to manage them poorly. The key is good water management!

This shows food-size fish being harvested from a pond. The harvest looks abundant! (Photo courtesy, James Lytle, Mississippi State University)

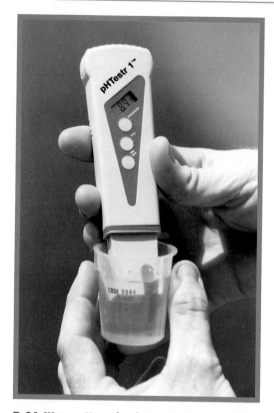

7–34. Water pH can be determined with a pH meter.

organisms. Selecting an aquacrop suited to the water that is available is best. Water from deep wells, springs, and melted snow is typically cold. It will warm if allowed to stand in ponds for a period in warm weather.

ACIDITY, BASICITY, AND HARDNESS

The acidity, basicity, and hardness of water are determined through chemical analysis of a sample of the water. Commonly, surface water is within the desired acidity, alkalinity, and hardness range.

pH

Water pH is the acidity or basicity of water. Most aquacrops will not thrive in water with a pH range to which they are not suited. The midpoint on the 14-point pH scale is 7. Most aquacrops will survive 2 points above or below 7. Since the pH of water in ponds and other facilities may vary during a day, most aquacrops are tolerant of short-term exposure to very high or very low pH values.

Some chemicals used to treat aquacrops for diseases or other purposes are more toxic in water that is not in the pH range of 5 to 9. If these will be used, having some understanding of water pH and hardness is important. Labels or material safety data sheets (MSDS) on chemicals tell whether they are approved and how they will react with the water.

Hardness

Hardness is the amount of calcium and magnesium in water. It is associated with a high pH. Hardness is measured in ppm, with a range of 50 to 300 ppm hardness being best. A water softener can be used if the water is too hard.

POLLUTANTS

A *pollutant* is any substance that contaminates water used in aquaculture. Some substances are harmful to aquacrops; others are not. Sometimes, aquacrops ingest (take in) harmful substances and pass them on to human consumers.

7–35. Bubbles on the surface of this water form in the presence of blue-green algae. In the morning, the bubbles contain CO_2, and in the afternoon they contain O_2.

Pollutants may come from industries, natural sources, ordinary life activities of humans in towns and cities, and agriculture. Some sources of pollution do not seem significant, but they can become significant with repeated exposure. For example, automobiles and trucks release gases into the air, produce used oil, and emit other substances. Used oil should be properly handled; otherwise, it may find its way into water used for aquacrops. Fuel storage tanks may develop leaks that allow fuel to enter sources of water.

Farming activities sometimes release toxic substances. Farmers who grow row crops near ponds or other aquaculture facilities should be very careful in using pesticides (primarily weed and insect killers). Harvested aquacrops found to contain excess amounts of toxic chemicals are unfit for human consumption.

Determining the possibility of pollution involves studying the source of the water. Water that might have come from areas where contamination could occur should undergo laboratory analysis. It is a good idea to have samples of water from any source tested before an aquafarm is started.

NITROGEN COMPOUNDS

The air contains 78 percent nitrogen, as compared with 21 percent oxygen. There will likely be more nitrogen gas in water than dissolved oxygen. Nitrogen compounds include ammonia, nitrite, and nitrate. These usually become problems in water used in intensive aquaculture, such as in tanks, where there is high organic waste. Spring and well water can become supersaturated with nitrogen and cause gas bubble disease in some aquacrops. If water from an aquacrop is reused, a strong possibility of nitrogen problems exists. Various tests and treatments are available. These are presented in Chapter 8.

CARBON DIOXIDE

Some carbon dioxide is usually found in water. The level is higher in water used in aquafarming. Carbon dioxide is produced by the respiration of plants and animals living in water. Safe levels of carbon dioxide range from 5 to 10 ppm. Toxicity to aquacrops depends on the amount of dissolved oxygen in the water. Most crops will tolerate a high level of carbon dioxide if the dissolved oxygen level is also high. If from calcium carbonate aquifers, spring and well water as they are pumped may have a carbon dioxide problem.

REVIEWING

MAIN IDEAS

As the environment in which aquacrops grow, water is very important. When deciding about aquaculture production, consider water supply, water cycle, and species of aquacrop.

Impoundments include ponds, raceways, tanks, vats, and aquariums. In addition, cages and pens are also used.

Selecting the kind of facility to use requires careful consideration of four areas: supply of available water, disposal of water, characteristics of the water, and species to be grown.

Sources of water include wells, streams, lakes and oceans, springs, industrial effluent, municipal water systems, recycled wastewater, and surface runoff. Wells are often considered the best sources of freshwater. They provide a more dependable supply than springs and surface runoff.

Water quality refers to the suitability of water for use with an aquacrop. Major concerns in water quality are dissolved oxygen; temperature; acidity, basicity, and hardness; pollutants; nitrogen compounds; and carbon dioxide. Some of these quality factors, such as dissolved oxygen, can be easily manipulated. Changing the quality of water is often expensive but may be essential.

QUESTIONS

Answer the following questions, using complete sentences and correct spelling.

1. Why is water quality important?

2. Why is it important for the aquacrop to be carefully matched with the characteristics of the water?

3. What is a water impoundment? What kinds of water impoundments are used?

4. What factors should be considered in the selection of a water facility?

5. What are the sources of water for aquaculture? Briefly describe each.

6. How is the capacity of a water pump measured? Why is this important?

7. What is dissolved oxygen? Why is it important? What levels are needed in water for aquaculture?

8. Why is water temperature important with aquaculture crops?

9. What is water hardness?

10. What are the sources of water pollution in aquaculture?

EVALUATING

Match the term with the correct definition. Write the letter of the term on the line provided.

a. aquifer
b. industrial effluent
c. gallons per minute
d. water cycle

e. impoundment
f. cage
g. well
h. water quality

_____1. The suitability of water for a particular use

_____2. The never-ending circulation of water on the earth

_____3. An underground formation that contains water

_____4. An enclosure that holds water

_____5. A container for aquacrops that floats in the water

_____6. The measurement of the capacity of a well to produce water

_____7. An opening in the earth to obtain water

_____8. Water released from manufacturing plants

EXPLORING

1. Assess the possible sources of water for aquaculture in your school district or county. Determine which aquacrops might be appropriate for the water. Evaluate the cost, quality, and other characteristics of the source to determine the feasibility of using it for aquaculture. Prepare a written report on your findings. Give an oral report in class.

2. Select a water facility and prepare a plan for using it to produce an aquacrop. Consider the costs of the facility, available water, the market, and other factors. Select a species that you feel would be appropriate. Prepare a written report on your findings. Give an oral report to your class.

CHAPTER 8

Water Quality and Management

OBJECTIVES

This chapter covers important areas of water quality and management. It has the following objectives:

1 Describe water quality

2 Describe important water management practices

3 Calculate water volume

4 Explain how weeds and algae are controlled

5 Describe how to prevent aquaculture water pollution

6 Describe how to dispose of used water

TERMS

aeration
ammonia toxicity
biological oxygen demand
biological weed control
biomass
chemical weed control
effluent
environmental weed control

eutrophication
gas bubble disease
mechanical weed control
nitrogen cycle
oxygenation
oxygen depletion
phytoplankton
plankton

supersaturation
turbidity
water biology
water chemistry
water management
water physical characteristics
zooplankton

8–1. Tests are often made on the sites of streams and ponds.

GETTING WATER and constructing facilities are important, but how the water and the facilities are used is likely more important! Water management is a key to successful aquaculture production.

Organisms that live in water change their environment. Life processes produce wastes. Problems are more likely in high-density populations. Particles of excrement and uneaten feed foul the water. Fortunately, steps can be taken to improve and maintain water quality.

Providing a good water environment for aquacrops is similar to providing a good air environment for yourself. Dusty, smoky areas are not good for your health. You try to breathe good air and keep it as clean as possible. A similar approach is needed with the water for aquacrops.

WATER QUALITY

Water quality consists of all the chemical, physical, and biological characteristics of water that influence how an aquacrop grows. It determines the suitability of water for aquaculture. Water can be unfit for aquaculture. This may be due to naturally existing qualities, pollution, or other factors. Any characteristic that influences how water is used in the production of an aquacrop is a part of water quality.

8–2. Fish continuously remove oxygen from water as the water moves through their mouths and out over their gills. This process can be easily observed with most species, such as these hybrid tilapia.

CHEMICAL CHARACTERISTICS

Water chemistry is the composition of water. Each drop of water contains millions of tiny molecules. These molecules are made up of atoms of hydrogen and oxygen. Pure water is a clear liquid that serves many important functions.

Normally, hydrogen and oxygen are gases. When they combine, they form a chemical compound known as water. The compound in pure form is written as H_2O. Sometimes, other substances get into water. It is no longer pure. Scientific processes are needed to detect impurities in water. These processes involve using applied chemistry.

Small amounts of various minerals and compounds may be found in water. Dissolved oxygen (DO), nitrogen compounds, hydrogen sulfide, carbon dioxide, and iron are often present in

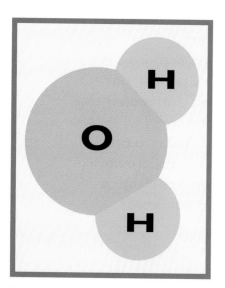

8–3. A water molecule (H_2O) is made of two atoms of hydrogen and one atom of oxygen.

water. DO is particularly important for many aquacrops. For example, fish must be able to get oxygen from the water, for without adequate oxygen, the fish will die.

Some chemical variations in water make it unsuitable for aquaculture. These, to some extent, depend on the environment needed by the crop being grown. An example of a hazardous component of water is a nitrite compound, which can kill a crop if the compound is present in a large amount.

Water chemistry includes pH, hardness, nitrogen compounds, oxygen forms, carbon dioxide, and alkalinity. Each plays a major role in maintaining water quality for aquaculture.

The important chemical characteristics are those that can cause the water to vary from the ideal environment. The ideal environment is different for different species. However, several areas are common among all species.

8–4. Kits are often used to determine the chemical characteristics of a water sample.

Nitrogen Cycle

Nitrogen is often present in aquaculture water. Sometimes the amount is sufficient to cause problems.

Nitrogen is present in four forms:

1. N_2—Nitrogen gas may be dissolved in water. The level should not be greater than 110 percent of saturation. Water from deep wells may have sufficient N_2 to pose a problem.

2. Ammonia—The breakdown of wastes and excess fish feed may form ammonia. It is typically present in ionized (NH_4^+) and un-ionized (NH_3) forms. The un-ionized form causes toxicity beginning at the concentration level of 0.01 mg/L (milligrams per liter) of total ammonia. Acute toxicity occurs at the 0.60 mg/L concentration. Avoid excess feed and aerate the water to control ammonia buildup in water. Some species are more sensitive to ammonia.

3. Nitrite—Nitrite (NO_2^-) results from the breakdown of ammonia in the nitrification process. Nitrite levels greater than 0.60 mg/L can be toxic to fish.

4. Nitrate—Nitrate (NO_3^-) results from the breakdown of nitrite, which is a product of ammonia breakdown. Nitrate is relatively nontoxic to aquacrops unless the concentration exceeds 3.0 mg/L.

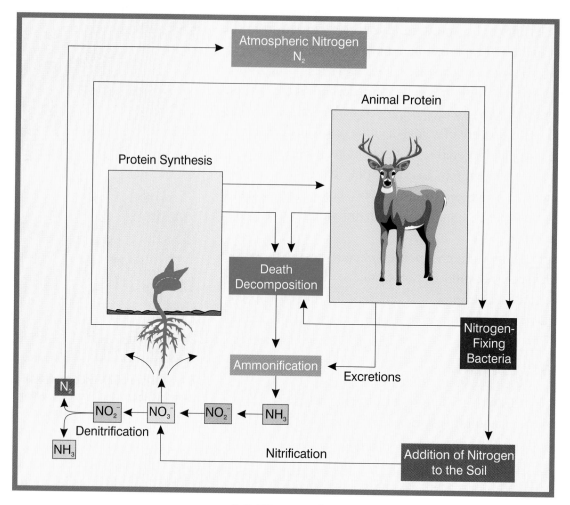

8–5. Nitrogen cycle.

8–6. A water sample has been carefully collected for testing.

Nitrogen can be a problem in some situations. Toxic compounds may result from the decomposition of wastes and uneaten feed that remain in the water. Microbe action in the water converts the nitrogen into forms less hazardous to fish. The processes involved with nitrogen are best explained in the nitrogen cycle.

The **nitrogen cycle** is the natural circulation or cycling of nitrogen through the earth's environment. The cycling includes the atmosphere, soil and water, and animals and plants. Nature has developed complex processes in the nitrogen cycle.

Though the atmosphere is 78 percent nitrogen, the elemental form (N_2) cannot be used by living organisms. Nitrogen must be combined with other elements in a form known as fixed nitrogen. Ammonia and nitrite forms are particularly dangerous to many aquatic species, especially fish. Microscopic organisms help in converting the forms into those that are harmless. (More details on the nitrification process are included later in the chapter.)

pH

With some aquacrops, the pH of the water is important. It is a function of the hydrogen ion concentration in the water. As explained in the previous chapter, numbers are used to describe pH. On a scale of 1 to 14, a pH of 7.0 is neutral. Numbers below 7.0 indicate that the water is acidic, while numbers above 7.0 indicate that the water is alkaline. For example, a pH of 5.2 indicates that the water is acidic.

Traces of minerals give water an acidic or basic quality. Most aquacrops prefer a pH of 6.3 to 7.5, but some will thrive in water with a wider pH of 5.0 to 8.5. Easy-to-use test kits and meters are available for determining pH.

8–7. A water sample from a tank system is being tested in a greenhouse facility.

Alkalinity

Alkalinity is often defined as a measure of the carbonates, bicarbonates, and hydroxyl ions in water. These affect pH and buffer against rather sudden changes in pH, which could destroy an aquacrop. Chemists refer to alkalinity as the amount of titratable bases in water expressed as milligrams per liter of equivalent calcium carbonate. *Titratable* refers to the presence of a dissolved substance in water that will bring about a reaction with a reagent.

8–8. pH is being assessed using a Color Comparator with color disc and pH indicator in a sample of water.

Test kits can be used in aquaculture to determine the levels of alkalinities in water. Commercial kits use a phenolphthalein indicator solution with a sample of water. In fresh water, alkalinities should range between 40 and 400 mg/L. Alkalinities may also be measured as grams per gallon (gpg), which can be converted to mg/L by multiplying the gpg finding by 17.1. High-range alkalinity tests report 1 to 20 gpg. Low-range tests report 0.4 to 8 gpg.

Alkalinity is one important indicator of the need for a water treatment. An example of such a treatment is the addition of lime to raise pH.

Hydrogen Sulfide

Hydrogen sulfide is a gas produced by the anaerobic breakdown of waste products in water. It becomes dissolved in the water and tends to escape from the surface with an odor similar to that of rotten eggs.

Hydrogen sulfide is toxic to fish and other aquatic organisms. Avoid overfeeding and keep water in good condition to control hydrogen sulfide buildup. Hydrogen sulfide levels can be lowered by aerating the water. The odor of hydrogen sulfide is usually sufficient evidence that steps need to be taken to alleviate any problems.

Salinity

Water may be classified based on its salt content. Fresh water has less than 3 ppt (parts per thousand) salt. Water from most wells and streams is fresh water. Salt water is the water found in oceans and seas, which typically has a salt content of 33 to 37 ppt. Water found where the two flow together has a salt content higher than that of fresh water but lower than that of salt water and is known as brackish water.

8–9. Various lab procedures may be used in testing water.

Chlorine

Chlorine is a disinfectant used in drinking water and aquaculture. It may be found in water from a municipal system. Tests can be made to determine the presence of chlorine. Chlorine levels should be less than 0.03 mg/L in aquaculture water. Sodium thiosulfate can be applied to water at the rate of 1 mg/L for each mg/L of chlorine to neutralize the chlorine.

Collecting water and allowing it to stand in an open container for a day or so will result in the chlorine escaping. This practice is often followed with small aquariums and other systems where time is available for the water to stand.

Supersaturation

Supersaturation is the condition in which water contains more gas than is soluble at a given temperature. The formation of bubbles occurs when barometric pressure and total gas pressure in the water are at levels conducive to bubble formation. Scientists use mathematical formulas to establish pressure levels and predict the likelihood of supersaturation problems. Water can be supersaturated with oxygen or nitrogen.

Supersaturation results from unusual natural or human-caused conditions. The major causes of supersaturation are the mix-

8–10. Water testing is underway using a portable lab in the back of a pickup truck.

ing of water of different temperatures, atmospheric or other pressure changes, excess aeration, photosynthesis of aquatic organisms, and bacterial action.

Supersaturation can result in **gas bubble disease** with fish and other aquatic animals. Bubbles form on the surface of the body or within tissues and the vascular system.

PHYSICAL CHARACTERISTICS

Water physical characteristics are the conditions of water due to temperature. Temperature determines the physical state of water: solid, liquid, or gas. Water becomes a solid when the temperature reaches 32°F (0°C) and it changes to ice. Water is a liquid when the temperature is between the freezing and boiling points of 32° and 212°F (0° and 100°C), respectively. Water becomes a gas (vapor) through vaporization. This process can be accelerated by heating water to the boiling point (212°F, 100°C).

Aquacrops cannot grow in extreme water temperatures. Most aquacrops grow in water between 50° and 90°F (10° and 32°C). The physical features of the available water influence the selection of an aquacrop. Knowing the temperature requirements of each aquacrop is important.

WATER BIOLOGY

Water biology is the living and nonliving organisms found in water and the processes they carry out. The organisms include the aquacrops plus other small and large plants and animals that may be present. In a pond or other growing facility, these are collectively called biomass. **Biomass** is the amount of living and nonliving biological material in a given location. The more fish and other organisms that are in water, the higher is the biomass.

8–11. The number and size of fish and other organisms in water determine the biomass.

Tiny plants and animals present in water are usually not visible without magnification, such as with a microscope. Bacteria, fungi, and algae are common examples. Some of these are beneficial in the production of certain aquacrops; others are harmful and cause diseased conditions in the crops.

Plankton is the tiny plants and animals that float in pond water. *Phytoplankton* (algae plankton) produces oxygen through photosynthesis and helps keep oxygen available for aquacrops. Phytoplankton shades the bottoms of ponds and helps reduce the growth of aquatic weeds. *Zooplankton* (animal plankton) is a natural food of some aquacrops. It is not present in sufficient quantity for high densities of fish.

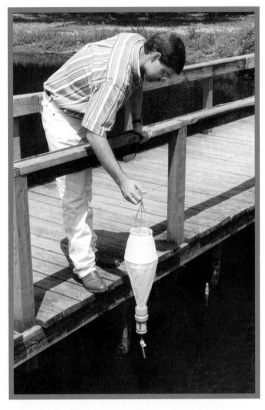

8–12. A plankton net can be used to collect plankton for study.

MANAGEMENT OF WATER

Once quality water has been obtained, production practices must be followed that will keep it in good condition for fish and other aquacrops.

Water management is the use of water in aquaculture to maintain a good environment for the

8–13. Regular and frequent observation of water is needed in providing good management. Here, a separate computer printout of DO for each pond is being analyzed.

aquacrop. It includes knowing and using the chemical, physical, and biological characteristics of water. Good water management can prevent problems that restrict production. Poor water management may result in little growth and, possibly, the loss of an aquacrop. Dead fish floating on the surface of the water may be the result of water problems that could have been prevented.

Major areas of concern in water management are oxygen depletion, buildup of nitrogen compounds, presence or excess of other compounds and substances, turbidity and color, growth of weeds and algae, and plankton bloom.

OXYGEN DEPLETION

Water must have adequate dissolved oxygen (DO) to support the growth of an aquacrop. *Oxygen depletion* has occurred when the DO level in water is below the level needed to maintain the living condition of the aquacrop being produced. Oxygen need varies with the species of aquacrop.

In any type of water facility, oxygen depletion will cause the death of fish in a few hours. Larger fish typically die first. Most of the aquacrops require 4 to 5 ppm of DO. Follow good practices to keep DO at an appropriate level.

Common Signs of Oxygen Deficiency

Some common signs of oxygen deficiency with fish are the following:

- Fish pipe (gasp) at the water surface for air.

- Fish group around the incoming water source.

- Fish go off feed (do not eat).

- Nonfish animals, such as crawfish and snails, crawl out of the water.

- Growth is slowed as a result of oxygen being deficient over the long term but not being low enough to kill the crop.

- Repeated outbreaks of health problems, such as those related to stress of fish, occur.

- Water color changes. (This indicates a plankton die-off.)

- Fish-eating birds are present. (The fish are near the surface and easy to catch.)

Causes of Oxygen Depletion

Biological oxygen demand (BOD) is the amount of oxygen used in the water for many natural purposes: decay of uneaten feed and vegetation, decay of plankton, respiration by the aquacrop and phytoplankton, and use by trash fish. (Trash fish are unwanted species of fish mixed in with the intended crop.) Ponds with dense populations of aquacrops have higher BOD than those with low-population density. Other conditions in the water may also influence BOD.

Among the causes of oxygen depletion are

- Overstocking—If water is stocked beyond its normal ability to provide oxygen, the fish or other crop will use up the oxygen. Most facilities are stocked far beyond the normal capacity of the water. Careful monitoring is needed to make sure that water problems do not develop.

- Weather—In production systems located outside, such as ponds, plant plankton produces oxygen by photosynthesis when the sun is shining. On cloudy days and dark nights, the water is lowest in DO because photosynthesis has not been taking place. Limited light may result in the death and decay of certain organisms. This ties up oxygen. Warmer water holds less DO; therefore, close monitoring is needed in warm, cloudy weather.

- Time of day—Natural supplies of DO vary greatly, depending on the time of day. DO is highest in a pond in the afternoon of a bright, sunny day. It is lowest in the early morning, just before sunrise. Plant plankton produces oxygen through photosynthesis during the day; it does not at night. Many producers monitor DO levels all night in the warm months of the year.

- Decay of feed—When an aquacrop is given more feed than it can eat, the feed decays. This process uses oxygen. Aquacrops should not be fed more feed than they will consume in a matter of a few minutes.

8–14. The decay of uneaten feed uses oxygen. This shows floating pellets on pond water.

- Feeding activity—The process of digesting food uses oxygen. As aquacrops consume feed, they require more oxygen.

- Competition—Some water facilities have trash fish and plants that use oxygen. These compete with the aquacrops for DO.

- Decay of vegetation—Dead weeds, leaves, grass, and other organic matter decay in water. This process ties up oxygen, just as does the decay of excess feed.

- Water temperature—Cold water holds more DO than warm water. Those crops that prefer warm water are more likely to have problems because they grow in water with a warm, nurturing environment for microorganisms.

- Salt content—Salt water holds less DO than fresh water. If fresh water is polluted by salt water, the ability to hold DO is reduced. This is seldom a problem with freshwater aquafarms. Systems using salt water will need to be monitored more closely.

- Chemical reactions—Certain chemical reactions in water may use oxygen. Although this is seldom a problem in aquaculture, it can happen with the addition of chemicals for various purposes.

- Equipment failure—DO problems can occur when the equipment used to aerate water fails. For example, when power outages for electric motors or breakdowns of motors or pumps happen, a tank or pond can quickly develop oxygen depletion.

- Corrosion—Equipment used in water aeration may become corroded and less efficient. This is particularly a problem in salt water because barnacles attach themselves to equipment.

DO can be easily measured. Several companies make meters and kits that are accurate. A DO meter often involves inserting a probe into the water and taking a reading using a battery-operated instrument. A kit may involve collecting water samples and using chemicals to test them.

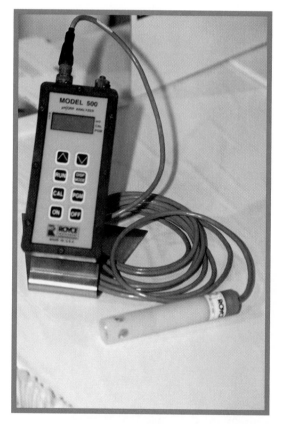

8–15. A DO meter can provide a quick indication of the oxygen level.

Normally, DO readings are made at least 6 inches below the surface of the water. Measurements should not be made near incoming water, close to aeration equipment, or next to the edge of the water impoundment. Required DO levels tend to vary for different crops; thus, knowing the desired level for the crop is important.

Overcoming Oxygen Deficiency

When an oxygen deficiency develops, steps should be taken to handle it immediately. Several ways are listed below. Sometimes combinations are needed.

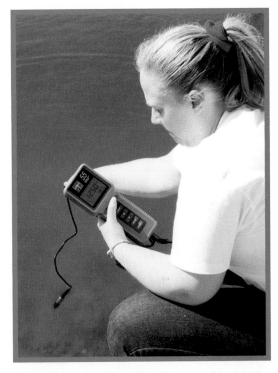

8–16. This meter shows that the water has 12.50 ppm of DO.

- Reduce the number of fish or other aquacrop in the water.
- Remove vegetation that competes with the aquacrop for oxygen.
- Inject oxygen into the water.
- Use mechanical aerators.
- Pump out bottom water and add new, aerated water to the surface.
- If the water level is below capacity, add aerated water to the impoundment.

8–17. Bubbles on this water in a hatchery suggest that biological processes are using oxygen and releasing carbon dioxide.

Oxygenation of Water

DO can be added to water with a variety of devices and methods. Some methods are more reliable than others; some are not very efficient. Several ways of adding oxygen are presented later in this chapter.

Oxygenation is adding dissolved oxygen (DO) to water. The chemical structure of water molecules is not changed. Methods are selected, depending on the situation, to increase the amount of DO in water. Water in tanks is oxygenated differently from that in ponds. Exposing water to the air so that it will pick up oxygen from the air is known as **aeration**. Large pond aquaculture production systems rely on aeration, while tank systems may use techniques that bubble oxygen into the water.

Common ways of getting DO into water include

8–18. Small, round tank being aerated by bubbling oxygen into the water. (Courtesy, National Oceanic & Atmospheric Administration)

- Splashing the water—New water being added to a facility can be splashed against a concrete slab or another structure. The purpose is to expose as much surface area (as many molecules) as possible to the air to get oxygen. Some splashing occurs when water is being pumped into a pond or through a raceway.

- Pumping air or oxygen gas into the water—This method is most often used with tanks or vats. Cylinders of oxygen can be placed on trucks with haul tanks. Sometimes aquacrops are shipped in large, heavy plastic bags. Pure oxygen can be injected into the bags after the fish and water are in place. Two ways of injecting air into larger bodies of water, such as ponds, are (1) bubbling compressed air through aeration tubes at the bottoms

8–19. This trailer for hauling fry is equipped with oxygen cylinders for direct injection into the water.

of ponds and (2) using pumps made with rotors or blades (impellers) to force air down into the water.

- Spraying the water into the air—This is a common method of aeration. The water is broken into as many droplets as possible to expose the maximum surface to the air. Various types of equipment, including electric-powered paddle-wheel aerators and floating pump sprayers, are used to throw the water. Some farmers have portable paddle-wheel aerators powered from the power shafts of farm tractors. These are on wheels and can be easily moved from one location to another. Portable units are particularly good to handle emergencies.

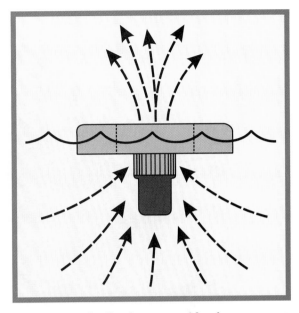

8–20. Design of a floating aerator showing movement of water from the pond, through the aerator, and into the air. (Courtesy, Kasco Marine, Inc.)

8–21. An electric-powered floating aerator anchored to a levee.

- Using chemicals—Using chemicals to restore DO can cause about as many problems as it solves. Potassium permanganate has been used at the rate of 1 to 3 pounds per acre in freshwater ponds. Fertilizers are sometimes used to increase plankton bloom, as this produces more oxygen. The rate is typically 40 to 50 pounds of superphosphate per acre. Fertilizers containing nitrogen should not be used with low oxygen. Chemicals tend to take longer than mechanical aerators for results.

8–22. The design of this portable tractor-powered aerator will move large volumes of water into the air for oxygenation.

NITROGEN COMPOUNDS

Nitrogen compounds are more likely to be problems in intensive aquaculture systems. This is because large amounts of organic wastes may build up. Fish excrement, as well as uneaten feed and other organic materials, also adds to nitrogen problems. As the wastes decompose, ammonia is formed and later converted to nitrites. Two forms of ammonia are found: un-ionized ammonia (NH_3) and ionized ammonia (NH_4^+), also known as ammonium. *Nitrosomonas* bacteria change the ammonia to nitrite (NO_2). Another form of bacteria, *Nitrobacter*, changes the nitrite to nitrate (NO_3). The nitrate form is relatively harmless to most aquacrops.

Ammonia and nitrite are the most harmful forms of nitrogen. Ammonia concentrations of 0.1 ppm may kill certain species of aquacrops. Concentrations of 0.0125 ppm may reduce the rate of growth and damage the ability of the aquacrops to function. *Ammonia toxicity* is a level of ammonia that injures or kills an aquatic species. Brain damage is among the first signs of ammonia toxicity. The gills of trout may be damaged at very low levels of un-ionized

8–23. Observing fish behavior provides evidence of water quality.

ammonia. Ammonia at 0.06 ppm can damage the gills of catfish, increase susceptibility to disease, and reduce growth rates.

High levels of nitrite may cause the hemoglobin in fish blood to oxidize. It will have a brown color and be unable to carry oxygen. In catfish, this condition is known as brown blood disease.

Many variables are involved in ammonia toxicity. Ammonia is more toxic in water when the temperature increases, the pH becomes more alkaline, the dissolved oxygen decreases, the carbon dioxide increases, and the salinity decreases.

Tests can be conducted to learn if nitrogen compounds exist in water. Since nitrogen forms may leave a water sample quickly, reliable methods of testing should be used. Samples should be collected in clean pint or half pint jars that can be sealed to prevent loss of nitrogen. The water samples should be taken at a depth of 1 foot.

Carefully monitoring feed consumption to prevent overfeeding is a crucial management tool in reducing nitrogen problems. Removing feces, uneaten feed, dead fish, and other organic materials that may decay and produce nitrogen compounds is important. Intensive systems must have considerable flow of water to remove the wastes. Tanks should be designed so that these materials can be moved to an area where removal is relatively easy, such as in the center of a round tank. Intensive systems that recycle water must have elaborate filtration and treatment systems to recondition the water for use.

OTHER COMPOUNDS AND SUBSTANCES

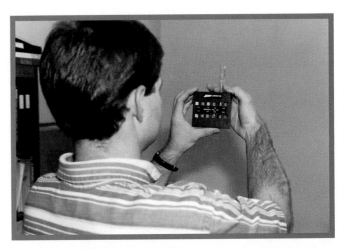

8–24. Observing the results of a test for phosphate.

Water used in aquaculture can contain any compound or substance dissolved by it or suspended in it. Some compounds and substances are harmless; others are dangerous to the crop. Some that are dangerous in large amounts are harmless in small amounts. Influence may be directly on the aquacrop or create conditions in the water environment that damage the crop.

Phosphorus, fluorine, sodium, potassium, chlorine, sulfur, and other compounds may be present. Hazardous heavy metals, such as lead and mercury, can also be in water. Water from manufacturing activity may contain other substances if not treated properly.

Phosphorus is usually in the phosphate (PO_4^{3-}) form. In most water used in aquaculture, phosphate does not directly damage the aquacrop. Higher levels of phosphate encourage excessive plankton growth, which damages water quality for aquaculture. Wastewater may contain high phosphate levels. Streams or lakes with wastewater flowing into them may have excessive plankton and eutrophication.

Eutrophication is excessive nutrient enrichment in water and is often caused by nitrogen and phosphorus. Plankton bloom ties up oxygen and often kills off fish and other aquatic organisms. Eutrophication is a greater problem with natural bodies of water than with managed fish ponds.

Chlorine in water from municipal systems can pose problems with ornamental fish or baitfish raised in the water. De-chlorination is needed. This may be by aging the water or adding chemical treatments. (More on de-chlorination is presented later in the book.)

Heavy metals, such as lead, mercury, and cadmium, in the water can result in harvested organisms that have high residues in their bodies. Such products are unfit for consumption. Water should be selected that is free of heavy metals. Avoid practices that contaminate water, such as using lead in plumbing fixtures or using water to dispose improperly of used batteries containing cadmium or lead.

Low levels of many substances in water cause no problems. Both the source of the water and the characteristics of the site, such as substances in the soil, should be considered. If problems with any substance are suspected, thorough laboratory analysis is needed.

8–25. A secchi disc is used to determine turbidity.

TURBIDITY AND COLOR

Turbidity is the presence of suspended particles of soil or plankton in the water. The water may appear muddy or cloudy. Some turbidity causes no problems. However, excessive turbidity reduces light that passes through the water. Thus, oxygen-producing plankton cannot carry out photosynthesis, thereby resulting in an oxygen deficiency.

Ponds that receive large amounts of runoff from rain are more likely to have turbidity problems because soil and vegetative matter are washed into the ponds. Sometimes, the vegetative matter will discolor the water, but this will not likely cause any problems. However, settling silt or soil may coat eggs, smothering them. The silt may also impair the growth of desired organisms.

Protecting aquaculture facilities from runoff by establishing grass covers on the soil around ponds is a practical way to reduce turbidity problems.

Various other treatments are also available. First, determine if the turbidity is due to silt or organic matter. With silt, gypsum may be used at the rate of 100 to 1,000 pounds per acre. Alum may also be used at the rate of 15 to 25 pounds per acre-foot. With organic turbidity, some producers broadcast 400 to 450 pounds of agricultural lime per acre. Note: The lime may increase the pH. It is a good practice to add the lime in increments, testing the pH between applications. The application of lime should stop when the pH reaches 9.0 to 9.5.

WEEDS AND ALGAE

Weeds and algae cause problems in aquaculture in several ways. Both compete with the aquacrop for oxygen, light, and nutrients. They also cause problems in harvesting. For example, weeds in ponds make it very difficult to pull a seine through the water; algae can clog a seine. Of course, weeds are usually not a problem in tanks, vats, and concrete raceways.

8–26. Riprap reduces erosion and protects the water from muddy runoff. This can eliminate turbidity problems. (Courtesy, National Oceanic & Atmospheric Administration)

Some plants growing in aquaculture facilities are desirable, particularly in the less intensive systems. Their role in producing oxygen is important. Desirable plants can create poor conditions if there are too many of them. (Another section of this chapter contains details on weed and algae control.)

8–27. Algae growing in ponds can cause problems. (Courtesy, National Oceanic & Atmospheric Administration)

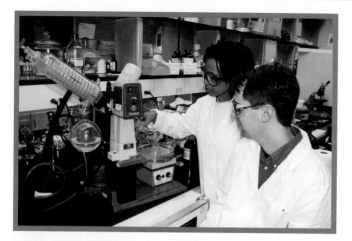

8–28. Sophisticated laboratory analysis with a rotary evaporator is sometimes needed to determine water qualities. (Courtesy, Emory University, Atlanta)

PLANKTON BLOOM

The beneficial tiny plants and animals that live in water can sometimes cause problems. When water is soupy green or brown, it may have too much plankton. Applying fertilizer high in nitrogen or phosphorus to a pond can cause too much plankton to grow. Plankton can be killed off with a chemical, but this may cause DO depletion. An approach used by some producers is to remove some water from a pond and add fresh water. This dilutes the concentration of plankton but does not work in large ponds.

CALCULATING WATER VOLUME

Operating aquafarms requires skill in making calculations about water. A producer often needs to know how long it takes to fill a pond or how much chemical to use in a tank.

The amount of water needed depends on the production system being used. Open systems, where the water continuously flows, require more water than closed systems. Raceways require more water than ponds.

Water requirements are typically stated as gallons, cubic feet, and acre-feet. (These can be converted to metric measurements using the information in Appendix A.)

- 1 cubic foot of water contains 7.481 gallons.

- 1 gallon contains 231 cubic inches of water.

- 1 acre-foot contains 325,851 gallons. (An acre-foot is the amount of water required to cover 1 acre with 1 foot of water.)

VOLUME OF TANKS AND VATS

Three measurements are needed to determine the amount of water in a rectangular tank, aquarium, or vat: length, width, and depth. Using a yardstick or tape measure, determine the length and width of the inside of the tank, aquarium, or vat and the depth of the water. (Some allowance is needed for a tank or other container with a sloping bottom or sloping sides. These measurements may need to be an average of the deepest and shallowest or widest and narrowest parts of the tank.) The formula to use is

$$\text{Volume} = \text{length} \times \text{width} \times \text{depth}$$

For example, a tank of water 10 feet long, 3 feet wide, and 2 feet deep would have a volume of 60 cubic feet. The number of gallons is found by multiplying 60 times 7.481. This tank has 448.86 gallons of water. The time required to fill the tank is determined by dividing the number of gallons in the tank by the gallons per minute (gpm) of the water source. Less than ten minutes would be required to fill the tank at a flow rate of 50 gpm.

The volume of a round tank or vat is determined somewhat differently. Two measurements—depth of the water and diameter of the inside of the tank—are needed. The formula to use is

$$\text{Volume} = 3.1416 \, (\text{diameter of tank} / 2)^2 \times \text{depth of water}$$

[Note: Diameter divided by 2 equals the radius (r).]

For example, a round tank 20 feet wide containing water 4 feet deep would have a volume of 1,256.64 cubic feet, or 9,400.92 gallons. At a pumping rate of 50 gpm (same as 3,000 gallons per hour), 3.14 hours would be required to fill the tank.

VOLUME OF PONDS AND RACEWAYS

The amount of water in ponds and raceways is determined much like the volume of rectangular tanks. Distances are often much larger and more difficult to measure. Averages of widths, depths, and lengths are often used. Slopes of levees and bottoms must be considered. In taking measurements, always use water dimensions and not locations without water. Measurements should be taken at the edge of the water.

Measuring at regular intervals along straight lines across a pond and then averaging the measurements will determine water depth. The design of a pond may provide for a certain depth of water. Information about depth, measurements, and slope of levee used in pond construction is very helpful. Volumes of rectangular ponds are more easily determined. The following is an example.

At the water level, a pond measures 506 feet in length and 306 feet in width. The levee has a 3-to-1 slope. The pond bottom is close to level, with water 4 feet deep. This means that the foot of the levee extends 12 feet into the water at the bottom all the way around the pond. The average length of the water is at the depth of 2 feet. Since the levee extends 12 feet, the amount it extends at 2 feet deep is 6 feet (one half of 12). This means that the average length of the water is 506 minus 6, or 500 feet. Average width is 306 minus 6, or 300 feet. The volume of water in the pond is 500 × 300 × 4, or 600,000 cubic feet. The number of gallons is 4,488,600 (600,000 × 7.481). Pumping time at the rate of 1,000 gpm would be 4,488.6 minutes, or 74.81 hours. Once a pond is full, water will need to be added occasionally to keep it up to the right level.

The volume of a raceway can be determined in much the same way. Since raceways involve flowing water, continual pumping is required. Water in raceways is often replaced twice each hour. In a 30,000-gallon raceway, a 1,000-gpm supply would be needed.

AMOUNTS OF CHEMICALS

Many chemicals are calculated as parts per million (ppm). Remember that 1.0 ppm is equal to 2.72 pounds per acre-foot, or 0.0283 gram per cubic foot. If a pond is treated, the acre-foot measurement is used. If a vat or tank is treated, the cubic-foot measurement is used. If a vat contains 300 cubic feet and the rate of application is 3 ppm, 25.47 grams will be needed for the entire vat (3 × 0.0283 = 0.0849 gram per cubic foot, or 300 × 0.0849 = 25.47 grams for the vat). (Several useful conversions are presented in Appendix A.)

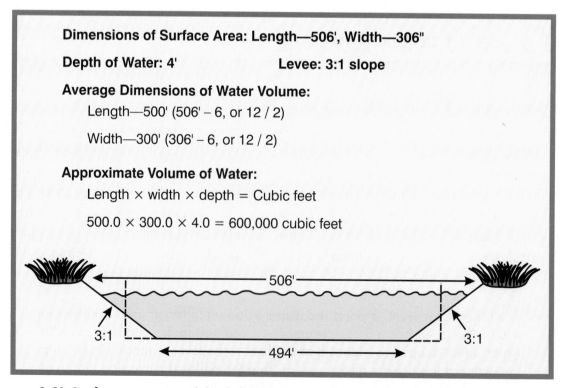

Dimensions of Surface Area: Length—506', Width—306"

Depth of Water: 4'   **Levee: 3:1 slope**

Average Dimensions of Water Volume:

　　Length—500' (506' – 6, or 12 / 2)

　　Width—300' (306' – 6, or 12 / 2)

Approximate Volume of Water:

　　Length × width × depth = Cubic feet

　　500.0 × 300.0 × 4.0 = 600,000 cubic feet

8–29. Good measurements and simple formulas are needed to calculate the volume of a pond.

CONTROLLING WEEDS AND ALGAE

Weeds and algae often resemble each other. Both are plants. Algae are tiny, one-celled plants or fillaments of cells; weeds are larger, many-celled plants. The free-floating phytoplankton algae are very useful in pond aquaculture because they produce oxygen. The filamentous algae are big pests because they compete with the desired plankton for light and nutrients. The long, stringy strands formed are sometimes known as pond scum.

Three kinds of aquatic weeds are submersed, emersed, and floating. Submersed weeds, such as hydrilla and fanwort, are rooted to the bottom of the pond and grow to the surface of the water. Emersed weeds, such as cattail and water lily, grow in shallow water. Their roots are attached to the bottom, and their tops go above the water. Floating weeds are not attached to the bottom; thus, they float on the water. They sometimes give the appearance of a green blanket on the water. Examples of floating weeds are duckweed and water hyacinth.

8–30. Narrow-leaved cattails are emersed weeds. (Courtesy, National Oceanic & Atmospheric Administration)

8–31. Duckweed almost completely covers this pond.

8–32. Water hyacinths float on the water and may form large masses of vegetation that interfere with harvesting.

Weeds and undesirable algae should be eliminated before a pond is stocked. Controlling them is much more difficult after the aquacrop is underway. Four methods of aquatic weed control that may be used are chemical, biological, mechanical, and environmental.

Chemical Methods

Chemical weed control involves using herbicides for weeds and algicides for algae. Several herbicides and algicides are on the market, but only a few are approved for use in aquaculture. Examples include the herbicide diquat and the algicide copper sulfate.

CONNECTION

POLLUTED WATER PROVIDES PLASTIC FOOD

Particles of raw plastic in water often resemble the food of fish. A hungry fish will eat the small pellets and gain no nutritional value from them. A case situation is Commencement Bay, on the coast of Washington.

Sumner High School agriculture student Hillary Fulk got busy and investigated the problem of plastic pollution in the bay. She found that the fish could not digest the pellets. She was also able to trace the source of the problem to industries in the area that used raw plastic. After careful study, she helped the industries see the problem and cut back on pollution. Today, the bay has better water because of one person's efforts.

Before chemicals are applied, correctly identify the weeds or algae to be controlled. The directions on the labels of containers should always be read and followed. Applications should be made according to the regulations of the U.S. Environmental Protection Agency. Only a few herbicides and algicides may be used around water with food fish. Most should not be used within 60 days of harvest. The chemicals are usually sprayed on the weeds or applied to the surface of the water. Water chemistry plays an important role in the use of chemicals.

Many producers feel that the use of chemicals is the safest, most economical, and most practical way to control aquatic weeds and algae. A note of caution: As the dead weeds decay, oxygen is used; as a result, the DO level may go below the level required for the aquacrop to live.

Biological Methods

Biological weed control is the use of plant-eating fish or other animals to control weeds and algae. This method does not pose the hazards of chemicals. The plant-eating fish must be sorted from the desired aquacrop at the time of harvest. They also compete with the crop for food and oxygen. Examples of fish used are grass carp (white amur) and Israeli carp. Small numbers (fewer than ten per acre) are used to prevent weed growth.

Mechanical Methods

Mechanical weed control is the physical removal of the weeds and algae from the water. In small ponds, the weeds and filamentous algae can be raked out and hauled away. Willow trees can be cut off and the tops removed. Usually, any roots or parts that remain in the water are likely to sprout and grow.

Environmental Methods

Environmental weed control involves creating conditions unfavorable to weed and algae growth. It is a practical approach to weeds and algae.

8–33. Pulling weeds with a hand rake may be a practical method of weed control in small ponds.

8–34. Regular water testing can be used to determine the presence of pollutants.

Designing ponds with a minimum of shallow water discourages the growth of certain weeds and algae. The edges of ponds should have water that is a minimum of 18 inches deep. A water depth of 2.5 feet or more (0.8 meter or more) discourages the growth of several kinds of weeds and algae.

Other environmental methods are (1) draining all the water from a pond and allowing the bottom to dry and (2) lowering the water level during cold weather to kill the weeds and algae by freezing. These methods never result in pollution but do interrupt the growth of the aquacrop.

CONNECTION

GETTING THE SALT OUT

Salt can be removed from salt water. The process is known as desalination. Two major approaches are used: reverse osmosis and distillation. Other approaches include electrodialysis and vacuum freezing. Desalination has been used only on a limited basis because of the costs associated with the process and the limited amount of salt-free water produced.

Desalination removes salt and other dissolved minerals. Distillation is the most effective desalination process. Desalinated water often goes through post-treatments to assure that it is appropriate for its intended use. Most desalination plants produce 15 to 50 gallons of salt-free water for each 100 gallons of salt water used. Considerable electricity and heat are required for the process of desalination.

This shows part of a desalination facility. Reverse osmosis, which requires less heat than distillation, is being used. Effluent from a reverse osmosis facility can be released without going through a time of cooling.

CONTROLLING POLLUTION

Controlling pollution involves preventing damage to both the aquatic environment and the terrestrial environment. Pollution may be a part of aquaculture in two ways:

1. The water used in aquafarming may be contaminated.

2. The water released from aquafarming may contain materials that pollute streams and lakes.

The water used in aquaculture should be free of harmful pollution. Contamination occurs when chemicals and other substances get into the water. All water used for aquafarming purposes should be free of contamination that would impair the growth of the crop or make it unfit for human consumption.

8–35. Water from a manufacturing plant is being released into a stream. Wild fish stocks in many streams have been killed by industrial pollution.

Reduce the possibility of water contamination by using only water from known sources that has tested free of harmful substances. Many producers rely on water from deep wells, but even well water can be contaminated. Good water also can be contaminated after it is pumped. Careless handling of chemicals, failure to control erosion on pond levees, and drift from nearby row-crop application of pesticides can pollute water. Pesticide containers should be disposed of properly. Allowing them to be thrown into ponds, streams, or lakes causes contamination that could have very easily been avoided.

Discharged water may contain uneaten feed, live fish, fish excrement, residues of chemicals used to treat the aquacrop, and dead fish. If run directly into a stream or lake, it can contaminate that water. Generally, the water released by an aquafarm should not appreciably alter the natural stream or lake. Many states have strict laws regarding effluent from aquafarms. The use of holding reservoirs or other treatment methods may be needed to prepare the water before it is dumped. Just as the water used to grow an aquacrop should be tested, discharged water should also be tested.

DISPOSING OF WATER

Properly disposing of used water is essential. Such water, also known as *effluent*, may come from aquafarms, processing plants, or other sources. Water from farms has often been used to produce aquacrops. It may contain various residues from the production process. Processing plants use water in washing the products, cleaning the facilities, and performing other functions. This water contains blood, fish tissue, excrement, and other materials that cannot be released into a stream or a lake.

Used water must be prepared for release. Solids must be removed from it. This is often done by allowing the water to stand in a lagoon so that the solids settle out or are otherwise removed. After removal, the solids may be disposed of in a landfill. Some treatment may also be needed to remove gases and chemicals from the water. Other filtration systems are sometimes used.

Released water should never introduce a non-native species into a stream, lake, or other natural body of water. Non-native species tend to destroy the habitats of native species by overeating food needed by native species and by excessively reproducing.

Water from an aquaculture facility should never be dumped into a stream or lake without being tested. All legal regulations must be strictly observed.

8–36. Water from an aquaculture facility should be released into streams or lakes only if it does not alter the natural condition of the water. Be sure to follow all regulations regarding water disposal.

REVIEWING

MAIN IDEAS

Water-quality management begins with understanding the chemistry of water. Pure water is formed when two molecules of hydrogen and one molecule of oxygen combine. Various substances get into water and make it impure. Some of these substances make water useful in aquaculture, such as dissolved oxygen; others make it unfit, such as excessive ammonia. Water quality consists of chemical, physical, and biological characteristics. Each affects the use of water in aquaculture. With good water management, the negative effects can be overcome and a good environment provided for an aquacrop.

How water is managed is a key to successful aquafarming. Important areas to manage are dissolved oxygen content, nitrogen compounds, other compounds and substances, turbidity and color, weeds and algae, and plankton bloom.

Skills with simple mathematical calculations are needed to determine water volumes and amounts of chemicals to use. Excess and used water should be properly disposed of by the producer.

QUESTIONS

Answer the following questions, using complete sentences and correct spelling.

1. What is water chemistry?
2. What are the physical characteristics of water?
3. What is water biology?
4. What is oxygen depletion? Why is it important? What are the causes of oxygen depletion?
5. What are the signs of possible oxygen problems in water?
6. How is oxygen added to water?
7. What can be done to prevent problems with nitrogen compounds?
8. What is turbidity? How can it be a problem in aquaculture?
9. How do weeds and algae cause problems?
10. How many cubic feet of water are in a tank 15 feet long and 3 feet wide with water 3 feet deep? How many gallons are in the tank? How long will it take to fill the tank at the rate of 100 gpm?
11. What methods are used to control weeds and algae? Briefly describe each.
12. What are the two ways water pollution is a concern in aquaculture?
13. How is used water released from an aquaculture facility?
14. What is supersaturation? How does it affect aquatic animals?
15. What is alkalinity?

EVALUATING

Match the term with the correct definition. Write the letter of the term on the line provided.

a. nitrogen cycle
b. water biology
c. water management
d. oxygen depletion
e. biological oxygen demand

f. turbidity
g. mechanical weed control
h. plankton
i. gas bubble disease
j. supersaturation

_____ 1. The study of living and nonliving plants and animals found in water

_____ 2. The use of water to maintain a good aquatic environment

_____ 3. Tiny organisms that live suspended or floating in water

_____ 4. Natural movement or circulation of nitrogen in the earth's environment

_____ 5. The condition that occurs when the DO level is below the level needed by organisms

_____ 6. The amount of oxygen used in the water for biological purposes

_____ 7. Suspended particles of soil and other materials in water

_____ 8. The physical removal of weeds from water

_____ 9. A water condition in which water contains more gas than can be dissolved in it

_____ 10. A disease of fish resulting from supersaturation

EXPLORING

1. Select a body of water that is, or could be, used for aquaculture. Study the quality of the water. Use meters and test kits to determine pH, DO, nitrogen compounds, alkalinity, hardness, and other qualities. Assess your findings in terms of the species that are growing, or could be growing, in the water. Prepare a report on your findings.

2. Design an experiment to determine the effects of aeration on the DO level in water. Let a small aquarium or a large jar of water stand for a day or so. Use a DO meter and determine the amount of DO in the water. Use an aquarium pump or splash the water with your hand for 15 minutes, and then make another DO measurement. What did you find? Why? Prepare a report on your experiment and findings.

PART FOUR

The Business
of Aquaculture

Aquaculture Production Requirements

OBJECTIVES

This chapter is about the "business" of production aquaculture. It has the following objectives:

1 Explain feasibility considerations with aquaculture

2 List and distinguish between ways of doing business in aquaculture

3 Describe general requirements for aquaculture

4 Explain how to select the aquatic species to produce

5 Describe economic considerations in aquaculture

6 Explain the importance of infrastructure

7 Explain the role of regulations and permits in aquaculture

TERMS

annual fixed cost
cooperative
corporation
decision making
Fair Labor Standards Act
feasibility
free enterprise
gross return

infrastructure
initial cost
management
net return
niche market
Occupational Safety and
    Health Administration
partnership

production cost
profit
return
risk
sole proprietorship

9–1. Aquaculture requires large investments in facilities and equipment. This shows a soft-shelled turtle farm in Japan. (Courtesy, National Oceanic & Atmospheric Administration)

IS AQUACULTURE a hobby or a business venture? It has been viewed as hobby, and to some people it continues to be a hobby. Overall, aquaculture has changed! It is now a major part of agriculture in the United States.

Aquaculture is a serious business venture. People may invest large sums of money in facilities and much time in planning. Their goal is to produce a product that can be sold for a profit. Success requires careful consideration of what is needed to make the enterprise profitable.

Aquaculture requires facilities, financing, and other resources. Knowledge is needed to make good decisions. Planning an aquaculture enterprise requires information. Knowing what to do and how to do it does not come easily.

FEASIBILITY OF PRODUCTION AQUACULTURE

Feasibility is a term that describes what can be done successfully. It answers these questions: "What holds the best possibilities for me?" "Which species can be grown?" "What is needed to grow the species?" "What returns can be expected?"

Important considerations also apply to nonproduction ventures. Various aquabusinesses (aquaculture supply businesses, aquaculture processors, etc.) have been started. Their owners also want them to be successful.

In assessing the possibilities of any aquaculture business, a person should look at feasibility from several viewpoints.

9–2. Freshwater shrimp may be feasible as an aquacrop in some locations. (Courtesy, U.S. Department of Agriculture)

PROFIT POTENTIAL

The potential to make a profit is important. *Profit* is the money left over after all costs of production have been paid. Examining the opportunity to gain a profit is a part of economic feasibility.

Unfortunately, some people have gone into aquaculture and not made a profit. Some have even lost huge amounts of money.

The species chosen, market potential, available facilities, labor costs, climate, and available natural resources (especially water) all play parts in determining profit potential in aquaculture.

AVAILABLE FINANCES

Deciding the way to start is important. Aquafarming is a business much the same as one that provides the supplies needed to produce aquacrops. Getting started is a serious matter. Money is needed. Many people have limited resources and must be creative in how they go about beginning.

9–3. Agricultural loan officers can help in assessing financial needs.

KIND OF CROP

The kind of crop to produce must be carefully selected. Aquacrops usually require certain conditions for best growth. Choosing a crop that is not suitable puts the grower at a disadvantage. For example, if only cold water is available, a crop that grows well in cold water should be chosen.

SUPPORTING RESOURCES

The resources available in the local area to support the venture must be considered. Resources may be needed from a variety of providers. Equipment, such as pumps, seines, and tractors, must be available. Seedstock, feed, medications, and other inputs are necessary. There must be buyers and processors for the produced crops. The

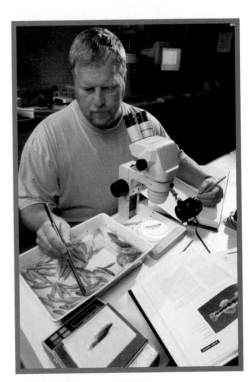

9–4. Experts in aquaculture research are valuable resources. (Courtesy, Agricultural Research Service, USDA)

assistance of experts in aquaculture is helpful. Local communities that do not have the resources pose a significant challenge.

WAYS OF SETTING UP A BUSINESS IN AQUACULTURE

People who are going into aquaculture must know more than how to produce a species. They must figure out how they are going to do business. Few individuals have the finances necessary to start a business. Most people must seek needed finances elsewhere. How an aquabusiness is organized helps in getting finances or other resources.

FREE ENTERPRISE

The United States has a free enterprise economic system, also known as capitalism. In *free enterprise*, individuals may privately own property. An owner may be one person or more. The owner has the freedom to make choices about the business. Government regulation is kept to a minimum, but some controls are needed.

In free enterprise, government controls provide for the general welfare of society. For example, regulations on uniform and wholesome aquafood products help protect the consumer. Good products help aquaculture prosper. A few bad products on the market can give it a bad reputation in a hurry, particularly if the information is carried as a news item by the media. Purchases of aquafoods can drop drastically in just a few hours!

WAYS OF DOING BUSINESS

There are three ways of doing business: sole proprietorship, partnership, and corporation, including cooperative. It is important to remember that farms are businesses. They are established to produce goods or services that provide monetary gain to the owner(s).

Each of the three ways of doing business involves some rules and regulations. There are more of these for corporations than for partnerships and sole proprietorships. Appropriate legal counsel is important. This involves additional cost for attorney fees. Certain reports may be required annually.

A wide range of regulations must be followed. Property taxes, income taxes, privilege taxes, and taxes in other areas must be paid. Social Security taxes must be paid for the employees. Most medium- and large-size aquabusinesses regularly use accountant services to help with these details. The largest ones may employ accountants full time.

Sole Proprietorship

A proprietor is an individual who owns and operates a business venture. A *sole proprietorship* is a business owned by one person. This person has the legal title to the business, whether it is a farm, a retail market, a processing plant, or a fish feed mill. The owner is responsible for all debts and receives all profits, if any profit is made.

9–5. A proprietor must be a good manager, know how to produce an aquacrop, and understand needed technology.

The sole proprietorship is the most common form of ownership for small and medium-size businesses. Most aquafarms are sole proprietorships.

Partnership

A *partnership* is two or more people in business together. This way of doing business allows people to pool their resources, which may be finances, skills, and/or facilities. When resources are pooled, more support is available. People with specialized skills can use them in a productive way.

Partnerships allow people to join with other people who have skills they do not have. An example would be an accountant going into partnership with a person who knows aquaculture. The accountant might know very little about aquaculture but would be very skilled in the accounting areas. The person skilled in aquaculture would provide the expertise with the water-farming enterprise and leave the financial details to the accountant.

In a partnership, the profits, if any, are divided among the partners. Likewise, any debts are shared by the partners. Individuals considering a partnership should carefully assess what they want to do. Normally, a written document that describes the partnership would be prepared and signed. Some aquafarms involve partnerships. Nonfarm aquabusinesses may also be partnerships.

Corporation

A *corporation* is a way of doing business by creating an "artificial person," or a legal entity. A charter of incorporation has to be obtained from the state government. All applicable laws, which vary from one state to another, must be met.

9–6. The sign shows that this business is a corporation.

The owners are known as shareholders because they buy shares in the corporation. A shareholder is eligible to vote on matters about the corporation. Each share entitles the owner to one vote. The more shares a person owns, the more votes that person has. Any profit is divided among the shareholders. An individual can lose no more than the amount invested in shares.

Corporations can get larger amounts of money through the sale of shares than individuals or partnerships are usually able to raise.

A board of directors is elected by the shareholders. The board establishes policy and appoints officers to run the business. The officers normally include a president, a vice president, and a secretary-treasurer. Larger aquafarms, processing plants, and equipment manufacturers may be corporations. The word *Incorporated* or the abbreviation *Inc.* appears after the name of the corporation, or the word *Corporation* may be used in its name.

A special form of corporation is the cooperative. A *cooperative* is an association formed to provide certain services to its members. For example, growers may

9–7. This fish feed manufacturing plant is a cooperative.

form a cooperative to manufacture feed or to process their crops. None of the growers might individually establish a feed mill or a processing plant, but by working together, they help each other. Cooperatives must be set up under applicable state and federal laws. In addition, the federal government has special financial assistance available to certain cooperatives.

Cooperatives are not intended to produce profits but to serve their members. To be a member, an individual must usually buy shares in the cooperative. Each member has only one vote, regardless of the number of shares owned.

A big advantage of a cooperative is larger volumes of fish, feed, or other items are involved when individuals join together. Financial advantages are usually found in volume buying and selling. For example, since a greater quantity of feed is needed collectively, the feed is usually available at a lower price. Very few aquafarms are large enough to use a feed mill of their own efficiently.

PRODUCTION AQUACULTURE REQUIREMENTS

Many factors contribute to success in production aquaculture. These essentials must be considered if a person is to "make it" in an aquaculture business. The requirements are in six areas: management, labor, land and water, species, markets, and financial resources.

MANAGEMENT

Management is the handling of a wide range of mental tasks to carry out aquaculture successfully. It involves planning, organizing, staffing, leading, and controlling. These are done to produce a profit. Managers must be qualified in several ways.

9–8. Management often involves getting assistance from government agencies. (Courtesy, U.S. Department of Agriculture)

Education

Education is the knowledge and skill an individual has in a particular aquaculture enterprise. An individual must be able both

Table 9–1. Important Areas of Education for Aquaculture

- Biology of the species under consideration
- Disease prevention and control
- Culture requirements for the species
- Harvesting and marketing procedures
- Facility and equipment needs
- Legal regulations associated with aquaculture
- Water management and quality
- Personnel and financial management
- Nutritional requirements and feed ingredients
- Communication skills

"to know" and "to do." Formal classes, work-shops, seminars, and field days are good ways to learn the basics.

"Learning to do" is gained by working in aquaculture. For example, an aspiring aquaculture manager will find it very beneficial to spend time working on an aquafarm. Firsthand experience teaches about the "real world." Some important areas of education for aquaculture are shown in Table 9–1.

Decision Making

Making decisions and then following through on them is important. Education and experience help a person to be a good decision maker. *Decision making* is choosing among alternatives for an aquabusiness. This includes selecting the species to grow, the production system to use, the size of business, the personnel to hire, and the time to market.

Any problem usually involves several possible solutions. The role of the manager is to select the possible solution that is in the best interest of the aquafarm. Several approaches are available in decision making. Routine decisions can be made by following a simple process. The process is shown in Table 9–2.

Table 9–2. The Decision-Making Process

Step	Action
Step 1	Become aware of the problem. This means that a good manager must keep up with what is going on. "Keeping in touch" requires putting time and energy into whatever is being managed.
Step 2	Get enough information on the problem. This involves being informed. The information should be accurate and used in making the decision.
Step 3	Determine alternatives. This involves identifying the possible solutions. What options are available?
Step 4	Evaluate alternatives. Some ways of solving a problem are better than others. Good information about the consequences of the different actions is needed. Seek the input of people who have had experience with the problem you are solving. In some cases, consultants may be hired to assist in solving the problem.

(Continued)

Table 9-2 (Continued)

Step	Action
Step 5	Choose the best alternative. Select the best alternative based on the situation that exists at the time. Risk is always involved. Every decision involves some uncertainty. Using a thorough process in making the decision can help reduce the risk.
Step 6	Implement and follow up. Good decisions are no better than how well they are carried out. Communicate the decision to others carefully, as appropriate. Follow up to see how well the decision is being implemented and if it is working out okay. This is the same as evaluation. On a small aquafarm, the manager may be the only individual involved. Decisions are still made to be carried out.
Step 7	Recycle through the decision-making process (optional). If a decision does not work, start over with Step 1 and repeat the process.

Energy and Enthusiasm

Good managers have high levels of energy. This means that they are capable of spending long hours at work on the aquafarm. Managers must use both physical and mental energy. Physical activity involves doing all the tasks that occur in an aquaculture operation. Mental activity refers to making decisions and recalling information.

Relating to Other People: Communication Skills

A manager must be able to relate to other people. This includes communicating effectively with employees. The ability to relate to the suppliers of feed and other inputs for the farm is essential. Good relationships are needed in marketing the crop, since the crop must be sold to yield a profit.

9–9. Managers must be good communicators. (This shows a packing shed manager relating to a customer while weighing a sack of harvested crawfish.) (Courtesy, U.S. Department of Agriculture)

Honesty and Other Personal Qualities

All actions in aquaculture should involve honesty and fairness with people. Ethical relationships are essential for the prosperity of individuals and the aquaculture industry. A few pointers on aquaculture ethics are presented in Table 9–3.

Table 9–3. Important Ethics for Successful Managers

- Financial obligations must be fulfilled in a timely manner.
- Managers must follow through on their word. (If they say they are going to do something, they must do it.)
- An aquacrop should be produced to ensure a nutritional, healthy product.
- Environmental considerations, such as getting and disposing of water, need to be observed.
- Animal crops should be produced in a manner consistent with animal well-being.
- Business agreements should be carried out as was the original intent unless both parties agree to changes.
- Legal regulations must be observed. (Aquaculture is different from row-crop or dairy farming. The beginning aquafarmer should spend time learning about the laws and rules that apply.)
- When others are involved, good communication and teamwork are important.
- Dealings should be fair to all concerned.

Personal Preferences

Personal preferences play a big role in decisions about aquaculture. Individuals need to assess their personal interests and preferences. If they do not like the nature of the work, they should not go into aquaculture. If they prefer to work with one kind of aquacrop over another, they should raise the one they prefer, provided it is economically feasible.

CONNECTION

OVERCOMING "FISH FEAR"

"Fish fear" is being afraid to catch, touch, and hold a fish. Overcoming this fear is essential for anyone raising most species.

How do you do it? Begin by studying the external anatomy of the species. Learn the fins that are most likely to be used by the fish to defend itself. Watch an experienced person who has no fear of fish. Study how the person picks up and holds a fish. Notice how he or she pushes dangerous fins down and grasps the fish out of reach of its fins. Because fish are slippery and active, they are sometimes not cooperative.

As you learn, be sure to avoid injuring the fish. Practice good animal well-being skills.

Lifestyle is influenced by aquafarming. Factors, such as length of work days, repetition of tasks, and risk taking, must be dealt with. To be successful, people in aquaculture must like what they do.

LABOR

Aquafarming involves much work. Labor needs vary with the size and nature of the farm. A small farm may need only one person—the operator-manager. A larger farm requires more labor.

The labor requirements for some crops are greater than for others. Education and training needs vary with the nature of the enterprise. Labor must be dependable. For example, some aquacrops require the nighttime monitoring of oxygen levels in the water. This duty must be accurately carried out on schedule during the night hours.

Some work, such as harvesting, can be handled on a custom basis. "Custom" means that independent contractors are engaged to provide equipment and do the work.

Activities requiring labor on a typical food fish farm are listed in Table 9–4.

Table 9–4. Activities Requiring Labor in Production Aquaculture

- Preparing facilities for stocking
- Calculating amounts of chemicals, etc., to use
- Stocking growing facilities
- Administering disease treatments
- Feeding
- Controlling predators, pests, and weeds
- Monitoring water
- Harvesting
- Maintaining pumps and aerators
- Operating trucks, tractors, etc.
- Collecting samples of aquacrops

9–10. Transferring stock requires labor. (Courtesy, National Oceanic & Atmospheric Administration)

LAND AND WATER

Adequate land and water must be available. The potential land site should be studied to determine water supply and quality.

9–11. Large earth-moving equipment at a fish farm construction site.

The amount of land depends on the production system to be used. Pond systems require much more land than tank systems.

The land should have the appropriate physical features for aquaculture. Different aquacrops have different requirements. Some require warm water, while others require cold water; some prefer flowing water, while others prefer still water. In general, level land is best for pond construction. Harvesting fish is easier in ponds on level land.

Selecting land for an aquafarm is a big decision!

Past Use of the Land

Some investigation is needed to learn the past use of the land. Land may retain hazardous materials for many years.

If the land was previously used for row crops to which high levels of pesticides were applied, it might be unfit for aquaculture. Pesticide residues might have built up in the soil. These residues could contaminate the water and the crop. A chemical laboratory analysis of the soil can tell if dangerous pesticide residues exist.

If the land was used for a dump site or landfill, careful study is needed. Pollution may be present that would damage the fish or make the site unsatisfactory.

Soil Characteristics

The soil at a site for a proposed aquaculture facility should be appropriate for the intended use. Soil high in clay content is preferred for ponds. Sandy and loamy soils do not hold water as well. Ponds on land with sandy or loamy soil may need to be lined with expensive liners. Of course, tank facilities can be set up on about any type of soil.

Site Flooding

A site above the flood plain of a creek or river should be selected. Sites for aquaculture facilities should not flood. Study the relationships to nearby streams. Water that overflows into a fish pond can result in the loss of the fish crop. The fish crop could just swim away in the flood water!

Flooding can also restrict access to the pond and make it impossible to feed the fish. If this occurs, the feeding habits of the fish are interrupted, and they may go off feed (stop eating even when fed). Several days may be required to get them back on feed.

Available Water

A good supply of suitable water is essential. Checking on the availability of well-drilling permits is a part of the selection process. Chemical analysis of the water may be needed to determine if it is suitable.

All aquafarms require water. The water must be available in adequate supply and be of appropriate quality and chemistry. Sources of water include wells, springs, rainfall runoff, lakes, oceans, streams, and industrial effluent (water released by an industry, such as an electric power generator).

Water should undergo thorough analysis before a final decision is made. Chapters 7 and 8 cover water environments and quality in detail.

9–12. An abundance of good water is needed in aquaculture.

Amount and Cost of Land

The amount of land required varies with the intended use for aquaculture. For example, a hatchery requires less land than a large food fish operation. Site selection should consider all needs—acreage in ponds, as well as that required for roads, storage buildings, and other uses.

The cost of land should be in line with the capability of the land to produce an aquacrop at a profit. Sometimes, land can return a higher profit if used for purposes other than aquaculture.

Land may be overpriced. Land near cities or in productive farming areas tends to be higher than land in other locations. Of course, a recreation facility should be near a population center to obtain adequate business.

9–13. This land is well suited for pond production.

Accessibility

Aquacrops must be tended in all weather conditions. A site should be accessible by all-weather roads. Electric power lines should be in the vicinity; otherwise, power line construction will be an additional cost.

SPECIES

Good information is needed to select a species. The one selected must be suited to the production system. Further, a ready market must exist for the species to be produced. If little information is available on a species, the risk of choosing it is greater. The culture of new species should first be carried out on a small scale to minimize financial risk.

Some fish farmers have established niche markets. A *niche market* is a specialized outlet for a crop. For example, tilapia grown in the southern United States may be shipped without processing to markets in the large cities.

Aquafarmers should usually produce species that have established market outlets. With aquafoods, processors should be available. In a few cases, farmers operate small roadside markets, but the potential of these is often small scale.

Individuals considering aquafarming should learn all they can about the environmental requirements of a species. Select a species that is well suited to production. With fish, adequate breeding stock or fingerlings should be available. (More information is presented on species selection later in this chapter.)

MARKETS

A market must be available for the aquacrop. The location of a potential site in relation to a market outlet is a major factor. If no market is readily available, the selection of a particular site should be reconsidered. Hauling harvested crops long distances cuts into profit.

It is impossible to operate profitably without appropriate markets. A superior aquacrop is of little value if no market exists.

In making decisions about which aquacrop to produce, consider the availability of markets. Determine the buyers that are available. Sometimes, contracts are made between growers and processors. These ensure the processors of an adequate supply of product and ensure the growers of a ready market outlet. (More information on marketing is presented in Chapter 11.)

FINANCIAL RESOURCES

Establishing an aquafarm may require a sizeable financial investment. The amount of money needed depends on many factors, including size; cost of equipment, production inputs, harvesting, and marketing; labor; and water availability.

Some lending institutions do not make aquaculture loans; others do. The interest rate and the number of years for repayment are definite considerations. Regardless, adequate finances must be available.

9–14. Considerable money is needed to begin and operate a food fish production facility.

9–15. Local banks may be sources of money for aquaculture.

SELECTING THE SPECIES

Success in aquaculture depends on producing an appropriate species. The species must "match" the conditions available for culturing it. Important considerations in species selection are climate, market, site, finances, and species potential.

CLIMATE

The major climate factor is temperature. Since aquacrops grow in water, the temperature of the water may be more important than that of the atmosphere.

Ground water may be too cool for some aquacrops if it is pumped directly into ponds or other growing facilities. In some locations, thermal springs and wells provide warm water. This water can be directly used with warmwater fish.

Cool well water can often be economically warmed by storing it several days in a large reservoir for natural warming by the sun. Of course, warming is needed only for warmwater aquacrops.

9–16. Arctic char is a species that prefers cold water and would not be suitable for production in areas with warm or cool water.

Table 9–5. Water Temperature Requirements for Selected Aquacrops

Species	Optimal Water Temperature (°F)
Alligator	80–90
Bullfrog	60–80
Channel catfish	70–85
Crawfish	60–80
Fathead minnow	65–80
Freshwater prawn	75–95
Striped bass	65–90
Tilapia	80–90
Trout	50–68

Crops preferring cool and cold water should be selected if the water temperature is satisfactory. Cool spring water may work well with those aquacrops that prefer cool water, such as trout.

Temperature requirements for selected species are shown in Table 9–5.

MARKET OUTLETS

A potential producer should be cautious in growing a crop that has no established market. Any decision to start producing a particular crop should be based on careful consideration of marketing possibilities. An aquacrop is of little value if it cannot be sold for a satisfactory price.

SITE

Aquacrops have characteristics that make them better suited to some sites than others. The species selected needs to "match" the site well. The type of production system to be used has a bearing on how appropriate a site may be. For example, an intensive system involving tanks can be established on land that would not be suited to pond culture.

FINANCIAL RESOURCES

Money is needed for start-up and operating costs. Start-up costs include land, facilities, and seedstock needed to carry out aquaculture. Operating costs include those for feed, electricity, labor, and other variable production inputs.

Establishment and operation of large-scale commercial fish farms require big financial investments. Individuals with fewer resources will need to select species and production systems within their means. For example, ornamental fish can be grown in spare rooms, garages, and basements. (More information is presented on finances later in this chapter.)

SPECIES POTENTIAL

The aquacrop grown must have the potential of making a profit for the producer. Some species have greater potential than others. Important considerations include adaptability of the species to culture, demand for the species, market price, legal regulations (some species are not legal in some states), personal preferences, and availability of technical assistance when problems arise. Aquaculture specialists with land-grant universities or regional aquaculture centers can provide useful information on species potential.

ECONOMIC CONSIDERATIONS

The potential to make a profit is the most important consideration in commercial aquaculture. Income from the sale of a crop must be greater than the cost of producing the crop. Profit is not a concern to the few individuals who grow aquacrops as a hobby.

Economic considerations should involve an analysis of both potential costs and potential returns, as well as sources of risk.

9–17. Constructing ponds is an initial cost with pond production systems.

9–18. Feed is a production cost.

Costs

Costs include initial costs, annual fixed costs, and production costs.

Initial costs, also known as start-up costs, include land and facilities. Among these costs are constructing ponds, drilling wells, buying or constructing tanks, purchasing hatchery equipment, buying aeration and feeding equipment, and establishing breeding stock. A large fish farm may cost millions of dollars. Good planning is essential in identifying all the initial costs of setting up an aquafarm.

Annual fixed costs occur every year, no matter the level of production. These include interest on loans, repayment of loan principal, property taxes, insurance, and depreciation of facilities and equipment. These costs are often overlooked but are important in getting a financial picture of a proposed aquaculture enterprise.

Production costs are the direct costs of producing the crop. Also known as variable costs, these costs vary with the size of the farm. Feed, seedstock, chemicals, electricity, and fuel are examples. Custom services (such as harvesting and hauling) are also production costs.

Returns

Return is the income from a crop when it is sold. Processors typically pay producers for the volume and quality of the aquafood. Producers of eggs, fry, or fingerlings receive income when they sell their product to growers. Operators of recreational lakes get income from the sale of fishing privileges and product caught. Income for bait and ornamental producers comes when they sell their product to recreational and commercial fishers.

Returns are measured as "gross return" and "net return." **Gross return** is the total money received for an aquacrop. **Net return** is the amount of money that remains after all expenses for the production of the crop have been subtracted from the gross return. The most important figure to a producer is net return—profit.

Aquafarms that have large gross returns do not necessarily have large net returns. Operating a farm efficiently involves keeping down costs and maximizing sales. Some aquafarms return sizeable profits each year; others do not.

FINANCING AQUACULTURE

Money must be available to set up and operate an aquaculture enterprise. Some producers have the money they need to establish and operate their aquafarms. Others must rely on credit to provide the needed finances.

Sources of credit include individuals, banks, the Farm Credit System, and aquaculture businesses, such as feed mills and processors. Short-term credit (sometimes called seasonal or production loans), intermediate-term credit, and long-term credit may be needed. Short-term credit is typically for a year or less. Intermediate-term credit is usually for more than one year but less than five to seven years. Long-term credit is used to finance the establishment of the aquaculture production facility, with repayment over a period of more than five to seven years.

RISKS IN AQUACULTURE

Aquaculture involves risk. **Risk** is the possibility of failure or loss. The producer can keep risk at a minimum by following good management practices. Areas of risk are listed in Table 9–6.

Carefully observing an aquacrop and using good management can minimize the loss of a crop. For example, fish in ponds must be regularly monitored for disease, oxygen depletion, and other problems. Once a problem is suspected, steps must be taken to correct it. An entire crop of fish can be lost quickly due to oxygen depletion in the water. Through proper aeration, these losses can be reduced, if not eliminated.

Water supply failure can be a catastrophe. It may be due to a power outage, a pump breakdown, a well going bad, or another cause. Back-up systems need to be

Table 9–6. Areas of Risk in Aquaculture

- Possible loss of a crop
- Contamination of the crop by dangerous chemicals
- Poor-quality seedstock
- Losses at time of harvest
- Failure of water supply
- Instability or loss of market
- Failure of electrical system
- Fluctuations in market price
- Loss of a supplier of inputs, such as feed
- Undependable labor

9–19. Emergency electrical generators are needed on aquafarms in case of power failure.

available. There should be electrical generators for use if the electric power fails and the pumps and aerators stop operating. Spare pumps and pump parts should be kept on hand. Personnel who can trouble-shoot and repair pumps, generators, aerators, and other mechanical devices need to be available or on-call for emergencies.

Once a quality crop has been produced, efficient harvesting procedures should assure a minimum of loss. Harvesting equipment should be in good repair and operated in the correct manner. Proper hauling equipment should be used.

In making financial plans for aquaculture, the amount to be received for the crop is important. Most plans use the current or predicted price level. An increase in price works to the advantage of the producer. A decrease in price can be financial disaster. Instability of price and market outlet is a concern. Some risk can be worked out ahead of time by agreements between the producer and the processor or other buyer.

AQUACULTURE INDUSTRY INFRASTRUCTURE

Infrastructure is the network required for an aquaculture commodity to become commercially important. Aquafarmers cannot go it alone. They must have finances, equipment, feed, chemicals, processing, and marketing. Without these to support the production phase, establishing an aquaculture enterprise is very difficult. New areas of aquaculture begin slowly, and the infrastructure develops along with the aquacrop. Not all of what is needed can be instantly put in place.

9–20. Properly equipped haul trucks are essential in marketing food fish. (This truck is refilling its oxygen cylinders from a large storage tank.)

Balance must exist among the infrastructure parts. For example, a large processing plant with only a few fish to process loses efficiency. A large farm without a market outlet has no place to sell the aquacrop.

A good example of the importance of balance in infrastructure is in a fish processing plant. A production standard is that a band saw operator in a processing plant should be able to remove the heads of about 45 catfish per minute. This translates into about 19,000 pounds a day and 5 million pounds a 365-day work year. With pond production, about 1,250 acres of ponds would be needed to keep this one band saw going. Some 8.5 million pounds of feed would be needed to raise the fish. Three million pounds of ice-packed fish or 2 million pounds of fillets would be produced. The market must be in place for this quantity of fish.

A first step is to develop a marketing plan. The plan determines the market demand for the aquacrop. It sets a production schedule. Credit can be arranged, seedstock obtained, water facilities built, feed mills put into operation, and processing and marketing facilities developed. Advertising can promote the aquacrop to the consumer.

9–21. Using a band saw in processing fish.

An aquaculture industry can emerge in a community when all the components are in place. These components must be balanced to accommodate the size of the industry. Growth results as each part expands and creates demand as one aspect gets a little out of balance.

Good communication in the industry is essential. Agreements among producers, providers, and processors are beneficial. Individuals involved at all steps must be educated.

Supermarkets must allocate market space. Restaurants must add items to their menus. Chefs must be trained in how to prepare the food. Interested parties must provide leadership for the industry.

Lending agencies must allocate money for aquaculture loans. Time and a proven record are required for a new aquaculture industry to emerge.

9–22. Seafood is readily available in this supermarket. (Courtesy, U.S. Department of Agriculture)

REGULATIONS AND PERMITS

All phases of aquaculture are subject to certain regulations and required permits. The intent of regulations is to provide for the general welfare of society. This may be by controlling pollution or assuring that a product is wholesome and up to standard. Information on the regulations in a particular state can be obtained from an aquaculture specialist at a land-grant university or a state or federal agency responsible for aquaculture.

The regulations are typically in four areas: environmental protection, worker health and safety, licensing, and product transportation.

ENVIRONMENTAL PROTECTION

Regulations in this area serve to protect the environment from pollution and to conserve natural resources. Water is the major area of concern.

Water for aquacrops must be obtained in a manner that complies with federal and state regulations. Aquafarmers cannot put pumps into creeks or rivers and start taking out water as they please. Wells cannot be drilled in just any way. Permits are needed to remove water from streams and to drill wells. An individual who owns property that adjoins a stream can usually have access to the water but must not alter the water or interfere with the rights of other property owners. State laws vary, and aquafarmers should become familiar with those of their own states. A good attorney may be needed to review applicable laws.

Discharging water from aquaculture facilities is also regulated. Water from aquacrop facilities often contains feed particles, feces, and other wastes, such as medications. Sometimes fish may be released with discharged water. The release of some species of fish is illegal, even if accidental.

Discharged water that would change the nature of the water in a stream cannot usually be released directly into it. Such water will need to be treated or held in a reservoir where it can be made suitable for release. Most states either have laws regarding effluent water or will have them soon.

The disposal of wastes from processing plants requires careful planning. A landfill may need to be constructed according to legal requirements. Both processing plants and farmers must properly dispose of fish wastes, dead fish, or other animals.

Construction of earthen facilities in certain locations is regulated. Altering the banks of streams or the shores of lakes, constructing levees on land designated as a "wetland," and altering flood plains require permits from the U.S. Army Corps of Engineers.

Aquaculture must be carried out so as not to threaten endangered plant or animal species. Predatory water birds that consume hundreds of pounds of fish are common problems. For example, cormorants are protected birds. They can consume 1 to 2 pounds of fish a day. Federal law protects them from being killed. However, when they develop into particularly big nuisances, special permits can sometimes be obtained. Creative ways that are legal have been tried in attempts to scare them away.

WORKER HEALTH AND SAFETY

Two federal laws shape the work environment in aquaculture. The first is the *Fair Labor Standards Act*. This Act sets minimum wage, overtime pay, equal pay, record-keeping, and child labor standards. Millions of workers in aquaculture and nonaquaculture occupations are covered. All employees of aquabusinesses engaged in interstate commerce

9–23. Carefully read and follow the instructions on all chemicals used in aquaculture.

are included. If the only employees of an aquabusiness are the owner's immediate family members, that business is not covered. Very small businesses are also not covered. A few exemptions exist.

The Child Labor Laws provisions of the Act provide specific details on the employment of children under the legal minimum age. The Secretary of Labor determines which occupations are hazardous. Although 16 has been established as the basic minimum age for employment, persons under the age of 18 cannot be employed in hazardous occupations. Examples of hazardous work include certain jobs in processing plants, the operation of motor vehicles in certain locations, and the operation of power-driven machinery. The Act also establishes the number of hours that underage youths may work. In some occupations, high school students can get learner permits when they are enrolled in agricultural education programs preparing for careers in aquaculture.

The major regulatory agency on worker health and safety is the U.S. Department of Labor through the **Occupational Safety and Health Administration** (OSHA). The regulations of this agency are designed to promote a safe and healthy work environment. Areas likely to receive attention in aquaculture include repetitive motions by workers in processing plants, noise protection, eye protection, protective clothing, and built-in safety features in buildings and facilities. Many states have established regulations approved by OSHA.

A problem that has received considerable attention in recent years occurs when workers repeatedly perform the same physical movements, such as in filleting fish. This repetitive-motion job-place health hazard sometimes results in carpal tunnel syndrome. This condition may develop when people quickly perform a single activity over and over, hour after hour, day after day. It can occur in any type of manufacturing or industry involving motion repetition. People with the problem have nerve damage and begin to experience pain and tingling in their hands. They may subsequently lose certain movements. Providing a variety of job tasks can help minimize the risk of repetitive-motion problems. Knives with new designs are being used to change the positions used by the workers when they are holding and cutting in fish processing.

LICENSING

Licensing requirements vary. In some cases, they depend on the size of the enterprise and type of aquaculture to be carried out. Retail markets must usually have licenses to operate as retail businesses. Fee-lake operators may be required to have permits for vending machines or other related sales at lake sites. Operating a processing facility usually requires a license. Certificates of inspection and sanitation may be needed in areas where food is processed. A license to produce an aquacrop is usually not needed in a state where aquaculture has been defined as agriculture.

PRODUCT TRANSPORTATION

Several areas of regulation apply to the transportation of aquacrops. These vary from one state to another. Hauling certain products across state lines may be prohibited. Health certificates may be needed to certify that a shipment is disease free.

International shipments may be subjected to the laws of different countries. Permits to import goods may be required. In some cases, importing certain species of fish is illegal.

All motor vehicles must be properly licensed to operate on public roads. Those that operate only within the confines of a farm may not need licensing, depending on state and local regulations. The operators of all motor vehicles should be properly licensed. Boats and other marine equipment may need to be registered with the appropriate offices.

Shipping aquaculture materials, such as eggs or fry, by common carrier requires appropriate packaging material. Air freight may be used for tropical fish, high-value food fish, and other items. Certain regulations apply to these shipments. Information is available from local shipping companies.

REVIEWING

MAIN IDEAS

Being successful in aquaculture requires good management. Adequate resources are needed to set up and operate an aquaculture enterprise. A good match between the requirements of the crop and the resources is essential.

The most important factor in commercial aquaculture is the ability to make a profit. This requires careful consideration of many economic matters. Overcoming risks is made easier when good culture techniques are followed.

All aquaculture production must have a network of support in providing the supplies needed to produce the crop and the marketing capability to get the commodity from the farm to the consumer. In some cases, consumer demand will have to be developed.

Certainly, no aquafarmer would want to violate the regulations that apply to aquaculture. The key is education!

QUESTIONS

Answer the following questions, using complete sentences and correct spelling.

1. What is feasibility?

2. What are the ways of doing business in aquaculture? Briefly distinguish between them.

3. Name the general requirements in aquaculture.

4. What is management? Why is it important to success in aquaculture?

5. Explain how an aquafarmer might go about making a decision.

6. What are some qualities of good aquafarm managers?

7. What major factors should a person consider in selecting land for an aquafarm? Briefly explain each.

8. Why is species selection important? What are some important considerations in species selection?

9. What costs are involved in aquaculture?

10. How is aquaculture financed? What are three sources of finances?

11. What is infrastructure in aquaculture? Why is it important?

12. What are the areas of regulations for aquaculture? Briefly explain each.

EVALUATING

Match the term with the correct definition. Write the letter of the term on the line provided.

a. initial cost
b. annual fixed cost
c. production cost
d. net return

e. risk
f. free enterprise
g. decision making
h. cooperative

i. sole proprietorship
j. niche market

_____ 1. The economic system used in the United States

_____ 2. The act of choosing among alternatives for an aquabusiness

_____ 3. A direct cost that varies with production

_____ 4. A cost that occurs every year regardless of production

_____ 5. A start-up cost associated with going into aquaculture

_____ 6. Money that remains after all expenses have been paid

_____ 7. The possibility of failure or loss

_____ 8. An association formed to provide services to members

_____ 9. A market with a specific focus

_____ 10. A business enterprise owned by one individual

EXPLORING

1. Determine the legal regulations that apply to aquaculture in your state. Contact a regional aquaculture center (see Appendix B) or an aquaculture specialist with the land-grant university in your state for information. Prepare a written report on your findings.

2. Plan a hypothetical aquafarm. Determine the facilities needed and the costs associated with the facilities, such as ponds, buildings, and tanks. Determine the total initial costs as well as the annual fixed costs and production costs. Calculate the amount of return needed to produce a profit. Prepare a report on your study.

CHAPTER 10

Aquaculture Facilities

OBJECTIVES

This chapter describes facility and equipment needs for aquaculture. It has the following objectives:

1 Describe the common types of facilities used in aquaculture

2 Discuss site selection

3 Identify and assess construction methods for aquaculture facilities

4 Describe the equipment needed in aquaculture

5 List and explain the components of recirculating aquaculture tank systems

TERMS

aerator
backflushing
biofilter
biofilter media
cage culture
fill

filtration
freeboard
levee-type pond
net pen
permeability
RAS

RBC
seine
seine boat
suspended solids
topography
watershed pond

10–1. Electronic monitoring and controlling are used at this aquaculture facility.

ALMOST ANY structure that will hold water has potential for aquaculture. Of course, in today's commercial aquaculture, not just any container will do! Actually, once the aquacrop to be produced has been selected, the type of facility is the most important decision to make.

Many factors influence facility decisions. The species chosen may require a certain type of facility. The money available is important. The available land, sources of water, and other resources must be considered. The amount and intensity of production are major factors in determining the type of facility needed. The soil type and local climate are also important.

People who work in aquaculture need a variety of skills. Not only do they need to know the biology of the species being produced, but, among other things, they also need to be able to operate equipment, repair pumps and aerators, maintain and use seines, and monitor water quality.

WATER FACILITIES

Five types of facilities are commonly used in aquaculture. These are levee-type ponds, watershed ponds, raceways, cages, and tanks. These facilities all have similarities, but each also has unique features. Brief descriptions of the different types of facilities, including information on some of the important species grown in those facilities, are given here.

In many cases, particularly with freshwater species, the producer must establish water facilities. With mariculture (ocean farming), the producer must gain access to the seawater and install the facilities needed for production. Gaining access usually requires leasing areas of water within the jurisdiction of state boundaries or the United States boundary from appropriate government agencies.

10–2. Containment is necessary when growing aquacrops in the ocean. (Courtesy, National Oceanic & Atmospheric Administration)

LEVEE-TYPE PONDS

A *levee-type pond* is made by forming an earthen levee on nearly level land. The material for the levee may be moved from another site. It is sometimes dug out of the levee site; therefore, the bottom of the pond is near the elevation of the surrounding land.

Levee-type ponds are usually built to hold water pumped from ground wells or other sources of surface water. Occasionally, the source of water is a separate watershed pond. Levee-type ponds may also be built to take advantage of natural springs, but this is less common. These ponds are usually built on relatively flat ground to reduce the amount of surface runoff into the ponds. A levee-type pond generally has four raised levees and a flat bottom.

10–3. Aerial view of catfish production ponds. (Courtesy, Agricultural Research Service, USDA)

Many early catfish producers believed that intensive catfish production was possible only in levee-type ponds located on flat, nearly level land. In the late 1980s and early 1990s, however, the largest increases in catfish production took place in the hill areas of Mississippi and Alabama. Many aquafarmers in the hills took advantage of the natural movement of water on the ground by building watershed ponds.

The most common food species grown in levee-type ponds in the United States is the channel catfish. Baitfish, ornamental fish, and freshwater shrimp also are produced. The other food fish commonly produced in levee-type ponds are tilapia, hybrid striped bass, trout (only in northern areas), and bream.

Watershed Ponds

A *watershed pond* is a pond created by damming a natural stream or valley. The primary source of water for watershed ponds is surface runoff, water that accumulates and flows along the ground after a rain. The surface runoff is sometimes supplemented with water from a spring or a well.

Watershed ponds may be used as the primary facility for aquaculture, or they may be used as feeder ponds. When they are used as feeder ponds, the water from them is pumped or flows by gravity to one or more levee-type ponds that serve as the primary facility for aquaculture production.

Watershed ponds may have one or more dams or levees, taking advantage of the natural topography of the land to keep water in the ponds. (*Topography* is the slope of the land on which a pond is built.) The bottom of a watershed pond is usually uneven, which makes harvest of the aquacrops more difficult. Thus, the ponds are usually drained to nearly empty

10–4. Watershed pond. (Note the gently sloping terrain, which provides the watershed.)

to facilitate harvesting. Many aquafarmers, however, use watershed ponds with success. One factor in their favor is the low cost of providing water for aquacrops.

Both levee-type ponds and watershed ponds can serve as standing or static systems. This means that the water is replaced with new water very slowly. Once the ponds are filled with water and production begins, water is added only to keep them full. Water loss from evaporation and percolation into the soil that is not replaced by rainwater is supplemented by water from ground wells or other sources. As a result, ponds do not use as much water as some other types of facilities.

The same species produced in levee-type ponds can be produced in watershed ponds, other factors (such as temperature and pH) being equal.

RACEWAYS

Raceways are enclosures where the water moves through at a rapid rate. Wastes are carried out at the lower end. The most common raceways are rectangular and used with coolwater or coldwater crops. Round tanks are sometimes used. Production is usually much more intensive, with higher stocking rates in raceways than in ponds because the wastes are removed and the water is oxygenated.

Raceways are known as flow-through or open systems because water is replaced every hour or so. A large supply of water is needed to provide for this exchange. Raceways usually take advantage of natural springs or streams, because few ground wells will have the necessary water required for an extended time.

Most raceways utilize the slope of the terrain to move the water out at the bottom, although round raceways use a manufac-

10–5. A raceway used for flounder production. (Courtesy, National Oceanic & Atmospheric Administration)

10–6. Raceway system with feeders and enclosed with chainlink fence to prevent loss of fish to predators and by theft. (Courtesy, Gary Fornshell, University of Idaho)

tured slope. Very few rectangular raceways are built on level or nearly level terrain because pumping the water through the system increases the cost. Raceways are usually constructed of concrete, but other materials may be used.

Brown and rainbow trout are the most common fish produced in raceways. Trout require a high level of dissolved oxygen and cold water, which makes raceways an ideal method of culture. Some species of salmon also do well in raceways, as do catfish (in warmer areas), but the culture of these is usually more profitable when other methods are used.

CAGES

Cage culture involves placing a cage made of netting on a metal, plastic, or wood frame in an existing water structure. Thus, cage culture is really more of a method of production than a facility. Cage culture is often used in levee-type ponds, watershed ponds, lakes, rivers, oceans, and estuaries, where intensive production outside the cages is difficult due to the size of the water facility or to predators. This type of culture is used primarily with fish.

Cage culture began in Japan as a way of producing saltwater species because the ocean was too large to try to raise aquacrops without cages or some type of enclosure. In the United States, most cage culture has been used to grow freshwater crops in ponds that are not particularly well suited to aquaculture. Cages often allow for the productive use of at least some of the water in these types of ponds.

Cages are sometimes used to produce aquacrops in the same facility where other crops are being grown in a polyculture that would not work in a natural setting. For example, a pond with bass and bream may be suitable for cage culture of channel catfish, but if catfish fingerlings were put in the open water with the bass, the bass would eat the catfish.

10–7. Fish in a net pen are being fed to assure an adequate diet.

Cage culture is usually more intensive than pond culture. With periodic movement of cages and maximum stocking rates, aquafarmers can produce about as many pounds of aquacrop per acre as they can in open ponds with intensive culture.

Very large cages, sometimes used in oceans or estuaries for saltwater and brackish-water production and in rivers for freshwater production, are known as net pens. A *net pen* is a large cage-type structure made with nylon or plastic netting over a frame of plastic or other sturdy material. The stocking rates and requirements vary, based on the rate of flow of water through the cages and the species cultured. Net pens are commonly used in Southeast Asia and increasing in use in the United States. The most common use of cages in the United States is in farm ponds that are not well suited to levee-pond aquaculture production methods.

One concern with cages is that the fish cannot forage for food throughout the water facility. This means that the fish have to be fed more. They also have to be fed a feed that is more nutritionally complete, because, by not being able to forage for food, they may be missing an important part of their diet.

Species that will grow in cages are those adapted to the water in which the cages are placed. Catfish, tilapia, bream, and several other freshwater species seem to grow very well in cages. Saltwater and brackish-water species, such as red drum, salmon, and shrimp, do well if the cages are placed in the right type of water. With shrimp, it is important to find a flow of water fast enough to compensate for the size of the mesh or netting, which must be very small to keep the shrimp from escaping.

TANKS

10–8. A small tank system complete with pump and filtration system.

A tank is an artificial water enclosure. Tanks used for aquaculture may have many different characteristics. Some tanks are used as flow-through systems, with many of

10–9. This fiberglass tank designed for raising tilapia has a see-through section on one side.

the same characteristics as raceways. A round tank is particularly well suited for this purpose if it has a bottom that slopes to a drain in the middle. This allows for excellent removal of the wastes.

Other tanks may be used in static systems, much like pond culture. Tanks are the primary water facility in closed systems. These recirculate more than 90 percent of the water used, removing wastes through mechanical or biological filters and pumping the water back through the systems. These systems make efficient use of water but are expensive to set up and operate. The use of closed systems for large-scale aquaculture is still considered experimental.

Tanks may be constructed from steel, concrete, fiberglass, or several other materials. Several manufacturers offer different-size fiberglass tanks that are reasonable in price and suitable for many types of aquaculture production.

Baitfish and ornamental fish adapt to tank culture well, usually requiring aerators and flow-through systems to enhance the intensive stocking rates. Tilapia, catfish, and hybrid striped bass adapt to tank culture. Softshell crawfish and softshell blue crabs have been cultured experimentally in closed systems with fairly good results.

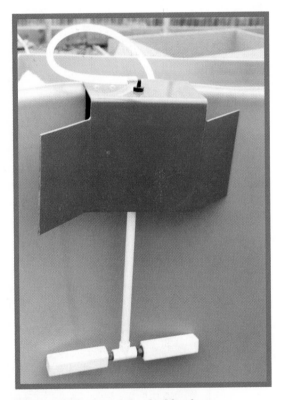

10–10. Arrangement of a double air-stone aeration device inside a small tank. (The air stones are rectangular and attached on each side of the T fitting.)

SITE SELECTION FOR AQUACULTURE FACILITIES

Although the site selection process may vary widely for the different types of facilities used in aquaculture production, several general considerations must be made regardless of the type of facility. Of course, an adequate supply of water is needed. Water requirements are covered for each type of facility.

10–11. Some aquaculture facilities make use of inflatable greenhouse-type structures, such as this ornamental fish operation in Florida. (Courtesy, National Oceanic & Atmospheric Administration)

Water used for aquacrops is often reused for other purposes, such as irrigating farm crops. If this is the case, the facility should be located close to the secondary use, if possible, to reduce the cost of moving water from one use to the other.

The location of the site in relation to others is very important. For example, service people should be close enough to the operation so equipment can be serviced or repaired in a timely manner. The suppliers of medicines, chemicals, equipment, and materials should be close enough so these goods can easily be transported. Also, the

10–12. An electric control panel is used to provide power for aerators. A source of electricity is often important in site selection.

markets for the aquacrops to be grown should be in fairly close proximity to reduce transportation costs.

A suitable site should be accessed by roads that are in good repair. Telephone lines and electrical lines should also be available, although diesel generators may be used to supply some of the power needed. Some specific site selection criteria for the different types of aquaculture facilities are given in the following sections.

SITES FOR LEVEE-TYPE PONDS

The three basic site requirements for levee-type ponds are an adequate supply of clean water, soil that holds water, and suitable terrain for pond construction.

For levee-type ponds, surface runoff is not normally a source of water. These ponds use either well water or spring water, with well water being the customary source. If well water is the source, a test well is usually drilled to evaluate the quality and quantity of the water. The depth of the well water may also be a factor in that the deeper the water is in the earth, the more it costs to pump it to the surface. Well water is often low in dissolved oxygen, but splashing the water into the air as it is being pumped into the pond will correct this. Well water should also be checked for pollution, although this is seldom a problem.

If spring water is the source, it should be observed several times during the year to make sure it has an adequate flow. Some springs almost stop flowing during certain times of the year, often in the fall. Spring water may be too cold for some warmwater species, such as catfish, freshwater shrimp, and tilapia. If so, the water can be held in a warming

CONNECTION

TIDES GIVE BETTER OYSTERS

Wilapa Bay, Washington, is a producer of top-quality cultured oysters. This shows a view of the bay during low tide.

Pristine water entering the bay and tides that keep it clean contribute to the bay's reputation. Tides (rise and fall in the Pacific Ocean water) move any wastes out to the open water and away from the oysters. This sheltered bay has tides that are several feet each day.

Shells from shucked oysters are returned to the bay. Old shells provide habitat for young oysters (spat). The shells are seeded with spat before being placed in the bay.

10–13. An electric paddle-wheel aerator is operating in a levee-type pond. Note the level terrain and the side-by-side construction of the ponds. Two ponds often share the same levee in commercial operations.

pond, where the sun warms it before it is pumped into the production pond. The spring water should be checked for nitrogen gas. Sometimes, spring water is supersaturated with nitrogen gas, which can lead to fish kills.

The soil type dictates whether a pond can be built on a particular site. Even if the topography is good and an adequate source of water is found, the soil type will determine if the pond will hold water well enough to produce an aquacrop. A quick look at a soil map for the area under consideration will tell much about the soil type and whether it is suitable for aquaculture.

Soil for ponds should have low *permeability*, or a slow infiltration rate, and a high run-off rate. To have a slow infiltration rate, the soil will usually have a high percentage of clay. A common recommendation is soil that is at least 20 percent clay. After selecting a tentative site, the aquafarmer can consult with experts from the USDA Natural Resources Conservation Service to provide soil tests and analyses to help determine whether the site is suitable. Soils with low permeability enhance water conservation.

The topography for a levee-type pond site should be relatively flat. Two important factors that should be considered are drainage and flooding. The pond should be able to drain by gravity during any season of the year. If it will not, drainage ditches may have to be dug, which will increase the cost of construction.

A pond should not be built in a low-lying area that is subject to periodic flooding. Flooding is hazardous to an aquafarmer. The aquacrop can leave the pond during flooding, and trash fish or other undesirable animals can enter. Care should be taken to make sure that rivers, bayous, and drainage ditches are at a lower elevation than the drain pipe of the pond. Also, a low-lying area may be classified as a wetland, and building a pond may not be allowed.

SITES FOR WATERSHED PONDS

Site selection for watershed ponds includes the same three factors as for levee-type ponds, but the desired characteristics are a little different. For watershed ponds, the topography of the site provides the source of water. Streams or surface runoff provides most of the water for watershed ponds. As a result, the ponds must be on land with at least a gentle slope that will carry the water into the ponds by gravity. The dam for the ponds is usually built perpendicular to a stream or natural flow of water to create a reservoir. The least expensive watershed ponds to build are in gently sloping valleys. Deep valleys require larger dams, which cost more to construct. Deep water is less productive than shallow water that is 2 to 4 feet deep.

The size of watershed required to fill a pond is also a consideration. Usually, between 5 and 25 acres of watershed is needed for each acre of water surface. This varies, depending on the soil type of the watershed, the amount of rainfall, and the number of trees on the watershed. The watershed should be sufficient to fill the pond during rainy times but should not let the level of the pond fall more than 2 feet during drier times of the year.

Watershed ponds also require soils that will hold water well. If a proposed site does not have enough clay in the soil, additional clay is sometimes brought in and added to the pond bottom and dam. Care must be taken to locate a site that does not uncover limestone, sand, or gravel areas, which will cause the pond to leak.

10–14. A watershed recreational trout pond built in a gently sloping valley. (Note the shallow edges, common with watershed ponds. These edges make it more difficult to harvest than with levee-type ponds. Cold well water is being added.)

Sites for Raceways

10–15. A concrete raceway system is used for trout production.

The primary concern for a raceway site is a source of water that can be consistently used to flow through the system. The two most common sources are streams that are diverted through the raceway and natural springs. Some aquafarmers use wells as their water source.

Another important site criterion is land that gently slopes so gravity will move the water through the raceway. A ground slope of 1 to 3 percent will accomplish this. In a series of raceways, the drain pipe of an upper raceway should be at least a few inches higher than the water level in the next raceway to oxygenate the water between the raceways.

10–16. A tuna cage 24 miles offshore of California is being checked by boat. (Courtesy, National Oceanic & Atmospheric Administration)

SITES FOR CAGES

When selecting a site for a cage, two primary considerations should be met to ensure water quality. First, the cage must have natural movement of new water through it, since the fish cannot really move through the water. In ponds and estuaries, this movement is accomplished by placing the cages where prevailing winds will keep water moving through them. Of course, in rivers, the natural flow does this job. In the ocean, the tide and the other natural movements of water are usually sufficient.

The second important criterion in cage culture is having water that is deep enough for the waste matter to move well below the cage. Feces and feed wastes use oxygen as they decay and would take up valuable space in the cage if it were placed on the bottom. A water depth of at least 6 feet is recommended for the most common type of cage, one that is 4 feet deep. With any cage, at least 2 feet of water space should be maintained below it.

Several other factors should be considered, although these may not be quite as important as water movement and depth. Cages should be placed at least 10 feet apart. Cages too close together may lead to low or even fatal dissolved oxygen levels. Cages should not be placed near coves and weed beds. Both may restrict the natural flow of water through the cages. If possible, cages should be kept away from high traffic areas where people and animals might disturb the aquacrop. This has to be balanced with being able to feed and check the aquacrop on a daily basis.

10–17. Juvenile fish are being stocked in a grow-out cage. (Courtesy, National Oceanic & Atmospheric Administration)

SITES FOR TANKS

The general criteria for selecting a site for a tank are access to roads, suppliers, and utilities; a source of water; and the use of the discharged water. Future expansion needs must be carefully considered, as tanks are often built in smaller areas.

Since many tank systems are inside buildings, the site must be appropriate for building construction. In some cases, buildings constructed and used for other purposes are converted to tank aquaculture facilities. A strong floor, an adequate water supply, and a method for disposing of water must be a part of any building.

10–18. Tanks with trout fingerlings. (The source of water is a natural stream.)

The primary source of water for tanks is usually ground wells. This availability must be considered in the selection of a site. Because tanks are usually smaller and require less land than ponds, they are often the choice where land prices are prohibitive, such as near large cities. Tanks may give proximity to markets and suppliers where ponds are not feasible.

CONSTRUCTION OF AQUACULTURE FACILITIES

Once a suitable site has been selected for an aquaculture facility, the facility must be built before aquaculture production can begin. Although the type of facility should have been decided on before the site was selected, the shape, the size, and the placement of the facility on the site may not have been determined.

This section discusses the construction of levee-type ponds, watershed ponds, raceways, cages, and tanks, including some design considerations for each that would allow the facilities to be better utilized in the production of an aquacrop.

LEVEE-TYPE PONDS

A levee-type pond typically has a levee on all four sides and a nearly flat bottom. This makes harvesting the aquacrop easier because a seine can be pulled across the bottom without losing the aquacrop underneath the seine. On flat land, these features usually mean lower costs of construction than for watershed ponds with similar production capacities.

Size

One of the first decisions to make is that of the size of the pond or ponds. The most common size of a levee-type pond used for catfish production is a 17½-acre pond built on 20 land acres. This size is somewhat of a compromise between ease of management and cost of construction. Smaller ponds are easier to manage and harvest, while larger ponds cost less per surface acre of water to construct. Ten-acre ponds are popular with higher stocking densities.

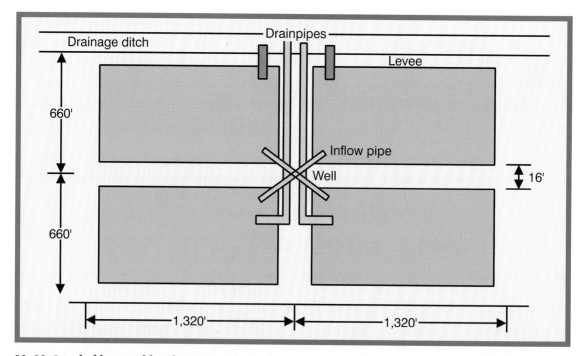

10–19. A typical layout of four levee-type ponds. (Source: "Construction of Levee-Type Fish Production Ponds," Southern Regional Aquaculture Center)

Depth

The normal depth for a levee-type pond is between 4 and $4\frac{1}{2}$ feet, with a freeboard of about $1\frac{1}{2}$ feet. **Freeboard** is the height of the levee minus the normal water level. It is the distance the top of the levee is above the waterline.

With allowance for freeboard, a levee is built to a height of about 6 feet from the pond bottom. The freeboard should not exceed 2 feet, as this increases the cost of constructing levees and makes it difficult to get equipment into and out of a pond. A levee with a freeboard of less than 1 foot is very susceptible to erosion.

Shape

The shapes of levee-type ponds vary. A square pond gets the most acreage out of the amount of its levees, but it requires a longer seine for harvesting than a rectangular pond of the same area. The most common shape is rectangular. However, property lines often force irregularly shaped ponds at the edge of the property.

Whatever the shape and size, if several ponds are built, they should be somewhat uniform. Otherwise, an aquafarmer might need several different seines to harvest the different ponds.

Location

The location of a pond is usually determined by the prevailing winds. The longer levees are usually placed parallel to the direction of the prevailing winds to minimize the erosion caused by wave action against the bank. Some aquafarmers argue, however, that this decreases the amount of oxygenation the pond receives from the wind, so they recommend putting the longer levees perpendicular to the prevailing winds. At present, there is not a hard-and-fast rule for deciding the orientation. This judgment may be left up to the aquafarmer's own unique situation, depending on how easily the pond is manually aerated, how concentrated the production is, and how intensive the prevailing winds are in the area.

Other factors may be more important than prevailing winds in determining a location within a site. Putting ponds as close as possible to roads usually minimizes the chances of

10–20. Main levees should be designed so that trucks, tractors, and other equipment can be moved over and operated on them. A paddle-wheel PTO-powered aerator is in operation.

poaching and/or vandalism. Of course, this is not always possible. Frequent checking of the ponds by night crews, in irregular patterns, is probably the best deterrent.

Levee Engineering

The main levees (where the wells are located) should have a top width of 20 feet or more. This width will support the traffic that occurs when the aquafarmer is feeding, harvesting, checking oxygen, and taking samples. Other levees should be at least 16 feet wide to allow for safety and to reduce the required maintenance. Often, the soil type dictates that at least two levees be graveled. (If the levees become impassable to two-wheel-drive vehicles when it rains, they should be graveled.)

Although it may not be obvious, a levee-type pond usually has a little slope at the bottom and contains a shallow end and a deep end. The bottom slope allows for better draining. A typical slope for the bottom would be about 0.2 feet of drop for every 100 linear feet along the long axis of the pond.

A pond with a good soil type for holding water will usually have levees with a slope of about 3:1. This means that for every 3 feet a levee extends horizontally (out into the water), it drops 1 foot. Therefore, a 6-foot-high levee extends 18 feet horizontally to the point at which the slope reaches the bottom of the pond. This point is called the toe. Soils that do not hold water as well may need a slope of 4:1 or even 5:1. With a greater slope, more cubic yards of *fill* (soil used to create the levee) must be moved in the construction of the levee, thus increasing the construction costs.

If the slope of the levee is the same on both sides, the formula for determining the number of cubic yards of fill needed per linear foot of levee is shown in Figure 10–21.

$$\frac{\text{cubic yards}}{\text{length (feet)}} = \frac{[(\text{slope} \times \text{height}) + \text{top width}] \times \text{height}}{27}$$

10–21. Formula for calculating cubic yards of fill per linear foot of levee.

An example of how to use the formula is presented Figure 10–22. The example uses a levee with a 3:1 slope, a 6-foot height, and a 16-foot top width.

Figure 10–23 shows how slope requirements can increase construction costs. The cubic yards of fill needed per foot for a pond levee with a 5:1 slope, a 6-foot height, and a 16-foot top width are calculated.

Obviously, the amount of slope is important. The total length of levee on a typical 20-acre pond is 3,960 feet. With a 3:1 slope, the levee would require almost 30,000 cubic

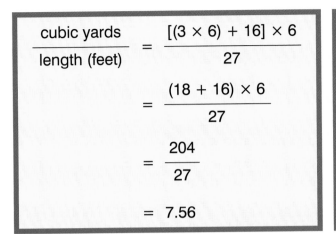

$$\frac{\text{cubic yards}}{\text{length (feet)}} = \frac{[(3 \times 6) + 16] \times 6}{27}$$

$$= \frac{(18 + 16) \times 6}{27}$$

$$= \frac{204}{27}$$

$$= 7.56$$

10–22. Example of using formula for determining the cubic yards of fill per linear foot of levee.

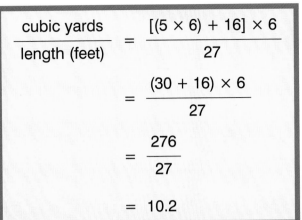

$$\frac{\text{cubic yards}}{\text{length (feet)}} = \frac{[(5 \times 6) + 16] \times 6}{27}$$

$$= \frac{(30 + 16) \times 6}{27}$$

$$= \frac{276}{27}$$

$$= 10.2$$

10–23. Example of how slope requirements can increase costs.

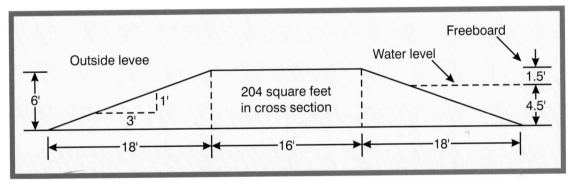

10–24. Cross section of a typical pond levee. (Source: "Construction of Levee-Type Fish Production Ponds," Southern Regional Aquaculture Center)

yards of fill. With a 5:1 slope, the levee would require just over 40,000 yards of fill. The money used for the extra fill may be the difference between making a profit and experiencing a loss!

Most levee-type ponds are constructed by self-loading pans, also called scrapers. Before a pan is used, all roots, stumps, and topsoil are removed. This allows a good bond between the foundation soil and the fill material. The pan compacts the soil as it carries the fill to build the levee, which is very important. Water places much pressure on the levee, so the soil must be compacted well. If a bulldozer is used to construct the levee, a sheep's foot roller can be used to improve compaction. For maximum compaction, the soil must be slightly moist (about 12 to 15 percent). When many ponds are being constructed on one aquafarm, a laser-guided pan should be used to improve the accuracy of the bottom slope and the slope of each levee.

10–25. A modified Canfield drain, where the water level in the pond is regulated by the standpipe located inside the pond. Note the netting to keep the aquacrop from escaping through the drain.

Drainage

Every pond must have some method of drainage that will regulate the water level in the pond at all times and that will be large enough to drain the pond in five to seven days when necessary. The drain will consist of a pipe that runs along the bottom of the pond through the levee and out the other side. Most drains are constructed from PVC pipe. The soil is hand compacted around the drain pipe for at least 1 foot so the equipment used to construct the levee above it will not damage the pipe. This also creates a good seal around the drain pipe to keep the pond from leaking. The outside end of the drain pipe should extend at least 5 feet past the toe to prevent erosion of the levee during draining. The drain will have a standpipe to regulate the water level in the pond.

On an inside swivel or modified Canfield outlet drain, the standpipe is located inside the pond at the desired water level. The standpipe can be turned down to drain the pond completely. On an outside drain, which is most common with a new pond, the standpipe is located outside the pond and connected to the drain pipe with a T joint. The outer end of the T has a valve to drain the pond completely. An outside drain may sometimes have a standpipe that is only 24 inches high and also has a valve. The valve must be opened slightly to regulate the water level. With either outside drain, the drain pipe should extend 5 to 10 feet past the toe to the bottom of the pond to prevent clogging. The inside end of the drain pipe should have a screen to prevent losing the aquacrop through the drain.

WATERSHED PONDS

Before constructing a watershed pond, the aquafarmer should use a level and stakes to mark off the waterline of the proposed pond. This is done to make sure that the size will suit the purpose of the pond and that the water will not encroach on the property of neighbors.

The first step in constructing the dam of a watershed pond is to remove all trees, stumps, and topsoil from the site. Then, a 3-foot deep trench is dug into a good clay base on the dam site. Clay is filled and compacted into the trench, and this core is continued all the way to the top of the dam.

The dam of a watershed pond should have a slope of 3:1 or higher and a top width of 16 to 20 feet. A spillway is necessary to handle flooding problems. The spillway is usually grassed and extends from 10 to 50 feet or more, depending on the size of the pond and the expected flooding of the watershed. The spillway must have some type of barrier to keep the aquacrop from escaping the pond during flooding. This barrier must be kept from clogging to prevent the water from running over the top of the dam.

A watershed pond typically has a drain in which the drain pipe has a T on the inside with a standpipe to handle small flows of excess water. The top of the standpipe is usually about 3 feet from the top of the dam. A sleeve pipe is usually fitted around the drain pipe near the bottom and extends a few inches above the drain pipe to ensure that the water being drained is the poor-quality water from the bottom of the pond and not the fresh water that is just entering the pond. As in a levee-type pond, the drain is fitted with a valve at the outside end and should be large enough to drain the pond within five to seven days.

An important step is to make sure that all areas of the pond are at least $2\frac{1}{2}$ feet deep. This will prevent weeds from taking up space in the water that could be used by the aquacrop.

Because watershed ponds often have an erratic water supply, creating a series of ponds in the same valley, instead of building a very large pond that is hard to manage, works very well. This method allows for the best use of available water. The lowest-level pond in a series is drained for harvest first, and water from the upper ponds is used to fill that pond so production can resume immediately. Temporarily extended drain pipes can be used to store water. When an upper-level pond is drained for harvesting, the water in it is used in the lower-level ponds. This keeps the aquafarmer from having to wait for a substantial rain to restock the ponds.

Raceways

The construction of raceways is normally much simpler than the construction of ponds. Once a suitable source of water is found, the site for a raceway is cleared. Because most raceways are constructed with concrete, the soil type is not as important. Some earthen raceways are used, but the rapid flow of water tends to erode them quickly. Earthen raceways work well in a less intensive culture system where there is a slower exchange of water. A few raceways are built of wood or other materials.

10–26. Raceway designed for efficiency, easy feeding, and minimal cleaning.

10–27. Baffles regulate the water level in a parallel series of concrete raceways. Netting is used over the raceways to keep fish-eating birds out.

Raceways are usually fairly long and narrow. They typically range from 75 to 100 feet in length and 10 to 30 feet in width, although some may be longer and/or wider. The depth of most rectangular raceways is 3 feet or less, although some may be as much as 6 feet. The amount of water available will determine the size of the raceways.

The layout of raceways may be parallel or in a series. In a parallel layout, water moves through only one raceway, and each raceway can be drained individually. This prevents wastes from one raceway from entering the next and keeps diseases from being transmitted between raceways.

In a series, water flows through several raceways before being discharged. Although this system allows for maximum use of water, it can lead to problems with diseases. If the aquacrop in the top raceway becomes diseased, then the crops in the raceways below it soon will also, because the water from the upper raceway flows directly into them. Most common is a combination of parallel and series layouts. This means that three or four series of raceways with two or three raceways in each will be laid out parallel to each other. This represents a compromise between disease control and maximum use of water.

Some tanks are really raceways because they are constructed as flow-through systems. Culture is just as intensive in these tank systems as in rectangular raceways, if not more so. Often, the culture is so intensive that the aquafarmer has to add oxygen to the tanks even though a steady supply of fresh water is coming into them. This type of intensive culture requires a very tight control on diseases and stress, but the construction of the system allows the aquafarmer to add medicines or supplements to the water very easily.

Round tanks built as raceways slope to drains in the middle. These systems remove wastes very effectively. They sometimes have a Venturi drain with an inner standpipe to regulate the water level in the tank and an outer standpipe to draw water and wastes from the bottom. The inner standpipe can be temporarily removed so the wastes, which get trapped between the two pipes, can be cleaned out. Some systems have a screened drain with a valve that regulates the water height by letting water escape at the same rate as it enters the tank.

The effluent is the water discharged from the raceways or other water facility. Because such a large amount of water flows out of raceways, the aquafarmer may need a permit to discharge into natural bodies of water. Sometimes, the water is pumped back through the raceways, but this is usually not profitable.

CAGES AND NET PENS

Cages come in many shapes and sizes. The most common shapes are round and rectangular, although some cages are square. Rectangular cages are usually 3 feet wide × 4 feet long × 3 feet deep or 4 × 8 × 4 feet. The most common round cages are 4 feet deep with a diameter of 4 feet. Square cages are usually 4 × 4 × 4 feet or 8 × 8 × 4 feet.

Offshore aquaculture uses much larger cages or net pens. Those in the open ocean may measure 80 feet across and 150 to 175 feet deep. A typical shape for the very large cage is known as spar. A spar-shaped net pen is usually rounded, though it may be hexagon shaped.

A cage may be constructed from a variety of materials, but the material must allow for adequate water movement through the cage and must keep the aquacrop from escaping. The material must also be nontoxic to the aquacrop. Materials for extended use of cage culture should also not rust or rot in water, so some types of wire and wood are not suitable.

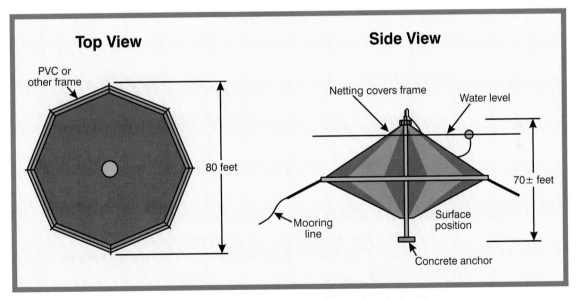

10–28. Example of a design for a large offshore (mariculture) net pen.

A cage consists of a frame, mesh or netting, feeding ring, lid, and some type of flotation. The frame helps the cage hold its shape as the water moves through it. A cage may have only a top frame for the lid but usually has a bottom and side frames as well. These frames may be constructed from PVC pipe, aluminum tubing, treated wood, or fiberglass. The frame of the cage may be used to help in the flotation, as when capped PVC pipe is used.

The mesh or netting is usually made of nylon, plastic, or some type of wire that is covered or galvanized. Solid plastic netting is most commonly used. Plastic-coated welded wire is

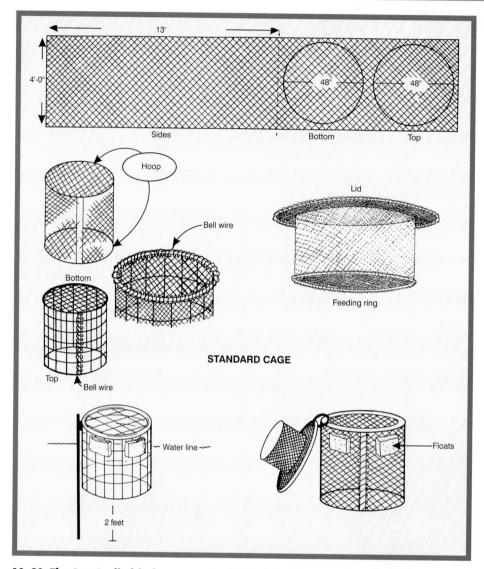

10–29. The 4 × 4 cylindrical cage, made with $\frac{1}{2}$-inch plastic mesh and bell wire, is simple to construct. (Source: "Cage Culture—Cage Construction and Placement," Southern Regional Aquaculture Center)

also a popular choice for cage construction. The size of the holes should be $\frac{1}{2}$ inch or larger, depending on the size of the fingerlings used to stock the cage. Netting with holes smaller than $\frac{1}{2}$ inch reduces the water circulation, which is important in keeping the water oxygenated through the cage.

Lids are used to keep the fish in the cages and to keep predators out. The lids should be securely fastened to keep people from stealing the fish. The lids may be constructed from the same type of material as the cages or from solid pieces of material, such as treated plywood. Some studies have shown that catfish grow better in cages if the lids are made of a solid material that they cannot see through. If the lids are solid, doors are usually put in for feeding.

The feeding ring is usually a band of fine mesh 10 to 12 inches wide, extending from a few inches below the water level to a few inches above it. This keeps floating feed from moving out of the cage before the fish have a chance to eat it. Another type of feeding ring is constructed of a floating material, such as Styrofoam®, and placed within the cage. Some feeding rings are attached to the lid and extend down into the water.

The flotation device is attached to the cage so it will keep the top of the cage about 6 inches above the water and in a level position. Flotation devices are very important in that they keep the aquacrop separate from the accumulated wastes at the bottom of the pond or other water facility. The most common material used is Styrofoam®, which should be covered with a canvas bag to keep it from breaking up and floating away from the cage. Other types of flotation devices include inner tubes, capped PVC pipes, and plastic bottles. Cages are sometimes suspended from docks.

Cages are placed in the water facility at least 10 feet apart and tied to concrete blocks to anchor them, or they are attached to docks. Docks should be avoided if the water level fluctuates greatly. Each cage should be anchored from at least two sides—four if the water flows very fast or if very windy conditions exist.

Tanks

Tanks can be built by the producer or purchased from a manufacturer. Most tanks built by the aquafarmer are either concrete or wood. Manufactured fiberglass and plastic tanks are readily available for purchase. Tanks are usually either rectangular or round, as these two shapes are the easiest to harvest and clean.

Before beginning any construction, determine the size and shape of tanks, water management practices, and location for tanks. Observe tank systems used by other producers. Plan the system on paper before beginning

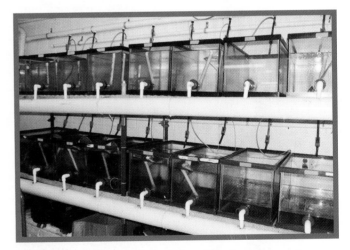

10–30. Aquariums are connected to share incoming and outgoing water lines.

tank construction. Fiberglass tanks, PVC pipes and fittings, and water treatment facilities will be needed. A good way to dispose of used water is essential.

The primary concern with constructing tanks is the drain and a suitable place to drain water from the tanks. A fiberglass tank usually has the drain built into the side or bottom.

10–31. Small tanks used in a hatchery for rearing paddlefish fry at Kentucky State University. Note that the hatching jars are adjacent to the tanks, which are held upright by a wooden frame.

10–32. Round tanks covered with netting to keep fish from jumping out. These tanks are used for broodfish being held for induced spawning.

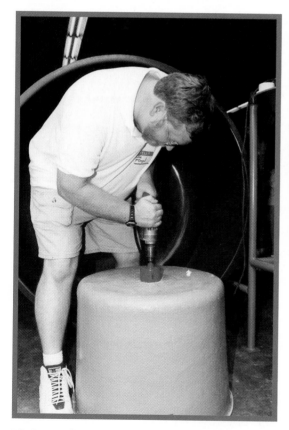

10–33. Cutting a drain hole in the bottom of a fiberglass tank to be used for aquaculture.

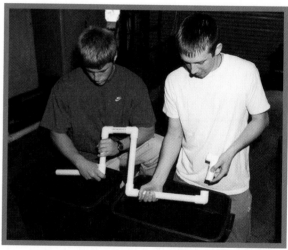

10–34. Skills in measuring, cutting, and joining PVC are needed in tank system installation.

Locate tanks where they will drain into suitable drainage ditches or holding ponds. Concrete tanks require a little more planning. If a tank slopes to the middle for draining, a ditch must be dug beneath the bottom and the drain installed before the concrete is poured. Such a drain usually includes a standpipe to control the water level in the tank.

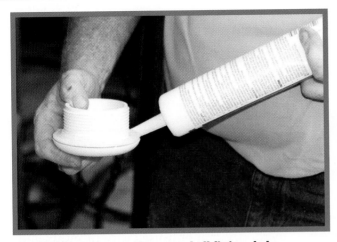

10–35. Using proper sealer around all fittings helps prevent leaks.

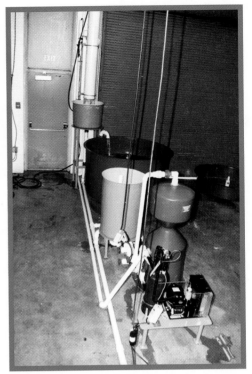

10–36. A small complete system for producing coldwater fish. Note that a chiller is in the foreground to assure proper water temperature.

Tanks in closed systems—those where the water is filtered and recirculated back into the tanks—require more construction. Because these closed systems reuse the same water, the wastes must be removed before the water is pumped back into the tanks. These systems each need a biofilter, which will be discussed later in this chapter. An issue with closed systems is the cost as compared with the amount of production, particularly when the amount of production increases.

Manufactured tanks are typically easy to install and use. The bottom of a tank should slope to a drain. A round tank may have a center or side drain. Tanks are set on platforms of wood or concrete masonry units to allow hooking up the drains. Dimensions of tanks are stated as gallons or in inches of depth and diameter. A round tank with a 650-gallon water capacity will likely be 85 inches in diameter and 30 inches deep. A round tank that holds 950 gallons will likely be 96 inches in diameter and 36 inches deep.

EQUIPMENT IN AQUACULTURE FACILITIES

Because some of the types of equipment discussed below are used in several different types of aquaculture facilities, they are not presented as equipment for levee-type ponds or

10–37. A hatchery building for the rearing of fry. Many hatcheries are located in metal buildings so the climate for the eggs and fingerlings can be carefully controlled.

equipment for raceways. Each type of equipment is described, and the facility or facilities in which it is needed are given.

AERATORS

Some type of aeration is necessary for all aquaculture systems. The need for aeration is greater with a higher stocking rate. The simplest form of aeration is by the splash method, commonly used with raceways and some closed systems. The splash method simply means that something is used to break water into small droplets as it enters the facility so as to oxygenate the water. With raceways, this is frequently the only type of aeration needed because the water is not in the facility long enough for the aquacrop to deplete the oxygen.

In other types of production facilities, more aeration is provided by aerators. An *aerator* is any device designed to add oxygen to water. In levee-type ponds, electric paddle wheels and floating spray-type surface aerators are commonly used. One of these will probably be found on every pond, ready to be used if oxygen levels get too low. Both of these simply throw oxygen-poor water into the air so it can be oxygenated. Contrary to the belief of some, outboard motors do not do a comparable job of aerating the water.

10–38. An electric paddle-wheel aerator. (Very energy efficient for the amount of oxygen they provide, electric paddle wheels are commonly used in large ponds with intensive production.) (Courtesy, Agricultural Research Service, USDA)

Besides the electric devices, portable paddle wheels that operate from the PTO shafts of tractors are used. Where dissolved oxygen problems have caused danger to the aquacrop, these portable aerators are moved to assist the regular aerators in oxygenating the water quickly. If this is necessary, a portable aerator should be placed right beside the regular aerator. This is done because the fish will be gathered close to the regular aerator and so the fish will not have to search the pond for oxygen if one of the aerators stops working.

10–39. Floating spray-type aerators are common in smaller ponds and in ponds with less intensive production.

Tank systems are not usually large enough to need big paddle wheels or splash-type surface aerators, although small splash-type surface aerators may be used. Tanks that are used as round raceways do not usually need additional aeration, although sometimes the stocking rates require it. If so, compressed oxygen is often injected or diffused into the water. This method is often used with closed systems as well.

If compressed oxygen is diffused into the water, the device used should create small bubbles. Large bubbles send most of their oxygen into the air when they reach the surface. If possible, a device to keep the bubbles from rising straight to the surface will also help. The longer the bubbles are under water, the more diffusion that occurs between the bubbles and the water.

10–40. A portable paddle-wheel aerator that operates from a tractor PTO.

10–41. A seine is being used in a small pond to harvest stocker sunfish.

10–42. This pond has been seined, and the fish have been gathered in a live car, or sock. (Courtesy, Agricultural Research Service, USDA)

SEINES AND SEINE HAULERS

A *seine* is a long net used to harvest an aquacrop. The size of the holes in the netting determines the size of the aquacrop that will be harvested. Small fish can escape through the holes; larger fish cannot. Seines are pulled either by hand or by a tractor and seine reel.

Seines are most often used in levee-type ponds or watershed ponds. In a levee-type pond, the water may be left at its regular level and the seine pulled through the entire pond. This requires a seine large enough to reach from the bottom to far enough above the top to keep the aquacrop from swimming or jumping over. In a watershed pond, a large portion of the water is usually drained from the pond before harvest, so a smaller seine is required.

The seine will have weights across the bottom to pull it down and keep fish from swimming underneath. A worker still must ride the seine at the toe of the levee to keep the aquacrop from swimming under where the seine starts to slope up to the bank.

The aquacrop is usually herded by the seine to a corner of the pond and held there for harvesting. Sometimes, a live car, or sock, is attached to the seine, and the aquacrop is forced into it. A live car, or sock, is a net with a bottom, which is used to hold the fish temporarily until they are harvested.

Once the aquacrop has been sufficiently crowded together for harvesting, steel rods are used to hold the sides of the seine or the sock above the water so the aquacrop cannot escape. These steel rods are usually made of reinforced steel with a Y welded to the end of each rod to hook the seine over. Then, the aquacrop is harvested, usually with a net attached to a powered boom, although dip nets are sometimes used to harvest the aquacrop by hand.

Seines are seldom needed with raceway, tank, or cage production methods. With a raceway, the aquacrop is usually herded to one end with a board and lifted out with a dip net. Dip nets are the predominant method for harvesting from tanks as well; lowering the water level makes it easier to use dip nets. With cages, the aquacrop is usually dumped into a boat or a hauling tank.

10–43. A powered seine reel is being used to harvest a large pond.

SEINE BOATS

A *seine boat* is a small boat used in seining. When a large seine is used, a seine boat usually travels along behind it and scares the fish as the seine crowds the fish together. It is important to keep the fish out of the seine, where they might get their gills caught in the netting.

Most seine boats are converted 14- or 15-foot-long aluminum fishing boats. A seine boat generally has an outboard motor and carries the sock (if used) and the rods to prop up the seine or the sock.

FEEDERS

Feeding time is very important in many types of aquaculture production, because this is often the only time the aquafarmer gets to check the aquacrop. The way an aquacrop feeds can reveal much about the health and well-being of the fish. As a result,

10–44. A typical seine boat.

10–45. An on-farm feed bin is built so a truck with a feed blower can drive under and load.

in most small systems, such as tanks and cages, the feeding is often done by hand. Feeds that are not commercially prepared, such as scraps from meat processing plants, are also usually fed by hand, as they tend to clog up automated feeding systems.

Most larger systems, however, require some automation to get the feeding done on a daily basis. These large operations usually feed commercially prepared pellets that float on the water.

The three most common types of automated feeders are feed blowers, demand feeders, and controlled auger systems. Feed blowers are often used with a large number of levee-type ponds or watershed ponds. Feed blowers are attached to trucks or tractors that drive around the tops of levees and blow feed out into the water. Feeders of this type are the most common on large-scale aquafarms that produce channel catfish. As the feed is blown on a pond, the fish respond almost immediately. If they do not, the driver knows that something is wrong with the fish.

A demand feeder stores feed inside the feeder, and the fish bump a rod (pendulum) to cause feed to be released. The fish usually have to be trained to bump the rod, but most species learn quickly. Demand feeders are common in raceways where trout are produced. To reduce wasting feed, some demand feeders have controls to regulate the amount of feed dumped during a certain period. Since the aquafarmer is not always present when the fish feed, the feeders must be checked regularly to make sure they are working properly.

10–46. A pull-behind PTO-operated feed blower is being moved along a levee.

Automated auger systems work just like those in poultry houses or dairy barns. A control panel is used to start the feed through the auger, which drops it into the water facility through a series of openings. An electronic system is used to regulate the amount of feed that goes to each water facility. Automated auger systems are most commonly found on aquafarms that use a series of tanks or raceways. Like demand feeders, these systems must be checked regularly to make sure that all openings are clear and that the augers are working properly.

10–47. A backpack feed blower can be used on small ponds.

MONITORING DEVICES

Since the most prevalent problem in intensive aquaculture production is low levels of dissolved oxygen, a means of quickly checking the dissolved oxygen is necessary. Dissolved oxygen may be checked with a chemical kit or an electronic meter. The chemical kit is very accurate and relatively inexpensive, but the procedure is time consuming. If many ponds or tanks must be checked, an electronic meter is essential. Good electronic meters cost several hundred dollars but are considered good investments. Any farm with more than a pond or two can justify the purchase of a meter to check for dissolved oxygen.

The dissolved oxygen in ponds should be checked at least twice a night, as the photosynthesis from the algae that produces oxygen during the day halts at night. The most common time for oxygen stress in ponds is just before daybreak.

Other monitoring devices or kits are commonly used to check nitrites, nitrates, and pH of the water. These may be needed with ponds and tanks, especially if the tanks are in closed systems. A nitrite test kit will tell if the biofilter has suddenly "died" and new water needs to be added to the system.

If a raceway is constructed properly and an adequate amount of water moves through the system, these monitoring devices are not as important. The water should be checked periodically, however, to make sure quality water is coming from the water source.

HAUL TANKS

Some aquaculture producers may find that haul tanks are never necessary. In fact, in a large-scale system, the producer usually has the fingerling supplier deliver the fingerlings

10–48. A truck equipped with haul tanks.

to the production facility and the processing plant pick up the finished aquacrop at the production facility. For many small-scale producers, however, the ability to haul live aquacrops to specialized markets or to pick up their own fingerlings may be an important way to save money.

10–49. Twelve-volt motors are being used to power aerators on haul tanks. (These motors operate from the electrical system of the truck.)

Live-haul tanks that can be loaded into a pickup truck or onto a flatbed truck often come in very handy. These tanks are usually made of aluminum or steel. Tanks that are more shallow provide for greater diffusion of oxygen during the hauling.

If the aquacrop is to be hauled very far, some means of adding oxygen to the water is necessary. Also, for even farther distances, the aquafarmer should plan on periodically replacing the water to avoid the buildup of ammonia.

Care must be taken not to shock the aquacrop with drastic changes of water temperature. Some species do not react well to sudden temperature changes of as little as 5°F. The aquacrop should be acclimated gradually by exchanging some of the water in the tank with that in the water facility in which it is to be placed.

ISH GRADERS

In many operations, fish must be graded—separated according to their size. This operation is done using fish graders. A fish grader is a device used to select fish above and below

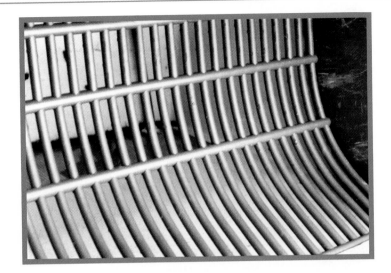

10–50. A large bar grader used to separate trout based on their size.

a certain size. In a trout raceway, a steel grate with slats is used. Fish that are below the required size can swim through the grates and those above the required size cannot.

With pond-raised fish, such as catfish or hybrid striped bass, grading is done using a seine with holes of a specific size. The seine will collect the larger fish desired for harvest and allow the smaller fish to remain in the pond.

10–51. A floating grader is used in a pond to sort stocker sunfish.

10–52. A small fingerling grader used in troughs or raceways.

OTHER EQUIPMENT

Aquaculture often requires equipment other than that previously covered in this chapter. Tractors with mowers are used to keep areas around ponds free of weeds. Computer systems are used to manage aquabusinesses. Various storage areas are needed for chemicals, equipment, and other items.

10–53. A tractor with a flail-type cutter is being used to keep down weeds and grass around a pond.

RECIRCULATING SYSTEMS

Recirculating systems filter, clean, and aerate water for circulating back through aquaculture growing facilities. They are used with ponds, raceways, and tanks. Most use is with tank systems. (Recirculating systems are sometimes known as **RAS**, or recirculating aquaculture systems.)

The goal of a recirculating system is to provide a near ideal environment for the health and growth of fish stocked at high densities. Feed must be provided. Water temperature may need to be controlled. Little new water is added to a system, though some must be added to compensate for the amount lost to evaporation, system leaks, and splashing.

Operating a recirculating system requires attention to a number of details. This is because the aquacrop is being produced in a controlled environment at high stocking densities. The system must be properly designed, constructed, and maintained.

COMPONENTS

A recirculating system must be able to accomplish all the processes that nature carries out in assuring quality water in ponds, lakes, and streams. It must do so with water that must support a much higher stocking density than is found in natural bodies of water.

The major components of a recirculating system are

- A water source
- Fish tanks
- Clarifiers (to remove solids wastes from the water, including wastes that settle and those that are suspended)
- Biofilters (to provide for growth of bacteria that convert ammonia and other harmful gases to harmless forms)
- Oxygenation/aeration
- Water pumps

The most important component of a recirculating system is the biofilter.

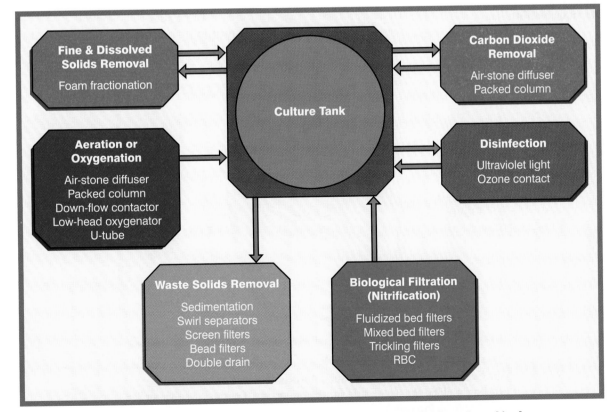

10–54. Processes (bold type) in a recirculating system and methods (standard type) used in the processes.

10–55. A small experimental system is being prepared to study biofiltration.

BIOFILTERS

A *biofilter* is any structure or material that uses natural organisms to improve water quality. The organisms are microscopic bacteria attached to structures or surfaces in the water. These organisms convert harmful substances in the water into less harmful substances.

The surface to which the microbes are attached is provided by the *biofilter media.* Small media provide greater total surface area than larger structures. Several kinds of materials are manufactured for use as biofilter media, including tiny polyethylene balls, nylon cords, and layered sheets of polyethylene. Sand and pebbles are common natural media.

In any fish culture, the primary waste product harmful to fish is ammonia. In closed or partially closed systems, biofilters convert ammonia into other nitrogen compounds less harmful to the aquacrop. The water can then be reused by the aquacrop. The ability of the biofilter to convert ammonia is the primary determinant of the intensity of production.

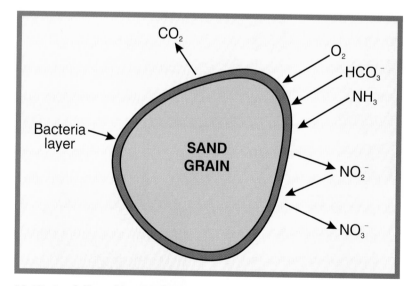

10–56. Sand, if used in a biofilter, has an important role filtering wastes. The bacterial film coating each sand particle removes ammonia and nitrites, making the water safe for the aquacrop. (Courtesy, Louisiana Sea Grant College Program)

10–57. One type of manufactured media used in recirculating systems is shown here. The design of this material provides maximum surface and water movement.

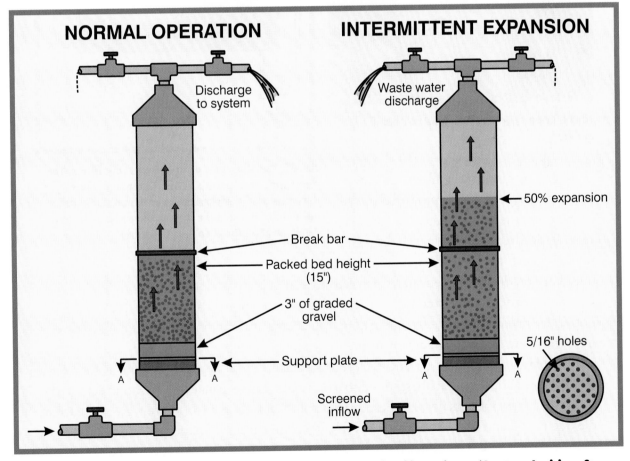

10–58. The two modes of operation of an upflow sand filter are normal and intermittent. (Courtesy, Louisiana Sea Grant College Program)

10–59. Inspecting the adjustment of a small biofilter.

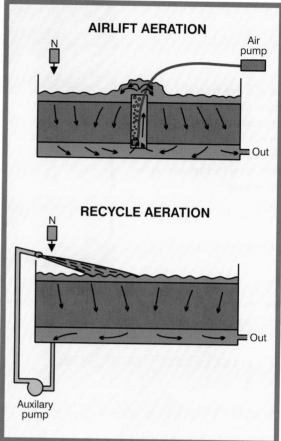

10–60. Two diagrams of submerged rock filters. The filter with an air pump, shown in the top diagram, has increased performance over the one without an air pump, shown in the bottom diagram. (Courtesy, Louisiana Sea Grant College Program)

Microorganisms in biofilters must convert nitrogen compounds produced by the aquacrop as the water is reused in the system. If not, the aquacrop will die. The toxic organic nitrogen compounds produced in a production system are un-ionized ammonia (NH_3) and nitrite (NO_2). Biofilters utilize two types of bacteria to convert these toxic organic compounds to nitrate (NO_3), which is not toxic. Bacteria from the genus *Nitrosomonas* convert ammonia to nitrite, and bacteria from the genus *Nitrobacter* convert nitrite to nitrate.

The pH of the water used in the closed systems must be kept stable. This is necessary because most aquacrops are best suited to a particular range, usually 7 to 8, and because the bacteria in the biofilters perform best at these pH levels. Because biofilters give off carbon dioxide (CO_2) and use bicarbonate ions (HCO_3), aquaculture production in closed systems tends to lower pH. Therefore, the calcium carbonate ($CaCO_3$) levels must be increased. This is usually accomplished by using calcareous gravel or shells in the filter or by periodically adding sodium bicarbonate ($NaHCO_3$) to the system.

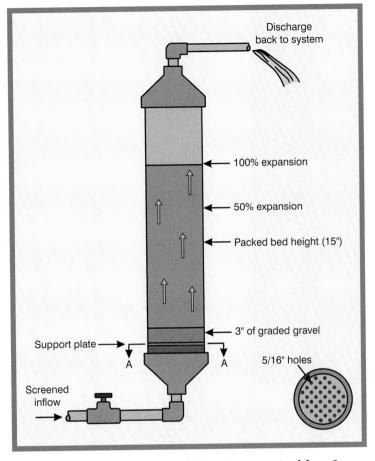

10–61. Diagram of a fluidized bed filter. (Courtesy, Louisiana Sea Grant College Program)

The four most common types of biological filters are submerged rock, upflow sand, fluidized bed, and rotating biological contactor. All four of these systems work by the growth of bacteria on the material in the filters.

- Submerged rock filter—In a submerged rock filter, the water passes through a bed of calcareous rock (or shells). The bacteria grow on the exterior of the rocks, where they convert the nitrite and ammonia to nitrate. Solid wastes accumulate in the spaces between the rocks and decompose. The calcareous rocks keep the pH of the water regulated.

   The submerged rock filter is widely used in specialized operations, such as softshell crab or crawfish shedding systems. The primary disadvantage is that it is very bulky and may lower the production capacity because not enough space is available.

- Upflow sand filter—In the upflow sand filter, the water flows upward through a coarse sand bed. The bacteria grow on the surfaces of the sand, which has a greater surface

10–62. Fluidized bed filters at shrimp tank production facility.

10–63. A rotating biological contactor, or RBC, as used on a recirculating system in West Virginia.

area than the rock, so the filter does not have to be as large. Because there is little void space between the sand grains for solids to accumulate, the solid wastes build up while a film of bacteria thickens, thus reducing water flow. For this reason, the bed must be expanded periodically for cleaning, usually once per day.

The upflow sand filter is expanded by increasing the water flow. When the water flow is increased, the solids, which are lighter than the sand, move on through the filter, while the grains of sand rub together to remove excess bacteria. When the bed is being expanded, the water is removed through a waste valve and is not recirculated through the system. The upflow sand filter does not regulate the pH of the water, so this must periodically be checked and sodium bicarbonate added.

- Fluidized bed filter—A fluidized bed filter is an upflow sand filter kept in a constant state of between 25 and 100 percent expansion. This prevents the buildup of solid wastes and the creation of a bacteria film. Because the water is in a constant state of expansion, very little maintenance is needed with the fluidized bed filter.

  Because the solids are constantly being moved through the system, another filter is needed to catch the solids. While the fluidized bed filter does an excellent job of removing the nitrites and ammonia, it is most often used in conjunction with an upflow sand filter, which does a good job of removing the solids.

- Rotating biological contactor (RBC)—An **RBC** is a motorized filter that rotates an open canister of material (usually plastic) so that the canister constantly goes from being submerged

10–64. A gravity separator is used as part of this recirculating system with an RBC.

to being in the open air. Although the RBC may be placed in the aquaculture facility, it is often located in its own water structure adjacent to the aquaculture facility. The RBC has become the biofilter of choice in most closed systems. The RBC does not remove solid wastes.

FILTRATION

Filtration is the process of removing solids and dissolved solids from water. Fine and dissolved solids are the most difficult to remove. Some solids are known as suspended solids. *Suspended solids* are those materials that do not float on top or sink to the bottom.

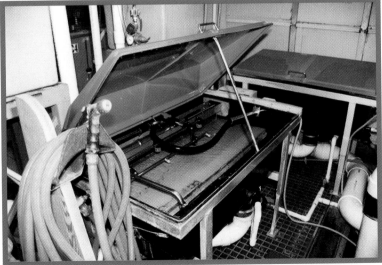

10–65. A filter with automatic backflushing.

10–66. A large bead filter system is used in this aquaculture facility.

Larger particles are easier to remove. The process may involve the water flowing through filter screens to remove solids or the water passing through granular solids. Water may be periodically pumped backwards through the filter to flush away the sludge that has accumulated. Backflushing may be automated with a timer system.

Suspended solids may be removed with bead filters. These filtering devices allow the water to be moved through a mass of small beads (BB size) that may be electrostatically charged to trap the suspended materials. Bead filters also promote nitrification at the same time that suspended solid materials are removed. The beads are normally made of polyethylene. The beads are cleaned by backflushing. *Backflushing* is forcing water to flow in reverse through a filter and/or system. Backflushed water is diverted into a drain for disposal.

10–67. Economical and dependable pumps powered by electric motors are needed to move water through a recirculating system.

REVIEWING

MAIN IDEAS

Having a good production facility is an important part of a successful aquaculture operation. An appropriate facility depends on several factors, including the aquacrop to be produced, the level of production desired, the time an aquafarmer has available for management, and the capital available.

For large-scale production, ponds and raceways are most common. Ponds are static systems where the water is held, with new water added only to maintain the water level. Ponds are primarily used for warmwater aquacrops, such as catfish and tilapia.

Raceways are open or flow-through systems that require much water for their operation. They are generally used for a coolwater or coldwater aquacrop, such as trout.

Smaller-scale operations, which may also be very intensive, generally use cages or tanks. Cages are placed in existing water facilities, such as farm ponds, rivers, oceans, and estuaries. The use of cages often allows aquaculture production in areas where production encompassing the entire water facility is not feasible.

Tanks, although they may be used as round raceways, are also commonly used as static systems, similar to pond culture, or as closed systems. Closed systems, which recirculate the water, require the use of biofilters to remove the wastes from the water before it is pumped back into the growing facilities.

Site selection for a water facility involves the consideration of many factors. The most common factors are an adequate source of water, the size of the facility needed, and the proximity to local markets, suppliers, and utilities. The different types of water facilities all have unique requirements that also must be taken into account.

Several types of equipment are necessary for aquaculture production. Mechanical aerators, seines, and seine boats are required in pond production. For a large-scale pond operation, a feed blower and an electronic dissolved oxygen monitor are almost mandatory.

Biofiltration is the use of bacteria to convert harmful forms of nitrogen into forms that are less harmful. Various biofilters are used, including submerged rock filters, upflow sand filters, fluidized bed filters, and rotating biological contactors. Solids and suspended solids are removed by mechanical filtration. Bead systems are often used.

QUESTIONS

Answer the following questions, using complete sentences and correct spelling.

1. How are watershed ponds and levee-type ponds different?

2. Why is soil type important in the selection of a site for a pond?

3. What type of topography is needed for a levee-type pond? For a watershed pond?

4. What is meant by a static system? An open system (flow-through system)? A closed system?

5. How deep should water be for cage culture? Why?

6. How far apart should cages be placed? Why?

7. Why should the freeboard on a pond be between 1 and 2 feet?

8. What determines the size of a drain pipe of a pond?

9. What is the purpose of a feeding ring on a cage?

10. What are biofilters? What types are used? How do they work?

EVALUATING

Match the term with the correct definition. Write the letter of the term on the line provided.

a. biofilter
b. effluent
c. fill
d. freeboard

e. permeability
f. backflushing
g. seine
h. topography

i. RBC
j. biofilter media
k. suspended solids
l. filtration

_____1. Earth used to make a pond levee

_____2. A long net used to harvest an aquacrop

_____3. The slope of the land on which a pond is built

_____4. The water draining out of an aquaculture facility

_____5. Any structure or material that uses natural organisms to improve water quality

_____6. The rate at which substances infiltrate the soil

_____7. The distance between the top of the water and the top of the levee in a pond

_____8. Forcing water to flow in reverse through a filter

_____9. The process of removing solids, suspended solids, and dissolved solids from water

_____10. Material in a biofilter to which microorganisms attach themselves

_____11. A rotating device that prepares water for recirculation

_____12. Materials that neither settle nor float in water

EXPLORING

1. Tour a local aquafarm to view the facilities. Ask the manager how the types of facilities used dictate the management decisions that are made. Give an oral report to the class.

2. Take photographs of the different types of aquaculture facilities found in your community. Develop a bulletin board for the classroom. In a written report, tell how the facilities are alike and different.

3. Build a cage for use in culturing an aquacrop in an existing water facility in your area. Follow the recommendations in the chapter for placement of the cage. Use the other chapters for information on feeding of the aquacrop.

CHAPTER 11

Aquaculture Marketing

This chapter emphasizes some fundamentals of marketing aquaculture products. It has the following objectives:

1 Explain the meaning and importance of aquaculture marketing
2 Discuss the importance of the *Regulatory Fish Encyclopedia* and give examples of information
3 Explain marketing channels used in aquaculture
4 Relate the role of economy of scale to aquaculture and describe how to select a market
5 Explain planning for marketing
6 Describe live aquaculture product forms
7 Describe processed aquaculture product forms
8 Explain how aquacrops are transported
9 Describe the role of promotion in marketing

TERMS

advertising
basic processing
B-to-B marketing
caviar
commercial producer
deheading
deveining
economic deception
economy of scale
eviscerating
eyed eggs
fabricating
fee-lake

fillet
fingerling
flavor testing
grading
live hauling
marketing
marketing channel
marketing functions
marketing plan
marketing planning
merchandising
misbranded food
packaging

pan-dressed
preservation
processing
product form
receiving
Regulatory Fish Encyclopedia
sampling
selling
shucking
skinning
stunning
viscera
yield

KNOWING how to produce an aquacrop is important; knowing how to market it is a must! Success in aquaculture is more than producing a quality aquacrop. It includes marketing the crop for a profit. A wise producer never begins producing a crop without a market for the final product.

Consumers—people who use products—make choices about what they buy. Smart marketing requires listening to consumers. Aquaculture products must be what consumers want or they will buy something else. Marketing is the link between aquaculture producers and consumers.

Early aquafarmers found that no marketing system existed. They began by developing their own markets.

11–1. Shucked, fresh, cultured oysters are packaged in a glass jar and kept on ice in a supermarket.

These were often small niche markets that wanted a steady supply of uniform product. The early aquafarmers found that marketing carefully and making a profit went together. Aquafarmers are in the business to make a profit!

11–2. Fish-and-seafood restaurants, such as this one in Seattle, are popular when people eat out.

MARKETING

As the link between producers and consumers, *marketing* includes all the steps needed to get a desired product to consumers. Marketing actually begins when deciding what to produce. Products cannot be produced independently of what consumers want. Of course, through advertising and other means, demand can sometimes be created. All the functions in moving aquacrops from the point of production to the consumer help make the concept of marketing.

Today's aquafarmers are commercial producers. **Commercial producers** raise fish and other crops for the money they can get when the crops are sold. They produce for specific markets. This makes them commercial producers rather than subsistence farmers. They are likely to buy their fish and other foods at a supermarket, just like other consumers!

MARKETING FUNCTIONS

Marketing is far more than selling an aquacrop. However, marketing includes selling. **Marketing functions** are the steps or processes that a product passes through before it reaches the consumer. Marketing aquacrops includes several functions, as presented in Table 11–1.

Table 11–1. Aquaculture Marketing Functions

- Planning what to produce
- Producing a quality aquacrop
- Sampling the aquacrop
- Assembling and grading
- Transporting (may occur several times in the marketing process)
- Advertising and promoting consumption
- Processing (also known as manufacturing)
- Selling (changing ownership)
- Storing (live and processed aquacrops)
- Developing products (such as easy-to-cook forms of fish)
- Following up with consumers

Planning Production

The key to successful marketing is producing something that is in demand. Good information is needed about the kinds of aquacrops consumers want. This requires serious study by a producer.

Begin by determining the aquacrops that will have the highest demand. Before deciding what to produce, consider the climate, available water, facilities, personal preferences, and other factors. Sometimes it is not possible to grow the crop with the greatest profit potential. This may be because of climate or other limiting factors. Grow the aquacrops that will result in the greatest returns in the long run.

Producing a Quality Product

Consumers want good-quality products. They do not want products with flaws. In aquaculture, they want products that have correct flavor, are free of hazardous substances, and provide good nutrition. The foods must be wholesome. They must also be attractive and appeal to consumers.

Sampling

Sampling is selecting a small, representative part of an aquacrop to determine if it is up to standard. Aquacrops may take on off-flavors or, in rare cases, contain hazardous chemical residues.

11–3. A producer has many decisions to make about aquaculture, such as when to harvest. (Courtesy, U.S. Department of Agriculture)

11–4. A quality moi (Pacific threadfin), cultured in an offshore cage in Hawaii, is ready for making sashimi. (Sashimi is a thinly sliced raw fish product.) (Courtesy, National Oceanic and Atmospheric Administration)

Processing plants usually take samples just before harvesting to check on the flavor. The samples may be quickly cooked in a microwave oven and tasted by people who are trained as tasters. An aquacrop that is off-flavor should not be harvested. Steps should be taken to correct the off-flavor problem so the crop can be harvested in a few days.

Scientists are not always able to explain what causes off-flavor. Sometimes it is attributed to feed and sometimes to water quality. The problem may be due to a number of different water-related factors. Research is beginning to find relationships in the production environment that lead to off-flavor.

11–5. Fish cultured in offshore cages are being graded before processing. (Courtesy, National Oceanic and Atmospheric Administration)

Sampling is used to check for dangerous residues or organisms in the aquacrop. Industrial chemical pollution has occasionally been found in wild fish. Sometimes, harmful organisms are present in other food items, such as oysters. Laboratory study is usually needed for accurate analysis. Care is needed in producing aquacrops to avoid any contamination of the crops. Only wholesome food should be marketed!

Assembling and Grading

Aquacrops must be gathered in uniform lots. With fish, assembling involves loading them into tanks for hauling. It may also include bringing together the fish from several different farms. This is most often the case at a processing plant.

Grading is an important step. Buyers, including processors, want fish that are of uniform size and species. Fish that are too small or too large must be culled out or assembled into other lots. Trash fish and diseased or injured fish must be removed.

11–6. A uniform lot of fish ready for processing. (Courtesy, MFC Services)

Transporting

As a marketing function, transporting involves getting the aquacrop from the farm to the consumer. This may involve stops along the way for other steps in the marketing process. The producer may be interested only in transporting to the nearest processing plant. What that plant will pay may be partially based on the distance that the processed product must be hauled. A processing plant must haul the processed product in refrigerated trucks to distributors, supermarkets, restaurants, and other outlets.

Recreational fee-lake operations are not as interested in transporting the product as they are in being convenient to the fishing public. In some cases, fee-lakes buy fish that are hauled and placed in the facilities.

11–7. Haul truck unloading fish at a processing plant.

11–8. Attractive signs promote sales.

Advertising

Advertising is calling the attention of possible consumers to a product and encouraging them to buy it. Advertising is usually part of a larger promotional program. Its purpose is to convince people to try what is being sold, such as an aquaculture food item or other commodity.

Many farmers may not be directly involved in advertising aquacrops. Yet, nearly all of them have some indirect involvement with it. Poor advertising can result in low consumption and lower profits to growers. Good advertising can result in increased consumption, profit, and expansion.

Farmers may help support some of the costs of advertising. For example, a fee may be added to each ton of feed for the specific purpose of product promotion.

Operators of fee-lakes are well aware of the value of good signs and other forms of promotion. Without good signs, the fishing public might not know where the fee-lakes are located.

11–9. Processing varies with the kind of aquacrop. Here, crawfish are being peeled by hand for packing. (Courtesy, MFC Services)

Processing

Processing is preparing the aquacrop into a convenient form for the consumer. It may involve only a few simple steps, or it may be a complex process that results in a precooked food item. What is done depends on the kind of aquacrop. Trout, for example, often have the head (with eyes) left on the whole fish. The scales and internal organs are removed. Shrimp may be whole, without heads and not peeled or without heads and peeled (outer crustacean shell removed).

Processed products may also be put into convenient packages for the consumer. This includes preparing the products for storage so they will be wholesome foods. (More on processing is presented later in this chapter.)

Selling

Selling is changing the ownership of an aquacrop. The seller and the buyer must agree on a price. For the producer who sells to a processor, selling is simply delivering the crop to the processing plant at a fixed price. The producer usually knows the price well in advance.

After a price has been established, the fish are weighed, the total value is determined, and a payment is made for the amount (less any harvesting or hauling costs, if the processor provided these services). Certainly the processor expects to receive a quality, uniform aquacrop. Some producers operate restaurants to sell their products. In this case, selling occurs when consumers buy ready-to-eat dinners.

Storing

Aquacrops must often be kept for a time before their use. Storing may occur on the farm or at the processing plant with live animals. It may also occur after processing, when the product is refrigerated or frozen. Processing plants often have high-tech freezing facilities that assure good products.

11–10. Scallops are displayed on ice in a supermarket to promote sales.

11–11. Fish are being stored live in these vats until processing at a plant.

Storage conditions vary with different aquacrops. Individuals must know the qualities of the product they are storing so as to maintain maximum quality. For example, processed fish that are improperly stored can take on off-flavors or undergo a change in texture. If this occurs, the consumer will not buy the product.

Developing Products

To enhance demand, food processors often develop new forms of products to appeal to consumers. These may involve new ways of packaging, easy-to-cook forms, and new kinds of products. A trip through the frozen food section of a local supermarket provides the opportunity to see many forms in which foods have been prepared for consumer convenience.

Following Up with Consumers

Follow-up with consumers is used to evaluate how consumers like a product. Often the label on a food product will tell how consumers can send in their comments.

A toll-free telephone number may be given so consumers can share concerns or suggestions. The toll-free number is also used to provide information to consumers on how to prepare the product for consumption. By knowing how consumers feel about a product and helping consumers prepare it, the processor can try to make the product better.

QUALITY IS ESSENTIAL

Only quality products should reach consumers. Poor quality damages the reputation of products. Fish with off-flavor may cause the customer to stop buying the product.

11–12. A sample is being checked for microorganisms in a microbiology lab as a step in assuring quality. (Courtesy, U.S. Department of Agriculture)

Any foods that are improperly stored, handled, or cooked might cause food poisoning. An outbreak of food poisoning can destroy the demand for an aquacrop.

The rule to follow is: Only quality, wholesome aquaculture products should be marketed.

THE *REGULATORY FISH ENCYCLOPEDIA*

The *Regulatory Fish Encyclopedia* (*RFE*) is a compilation of information that provides accurate identification of fish products in marketing. The information helps to identify processed fish products to assure accurate labeling. The *RFE* was developed by the Center for Food Safety and Applied Nutrition of the U.S. Food and Drug Administration.

CONSISTENT MARKET NAMES

The *RFE* helps provide consistent labeling of fish products in the marketing process. Retail products have uniform names in all markets in the United States. This is important because unscrupulous marketers may incorrectly label fish products. In particular, the *RFE* helps protect the consumer. The consumer is assured that a product has been correctly labeled.

The *RFE* includes nearly 100 species of fish. For each, it lists the market name, the common name, and the scientific name. Of course, there are many other species of fish, but the list includes those that are most commonly sold for human food.

Incorrectly labeling fish and other seafood is said to be economic deception. *Economic deception* is the substitution of a less expensive species for a more expensive species. This creates a practice known as misbranding. *Misbranded food* is a product offered for sale under the name of another product. Using a label that identifies a product as a more expensive species when it is a less expensive species is illegal.

A major problem occurred in the late 1990s with imported fish being labeled "catfish" when they were not catfish. New legislation was enacted to assure that products are labeled properly. Now, a product labeled "grouper" in a grocery store in Atlanta is the same species as products labeled "grouper" in New York and San Francisco.

INFORMATION IN THE RFE

The *RFE* provides a large amount of information. As stated above, it lists market names, common names, and scientific names of species routinely used for human food. The *RFE* also contains the following identifying information for each species:

- Image (picture) of live (unprocessed) form.

- Image of processed forms, such as fillets, to reveal tissue features.

- Taxonomic description to help identify unprocessed form. (This includes size, shape, color, fin structure and arrangement, etc.)

- Chemical pattern information obtained by appropriate laboratory analysis, including patterns from isoelectric focusing (IEF) and restriction fragment length polymorphism (RFLP). (Electrophoresis is used to develop gel banding patterns. The bands are studied for peaks and multiplicity of patterns in species determination.)

- DNA fragment patterns and sequence information (some species).

- List of other sources of information on the species.

The *RFE* is a searchable data base available through the Internet at **www.cfsan.fda.gov/**.

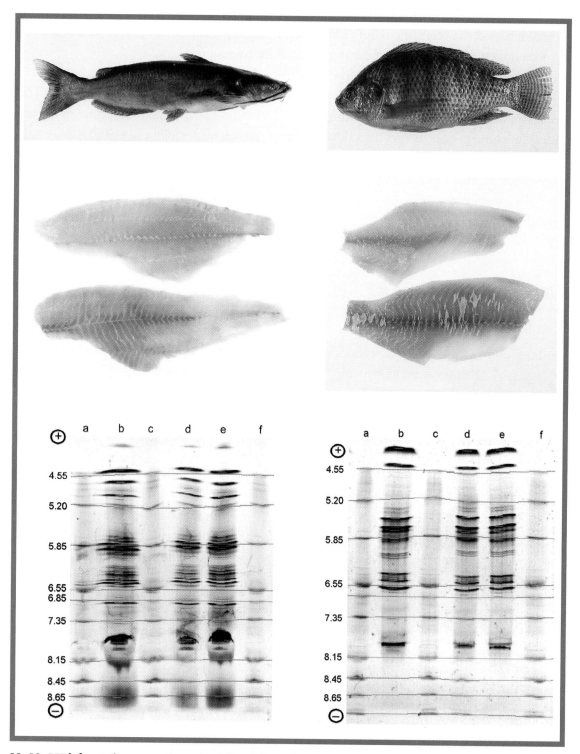

11–13. *RFE* information comparing external and tissue features and protein gel patterns of the channel catfish (left) with those of the Nile tilapia (right). What differences do you see?

AQUACULTURE MARKETING CHANNELS

Marketing—linking the producer and the consumer—can take place in several ways. In this chapter, the major emphasis is on marketing freshwater fish.

The *marketing channel* is the route or procedure followed to get a product to the consumer. Several channels are available to the fish producer. No doubt, the large-scale producer will enter into a contract with a processor to assure an outlet for the aquacrop when it is ready.

MARKETING THROUGH PROCESSING PLANTS

Most cultured food fish are sold by producers to processing plants. These plants may handle thousands of pounds of fish a day. Expensive automated machinery is used in processing. Sanitation and safety procedures are strictly enforced to ensure wholesome food products.

The typical processing plant buys fish from the farmer, dresses them, puts them in attractive and protective packages, and sells them to wholesalers, restaurants, supermarkets, and institutional food services. Processors may have trucks that deliver the processed fish to the point of sale. Fish that are sold wholesale go to a distributor, who usually sells them again to a retail outlet. Wholesalers often buy in large quantities. Retailers may buy only a few pounds a week. Some processors may also operate retail outlets.

11–14. Processing plants have modern refrigerated trucks that deliver nationwide.

Some processing plants have harvesting crews that will go to farms and harvest fish crops. The farmers are charged for this service. Most of the time the charge is only a few cents per pound of fish. This allows farmers the freedom of investing their money in production facilities rather than in expensive harvesting equipment.

An attractive advantage of marketing through a processing plant is that the plant will often sign a contract with the producer, ensuring a sale for the crop when it is ready. The contract usually specifies the price and the amount of fish that will be bought. The price might not be as high as the prices at some other market outlets, but it is fairly well guaranteed. In other words, the risk of having a crop and no place to sell it is virtually eliminated.

Sometimes, farmers pool their resources and build processing plants. They have more control over processing and share in any profits.

LOCAL RETAIL MARKETS

Aquafarmers may set up local retail markets. They may operate roadside stores or restaurants where all or some of their crops are sold, or they may sell only on an order basis to individuals or groups.

Roadside Stores

Roadside fish markets are small businesses that sell aquaculture products to the public. The products may be sold dressed or live, according to the wishes of the customers.

A roadside store adds another dimension of management to an aquafarm. The store must be operated efficiently. Good workers must be employed. Equipment must be obtained. Licenses must be purchased. Tax documents and other government reports will need to be prepared. Advertising and public relations will be important.

When properly operated, roadside stores can produce increased returns to the farmers. By selling directly to consumers, aquafarmers can get all the profits that would otherwise go to the processors and distributors.

One of the biggest problems with roadside markets is that considerable effort is necessary to make them successful. Regular store hours must be set and observed. The stores must be in prime locations convenient to customers. Only top-quality, wholesome products should be sold.

The volume of aquacrops sold through roadside stores operated by growers is small. However, a few such stores are able to make good profits.

11–15. Cultured oysters are being sold through a retail food store operated in conjunction with a processing facility in Washington.

Restaurants

A few enterprising aquafarmers operate restaurants in conjunction with their aquafarms. Most often, these are fish, shrimp, crawfish, or crab businesses. The restaurants may be located on the farms or in nearby towns. Besides the aquaculture items, the restaurants often have other foods on their menus. These restaurants, however, usually specialize in only a few choices of foods.

The big concern for an aquafarmer who has a restaurant is management. Facilities, equipment, personnel, and a good location are needed for the business to be successful. The farmer must also keep records and comply with regulations on food preparation and sanitation. Skills of a good aquafarm manager are different from those of a good restaurant manager. Regardless, a few farmers are able to be successful with this type of venture.

Selling on an Order Basis

A few aquafarmers sell large orders of live, dressed, or cooked products to groups for special functions. Civic clubs, church groups, and others may contract for a given amount of product, either raw or cooked. Facilities, equipment, and personnel are needed to fill orders. Records and other business matters must be handled.

11–16. A restaurant that specializes in farm-raised catfish.

11–17. A portable fish cooker is used to cater picnics and other events.

INTERNET-BASED BUSINESS TO BUSINESS

Internet-based marketing has opened new opportunities in aquaculture marketing. It is used for wild catch as well as for farm-raised products.

Business-to-business (B-to-B) companies are opening new opportunities via the World Wide Web. *B-to-B marketing* is a World Wide Web approach that connects those that

11–18. Alligator skins boxed and ready for shipping. (Courtesy, MFC Services)

have fish and seafood to sell with those that wish to buy fish and seafood. These companies help sellers and buyers locate each other. They expand the buying base available to a local producer from one or two local buyers to all buyers who use the Internet. B-to-B operates like a virtual marketplace.

Some Web sites have fees for participation; others merely sell advertisements. Buyers and sellers must register before using a B-to-B Web site. An example is Fishmonger, which is located at **www.fishmonger.com**.

LIVE HAULING

Live hauling is providing live aquacrops to others who will likely use them in recreational fee-lakes. Live haulers do not usually harvest or grade the fish. Sometimes the producer may have a haul truck and deliver the fish to the fee-lake. More often, the owner of the fee-lake or a custom hauler hauls the fish.

The fish must be in excellent condition because they often travel long distances and must be readily available for the fee-lake. Live haulers often pay slightly more per pound for fish than processing plants. The volume of fish that can be marketed this way is considerably less than the volume that can be marketed for processing.

11–19. Live hauling requires a truck (or a truck with a semitrailer) equipped with tanks and aerators.

RESTAURANTS AND SUPERMARKETS

Marketing through restaurants and supermarkets is attractive for some producers. The products are harvested, dressed, and made into the forms desired by the restaurants or supermarkets and then delivered. This type of marketing may involve making sales calls on restaurants and supermarkets to see if they will buy. Harvesting, processing, and hauling equipment is needed. Conditions must be clean to ensure that wholesome products will be produced.

11–20. An outdoor cooking facility for lobster.

The volume that can be marketed this way is often small; however, some producers develop niche markets with restaurants. For example, restaurants in large cities may cater to ethnic groups that want a specific fish. The fish may be grown hundreds of miles away and shipped in at a premium price. Good examples include tilapia and hybrid striped bass. Some restaurants will buy these fish without any processing. Of course, grading, packing, and transporting will be needed.

Other than for special situations, the volume of aquacrop marketed directly from farm to restaurant or supermarket is relatively small.

RECREATIONAL FEE-LAKES

A *fee-lake* is a facility where consumers fish for recreational purposes. A few aquafarmers operate recreational fee-fishing businesses. Typically, a fee-lake is a small pond that has been heavily stocked with eating-size fish. Individuals pay a fee to get to the pond and a price per pound for the fish caught. For a fee, the operator may also provide dressing services for the fish caught. Usually fee-lakes are open only certain hours on certain days of the week. A few are open every day year-round.

11–21. A good fee-lake is popular with customers. (Courtesy, James Tidwell, Kentucky State University)

Fee-lakes must be conveniently located, such as on major highways or near towns or cities. To the large aquafarmer, a recreational facility adds another management dimension. Employees must be on hand to run the fee-lake and provide whatever services the fishing public wants. Restrooms, bait sales, and refreshment vending machines should also be available. Areas around ponds must be kept well mowed, clean, and neat. Advertising will be needed to attract customers. There must be good driveways and parking areas to handle automobiles. One further item is the necessity of insurance. Allowing the general public on a farm increases the chances of liability in case an accident occurs.

Fee-lakes must be different from facilities used for growing fish. They should be separated by some distance. Fences to restrict access may be needed. There is always the chance that a disease or trash fish may be transported by the fishing public.

ECONOMY OF SCALE AND MARKET SELECTION

Choosing a market is an important management decision. In some cases, only one possibility exists. In most situations, several alternatives exist. The volume of production may be a major factor in making marketing decisions.

ECONOMY OF SCALE

Economy of scale is a concept relating the size of a fish farm and the marketing alternatives to the profit made. The volume of fish produced and the ability of the market to use the fish must be balanced. At a minimum, a farm must not produce more than can be marketed through the available channels. What is economical to one farm situation may not be to another. The key to looking at economy of scale is profitability.

Many factors go into making a profit. Larger farms usually have lower per pound costs for growing fish than smaller farms. Certainly, this depends on the management and the costs of production. Sometimes, smaller operations return higher rates of profit because the owners are able to follow good management practices and to keep costs of production low. A few possibilities are given here.

Economy of scale deals with marketing alternatives and costs of production as related to the size of the business. Careful study of a situation is needed to determine if a proposed aquafarm will be profitable.

Small-Volume Producers

Small producers may not produce enough fish to be attractive to processors. They may need to find other marketing alternatives. Smaller producers may get into more direct marketing through roadside stores, fee-lakes, and farmer-owned restaurants. Per pound prices are often higher when fish are sold through these marketing channels.

By virtue of not having to hire much labor and invest in expensive equipment, smaller farms may be profitable. For a family aquafarm, the big question is, "Will the farm produce enough profit for the family to have a good level of living?"

Large-Volume Producers

Large-volume producers often have lower per pound costs of production. They can sell to wholesalers or to processors, if the volume is substantial, at lower per pound prices than those paid by retail outlets.

The larger producers should have lower per pound costs for feed and other inputs because of buying larger volumes. On the other hand, larger farmers may find that local sales

11–22. Large-volume producers may use expensive machinery to handle fish. (Courtesy, U.S. Department of Agriculture)

to retail stores and restaurants are not economical. These market outlets often do not demand enough fish to justify the work required for a large-volume producer to serve them.

11–23. Compressed air tanks are being loaded onto a boat to supplement oxygen while transporting harvested cobia from offshore culture facilities. (Courtesy, National Oceanic and Atmospheric Administration)

SELECTING A MARKET

Marketing is the detailed process of getting aquacrops from the producer to the consumer. The marketing alternatives that are available may vary greatly. These must be studied in relation to marketing goals. The best market for a producer must be selected.

Here are questions to answer in selecting a market for an aquaculture product:

- What is the size of the market? How much can be sold retail, and how much wholesale? How does this fit into my farming operation?

- Where is the market located? Will some of the aquacrop be sold locally? Will the crop need to be hauled long distances? Will the returns from the crop cover the extra hauling costs?

- What processors are available? Will the processors agree to a minimum price for the aquacrop?

- What equipment and facilities will be needed to process on the farm? Will on-farm processing be profitable?

- What are my personal preferences? (Some people like to operate retail facilities; others prefer to sell to processors and avoid the hassles that go with retailing.)

Many small- to medium-size producers cater to the needs of niche markets. A niche market is a specialized outlet for a crop. The market may be small and involve only a few customers. An example of selling to a niche market would be selling tilapia to ethnic restaurants that have clientele who will buy tilapia meals. Another example is providing crawfish to fish markets that have clientele who will buy crawfish for home food preparation.

Market development is often needed to identify and serve niche groups. A local telephone directory may be a good place to begin identifying potential customers. Producers must usually make contacts with the potential customers to determine needs and produce products that meet those needs. This involves going to the potential customers' places of business and meeting with them. Participating in restaurant associations, chambers of commerce, and civic clubs made up of local businesspeople helps identify potential customers. Regular delivery of the desired products is also needed. A niche market may focus on a particular species or size of aquaculture product. A unique need exists that no other producer is meeting.

PLANNING FOR MARKETING

Successful marketing involves trying to determine the preferences of consumers in order to provide a product they will buy. In some cases, producers can try to create demand for their products. Various promotional efforts may be needed at the retail level to create demand.

Preparing a marketing plan can go a long way in helping to assure success. A *marketing plan* is a written statement that guides the marketing process. Such a plan must be thoughtfully created and followed.

Marketing plans may be simple or complex. A contract with a processor may be the only marketing plan of a particular grower. Without careful attention to a plan, opportunities for additional income may be overlooked.

Marketing plans may range from 5 to 50 pages or more. Large processors may have elaborate marketing plans. A marketing plan should be realistic and based on sound information. Once the plan has been made, there must be a commitment to carry it out.

Marketing plans may be created annually for products already being produced and marketed or as needed for new products. The purpose of a plan is to help spell out how an aquaproduct is to be marketed. A plan typically has four parts: situation, objectives, strategy, and assessment. These are briefly described in Table 11–2.

Table 11–2. Parts of a Marketing Plan

1. Situation—The situation statement describes current conditions. It analyzes the market situation and answers the question, "Where are we now?"

2. Objectives—The objectives indicate what is to be accomplished in marketing. They should be specific statements. The objectives are sometimes known as the business proposition and answer the question, "Where do we want to go?"

3. Strategy—The strategy part of the plan explains how the objectives will be achieved. Resources will need to be allocated to market the product. It will not just happen; people must work at marketing. The strategy part of the plan answers the question, "How do we achieve our objectives?"

4. Assessment—This part of the plan spells out how the marketing effort will be evaluated. There is normally a procedure for assessing each objective. The assessment part of the plan answers the question, "How well did we do?"

THE PROCESS OF PLANNING

Marketing planning is the process used to develop a marketing plan. It provides for a focus of efforts in marketing an aquacrop. Time and other limited resources are allocated to the highest priorities. Limited production resources are utilized more effectively.

Reliable information from reports published by government agencies, aquaculture associations, and other sources must be used in marketing plan development. Discussions with people who are already in the business, processors, and other possible market outlets will be helpful. Study the successes and failures of others who have ventured into aquaculture. Note their strengths and weaknesses, and make comparisons to the current situation.

The objectives and strategies should be carefully developed. Deadlines should be set for reaching objectives. Ways to reach the objectives must be realistic. Resources must be allocated to marketing.

At the end of the year (or other market period), some means of assessment must be specified. The most important factor to

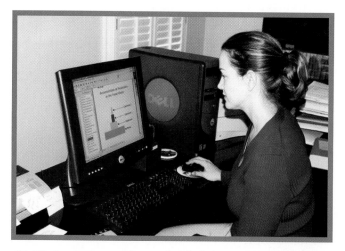

11–24. Computers can be used to help in marketing planning.

assess is how well the plan worked financially. Was a profit made? The information gained from the assessment can be used to develop a revised marketing plan for the following year.

In developing a marketing plan, every producer has a different situation. The differences are important in developing a marketing plan.

Here are important questions to consider in developing an aquaculture marketing plan:

- *What are the preferences of the aquafarmer?* This factor deals with a person's likes and dislikes of people. For example, the small aquafarmer who likes to work with the public might do well to have a retail roadside market or fee-lake.

- *What opportunities are available in the local area, and what opportunities are available that will require working with someone a distance away?* For example, the best opportunities might involve working with a distributor in a large city a long way from the farm.

- *What aquaculture currently exists in the area?* For example, if tilapia are currently being successfully grown in the area, this crop must be adapted to the climate and other environmental factors.

- *What are the local, national, and international trends that could have an impact on the proposed aquafarm?* For example, a shortage of an aquacrop that could be produced may be a good signal that the crop might be profitably grown and marketed.

- *What resources are available to start the aquafarm and market the crops?* Can additional resources be obtained? For example, will the banks or other lending agencies provide the money needed to carry out the marketing plan?

- *How well are the proposed aquacrops suited to the climate, water, and other available resources?* Some aquacrops may be well suited and in demand by the market.

LIVE AQUACULTURE PRODUCT FORMS

Product form is the form in which an aquacrop is marketed. Product form varies with the kind of crop produced. Consumer demand also plays an important role.

Aquacrops that are alive are said to be in live product form. They have not been processed to get them ready for consumption.

EGGS

The egg form of an aquacrop may be in demand by hatcheries and by humans. Hatcheries often buy **eyed eggs**. These are fertile eggs that are beginning to show the development of the fish. The hatcheries continue with the incubation process and grow the fry into marketable fingerlings.

11–25. Some producers market fish eggs to hatcheries. (Courtesy, U.S. Fish and Wildlife Service)

Some kinds of eggs are eaten by humans as food products. These fish eggs are often referred to as **caviar**, a rather expensive restaurant appetizer or entree. Caviar is usually the roe (egg mass) of large fish, such as the sturgeon. Sometimes, fish are harvested exclusively for their roe. An example is the mullet, caught in the Gulf of Mexico by commercial fishers of the United States. The roe is removed intact from the fish and exported to Japan, and the fish are used in various products or disposed of as waste.

Demand for caviar may be greater than the supply of fish can sustain. Shortages of caviar have developed in Russia because demand has resulted in destruction of the fish population used to produce caviar, especially the sturgeon.

BROODFISH

A few aquafarmers produce broodfish to be sold to other farmers for reproduction. This may be a good marketing alternative if the fish are of good quality, improved through selection, or of a selected strain. With most species, the volume of broodfish that could be marketed is often limited. Careful study of the possibilities would be needed before a broodfish farm could be launched. Marketing often depends on having a good reputation and making personal contacts with growers.

Fry

Newly hatched fish are sometimes sold to fingerling growers. Fry are very small and difficult to see. The basis for selling is usually by the thousand. Being so small, they are difficult to count. The number is often established by collecting a small sample in a container (such as a graduated beaker or a small cup) and then counting the number in the sample. This count is then used to calculate the number of fry in a larger volume. When the fry reach an inch in length, they become fingerlings.

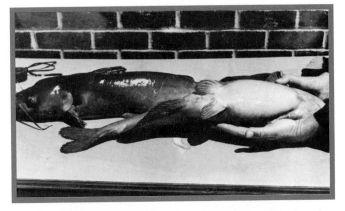

11–26. Broodfish are marketed by a few growers. The female on the right has a large abdomen, which indicates that she is near spawning. (Courtesy, U.S. Fish and Wildlife Service)

11–27. Fry being measured at the time of hauling by using a graduated beaker.

Fingerlings

A fish that ranges from 1 to 8 or 10 inches in length is usually referred to as a *fingerling*. Fingerlings are sold as individual fish, with the price usually being an amount per fish based on the length of the fish. Where food fish are grown, there is a demand for fingerlings. Some farmers produce their own fingerlings; others buy them ready for the grow-out ponds.

A fingerling producer must have a quality product. A producer who markets poor-quality fingerlings will not have much repeat business from growers. A good reputation is essential!

11–28. A tank of tilapia fingerlings.

Contacts with buyers of fingerlings may be on a local neighbor-to-neighbor basis, through advertisements in aquaculture publications, or through direct calls to food fish farms to see if fingerlings are needed. The fingerling producer will likely need to provide hauling to the fish farms; however, some fish growers have their own hauling equipment. Hauling and treating fish to prevent disease during hauling are part of fingerling marketing.

FOOD FISH

The major market for fish is for human consumption. Cultured food fish usually weigh from $^3/_4$ to 2 pounds or so. Uniform sizes are essential in processing plants. Fish weighing more than 4 pounds may be penalized with a lower price. Many farmers have hundreds of acres devoted to food fish production. They carefully make decisions about production based on the market available. (More information is presented elsewhere on marketing food fish.)

11–29. A food-size channel catfish ready for market. (Courtesy, Agricultural Research Service, USDA)

11–30. Ornamental fish are popular with some people.

11–31. Lobsters are being measured prior to harvest. (Courtesy, National Oceanic and Atmospheric Administration)

OTHER FORMS

Depending on the crop, several other forms of live products may be marketed. Some fish are marketed for use as bait by sport fishers. Other live fish, particularly exotic species of fish, are marketed as pet fish.

Bait producers may sell to retail bait shops. This most often involves hauling the baitfish to the shops. The sale price is usually on a per fish basis. This means that the baitfish are counted, usually at the point of delivery. Baitfish must be properly hauled and kept healthy.

A large number of species are used as pet fish. These are typically very small fish sold to pet stores, discount chains, and other outlets. They are most often sold on a per fish basis. The producer usually arranges transportation to the outlets. This may be by truck or air freight, with the fish packed in plastic bags containing water and oxygen. Sometimes, a few pieces of ice are added to the bags or the bags of fish are placed on ice.

PROCESSED AQUACULTURE PRODUCT FORMS

Processing involves a wide range of activities in getting an aquacrop ready for the consumer. Specialized processing plants are needed. The trend is toward aquacrops being processed by larger plants, with less on-farm processing. Processing facilities are usually impractical for individual farms unless there is a large volume. Processing prepares the aquacrop and preserves it for the consumer. The focus here is primarily on processing fish.

WHAT HAPPENS AT A PROCESSING PLANT?

Large-scale processing plants are modern facilities with the latest in technology. Most specialize in one species or product. This is in contrast to the older seafood plants that handled several different products. The modern plants have various types of labor-saving equipment to perform many activities. However, even the most modern plants need considerable labor.

Fish

With fish, the term *dressing* is often used. Dressing is essentially the same as **basic processing**. With fish, basic processing usually includes **deheading** (removing the head), **eviscerating** (removing the internal organs—also known as gutting), and skinning or scaling. **Skinning** is removing the skin from the flesh.

Processing involves additional work to prepare aquacrops for consumption. Several steps in processing fish are listed here.

Receiving. *Receiving* is taking delivery of the aquacrops from the producers at the processing plant. The fish are unloaded into baskets for weighing and moved to a vat or tank for holding. The fish may be held several hours or up to a day.

Producers are paid based on the weight of the fish received. A receiving clerk must keep careful records of the weight received from each farm. Fish are normally kept alive until processing, which usually occurs within a few hours of delivery.

Flavor Testing. *Flavor testing* is conducted to assure that the fish have the desired flavor. Though the fish are checked before being hauled to the plant, they are checked again before being unloaded. A sample of three or more are quickly cooked and tasted and smelled by trained samplers. A small sample of fish can provide some indication of the flavor of all the fish from a pond, raceway, or tank. Fish with off-flavor are rejected and usually hauled back to the farm. Off-flavor fish are not processed. After several days, the off-flavor may be corrected and the fish can be processed.

11–32. Fish sample being prepared for off-flavor testing.

Grading. In most cases, farmers are expected to deliver uniform lots of fish to the processing plant. If not, the plant must grade the fish.

Grading is sorting into batches of uniform size and species for processing. Fish with diseases, with injuries, and of mixed species are usually refused by the receiving clerk. Small numbers of injured or wrong species fish are removed and discarded.

11–33. Stunned fish are ready for deheading.

Stunning. Stunning is the first step in the processing line at a plant. *Stunning* involves using an electric shock to paralyze fish. Large tubs or tanks of fish are shocked at one time.

Stunning allows the fish to stay alive but makes them lifeless. Dead fish deteriorate quickly. Stunning makes it easier for the deheader to handle the fish and provides a better food product.

Deheading. The first step in preparing some fish is to remove the head. A band saw, fish-head saw, or automated saw is used to cut the head off at the proper place. Workers usually dehead fish by pushing them into the saw blade. These workers must learn to perform this step very rapidly. Not all species—trout, for example—are deheaded; therefore, this step may not apply.

11–34. Processing plants use automated equipment to dehead, remove internal organs, and make a fillet (boneless side).

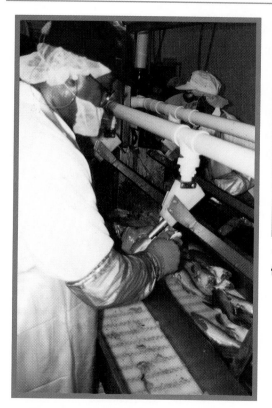

11–35. Some processing plants use vacuum eviscerating systems that make processing quick and efficient.

11–36. A machine that removes the skin without damaging the flesh.

Eviscerating. Most modern processing plants use a vacuum eviscerating process. The process vacuums or "sucks" the **viscera** (internal organs, especially the stomach and intestines) out of the body cavity. Evisceration is through a slit cut in the belly area or through the opening where the head was removed.

Scaling or Skinning. Depending on the species of fish, the scales or skin is removed. Most processing plants use mechanical methods to eliminate hand scaling and skinning. Sometimes, final scaling or skinning is by hand to remove areas skipped by machines. The machines must be precisely adjusted to avoid damaging the flesh and to remove the scales or skin as completely as possible.

11–37. Fish are carefully washed and chilled after evisceration.

Washing. Washing with water is done throughout processing to keep the fish products and equipment clean. Sanitation is important in all areas of a processing plant. Otherwise, microorganisms that spoil food can quickly grow.

Inspecting. After fish have been washed, they are inspected to ensure that all skin or scales and internal organs have been

11–38. Inspection in modern processing plants often involves passing fish products over a light table and viewing through the flesh. Imperfections are easily seen. Defects are cut away or the product is removed and not used for human food.

removed. If parts remain, they are removed. Damage is also noted. If injury or disease evidence is found, the fish are culled and go into the viscera for disposal.

Fabricating. *Fabricating* includes a wide range of activities to prepare the fish into suitable pieces. It is frequently known as cutting. Size, weight, and shape of the pieces are important. Pieces must be of the size desired by the consumer. Cuts must be made in a way that avoids wasting valuable fish product. For example, not cutting close enough to bones may waste high-value product.

Increasingly, fabrication includes preparing products for easy cooking. Some fish products are seasoned, such as catfish fillets with Cajun spice. Precooking may be used to cook fish partially or fully. Smoked salmon and trout are marketed as gourmet, ready-to-eat foods.

Packaging. *Packaging* is placing processed fish or other products in containers. The packaging may involve using large boxes; small, plastic-wrapped packages for supermarket sales; cans or jars; or other containers. The kind of packaging used depends on how the fish products are to be preserved.

Packaging also includes the addition of an appropriate label on the container. The label should comply with legal regulations in describing the product, the amount of product, and the way the product is to be stored.

Laser beams are now being used to count fish or fish portions to ensure that each package has a uniform number of items.

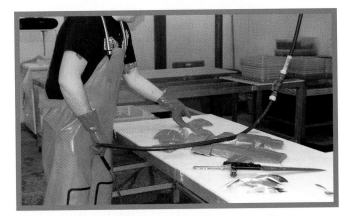

11–39. Hand preparing salmon fillets at an Alaskan market.

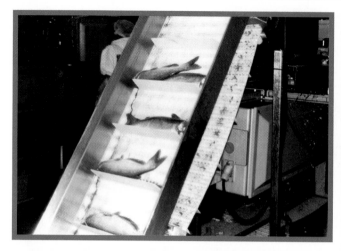

11–40. Conveyors quickly move processed fish for freezing and packaging.

11–41. Processed fish may be packed in 40-pound boxes for shipping.

11–42. Cultured clams are bagged and ready for selling. (Courtesy, National Oceanic and Atmospheric Administration)

Preserving. *Preservation* is the technique of keeping food from spoiling. Fish that have spoiled are not wholesome for human consumption. Spoilage is usually due to the presence of bacteria, yeast, and/or mold. An example is salmonella, dreaded bacteria that cause food poisoning in humans, sometimes resulting in death.

Following procedures that are unfavorable to the growth of bacteria, yeast, and mold will help prevent their growth in fish products. Extreme heat or cold will kill many of these organisms. Inadequate moisture and excess saltiness or acid will also kill or prevent the growth of these organisms.

Preservation methods include refrigerating, freezing, canning, smoking, drying, and pickling fish products. Fresh fish products are preserved by refrigerating or freezing. The quick freezing of individual fillets has gained wide consumer acceptance. These fillets can be kept

11–43. Individual pieces of fish are being quick-frozen.

11–44. Quick-frozen, high-quality fillets.

frozen from several weeks to a few months with little deterioration. Products that have been canned can be stored for quite a while before they must be used.

The kind of packaging used is closely related to the method of preservation. Canned products are packaged in cans or jars. Frozen and refrigerated products are packaged in plastic or paper containers.

Storing. How fish are stored is based on how the fish have been preserved. Frozen fish must be stored at 0°F or below. Canned fish should be stored in relatively cool warehouses and not exposed to heat. Proper storage is essential. Fish will deteriorate rapidly when improperly stored. Improper storage causes spoilage, thus making the fish unfit for human consumption.

Delivering. Transporting fish to the consumer is an essential step in marketing. Trucks must be properly refrigerated to keep the product at the appropriate temperature. Air freight may be used for high-value fresh fish products. Small batches may be shipped in insulated chests containing dry ice or some other means of keeping the products cool.

Merchandising. *Merchandising* is promoting the sale of processed aquacrops. Attractive packages in supermarkets are helpful. Posters and banners may be used by supermarkets and restaurants. Advertisements may be put in newspapers, on radio or television, or on billboards. Clean, modern delivery trucks can certainly help in promoting sales.

11–45. Attractive packaging in a supermarket promotes sales.

Crustaceans and Mollusks

With crustaceans, such as shrimp or crawfish, processing includes deheading, peeling, and *deveining* (removing the vein under the dorsal side of the shell). Some crustaceans are marketed with little processing; others undergo considerable preparation, such as freezing, canning, and precooking. The shells may be discarded, but they are increasingly used in manufacturing other products. Chitin is removed from shells and used in products such as hairspray.

CONNECTION

	Gallon	1/2 Gallon	32 Oz.
Large	64 & under	32 & under	16 & under
Medium	64 to 96	32 to 48	16 to 24
Small	96 to 144	48 to 72	24 to 36
Extra Small	144 & up	72 & up	36 & up
	16 Oz.	10 Oz.	8 Oz
Large	8 & under	5 & under	4 & under
Medium	8 to 12	5 to 10	4 to 6
Small	12 to 18	8 to 11	6 to 9
Extra Small	18 & up	11 & up	9 & up

OYSTER PACKING

Removing the oyster from its shell is the beginning of the packing process. Machinery is not available to shuck oysters. Skilled hand labor is needed to pry open the shell and remove the delicate oyster. Shucking requires fast, efficient movements of the hands and arms. Processing plants pay shuckers based on the number they shuck.

Once shucked, the oysters are graded. Grading involves sorting the oysters by size, as well as removing any imperfections. Four sizes (based on volume and weight) are used in the plant shown here. Once sized, the oysters are placed in jars and boxes for refrigeration and shipment.

11–46. Scallop size is being measured with outside calipers. (Courtesy, National Oceanic and Atmospheric Administration)

With mollusks, such as oysters and clams, **shucking** is used to remove the edible portion from the shells. The product may be refrigerated, frozen, or canned. The shells are discarded or used in restoring production beds. In some cases, the shells are used in manufacturing feed because of high calcium content. Ground oyster shell is often added to the ration of laying hens so they will lay eggs with stronger shells.

PROCESSED FORMS AND CUTS

Fish may be processed into several different forms and cuts. The forms used often depend on the kind of fish and the way the product is intended to be cooked.

Yield

Yield is the amount of high-value product remaining after processing. A processor wants to get as much product from each fish as possible. Yield is also known as dressing percentage. About 40 percent of a fish is head, internal organs, fins, scales or skin, and other parts that may be cut away. This means that only 60 percent of a live fish is left after dressing.

The more desirable, often boneless forms, such as fillets, result in lower yields. These products sell for much higher prices than forms with higher yields.

Forms and Cuts of Fish

Fish can be marketed with little preparation or fabricated into cuts that bring premium prices. How they are fabricated may vary with the species and market demand. Catfish, for

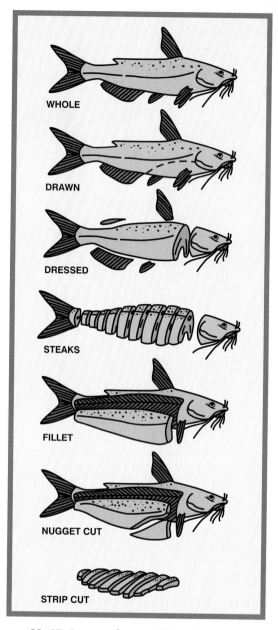

11–47. Common forms of fish fabrication.

example, are often sold as whole fish, round (head on) and gutted, whole dressed, steaks, and nuggets.

Several common forms and cuts of fresh fish are described here.

Whole. Whole fish have not been dressed. The scales or skin, head, and internal organs are still in place. The fish are usually not fed within 24 hours of harvesting. They are washed, chilled (often at 34°F—body cavity temperature), and boxed for shipment. Refrigerated trucks or insulated containers with ice added are used to transport the products.

The restaurant chef or the home preparer does the desired dressing. Tilapia and hybrid striped bass are frequently processed in the whole form.

Drawn. The drawn form involves removing the internal organs and leaving the head. Removing the skin or scales is optional with the drawn form. Drawn trout should have the eyes left to serve as positive identification of the species.

Dressed. The internal organs, head, scales or skin, and fins are removed with the dressed form. This is one of the most popular ways of preparing fish. Sometimes, this form is referred to as *pan-dressed*.

Steak Cut. The steak cut is made by slicing across a dressed fish. The slices are $3/4$ to 1 inch thick. A section of backbone and other bones may be present in steaks. This method of cutting is not as common as it was a few years ago. It is more frequently used with wild fish.

Fillet Cut. The fillet cut, or *fillet*, is made by slicing parallel with the backbone of a fish. Most fish produce fillets without bones. This cut yields a low dressing percentage, but it is a very high-quality cut. Prices for fillet cuts are usually considerably higher than for steaks or dressed fish.

Nugget Cut. This cut may be made from parts of the fish that do not go into the fillet cut. The belly area of the fish is the chief source of the nugget. It is sometimes called the belly flap.

Strip Cut. The strip cut is made from a fillet sliced into narrow strips of fish. This is a high-quality, premium-priced cut of fish. Since strips are made from fillets, they do not have bones.

11–48. Fillets are being carefully inspected for quality. (Courtesy, U. S. Department of Agriculture)

TRANSPORTING AQUACULTURE PRODUCTS

Getting aquacrops from the point of production to the consumer requires hauling. The products are hauled live to the processors, and the processed products are delivered to the market outlets. In all cases, quality products must be delivered. Live products are transported differently from processed products.

TRANSPORTING LIVE AQUACROPS

All forms of live aquacrops may be transported. Having good live ability requires following a few approved practices.

Common live aquaculture forms that may be transported are listed below.

- Fertile eggs may be hauled from a spawning operation to a hatchery. (Eyed eggs are also frequently shipped long distances.)

- Fry may be shipped from a hatchery to a fingerling grower.

- Fingerlings may be hauled to a grow-out farm.

- Food-size aquacrops must be hauled to the processing plant.

- Recreational fish must be hauled from the farm to the fee-lake.

- Pet fish must be transported from the producer to the pet store.

- Broodfish may be shipped from one farm to another.

What to Consider

Aquacrops are hauled in different ways. How an aquacrop is hauled depends on the species, life stage of the species, distance to be hauled, climate, and medication needs. The transportation of any aquacrop should always meet legal requirements.

Stress. When loading or unloading, transfer fish as rapidly as possible. Exposing fish to air for only a few seconds can increase stress. Get all equipment ready before capturing, lifting, and moving fish.

Water quality and temperature should be appropriate for the species. The water should be free of harmful substances. Some species can tolerate rather sudden changes in water temperature. As a rule of thumb, water temperature should vary no more than 5°F. Fish are conditioned by gradually changing the temperature of the water to that used in hauling. Haulers need to realize that species are adapted to certain temperatures. For example, trout

CONNECTION

HAULING FRAGILE FRY

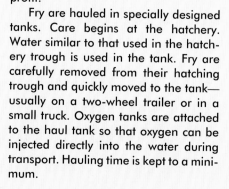

Fry are fragile. Extreme care is needed to haul them. Growers can prevent many losses when moving them to tanks or ponds for growing into fingerlings.

Tiny fry are moved from hatching troughs a few days after the yolk sac is absorbed and they have learned to eat. If the fry are not handled properly, stress can cause big losses. Any losses cut into profit.

Fry are hauled in specially designed tanks. Care begins at the hatchery. Water similar to that used in the hatchery trough is used in the tank. Fry are carefully removed from their hatching trough and quickly moved to the tank—usually on a two-wheel trailer or in a small truck. Oxygen tanks are attached to the haul tank so that oxygen can be injected directly into the water during transport. Hauling time is kept to a minimum.

grow in cool water, while tilapia prefer warm water. Hauling in water not suited to the species increases stress.

Life Stage. Life stage refers to whether eggs, fry, fingerlings, or food fish are being hauled. Equipment for hauling eggs is certainly different from that needed for hauling food fish. Small compartments that keep egg masses intact may be used. Large tanks are okay for food fish. The number and the size of fish determine the size of the container needed.

Crowding. Aquacrops can endure crowded, stressful conditions better for shorter distances and shorter periods than for longer distances and longer periods. Moving fish from one side of a farm to another is different from moving fish several hundred miles. The conditions of hauling must be good for long trips. A general rule is that no more than 3 pounds of fish should be hauled per gallon of water. The DO level in the water must be maintained. Oxygen is often injected from cylinders into the water.

11–49. Small ornamental fish may be transported short distances in small plastic bags with water.

Weather. Weather has some effect on hauling. Hot weather can be particularly harmful. Hauling at night or early or late in the day reduces exposure to heat. Sometimes, tanks have special equipment to provide the best temperature for the aquacrop.

Medications. Medications are sometimes put in the water in haul tanks to prevent bacterial growth and other disease problems. Only approved products should be used. Directions should be carefully read and followed. Disease organisms on fish that are constantly subjected to medicated water are beginning to develop resistance to the medications. Treating fish only during hauling is probably a good way to reduce the development of resistance by the disease organisms.

Equipment Needed

Fish are typically hauled in tanks or plastic bags. Tanks are made of fiberglass, aluminum, or wood. These tanks often have partitions so different sizes and species can be separated. The water in the tanks should be changed every 24 hours if the fish are in them that long.

11–50. Live oysters in crates are being shipped using methods that help retain their quality. (These premium oysters will be used in fine restaurants for raw consumption or cooked.)

11–51. A forklift loading frozen fish into a semitrailer for hauling.

Aerators and/or oxygen systems must be used. Tanks may have refrigeration units attached to keep the water cool.

Plastic bags are used to ship small quantities of fish. Often they are used with exotic pet fish or eggs, fry, or fingerlings. Plastic bags also may be used to handle individual large fish when moving them from one pond to another. The bags have water and pure oxygen added to them. They are frequently placed on ice, or a piece of ice is added to each bag. When used with certain species, the bags should not be directly on ice, and ice should not be put into the bags. Polyethylene bags, 4 millimeters thick, are usually preferred. Fish bags should be handled carefully to prevent bursting.

TRANSPORTING PROCESSED AQUAFOODS

Processing plants are careful to produce only wholesome food products. The quality must be maintained as the products are moved to consumers. As they leave the plants, they are packaged for shipping.

Transportation is selected on the basis of how the products have been processed. Fresh products may be shipped in refrigerated trucks or trucks with ice. There should be no delay in moving the fresh products to consumers. These products will begin to deteriorate rapidly if the temperature rises above 40°F. Frozen products must be shipped in trucks equipped with freezing units that keep the temperature near 0°F. Canned fish products can be hauled in trucks without refrigeration; however, they should not be exposed to excessive heat or be allowed to freeze.

Processing plants often ship boxes of frozen fish on pallets that are convenient to move. Forklifts can unload hundreds of pounds at a time, saving expensive labor.

PROMOTING AQUACROP CONSUMPTION

Promoting consumption involves trying to get consumers to buy certain products. When consumers buy, there is a greater demand for the products. Prices should be good, and growers should find production more profitable.

Various promotional efforts are used. Retailers, wholesalers, processors, marketing associations, and government agencies often get involved in the promotional process. Several methods are described here.

- Advertising—Radio, television, newspapers, magazines, and other media may be used to try to influence people to buy a product. Some advertisements target national audiences; others are intended for the local area served by a restaurant or a supermarket. Advertising costs can run into a significant amount of money.

- Chef training—Associations of aquacrop producers or processors may hold cooking schools for restaurant chefs. The schools train the chefs in ways of preparing a product. This is a good promotional strategy. It helps chefs know how to prepare a tasty aquafood so consumers will repeat as buyers. It also encourages chefs to try preparing a new food or to try new ways of preparing a familiar food.

- Supermarket tasting—Local supermarkets may provide samples of products for customers to taste in their stores. The arrangements are made by distributors or processors to promote products among people who are not now consuming them. Sometimes, new methods of preparation are introduced with supermarket tasting.

11–52. Nutrients in fish promote good health and weight control. (Courtesy, U.S. Department of Agriculture)

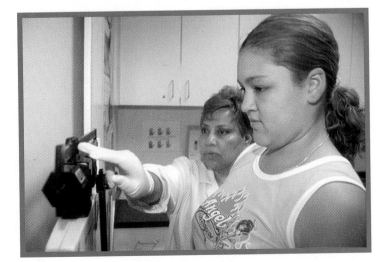

11–53. Attractive presentations of fish promote consumption. This shows cultured moi being used as a traditional dish in Hawaii. (Courtesy, National Oceanic and Atmospheric Administration)

- Educational literature—Pamphlets or booklets of recipes can be helpful in encouraging consumption. Cooks may not know how to prepare a product in certain ways. Thus, literature that provides preparation information, as well as nutrition information, may be beneficial. The food sections of newspapers often contain new recipes and new product information.

- Meal functions—Aquacrop marketers will sometimes sponsor meals for various groups to introduce them to a product. In addition, a variety of recipes can be used to let the group members know about the versatility of the product.

11–54. Fish nuggets have been prepared for a mealtime gathering.

REVIEWING

MAIN IDEAS

Aquacrops should be produced only if there is a market for them. Marketing is the link between the producer and the consumer. The goal is to try to meet consumer demand. Without considering the consumer, products may be produced for which no market exists.

Many steps are involved in getting aquacrops to the consumer. These include planning what to produce, producing it, and then getting it to the consumer in a quality, wholesome form.

Various channels are available to the producer. These may involve going from the farm through the processor to the consumer. Sometimes, a farmer markets directly from the farm to the consumer, a roadside store, or a restaurant. B-to-B marketing is opening wide new marketing opportunities via the Internet. Recreational markets are good outlets for a few farmers. Regardless, the channel used must be appropriate to the size of the farm and the amount the market will handle, also known as economy of scale.

The profitable aquafarmer develops and carries out a marketing plan. A good plan allows the farmer to study the situation, set marketing objectives, develop a strategy for marketing, and evaluate how well the objectives were achieved.

Aquacrops are marketed in several forms. These forms may be based on life cycle, such as eggs, fry, fingerlings, or food fish. Transportation is required to get these to the customer in wholesome condition.

Processing is used to get an aquacrop ready for the consumer. The extent of processing depends on the forms and cuts desired by the consumer. More and more often, the consumer wants easy-to-use forms. Consumer preferences are definitely important. Promotion is used to increase consumption of the aquacrop.

QUESTIONS

Answer the following questions, using complete sentences and correct spelling.

1. Why should the producer consider marketing in deciding which aquacrop to produce?
2. What are the marketing functions? Briefly describe each.
3. What marketing channels are available for aquaculture products? Distinguish between them.
4. What is economy of scale? How is it important in the selection of a market?
5. What questions should the aquafarmer answer in selecting a market?
6. Why is marketing planning important? What is a marketing plan?
7. What is meant by product form? Briefly describe several product forms.
8. What is processing? Describe what happens at a processing plant. What processed forms and cuts are used with fish?
9. How are aquacrops transported? What factors should be considered in the hauling of live fish products? Processed fish products?
10. What is promotion? How is it important?

EVALUATING

Match the term with the correct definition. Write the letter by the term on the line provided.

a. caviar
b. eviscerating
c. yield
d. deveining

e. shucking
f. marketing plan
g. flavor testing
h. marketing

i. commercial producer
j. selling

_____1. All the steps to get a desired product to a consumer

_____2. Changing ownership

_____3. Producer of aquacrops for sale to specific markets

_____4. Removing the internal organs of a fish

_____5. Written statement that guides the marketing process

_____6. Fish eggs used for human consumption

_____7. Determining that a sample of fish is not off-flavor

_____8. Removing a large vein under the dorsal side of a crustacean

_____9. Amount of high-value product remaining after processing

_____10. Removing the edible portion from a shell

EXPLORING

1. Study the procedures followed in marketing aquaculture crops in your local area. The procedures could relate to ornamental species in a local retail store, cultured food species on a large aquafarm, or other aquacrops. Prepare a written report on your findings.

2. Survey your classmates to determine their preferences for fish, crustaceans, and mollusks. Determine what could be done in processing to increase the amount they eat. Devise a plan to increase consumption. Prepare a written report on your findings. Give an oral report in class.

3. Tour a local supermarket and observe the kinds of aquaculture products, the ways they are preserved and packaged, and the pricing based on yield and other factors. If possible, interview the manager of the seafood area about the merchandising of fish and other products in the store. Prepare a written report on your observations.

4. Explore a B-to-B aquaculture marketing Web site, such as **www.fishmonger.com**. Prepare a report on your findings. Indicate your assessment of the Web site and how you feel it would be useful to aquaculture producers.

PART FIVE

Production
in Aquaculture

CHAPTER 12

Warm-Freshwater Aquacrops

This chapter covers the basic cultural practices with several species of freshwater aquacrops that require warm water. It has the following objectives:

1 Describe general environmental requirements for warm-freshwater species

2 Discuss the production of catfish

3 Discuss the production of crawfish

4 Discuss the production of prawns

5 Discuss the production of tilapia

6 Discuss the production of striped bass

7 Discuss the production of other warmwater finfish species, including sunfish and paddlefish

TERMS

burrow
C × B hybrid
chelas
detritus
dormancy
forage
fry
geothermal water

hapa
hollow tail
manured pond
monosex culture
mouthbrooder
neutral buoyancy
photoperiod
polytrophic

rice pond
self-perpetuating
sex reversal
softshell crawfish
spawning container
substrate spawning
warm-freshwater aquacrop
wooded pond

12–1. Warmwater fish are often raised in ponds, as shown in this broodfish harvesting scene. (Courtesy, Texas Department of Agriculture)

RAPID EXPANSION of aquaculture in the United States has been with species that grow in warm fresh water. Very few were cultured until the late 1900s. Today, annual production of selected species has zoomed to many millions of dollars.

The warm-freshwater species are used for food, bait, recreation, and other purposes, such as aquatic vegetation control. Food fish account for most of the production. Several species are involved, and the potential of other species is being studied.

Exciting new possibilities in aquaculture are unfolding each day! Success depends on knowing the basics of freshwater aquaculture plus the unique cultural requirements of the warmwater species.

GENERAL REQUIREMENTS FOR WARM-FRESHWATER SPECIES

12–2. An abundant harvest is a reflection of how well the requirements of a species have been met. (Courtesy, U.S. Department of Agriculture)

A *warm-freshwater aquacrop* is a species that requires warm fresh water with a temperature range of 70° to 90°F (21° to 32°C). Water temperature may reach this level on a seasonal basis in the summer with pond culture. The rate of growth is slower in the cool winter months. Species grown in tanks or other facilities where the water is warm year-round are not affected by seasonal temperature variations. Some warmwater species cannot survive in cold water. (Warm-freshwater ornamental and bait species are covered in Chapter 15.)

Catfish are, by far, the most important species in acreage, investment in production, and value of harvested product. Of the catfish, the channel catfish is the predominant species. Some blue, white, and flathead catfish are also grown. Improved strains of catfish are now being produced. Crawfish, tilapia, carp, buffalofish, minnows, bass, and sunfish are other species grown in warm fresh water.

Table 12–1. Selected Species Produced in Warm Fresh Water

Common Name	Scientific Name	Major Use
Bass,		
largemouth*	*Micropterus salmoides*	Sport
smallmouth	*Micropterus dolomieui*	Sport
striped hybrid	*Morone chrysops*♂ × *M. saxatilis*♀	Food, sport
white	*Morone chrysops*	Food, sport
Carp,		
bighead	*Aristichthys nobilis*	Some food
common	*Cyprinus carpio*	Food
grass	*Ctenopharyngodon idella*	Aquatic weed control

(Continued)

Table 12-1 (Continued)

Common Name	Scientific Name	Major Use
Catfish,		
blue	*Ictalurus furcatus*	Food
channel	*Ictalurus punctatus*	Food, sport
flathead	*Pylodictis olivaris*	Food, sport
white	*Ictalurus catus*	Food, sport
C × B hybrid	*Ictalurus punctatus* × *I. furcatus*	Food
Crawfish,		
red swamp	*Procambarus clarkii*	Food
rusty	*Orconectes rusticus*	Food
white river	*Procambarus acutus acutus***	Food
Paddlefish	*Polydon spathula*	Sport, roe
Prawn, freshwater	*Macrobrachium rosenbergii*	Food
Sunfish,		
bluegill	*Lepomis macrochirus*	Sport
green	*Lepomis cyanellus*	Sport/bait***
redear	*Lepomis microlophus*	Sport
warmouth	*Lepomis gulosus*	Sport
Tilapia,		
blue	*Tilapia aurea****	Food
Congo	*Tilapia randalli*	Food
Java	*Tilapia mossambica****	Food
Nile	*Tilapia nilotica****	Food
red hybrid***** (Cherry Snapper®, Pennyfish™)	*Tilapia mossambica*♂ × *T. hornorum*♀	Food
Royal Chocolate Hybrid™	*Tilapia nolitica*♂ × *T. hornorum*♀	Food
White Chocolate Hybrid™	*Tilapia nilotica*♂ × *T. aurea*♀	Food
Zanzibar	*Tilapia hornorum****	Food
Zill's	*Tilapia zillii*	Food

*Also grow in cold water.
**Sometimes classified as *Procambarus zonangulus* or *Procambarus blandingi*.
***Use as a baitfish prohibited in states where it is classified as a game fish.
****Mouthbrooders.
*****Salt-tolerant species that can be reared in coastal areas.
® indicates registered trademark of Mike Sipe.
™ indicates trademarks of Mike Sipe.

Animal aquacrops have similar general requirements for culture. Specific requirements, however, vary from one species to another. Knowing the basic cultural requirements is essential. Several fundamental requirements for aquaculture are described here.

SPECIES SELECTION

The species must be suited to the environment in which it is to be grown. Most species have preferences within the broad warm-freshwater group. Aquacrops may be grown in artificial environments that are carefully controlled even if the natural climate is not ideal.

The temperament of a species has some influence on suitability. Species that attack each other may not be adapted to confinement systems. Nearly all species have some tendency to destroy their eggs or young.

Table 12–2. Principles of Warm-Freshwater Species Selection

1. Select only a species adapted to the production system to be used.
2. Select only a species adapted to the warm fresh water available.
3. Feed an aquacrop on the basis of its nutritional needs.
4. Ensure good health by following management practices appropriate to the species being produced.
5. Maintain quality water by using production practices that minimize the possibilities of problems and make water more suitable for the species being produced.
6. Select a species for which there is a market.

AVAILABLE WATER

Since water is the environment in which aquacrops grow, having the "right" water is a must. Natural supplies of water often reflect the climate of the area. For example, ponds reflect the temperature of the atmosphere. Warmer climates will have bodies of water with

12–3. A tank-raised tilapia is being weighed to assess how well its needs have been met for growth.

warmer temperatures, and cooler climates will have bodies of water with cooler temperatures.

Available water can make production of a species possible in a climate that is too cold or too hot for the species to grow naturally. Some sites have **geothermal water**. This water is naturally heated in the earth. Geothermal water in cooler climates can be used to grow fish that would not normally live in those climates. Besides natural water, a few sites have industries that produce heated effluent suitable for aquacrops.

NUTRITIONAL REQUIREMENTS

Aquacrops must have the right nutrition to grow efficiently. Streams and lakes have some natural food supply used by wild fish and other life. In aquaculture, the levels of stocking in ponds and other growing facilities are greater than the ability of the water to provide natural foods to the aquacrops. Thus, commercial feed must be provided.

Not just any feed will do. Aquacrops must have the appropriate nutrients for their growth. Research has shown the dietary requirements of some aquacrops.

GOOD HEALTH

Good health is the absence of disease. Diseases reduce the rate of growth of aquacrops. In some cases, a crop may be killed by a disease. Aquacrops must be healthy to grow efficiently. Each species has different health needs.

Promoting good health is a part of good management. Species vary in their reaction to stress and to changes in the environment. The growth environment must be managed so unfavorable conditions do not develop.

WATER MANAGEMENT

Water should be managed to maximize its suitability for aquaculture. Dissolved oxygen should be maintained at the appropriate level for a species. Ammonia and nitrites may need to be monitored and regulated. Water pH and minerals may need to be controlled. Other water factors may need to be considered, depending on the species.

12–4. Good water management includes regularly checking the DO and taking steps to prevent problems from occurring.

Water management is more critical with high-intensity aquaculture. Fish stocked at high rates use more oxygen and excrete more wastes than those stocked at lower densities. The water management needs of an aquacrop may also be affected by weather and by other organisms growing in the water.

AVAILABLE MARKET

The demand for a species has much to do with making a profit. The prospective grower should answer this question: "Will someone buy what I produce at a price high enough for me to make a profit?" If a species grows well but is not wanted by consumers, it is not an appropriate aquacrop. Success in freshwater aquaculture depends on the selection of an appropriate species from a marketing perspective.

Aquacrops may be marketed in a variety of ways. Some are sold directly to consumers; others are sold to processors. Since processing plants want a year-round, uniform supply of fish, contracts between producers and processors may be used. The contracts will specify various conditions, including the prices that will be paid to the farmers.

CATFISH

Catfish production leads all freshwater aquacrop production in the United States. The value of the crop has increased annually for more than two decades. The culture of catfish began to emerge in the late 1950s. In 1960, there were only about 600 acres in catfish farming. By the late 1990s, the figure had reached 165,000 acres. In the early 2000s, 175,000 pond acres were used for catfish production.

12–5. Channel catfish. (Courtesy, Agricultural Research Service, USDA)

Nearly 450 million pounds (processed weight) are annually produced. An entire industry, supported by fish equipment manufacturers, feed mills, processing plants, product promotion, and other areas, has emerged. The leading states in catfish farming are Mississippi, Arkansas, Alabama, Louisiana, California, Missouri, Texas, and Oklahoma. Small amounts are produced in a number of states.

SPECIES GROWN AND IDENTIFICATION

Nearly 50 species of catfish are found in the United States. Of these, only a few have been farmed. The predominant species in aquafarming is the channel catfish (*Ictalurus punctatus*). Other cultured species are the blue catfish (*Ictalurus furcatus*) and the white catfish (*Ictalurus catus*). Catfish species known as "bullheads" are generally not good species to grow.

Genetically improved and hybrid catfish are increasingly being used. The **C × B hybrid** is a catfish produced by crossing the female channel catfish with the male blue catfish. The C × B exhibits superior characteristics in several ways: faster growth, better feed conversion, greater tolerance of low DO, increased resistance to disease, higher dressing percentage, and more uniform size and shape. The C × B has fewer spots than the channel catfish and has a straight-edge anal fin, which is characteristic of the blue catfish. Most first generation (F_1) C × B catfish spawn and produce a second generation (F_2). The F_2 C × B hybrids do not perform as well as the F_1s. Aquaculture scientists at Auburn University have taken the lead in developing the C × B hybrid.

Another genetically improved catfish is the USDA 103 (also known as the NWAC 103). This catfish is said to be a high-performing fish in commercial farm situations. The first USDA 103 catfish were released to selected producers in February 2001 to encourage several years of trial. Results indicate a growth rate 10 to 20 percent faster than that of unimproved catfish. This means that the crop is ready for marketing sooner. The fish does consume more feed, but this is offset by the increased growth rate. The USDA 103 was developed by scientists at the National Warmwater Aquaculture Center in Stoneville, Mississippi. (Refer to Chapter 3 for more information.)

Species Identification

One of the distinguishing features of catfish is the presence of barbels about the mouth. These are sometimes incorrectly referred to as "whiskers." (They are actually feelers that help the fish in its natural habitat maintain its position in the water and find food.) Distinguishing between species of catfish is not always easy. Fin shape and color are important in making distinctions.

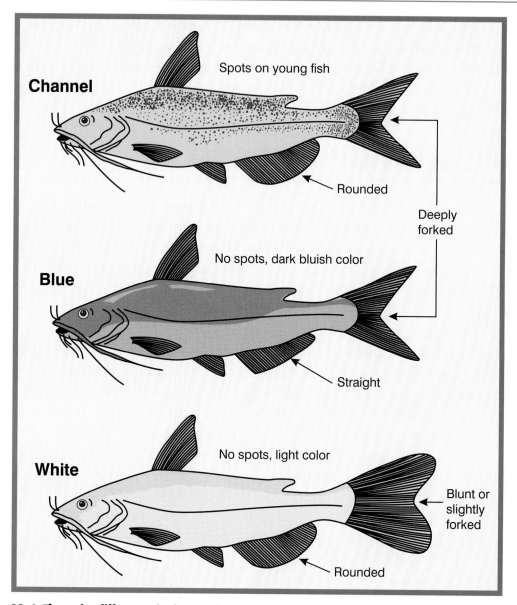

12–6. The major differences in three catfish species are shown here based on the shape of the anal and tail (caudal) fins.

The channel catfish has a deeply forked tail and a rounded anal fin. The dorsal part of the body has a bluish color that changes to silver on the sides and white on the belly (ventral side). Younger channel catfish have spots, but these are usually gone by the time the fish weigh 5 pounds (2.2 kg).

Similar to the channel catfish, the blue catfish has a forked tail. Different from the channel catfish, the blue catfish has a straight anal fin. The blue catfish also has a darker, bluish color than the channel catfish.

The white catfish is easily distinguished from the channel catfish and the blue catfish because its tail is not deeply forked. The white catfish also has a lighter color than the channel catfish and the blue catfish.

Size

Adult channel catfish range from 11 to 30 inches (28 to 76 cm) long and weigh up to 15 pounds (6.8 kg). On rare occasions, channel catfish may reach weights of 50 to 60 pounds (22.7 to 27.2 kg).

The desired food fish size is 1 to 3 pounds (0.5 to 1.5 kg). This size can be obtained in less than two years under good growing conditions. In the first year, the eggs are hatched and grown to fingerlings. In the second year, the fingerlings are stocked in growing ponds, where they should readily reach market size.

The size of the fish is important in determining how the fish will be processed and the forms and cuts that will be made. Small fish of $^3/_4$ to 1 pound (0.34 to 0.45 kg) may be left whole. Slightly larger catfish are processed into higher-priced fillet and nugget products. Other sizes may be cut into steaks.

Catfish yield (dress out) at 55 to 60 percent of their live weight. This means that the skin, head, and viscera are 40 to 45 percent of the weight of a live fish. A fish weighing 1 pound (0.45 kg) would yield a dressed fish weighing slightly more than $^1/_2$ pound (0.23 kg).

12–7. Cages being used to raise catfish.

ENVIRONMENT REQUIRED

Channel catfish grow best in water that is 75° to 85°F (24° to 29.4°C). When the water temperature is below 60°F (15.6°C) or above 95°F (35°C), channel catfish virtually stop eating. And when they do not eat, they do not grow! Sites where there is a minimum of time when the water temperature is below 70°F (21°C) are preferred for catfish culture. Short winters and long summers are most desirable.

Channel catfish will grow in ponds, streams, raceways, and other water facilities. The water should be free of pollution and have adequate dissolved oxygen (DO). Catfish will survive for a short time in water as low as 1 ppm DO, but the level must be at least 4 ppm for them to grow efficiently. The most desirable pH range for the water is 6.3 to 7.5; however, 5.0 to 8.5 may be used under certain conditions.

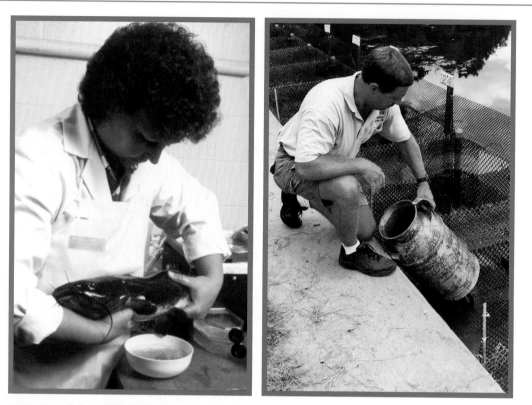

12–8. Female broodfish being expressed to provide eggs for artificial fertilization. (Courtesy, Agricultural Research Service, USDA)

12–9. Old milk cans are often placed in spawning pens as spawning containers.

EEDSTOCK

Broodstock were initially obtained from rivers and lakes as wild fish. The quality of the broodfish has been improved as catfish have been domesticated. Through selection, only the best broodstock have been used to produce eggs. Farmers may maintain their own broodfish and produce seedstock or buy their fingerlings from fingerling producers.

Natural Spawning

Catfish naturally spawn in the spring, when the weather begins to warm. In the wild, they seek out hollow logs, stumps, or other secluded places in the water. The female lays the eggs. The male swims over them, depositing sperm on the egg mass, which is also known as a spawn. One egg mass may contain thousands of eggs. A rule of thumb is that a female catfish will produce 2,000 eggs per pound of body weight.

In nature, the male catfish tends the spawn until it hatches. He swims immediately above the egg mass, fanning the water with his fins and occasionally bumping the mass.

Farm Spawning

On catfish farms, the broodfish may be kept in broodfish ponds until spawning season. They may be moved in pairs (one male and one female in each pair) to a pen with a *spawning container* (artificial nest). Common spawning containers are milk cans, ammunition cans, and similar containers. Spawning containers are regularly checked during the spawning season.

12–10. An egg mass (spawn) is being removed from a spawning container and collected in a tub. (Courtesy, *Progressive Farmer Magazine*)

12–11. Two large catfish spawns are shown here. (Courtesy, *Progressive Farmer Magazine*)

Hatching

The eggs may be allowed to hatch naturally in the pond or may be moved to an artificial hatchery. A hatchery creates and improves on the conditions of natural spawning. The water is kept moving—not flowing—and at a temperature of 75° to 85°F (24° to 29.4°C). Hatching occurs in six to ten days, depending on the water temperature. The warmer the water, the shorter the hatching time.

12–12. Two kinds of artificial hatching are shown here: paddle type and air stone. Hatching troughs are similar with both. The difference is how the water is moved. At the top, paddles on a rotating shaft that extends the length of the trough move the water. At the bottom, air is bubbled through air stones into the water to cause movement and ensure plenty of dissolved oxygen. Both systems work well if properly managed.

Caring for Fry

A newly hatched fish with egg sac attached is known as a *fry*. This sac provides nutrition for a few days. When it is gone, the fry is ready to start eating. Feed must be provided. A fine meal feed of 49 percent protein is fed every two to four hours around the clock for the first two or three weeks. This is followed by 38 percent protein feed the next three to six weeks. Afterward, a 35 percent protein feed is used.

Fry may be reared in ponds or in troughs. Some producers prefer trough rearing because of better control over the conditions in which the fragile fry live.

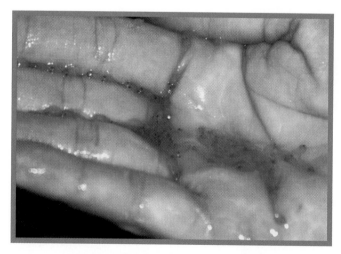

12–13. Catfish fry with egg sac attached.

Over a few summer months, the fry grow into fingerlings. Nearly a year after the fry hatch, the fingerlings are stocked in growing ponds.

CULTURE AND STOCKING

Most channel catfish are produced in ponds filled with fresh well water. They may also be grown in raceways, tanks, and cages.

Fingerling catfish 5 to 8 inches (12 to 20 cm) long are stocked in ponds at a rate depending on the level of management. It is possible to stock 5,000 or more fingerlings per acre if careful management is to be followed. Lower stocking rates of 1,000 to 2,000 should be used if the water is not to be aerated.

The natural food supply typically available in catfish ponds will support only a few hundred fish per acre. Catfish do not usually have other fish stocked in the same pond with them.

Water management is critical with intensive catfish farming. The oxygen level must be maintained. Round-the-clock monitoring of catfish ponds is essential in the warmer months of the year. This involves testing for dissolved oxygen. Aerators that splash the water, throw water into the air, or inject oxygen into the water may be used to add dissolved oxygen. When the oxygen gets too low, the fish "gulp" at the surface in an attempt to get oxygen from the air. Catfish will die if the oxygen problem is not solved quickly.

12–14. Catfish fry are fed a finely ground feed.

12–15. Channel catfish fingerlings that are ready to be moved to a growing pond.

FEEDING

Catfish need a ration that meets their nutritional needs. The natural food supply in pond water is far below what a crop of catfish needs.

Catfish are typically fed a ration that is 28 to 32 percent protein. Younger fish should receive the 32 percent feed the first two months after stocking. The second two months they should receive a 30 percent protein feed. After four months, older fish may be fed a 28 percent protein feed. The major ingredients in the feed are soybean meal, corn, and fish meal. Some of the protein in any ration should be provided by fish meal, as catfish grow better with some protein from an animal source.

Feed for catfish is commercially available from a number of suppliers. It may be manufactured as pellets that float, sink, or have neutral buoyancy. (**Neutral buoyancy** means that the pellets neither float nor sink. They remain in a stable position in the water for a while.) Floating pellets are preferred because the fish must come to the surface of the water to feed, allowing observation of their behavior. Catfish that do not feed in warm weather are likely to have some problem, such as oxygen deficiency or a disease.

12–16. A truck-mounted feeder that blows feed out into a pond.

12–17. Pellets for feeding catfish.

Large catfish farms use truck-mounted power blowers to blow carefully measured amounts of feed out into the ponds. Smaller farms with only a few acres may throw the feed into the water by hand. A few farms use automatic self-feeders.

Catfish should be fed once or twice daily and at the same time each day. Many producers feed only once per day, but research has shown that two feedings increase the rate of growth. The total weight of the feed on a daily basis is the same with two feedings as it would be with one feeding.

The amount to feed is usually based on the estimated weight of the fish, water temperature, and other factors. Fish should be fed only the amount they will consume in a few minutes and no more. The amount as a percentage of body weight decreases as the fish grow. Fingerlings 3 inches long will consume feed at the rate of 10 percent of body weight. In warm weather, growing catfish under 1 pound (0.45 kg) are fed at the rate of 3 percent of body weight. If the fish weigh more than 1 pound (0.45 kg) each, the feeding rate is dropped to 2 percent of body weight. For example, if a pond is stocked with 4,000 fish that average $1/_2$ pound (0.23 kg) in weight, the pond contains approximately 2,000 pounds (907 kg) of catfish. The total amount to feed a day is 3 percent of 2,000, or 60 pounds (27 kg). Overfeeding should be avoided. Uneaten feed contributes to water problems.

Table 12–3. General Feeding Guidelines for Catfish

- Use feed with 28 to 32% protein.
- Use feed that is nutritionally complete.
- Use pellets that are 5/32 to 3/16 inch in diameter.
- Use floating feed when the water temperature is above 65°F.
- Use feed with a mix of sinking and floating feed when the water temperature is 60° to 65°F.
- Use sinking feed when water temperature is below 60°F.
- Distribute feed over the water as evenly as possible.
- Use the amount of feed that the fish will eat in 20 to 25 minutes.
- Use 3% of body weight of fish as guideline for amount to feed when water temperature is 70° to 86°F; reduce percentage fed when water temperature is below 70°F or above 85°F.

Source: Developed from information by William A. Wurts, of Kentucky State University, in *The Aquaculture News,* September 2001.

DISEASES

Several different diseases may attack catfish. Using plenty of good water can help eliminate many disease problems. Use only healthy fish to stock ponds. Any new fish should be held in isolation for a few days to see if any diseases develop. Catfish may be stressed when handled, such as when harvested and hauled. Following good practices can reduce the possibility of stress and the diseases that may result.

The most common catfish diseases are those caused by bacteria, viruses, fungi, algae, parasites, nutritional deficiencies, and environmental problems. Only treatments approved for use with food fish should be used. Food fish that have been improperly treated may be ruled unfit for human consumption.

HARVESTING

Catfish are typically harvested from ponds by seining when they weigh 1 to 3 pounds (0.45 to 1.5 kg). Whole ponds are seined without removing the water. Power seine haulers attached to farm tractors are typically used. Once the fish have been concentrated into a small area of a pond, they are moved into a holding net and later lifted with a brailing bag to a haul truck.

12–19. Catfish being harvested from a live car for loading on a haul truck. (Courtesy, The Catfish Institute)

12–18. A seine is being pulled in a pond with a power seine hauler and help from a small boat.

Before catfish in a pond are harvested, samples should be checked for off-flavor. This merely involves quickly cooking a few samples and then tasting them. The trained taster can determine if the fish have the right flavor. Fish with off-flavor should never be harvested. Processors will not accept them.

MARKETING CATFISH

A vast industry has developed to support catfish marketing. Organizations have been formed to promote consumption, such as The Catfish Institute.

Catfish farming has expanded rapidly because of the quality of the product that has been produced. Catfish are good sources of protein in the human diet. Recent research shows that cultured fish promote good health better than wild catch. The flesh has an excellent mild flavor and can be prepared in a variety of delicious dishes. Catfish may be sold to the consumer whole, cut into steaks or fillets, or fabricated into other easy-to-cook forms.

Most large-scale growers have contracts with processing plants to ensure a market for their crops. The contracts often specify price, quality of crop, time of harvest, and other details.

Marketing the catfish crop may occur at a number of stages of production:

1. Broodfish may be sold to hatchery operators.

2. Hatcheries produce eggs and often fry and fingerlings.

3. Fingerling producers obtain eggs or fry from hatcheries and grow them to the size needed for stocking in growing ponds.

4. Food fish growers stock ponds with fingerlings and grow them to food size for sale to processors, fee-lake operators, and live haulers. (This is by far the major area of catfish production.)

5. Recreational fee-lake operators obtain fish from growers who may be producing food fish or fish especially for the fee-lake market.

6. Live haulers buy fish from growers for resale to fee-lakes, fish markets, and others.

7. One or more of the above marketing stages/outlets may be combined to serve market and producer needs.

CRAWFISH

Crawfish (also called crayfish) are the most widely raised freshwater crustaceans in the United States. Limited production is scattered throughout the country. Louisiana is the leading state. California, Texas, Oregon, Washington, Wisconsin, South Carolina, and Mississippi also have some crawfish production. The red swamp crawfish is widely raised in the South. Other species include white river crawfish and rusty crawfish.

12–20. Red swamp crawfish viewed from side and underneath (ventral side).

Crawfish are harvested from the wild as well as cultured. Production in the United States is approximately 110,000 metric tons annually, with about 55 percent from Louisiana.

Some 300 species of crawfish are found in the United States. Each has its own local environmental adaptations. The crawfish industry is not as developed as the catfish industry.

SPECIES GROWN

The predominant cultured species are the red swamp crawfish (*Procambarus clar ii*) and the white river crawfish (*Procambarus acutus acutus*). The red species may also be referred to as the red crawfish or the crawdad. This species is native to the Mississippi and Ohio River valleys. It has been introduced into several western states, including California and Nevada. The red swamp crawfish thrives in the climate of south Louisiana and is the major cultured species.

The white river crawfish is also known as the white crawfish. It is found in the Mississippi River Valley, in the Great Lakes area, along the Atlantic Coast, and into Florida. It has a much lighter color than the red swamp crawfish. It is better adapted to cooler climates. In nature, the white river crawfish is more likely to be found in rivers than the red swamp crawfish.

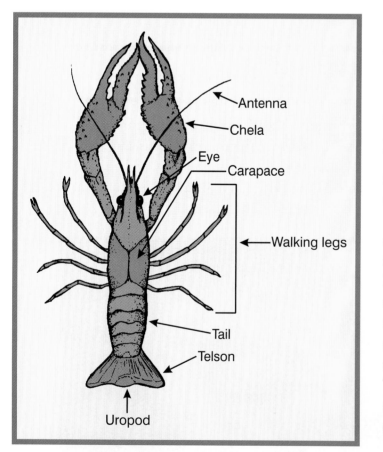

12–21. Detail of crawfish body structure and chelas.

IDENTIFICATION AND SIZE

The crawfish is a crustacean similar to shrimp. Its body is covered with an exoskeleton. This hard structure, or shell, protects the soft tissues of the body from injury. Species differentiation is not as important with crawfish culture as it is with catfish.

The crawfish has five legs on each side of the body, with the two front legs forming pincers (sharp claws, also known as **chelas**). If the crawfish loses a leg, or pincer, it grows back. There are two long antennae, or feelers, and two short ones on the head. Underneath the abdomen, the crawfish has swimmerets. The color may vary, depending on the species, but the red swamp crawfish is a deep red.

Molting

A crawfish molts as it grows. Molting is losing and regrowing the exoskeleton (shell). The shell of a crawfish does not expand as the crawfish grows and must be shed to allow the body to get larger.

A very young crawfish molts every 5 to 10 days, while an older crawfish that is still growing may molt every 20 to 30 days. The new shell hardens about 12 hours after the old shell is shed. A crawfish molts about 11 times before it reaches maturity.

12–22. A crawfish in a softshell phase of development. (Courtesy, U.S. Department of Agriculture)

Size

Crawfish seldom reach a length greater than 6 inches (15 cm). The desired weight for harvesting is about 10 crawfish per pound (0.45 kg).

ENVIRONMENT REQUIRED

Crawfish are naturally found in shallow, weedy swamps and ponds. They will grow in a wide range of soil types, but the soil must retain subsurface water that is available to crawfish when the area is drained. They typically prefer warm water with a temperature of 65° to 85°F (18.3° to 29.4°C), but they will grow in a wide range of water temperatures.

Crawfish will go dormant in water below 45°F (7.2°C). **Dormancy** is a state of rest or inactivity when crawfish do not eat or grow. Above 88°F (31.1°C), they burrow into the earth. White river crawfish tend to grow better at cooler temperatures.

Most pesticides are highly toxic to crawfish. Fields that have had pesticides applied to crops grown on them are not suitable for crawfish until all residues are gone.

Good-quality water is needed. The presence of some salt will not pose a problem. Water with too much iron or sodium bicarbonate is not suitable. Water in the pH range of 5.8 to 8.2 has been found satisfactory.

12–23. Crawfish ponds. (Courtesy, U.S. Department of Agriculture)

SEEDSTOCK

Adult crawfish may be obtained from the wild or from crawfish growers. Artificial hatching of crawfish is usually not needed. Once in a pond, the crawfish are *self-perpetuating*. This means that they reproduce in sufficient numbers to provide an adequate population of crawfish.

12–24. A crawfish burrow chimney.

Burrowing

Mature female crawfish form burrows for hiding and reproduction. A *burrow* is a tunnel system made in the earth that connects to the surface with a hole that may be capped with a mound, or "chimney." Crawfish make the burrows near the edge of the water. Burrowing is a natural part of their life cycle. They typically come out of their burrows at nightfall and daybreak. Their burrowing may weaken pond dams or other earthen structures.

Mating

Crawfish mate in the late spring. During mating, the male deposits sperm in a receptacle on the female. In the summer, the female lays the eggs in the burrow. As the eggs are released by the female, sperm are released from the receptacle to fertilize the eggs.

Hatching

The eggs are attached to the underside of the tail of the female crawfish until hatching. Red swamp crawfish hatch in 14 to 21 days, while white river crawfish hatch in 17 to 29 days. Each female may hatch 400 young, with 700 being the maximum. Red swamp crawfish may hatch a few more than white river crawfish. Survival of the young is much better if open water is available.

CULTURE

Water management is the most critical part of crawfish culture. The level of the water in a growing facility has much to do with the stages the crawfish go through.

Four kinds of grow-out facilities may be used, as follows:

1. Permanent ponds—These are specially constructed ponds for crawfish production, with a maximum water level of 24 inches (62 cm). Rice may be planted in them for forage. These ponds have no trees or bushes in them and may grow 1,200 pounds (544 kg) of crawfish per acre annually.

2. Rice ponds—A **rice pond** is a facility that is rotated for rice production. The crawfish eat the rice forage remaining after the rice crop has been harvested. Rice ponds produce about the same number of pounds as permanent ponds and can sometimes produce more.

3. Wooded ponds—A **wooded pond** is a natural pond found in a low area where trees and other vegetation are present. Trees and bushes in a wooded pond may interfere with management practices. Wooded ponds produce 400 to 600 pounds (181 to 272 kg) of crawfish per acre annually.

4. Marsh ponds—These are created by damming low areas of land that is often of little value for other uses. An acre of marsh pond may produce 300 to 500 pounds (136 to 227 kg) of crawfish a year.

Crawfish are often grown in permanent ponds or in rice ponds that can hold water 18 to 24 inches (46 to 61 cm) deep. A good size for a pond is 20 acres. The levee around the pond should be wide enough for tractors or small trucks to travel for easy access to the pond. Since most crawfish are harvested with traps, a smooth bottom in the pond is not essential. Clay soils hold water and make better ponds than sandy soils.

When construction of a pond is completed, the bottom should be disked or rotary tilled before the pond is filled with water. Water from sources that might contain trash fish should

12–25. Construction of a permanent crawfish pond requires a levee of about 24 inches (61 cm). Approximately 1,200 pounds (544 kg) of crawfish per acre may be grown annually in a pond.

be filtered. Once the pond is filled, in May or June, 25 to 50 pounds (9 to 18 kg) of both male and female brood crawfish should be stocked per acre. After stocking, the crawfish will begin burrowing. At this time, the water level should be drawn down to just a few inches. The area will later be flooded to a depth of 18 inches or so in September to encourage maximum growth during the fall and early winter months.

New systems of growing softshell crawfish in water trays in greenhouses are being studied. The current systems are labor-intensive but do result in the growth of quality crawfish crops. Production of softshell crawfish is greater at water temperatures of about 80°F (26.7°C). The key to producing softshell crawfish is to identify the molting phase and harvest at that time.

FEEDING

Crawfish are *polytrophic*, which means that they eat a variety of animal and plant materials, including detritus. *Detritus* is small particles of decaying material, primarily from plants. Crawfish also require some animal protein in their diets. In nature, the animal protein is primarily obtained from zooplankton. Crawfish will occasionally eat dead animals or trapped fish. Commercial feeds are not widely used in crawfish culture.

Some kind of forage is usually planted in the water where crawfish are raised. *Forage* refers to plants grown for leaves and stems and eaten by crawfish. Grain sorghum or millet may be planted, but rice is most common. The rice is planted when the water level is about 4 inches (10 cm) deep (after the draw down) and seeded at the rate of 100 pounds (45.3 kg) per acre. After the pond has been seeded, the remaining water is removed. Sometimes fertilizer is applied when the rice is planted. Since the purpose of the rice is to feed the crawfish, producing a high yield of rice is not a concern. (In some cases, rice and crawfish are double-cropped.)

12–26. Crawfish farm with rice planted as forage. (Courtesy, U.S. Department of Agriculture)

As the rice grows, water is added back to the field to a depth of about 4 inches (10 cm) for the remainder of the summer. More water is added in September and October. This flooding causes the crawfish to come out of their burrows and release their eggs. The crawfish feed on the green rice, other organic matter, and microorganisms that are in the water. As the water level is increased, rice stems and leaves begin to decay. This ties up oxygen in the water. Occasionally, aeration of the water is needed to keep the level of dissolved oxygen above the 3-ppm minimum.

Crawfish feed on the vegetation of rice plants throughout the winter. In heavily populated ponds, all the forage may be gone by late winter or early spring. In this case, some supplemental feeding may be needed. Commercially prepared crawfish feeds are available. Cattle range pellets may also be fed.

Crawfish are sometimes polycultured with freshwater shrimp. The shrimp are seined during hot weather when the crawfish are burrowing. This approach helps make culture of both crops more profitable.

DISEASES

Though disease problems are few, crawfish are subject to several diseases, parasites, and predators.

Nutritional diseases result when the crawfish do not receive the proper diet. Plenty of edible plants must be available, or the crawfish will have tails that are not filled out (a condition known as *hollow tail*). In some cases, inadequate forage will cause their livers to be brown or black. Well-nourished crawfish have full tails and yellow livers.

12–27. A crawfish encrusted with zebra mussels. (Courtesy, Don Schloesser, U.S. Fish and Wildlife Service)

Very few diseases cause problems in crawfish. Sometimes, bacterial diseases may attack crawfish, causing some decay. These can readily be controlled by treating with a 3-ppm potassium permanganate solution.

Zebra mussels sometimes attach themselves to crawfish. In some cases, the crawfish may be almost totally encrusted with these small creatures. Crawfish infested with zebra mussels do not have value. The presence of the mussels also reduces growth and can lead to a weakened condition.

Crawfish may also be subject to damage from pollution in the water, such as agricultural chemicals, and to attack by predators. Common predators are trash fish that get into the growing pond, as well as birds, raccoons, frogs, snakes, turtles, and water beetles.

12–28. Harvesting crawfish involves using traps baited with dead fish or other flesh. The top photo shows mullet (a trash fish) to be used as bait in traps that are "run" with a "go-devil," shown in the bottom photo. (Courtesy, U.S. Department of Agriculture)

HARVESTING

Market outlets should be arranged before the crawfish are harvested. Harvesting can begin in the late fall or early winter after stocking in the previous summer. The original broodstock are harvested first. The minimum size to harvest is a length of 3 inches (7.6 cm).

Most crawfish are harvested with traps. The traps are constructed of screen wire or $^3/_4$-inch (1.9-cm) chicken wire that allows smaller, young crawfish to remain in the growing pond. About ten traps are used for each acre. The traps are baited with fish heads, internal organs of beef animals, or dead trash fish. The traps are checked daily, with the crawfish being removed for marketing. The harvesting season ends by May or June. (At this time, the pond is prepared for the next crop of crawfish.)

Estimating the quantity of crawfish in a pond is difficult. The rate of reproduction, loss to disease and predators, and other factors are not easily determined.

MARKETING

Growers market crawfish to consumers, restaurants, and wholesalers. The markets tend to be local, though some regional distribution through seafood brokers or wholesalers takes place during crawfish season. The minimum size for marketing is a weight of about $^1/_2$ ounce (14 g). The preferred size is 1 to $1^1/_2$ ounces (28 to 42 g). Six to 14 months are required for crawfish to reach this size.

Crawfish may be graded based on the number required to weigh a pound. The count ranges per pound are

Number 1 or Large = 15 or fewer crawfish per pound
Number 2 or Medium = 16 to 25 crawfish per pound
Number 3 or Small = More than 25 crawfish per pound

Larger crawfish are marketed live to dealers, restaurants, and others. Some large crawfish may go into export trade. Small crawfish may go to peeling plants for processing. Some small crawfish are used as bait in fishing.

A new marketing niche is developing for *softshell crawfish*. These are crawfish in the 12-hour stage between hard shells that occurs when crawfish molt. Research has resulted in improved ways of getting crawfish in a pond to molt at the same time. The soft shell is not removed from the crawfish for eating.

Crawfish may be sold in a variety of forms. Most are sold live, but boiled and peeled-tail forms are sold to dealers and restaurants. Mechanical processing is needed to expand the market for peeled forms.

12–29. Crawfish are being graded in preparation for shipping. (Courtesy, MFC Services)

PRAWNS

Freshwater prawns are produced on a limited basis in the United States. Research is producing findings that support expanded freshwater prawn production. Both ponds and tanks have been used for prawns.

12–30. A market-size freshwater prawn.

Freshwater prawns are also known as freshwater shrimp. Commonly, a prawn is the name given to a large shrimp. Most shrimp species live in salt water. Freshwater prawns spend parts of their lives in salt water.

SPECIES GROWN

Several species of freshwater prawns are native to areas of the United States. Commercial production has largely focused on the imported Malyasian prawn (*Macrobrachium rosenbergii*) species. It grows larger than the native species and has greater market appeal.

Several species of prawns that grow in salt water are well known, such as the tiger prawn (*Panaeus esculentaus*) and spot prawn (*Pandalus platyceros*). These compete with the cultured Malaysian prawn in marketing.

IDENTIFICATION AND SIZE

Prawns are crustaceans similar to crawfish and shrimp. They go through molting as they grow. This tends to make growth appear in spurts. Freshwater prawns are harvested when weight reaches 1.2 ounces or more (30 to 40 g) each or at 10 to 13 prawns per pound (22 to 28 prawns per kg). Mature Malyasian prawns may be up to 12 inches (30 cm) long.

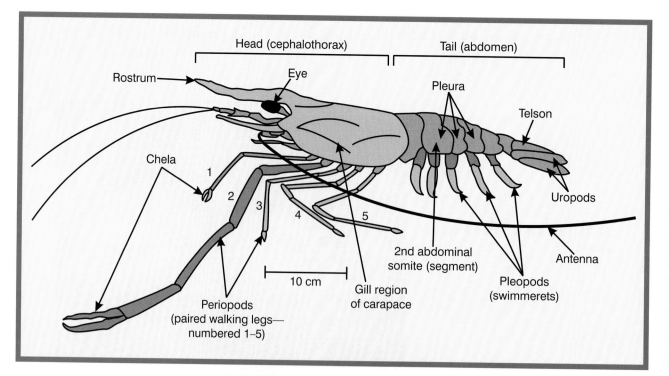

12–31. Major external anatomy of a prawn.

The body of a prawn is divided into the head and tail regions. A prawn has five pairs of walking legs. The second pair of walking legs (chela) is quite long. Prawns have long antennae.

Malaysian prawns have a distinct blue-green color, though the color may sometimes appear brown. To some extent, color is related to diet. Males grow larger than females. The heads and second walking legs of males are larger than those of females. Females tend to have greater space between walking legs. Experienced growers can distinguish between genders based on these secondary characteristics.

ENVIRONMENT REQUIRED

Meeting the environmental needs of prawns is essential for them to live and grow. Freshwater prawns are primarily produced in water with less than 5.0 ppt salt. However, salt water is needed during the first few weeks after hatching.

A water temperature range of 75° to 85°F (24° to 29°C) is usually preferred. Prawns can tolerate lower temperatures, though growth rate will be reduced. Water temperatures vary depending on the life stage of the prawns.

Eggs hatch as small larvae. The larvae do not usually survive more than 48 hours in

12–32. A greenhouse with an arching roof covered to provide shade is used to tank culture prawns.

fresh water and need water with 9 to 19 ppt salt. After larval development, freshwater prawns will not tolerate water with more than 5.0 ppt salt. Prawn producers move them into fresh water as they reach 0.3 to 0.4 inches (7 to 10 mm) in length.

12–33. Lined vats with water movement provide a good environment for freshwater prawns in this greenhouse facility. Note that a fine meal is being fed to these juvenile prawns.

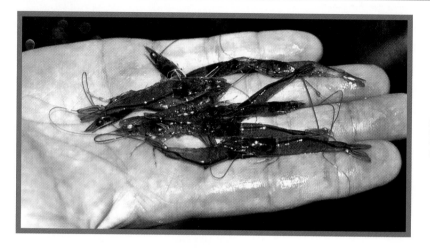

12–34. A sample of rapidly growing, tank-raised juvenile prawns is being examined.

SEEDSTOCK

Seedstock should be selected from a healthy broodstock population. An individual just going into prawn production can buy needed seedstock from a current producer. In some cases, the broodstock may be captured wild, but that is usually not very practical in the United States. Prawn producers may hold over selected mature prawns as seedstock.

Prawns can be kept through the winter in tanks or raceways at 77° to 82°F (25° to 27.8°C). Stocking density is 1.15 ounces per gallon (1 g/L). More females than males should be kept, with the ratio of two or three males for every ten females. The prawns should be fed a complete pelleted feed with 35 percent protein. Rate of feeding is 1 to 3 percent of body weight each day. Most producers use a twice-a-day feeding schedule. Tanks and raceways should have materials that allow the prawns to use all areas of the water. Most producers place plastic fencing or something similar in the water facilities to allow the prawns to escape from each other and have a place to inhabit.

Males go through a three-claw stage. The blue-claw (BC) males have long, spiny blue claws. These males transform into orange-claw (OC) males and strong orange-claw (SOC) males. BC

12–35. Examining a brood prawn that has been kept over winter.

12–36. Safety fence material is sometimes spread across ponds to increase area for prawns to inhabit. This material is being lowered from the surface into the water.

males are the most successful in mating. Mating occurs while the female is in the softshell stage but while the male has a hard shell. Females can reproduce at six months of age.

Mating is typically in the early spring but can occur throughout the year in warm water. The female is capable of multiple spawns each year. The male deposits sperm in a gelatin-like mass on the underside of the female's body between the fourth pair of walking legs. A female produces 28,000 eggs per ounce (1,000 eggs/g) of weight. The eggs are laid within a few hours of mating. The fertile eggs remain on the underpart of the female's body. When carrying eggs, females are referred to as "berried." Newly laid eggs are bright yellow. The color gradually changes to orange, brown, and gray as hatching approaches. Eggs hatch in 20 to 21 days in water that is 82°F (27.8°C).

Water facilities need to be prepared for the arrival of larvae. Fine screens should be placed around drains and other steps taken to prevent the loss of tiny larvae.

After hatching, the larvae swim upside down and backwards. They are separated from the hatching water and moved to water with 9 to 19 ppt salt. Use care with screen seines, strainers, and other devices to capture them. Avoid changes in water temperature and quality. Gradually introduce them to the salt water. Larvae feed on plankton and the larval stages of other organisms in the water. Water temperature should be 82° to 87°F (28° to 31°C) for best larval growth. Larvae undergo 11 molts in their gradual growth and change into the postlarval form. Depending on available food and water quality, larvae reach the postlarval stage in 15 to 40 days.

Postlarvae resemble miniature adults. They are 0.3 to 0.4 inch (7 to 10 mm) long. A pound will contain 50,000 to 76,000 prawns (each weighs 6 to 9 mg). Postlarvae can tolerate some salt water but migrate to fresh water as they develop. Postlarvae continue eating the foods of the larvae but add larger pieces of plant and animal material. At high population densities and with limited food, prawns become cannibalistic. The postlarvae or juveniles gradually become adults over a few weeks and are ready to move to a grow-out pond or tank.

12–37. Large round tanks are being used to culture prawns.

CULTURE

Freshwater prawns can be cultured in tanks or ponds. Most tank culture revolves around broodstock, larval, and juvenile keeping. Ponds are typically used to grow juvenile prawns to market size.

Grow-out ponds should be established and constructed much as those for catfish and similar species. A good supply of fresh water is needed. Sites should be in areas that are not subject to flooding. The soil should have a pH of 6.5 to 6.8. If not, add lime to raise the pH. Ponds should be constructed on sites where the soil holds water so that the need for adding water is reduced. Prawn ponds are typically 1 to 5 acres (0.4 to 2.5 ha) in surface-area size. They are 2 to 3 feet (0.6 to 1.0 m) deep at the shallow end and 3.5 to 5 feet (1.1 to 1.5 m) deep at the deeper end.

12–38. Careful records are kept of water measurements.

Once a pond is filled, use liquid fertilizer of 10-34-0 or 13-38-0 to promote abundant plankton and other organism growth. Apply 0.5 to 1 gallon of liquid fertilizer per acre. The application should be 1 to 2 weeks before the juvenile prawns are stocked in the pond. The organisms that grow serve as natural food for prawns. With a new pond, water from an older pond may need to be added to "seed" or assure that the desired organisms are present in the water. (Highly water soluble powder fertilizer can also be used. The analysis should be 12-49-6 or 10-52-0.)

Good water quality is just as important with freshwater prawns as with other species. The DO level in the bottom foot of water should not fall below 3.0 ppm. Otherwise, all water should be above 3.0 ppm. A DO level somewhat below ideal will result in lower prawn yields. DO can be a particular problem because of the need for the water to support plankton and other organisms used for prawn food. Aeration will be needed to maintain the desired DO level. Nitrogen compounds need to be kept very low. Un-ionized ammonia levels must be below 0.26 ppm at a pH of 6.83. If they are not, a large portion of the prawns will die. Prawns also suffer from pH toxicity. It is best to maintain pH between 6.5 and 9.5.

Polyculture is sometimes used with prawns. Catfish and crawfish have been produced with the prawns. Production results have been mixed.

FEEDING

When first stocked in a pond, juvenile prawns may be able to get sufficient nutrition from natural foods in the water. Supplemental feeding is needed when individual prawns weigh 5.0 grams or more. Sinking catfish feed with 28 to 32 percent crude protein is an effective feed. This feed is readily available to growers and relatively economical. The feed should be scattered over the water area.

The rate of feeding varies with size. At individual weights of 5 to 15 grams, prawns are fed at the rate of 7.0 percent. The percentage decreases to 5 percent when the prawns weigh 15 to 25 grams each. Above 25 grams, the daily rate of feeding is 3 percent.

12–39. Regular monitoring of water is needed to assure proper DO in prawn grow-out facilities.

DISEASES

Prawns are affected by a few diseases. Blackspot, or shell disease, is caused by bacteria in the outer skeleton. It often follows rough handling. Using care to avoid injuring shells helps reduce the likelihood of blackspot.

Prawns can be affected by nutritional deficiencies. Rate of growth is related to available food. Algae and insects can be on shells when the prawns are stunted due to a lack of proper food.

HARVESTING

Prawns are typically harvested in the fall when they weigh 35 to 45 grams each or 10 to 13 per pound. The water in the pond may be drawn down and a seine used to capture most of

12–40. A harvested basket of prawns.

them. Afterward, all water may be removed and individual prawns picked up from the muddy bottom of the pond. Harvested prawns must be transported in a tank, much as other fish.

Traps may also be used to harvest prawns. Traps may be obtained from manufacturers specializing in equipment for harvesting prawns.

12–41. Hand collecting the prawns that remain after seining and water draw-down in a pond.

MARKETING

Prawns are often marketed whole and with little processing. They are kept alive until they reach a restaurant, distributor, or retail market. Some prawns may be processed by removing their heads and/or shells and may then be individually frozen. This processing requires more equipment than would be available on a typical prawn farm. In such a case, the prawns would be sold to a processor, who would handle the preparation.

Live prawns may be transported in tanks at a density of 0.5 pounds of prawns per gallon of water. Keeping prawns in a haul tank as long as 24 hours shows little adversity if the water is properly managed. The desired temperature of haul-tank water is 68° to 72°F (20° to 22°C). Aeration is needed to assure sufficient DO.

TILAPIA

Tilapia are the most widely raised warm-freshwater fish in the world. Popularity of tilapia in the United States is increasing. Four mouthbrooding species are grown more widely than the others: Java, Zanzibar, blue, and Nile. The red hybrid is also raised in some locations. Tilapia, relatively new in North America, are also known as St. Peter's fish.

Much of the tilapia production in the United States is in small-scale, closed-tank systems inside buildings in northern states. Since tilapia grow rapidly and tolerate a wide range of conditions, they are viewed as good species for intensive culture in tank facilities. Tilapia are also widely used in school laboratories for teaching fish culture.

12–42. A food-size tilapia.

Tilapia were first cultured some 4,000 years ago in Africa. An Egyptian tomb dated about 2,500 years ago depicts a tilapia. From the ancient days, production has expanded in some areas of the world to make tilapia a major source of protein in the human diet. The species have been valued for many years in Africa, Israel, and the Far East. Tilapia are grown in more than 100 countries.

Some states have laws forbidding the possession of tilapia and their release into streams. This is because tilapia will take over warmwater streams and lakes. Native vegetation is destroyed, and the habitat for native wild species deteriorates, resulting in loss of the native fish. This is true only in warmer climates, as tilapia cannot live in water below 50° to 55°F (10° to 13°C).

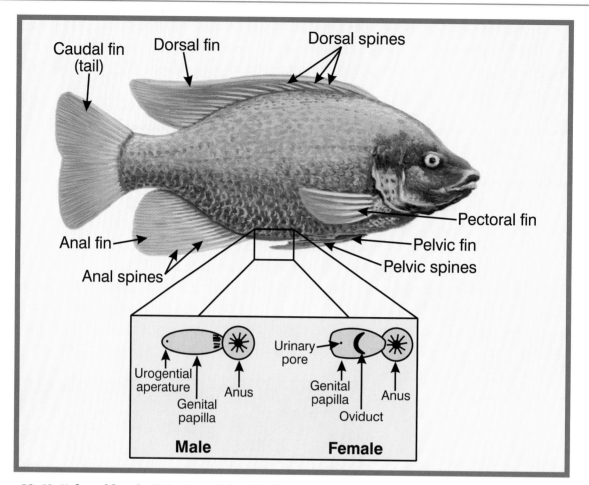

12–43. Male and female distinctions of the Nile tilapia. (Courtesy, Southern Regional Aquaculture Center)

CONNECTION

BOYS ONLY

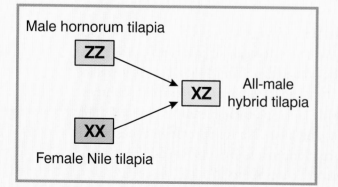

Male-only fish populations are sometimes used with tilapia. This is known as monosex culture. Problems with excessive reproduction while the fish are quite small are overcome. No females are present to produce eggs in male-only monosex culture.

Sorting tilapia by sex is no easy task when there are many thousands to sort. Handling and visually inspecting each fry to determine gender is time consuming. Scientists have found that hybridization can be used.

Crossing a male hornorum (*Tilapia hornorum*) with a female Nile (*T. nilotica*) will produce all-male offspring. This hybrid also grows faster than either the hornorum or Nile species.

IDENTIFICATION AND SIZE

Many species of tilapia exist. The Java tilapia (*Tilapia mossambica*) and the blue tilapia (*Tilapia aurea*) are the most common species. Cultural practices tend to be the same with both species. Some differences in feeding and reproduction are needed. The blue tilapia is considered the most tolerant of cool water.

Species Distinctions

The tilapia is a scale-covered finfish resembling the North American sunfish. It is a thin, flat fish with depth from dorsal side to ventral side. Wide vertical bars are on the sides of fry and fingerlings. Adult tilapia may also have the bars.

The Java tilapia is greenish-gray with three faint vertical bars. It has a dull gold edge to the tail. The fins may sometimes have red edges but not of the same intensity as the blue tilapia.

In cooler water, the blue tilapia is bluish-gray with black vertical bars. A blue bar may appear across the cheek in high water temperatures. Crimson borders may appear on the dorsal and caudal fins of healthy blue tilapia. Some tilapia are very colorful.

Size

When mature, the tilapia weighs a maximum of 5 pounds (2.2 kg) or a little more. It can grow rapidly, reaching a weight of $1/_2$ pound (0.22 kg) in six months.

12–44. A large divided tank is being used to raise tilapia.

12–45. Tilapia may be grown in highly intensive tank systems. The quality and quantity of the available water are limiting factors in such production systems. (Courtesy, *Aquaculture Magazine*)

ENVIRONMENT REQUIRED

Tilapia prefer shallow, fertile ponds and lakes where the water temperature never goes below 50°F (10°C). They are tolerant of poor-quality water. They will survive in water with a dissolved oxygen content as low as 1 ppm but thrive in 3.0 ppm and above DO. Carbon dioxide needs to be below 15 ppm.

Tilapia need water pH near neutral (pH of 6.0 to 8.5). They do not grow well in acid water. Alkalinity should be 50 to 700 ppm. Tilapia will grow well in small ponds and in confinement tanks at heavy population densities. As mentioned, they are more tolerant of poor-quality water than other species. However, they are susceptible to ammonia toxicity in water with a high pH.

In nature, tilapia feed on a wide range of plankton, soft green plants, and invertebrates. Young tilapia typically favor zooplankton. Due to their huge appetites for many aquatic plants, tilapia are sometimes used to control aquatic weeds.

SEEDSTOCK

Adult tilapia may be obtained from wild sources in some countries and from food fish stocks, fish breeders, or importers. Tilapia are fairly easy to breed in captivity. In some cases, aquafarmers have problems with too many young being produced. Some aquafarmers buy fingerlings from fingerling producers; others have broodfish and hatcheries. The fingerling producers operate hatcheries and fingerling grow-out ponds.

Spawning

Tilapia are normally easy to spawn. Crops can be started about any time of the year in warmer climates.

12–46. A tilapia female spawning in an aquarium. (In this case, the eggs are eaten as soon as laid.)

Tilapia females may reach sexual maturity at two to three months of age and at the small size of $2^1/_2$ to 4 inches (6.35 to 10.0 cm) in length. They can produce many offspring during the warm season when the water temperature is 75° to 85°F (23.9° to 29.4°C).

Photoperiod influences spawning. *Photoperiod* is the amount of light organisms are exposed to in one day. Tilapia begin spawning at 10 to 16 hours of light a day. In aquariums, exposing them to good artificial light will induce spawning.

The number of eggs produced depends on the size and age of the female. Frequency of spawning is also a factor in the number of eggs produced, with fewer eggs produced when the female spawns frequently. Tilapia produce 100 to 1,500 eggs per spawn.

Hatchery Systems

Four approaches are used to spawn tilapia: small ponds, small tanks, hapas, and aquariums. The pond method is probably most widely used, though many are spawned in tanks and aquariums. With a pond, one male is used for every two females. The stocking rate is about 28 females per 1,200 square yards (1,000 m²) of pond area.

Producing large numbers of fry in tanks and aquariums may be impractical. A big advantage is the producer has more control over the spawning and hatching process. Usually, one male is placed in an aquarium or tank with three to

12–47. A hatching jar with newly hatched tilapia fry.

five females. Cannibalism of eggs and fry increases with crowding. Successful tank or aquarium spawning year-round requires a temperature of 77° to 84°F (25° to 29°C) and a photoperiod of 12 to 14 hours a day.

A *hapa* is a nylon-type net enclosure that allows fry to escape from larger fish in an aquarium or tank. The fry can swim through the mesh in the net, but larger fish cannot. This keeps the fry from being eaten.

Mouthbrooders. Tilapia species vary in how they care for their spawns. Some species spawn and care for their eggs and young in nests. Other species spawn into nests, but the females hatch the eggs in their mouths. A fish that incubates eggs in its mouth is known as a *mouthbrooder*.

12–48. A mouthbrooder with eggs obvious in her mouth. (Courtesy, Aquanic)

The blue, Java, Nile, and Zanzibar tilapia are mouthbrooders. As such, the female lays eggs in a nest, over which the male deposits sperm. The female takes the eggs and sperm into her mouth for fertilization and incubation. The fry remain in her mouth until the yolk sacs are absorbed.

Hatchery operators check the mouths of females for eggs every day or so. Some hatcheries remove the eggs and place them in standard hatchery jars. Others allow the females to incubate the eggs in their mouths and then collect the fry when they are released by the females. Eggs usually hatch in three to five days. Some hatcheries may get hatching rates as high as 90 percent.

Substrate Spawning. *Substrate spawning* is nesting on the bottom of the water for spawning and hatching. Two common species of tilapia that substrate spawn are *Tilapia randalli* and *T. zillii*.

The spawning pair form a nest by making a depression in the sediment at the bottom of the pond or stream. The eggs are laid in the nest, and the male deposits sperm above them. The pair guard the nest until hatching.

Some producers use aquariums for producing seedstock. The tilapia form a nest in the sand in the bottom of an aquarium and spawn much as in the wild. Aquarium spawning is best in water of 75° to 85°F (23.9° to 29.4°C). Few or no eggs will be hatched in an aquarium with several tilapia. The other fish eat the eggs as soon as they are laid.

Fry Care

Fry need a good environment to live and grow. They must be protected from larger fish and other predators. This is often accomplished by isolating them with hapas or in separate containers.

Young fry feed on plankton and detritus material in the water. In hatcheries, finely ground feed with about 60 percent protein is often used. Some hatcheries use small pellets, allowing them to disintegrate in the water and reach a size that the tiny fry can consume. Research is underway to learn more about the nutritional needs of tilapia fry.

CULTURE

Tilapia are commercially grown in ponds, tanks, and other facilities, with tank culture being widely used in the United States. Much of the culture is with closed production systems using heated water and intensive stocking rates.

Tilapia are adaptable to a wide range of cultural situations. The major requirement is that the water temperature be above 50°F (10°C), with the preferred temperature being 80° to 90°F (26.7° to 32.2°C). Thus, unless the water is heated, tilapia must be grown in tropical and semitropical climates. In tanks with flowing water, tilapia can be stocked at heavy densities. They will tolerate low oxygen, high ammonia, and other conditions that would be lethal to many species of fish.

12–49. Small round tanks are being used for tilapia culture.

Preventing Overpopulation

Tilapia normally reproduce profusely. Overpopulation is often a problem when males and females are raised together. Even tiny females spawn, beginning at two to three months of age. Overpopulation impairs growth. An overstocked pond or tank may have huge numbers of small, stunted tilapia. Males grow faster than females. Segregating by sex is often used to overcome overpopulation.

Some research has involved stocking predatory fish with the tilapia and allowing the predatory fish to keep the population down by consuming them. A proper balance is hard to achieve, as the predators may consume too many.

In most production systems, only the males are grown. The females may be discarded. Growing all-male populations is used to overcome overpopulation problems. Growing all fish of the same gender together is known as *monosex culture*. To have monosex culture, the tilapia must be sorted by sex.

Tilapia are sorted by sex in three ways: hand sorting, using hybrid fry, and altering the sex of the females.

Hand Sorting. Hand sorting fry by sex involves separating the male and female fry. It is usually done when the fry weigh about 1.4 ounces (40 g). Hand sorting is time consuming but not too difficult. Sorting is not 100 percent accurate, allowing some females to end up in the growing facility. Training is needed to distinguish between the males and the females.

Hybridization. Hybrid tilapia tend to be nearly all males. The most common hybrid is obtained by crossing a female *Tilapia nilotica* with a male *T. hornorum*. Besides producing a high percentage of males, hybrid tilapia tend to grow faster and resist cooler water.

Sex Reversal. *Sex reversal* is changing an organism from one sex to another. In this case, the young females are changed to males. This is not yet an acceptable practice with some consumers. A big advantage is the high success rate. Nearly 100 percent of the fry treated with androgen (a male hormone) at 20 to 30 days after hatching will be males. Restrictions of the Food and Drug Administration in the United States require specific approval. Tilapia producers in some countries make wide use of sex reversal hormones with fry.

Pond Culture

Tilapia are stocked at 4,000 to 8,000 per acre in ponds. With careful management, the stocking rate can be increased to as high as 20,000 per acre. Considerable aeration is needed at the higher stocking rates.

Special management is needed where the water temperature may go below 55°F (12.8°C) in the winter. The tilapia cannot survive in cold water. Producers must heat the water in ponds—which is impractical in most cases—or move the fish to tanks where providing heated water is easier. Often, only broodfish are kept through the winter in cold climates.

12–50. Ponds are used for tilapia culture in warm climates. Note that legal regulations may restrict keeping tilapia in ponds.

Legal regulations may apply to pond production of tilapia. Some states do not allow tilapia production. Other states may require permits and assurances that practices are followed to prevent the accidental or intentional release of tilapia into native streams and lakes.

Tank Culture

Tilapia may be cultured in recirculating or flow-through tanks in greenhouses or other buildings or outdoors. Greenhouse culture makes tilapia production possible in cold climates year-round. Maintaining water temperature is easier. *Tilapia nilotica*, *T. aurea*, and certain hybrids have been found best suited to tank production.

Research is providing useful information on tilapia stocking rates in tanks. Higher stocking rates are used with fry. Stocking rate decreases as the tilapia grow. Tanks are typically stocked at a rate of 0.3 pound (0.13 kg) per gallon of water (3.8 L), with constant aeration of the water. Many growers learn by trial and error, but that can be a costly way to learn, especially if fish crops are lost or fail to grow. In a good growing situation, tilapia will reach $1/2$ pound (0.22 kg) in six months. A weight of 2 pounds (0.9 kg) can be achieved in 12 months or so from the date of hatching.

FEEDING

In ponds, tilapia feed on plants, insects, detritus, and plankton. Fertilizing ponds with a complete mixed fertilizer can stimulate plankton, algae, and aquatic plant growth. When fertilized, a pond can produce up to 2,700 pounds of tilapia per acre (3,000 kg/ha) without using manufactured feed. Tilapia gills secrete a mucous that traps plankton. A capsule-like mass forms and is swallowed. Digestion occurs in the stomach and intestines. Commercial producers, however, will provide supplemental feed to increase production greatly. Feed is essential with tanks.

Tilapia require the same nutrients as other warm-freshwater species. Nutrient consumption is related to water temperature. Below 63°F (17.2°C) tilapia stop feeding.

12–51. A directional time-released feeder may be used on a tilapia tank. (Rather than the feed being dropped at one place, the feed is spread out over the tank.) (Courtesy, Fischer ATR Feeders, St. Michaels, MD)

Commercial Feeds

Commercially available feeds are used to supplement natural growth in ponds or to feed intensive tank production systems. Feed with 32 to 36 percent protein is essential in intensive farming, though some tilapia producers use feed with a higher protein content. Tilapia raised in tanks are fed feed slightly higher in protein than those raised in ponds. The daily rate of feeding varies with the size of the tilapia. Tiny fry are fed at the rate of 15 to 20 percent of body weight each day. Those weighing about 4 ounces (100 g) are fed at the rate of 3 to 5 percent of the weight of the tilapia in a pond or tank. For example, if the tilapia in a pond weigh 100 pounds (45 kg), 3 to 5 pounds (1.4 to 2.2 kg) of feed are fed.

Small tilapia are fed more frequently than larger tilapia. Tiny fry are fed about eight times a day. This declines to four times when they weigh 1 ounce. Most growers feed twice a day after the tilapia weigh 2 ounces. The rate of feeding varies with size. Up to 30 days of age, when the weight of an individual fry is 1 gram or less, fry are fed at the rate of 15 to 20 percent of body weight. The rate decreases to 10 to 15 percent after 30 days. It is reduced to 7 to 10 percent for 60 to 90 days of age, 4 to 7 percent for 90 to 120 days of age, 3.5 to 4 percent for 120 to 150 days of age, 1.5 to 3.5 percent for 150 to 200 days of age, and 1.0 to 1.5 percent after 200 days of age. Of course, feeding rates vary with water conditions and other factors.

Growth rate varies widely. Under ideal conditions, a tilapia may gain nearly 2 pounds (850 g) in a year! Most producers do not reach this level, though many raise tilapia that grow a pound or more in one year. A weight of 1.5 pounds (680 g) is a good market size, especially if a tilapia is to be made into fillets. Two fillets of about 5 ounces (140 g) can be made from a tilapia weighing 1.5 pounds (680 g).

Manured Ponds

Some producers use chicken, hog, and duck manure as part of the food for tilapia. The system for doing this, known as a **manured pond**, involves constructing pens for chickens, hogs, and ducks over the water where the fish are being grown. Manure falls through the slated floor of the pens into the water. The fish use the manure as food.

Manured ponds are widely used in some Asian and developing areas. Many people in the United States do not find the practice acceptable. It has the advantages of providing a method of manure disposal as well as making nutrients available to fish. Some people feel that this method of production damages the reputation of tilapia as a food fish.

Diseases

Tilapia are resistant to many diseases. They are tolerant of poor-quality water. Very low oxygen levels and water temperatures below 50°F (10°C) are the two principal causes of loss.

Sometimes, tilapia become stunted. This is a result of overpopulation for the amount of feed available. Providing sufficient feed will usually overcome this problem.

Internal and external parasites are sometimes problems. Using good water and providing adequate feed helps keep parasites under control.

HARVESTING

How tilapia are harvested depends on the system in which they are grown. Seining is used where possible. Seining can be used in ponds. Casting nets are sometimes used, but tilapia are quick and often escape the nets. Draining methods may be difficult because the fish may try to burrow into the mud. In intensive systems of raceways, the fish may be dipped with nets from the water. With ponds and streams, hooks and lines can be used for a few fish, but this method is not practical for commercial aquafarms.

Tilapia are harvested at a weight of 1.25 to 2 pounds. This size is large enough to make nice, portion-cut fillets. In some areas, small tilapia are harvested and cooked whole without any processing.

12–52. Tilapia may be dipped from vats.

12–53. Food-size tilapia are being transported in plastic bags with a small amount of water and wet paper. They will remain alive many hours in this condition. Note: Some growers may question this practice as it relates to the well-being of the fish. What do you think? (Courtesy, Aquanic)

12–54. Farm-raised tilapia are promoted with signs at this farmers market.

Tilapia are not as easily stressed by harvesting and handling as other species. Regardless, caution should be followed to assure their well-being and to make certain that quality is maintained. Haul tanks should be aerated and should be kept within acceptable temperature limits.

MARKETING

Tilapia have been promoted in niche markets in the United States. These are typically ethnic markets in the large cities. Efforts are underway to expand the demand for tilapia into other markets. More restaurants are including tilapia on menus. Supermarkets are increasingly stocking tilapia in their fish and seafood sections.

A marketing structure for tilapia does not exist as it does with catfish. Some tilapia now being distributed undergo very little processing before sale to the restaurant or the fish market. The farmer will likely stop feeding about 24 hours before harvesting, chill the whole fish, and ship it under refrigeration to the buyer. No preparation is done to the fish; the head, internal organs, and skin are left intact. The buyer is responsible for all preparation. In other cases, tilapia are prepared much as catfish products, and this is becoming a more common practice.

BASS

Several species of bass are raised. Largemouth bass, striped bass, white bass, and hybrid striped bass are most often considered.

Hybrid striped bass, commonly known as stripers, are increasingly popular as food and sport fish. The hybrid striped bass is a product of crossing a male striped bass with a female white bass. Good growth rates and adaptability to cultural situations are encouraging more producers to consider the hybrid striped bass.

Bass have been important sport fish for quite a while. Their use in commercial food production is relatively new. Some species produce high-quality food for restaurants, supermarkets, and other outlets.

12–55. A hybrid striped bass. Note the presence of broken or jagged stripes that distinguish the hybrid from other species.

SPECIES AND SIZE

Several species of bass are grown. The largemouth, smallmouth, and white bass are primarily grown for sport fishing. The striped bass is grown for sport fishing and food production. Attention has focused on the hybrid striped bass as a food fish.

Hybridization

Two hybrids have been used: palmetto and sunshine. The palmetto hybrid striped bass results from crossing a female striped bass with a male white bass. The sunshine hybrid striped bass is from crossing a female white bass with a male striped bass. The sunshine hybrid has become the more popular. Physical appearance is identical.

12–56. A female striped bass (left) and a male white bass (right) are shown here. Compare the coloring of the two with that of the hybrid striped bass shown in Figure 12–55. (Courtesy, U.S. Fish and Wildlife Service)

Identification

A striped bass is silvery-white to grayish with black stripes that extend to the tail from behind the gill cover. A hybrid striped bass has much the same coloring except that the stripes tend to be broken or jagged. The body is covered with scales and has a somewhat forked tail.

Size

A striped bass can grow rather large, weighing 30 pounds or more. At the end of the first growing season, a hybrid striped bass may weigh $\frac{1}{2}$ pound. Marketable size is considered $1\frac{1}{4}$ pounds. In 18 months, the hybrid striped bass will grow to a weight of 2 pounds. A typical brood female weighs 15 to 30 pounds.

ENVIRONMENT REQUIRED

Striped bass grow well in a variety of situations. They can grow in salt water, brackish water, or fresh water. Most commercial production is in fresh water.

Hybrid striped bass grow best at a water temperature of 77° to 88°F (25° to 31°C). They will survive temperatures as low as 40°F (4.4°C), but feed consumption is reduced and growth is slowed below 60°F (15.6°C). Growth is also slow above 95°F (35°C).

Water quality is important. Dissolved oxygen should be no lower than 4 ppm for good growth; however, hybrid striped bass will survive for short periods at an oxygen level as low as 1 ppm. The best pH is 7.0 to 8.5, but hybrid striped bass are tolerant of a pH range of 6 to 10.

Water alkalinity of 100 milligrams per liter or above is desirable, but the fish will survive in extremely low water alkalinity. Transferring the fish from high-alkalinity/hardness water to low-alkalinity/hardness water can cause death.

As hybrid striped bass age, they become more tolerant of increased ammonia levels in the water. Severe stress can result if ammonia levels reach 0.5 ppm. A nitrite concentration greater than 2 ppm impairs the ability of the blood to transport oxygen. The carbon dioxide level should be 20 to 40 ppm to prevent stress and gas bubble disease.

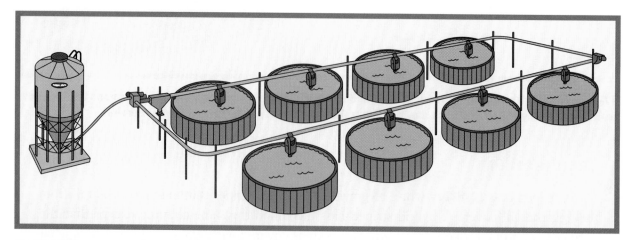

12–57. Highly automated round tank systems may be used to intensively produce hybrid striped bass. (Courtesy, Chore-Time Equipment)

SEEDSTOCK

Reproducing hybrid striped bass requires greater technology than reproducing some other aquacrops. Fingerling and food fish producers often rely on specialized hatcheries for their stock.

Two methods of spawning are used: tank and manual. With the tank method, broodstock ready to spawn are taken from the ponds to a hatchery, where spawning is induced. This involves injecting the female fish with human chorionic gonadotropin (HCG) to induce ovulation some 25 to 40 hours later. The fish are placed in tanks at the ratio of two males for each female. The female lays eggs that are naturally fertilized by the males.

The manual method involves bringing the females from the ponds, injecting them with HCG, regularly checking for ovulation, and hand stripping the eggs from the females. The stripped eggs are artificially fertilized with sperm induced from a male. The eggs are incubated in hatching jars at the rate of 100,000 to 250,000 per jar (this is equal to 200 to 300 ml per jar). At a water temperature of 65° to 70°F (18.3° to 21.1°C), the eggs hatch in 40 to 48 hours. The water should be kept flowing in the jar so that eggs are lifted and gently moved about.

After hatching, fry are moved to ponds in five days at a per acre stocking rate of 200,000 to 300,000. Survival depends on the availability of plenty of zooplankton. Many hatcheries will lose 50 to 75 percent of the fry in the first 45 days. At 45 days, the fingerlings are $1^1/_2$ to 2 inches (3.8 to 5.0 cm) long. They can then be stocked into growing ponds or moved to ponds at a stocking rate of 10,000 per acre to grow into 6- to 8-inch (15.2- to 20.3-cm) fingerlings. Maximum growth occurs at a water temperature of 82°F (27.8°C).

Fry feed on plankton in ponds until about 1 inch (2.54 cm) long. At that size, they are given a commercial feed appropriate for fry or small fingerlings.

CULTURE

Hybrid striped bass can be grown in a variety of culture systems, including ponds, cages, raceways, and tanks.

With ponds, stocking rates may be 1,000 to 1,500 fingerlings per acre for low intensity. The rate may be increased to 3,000 to 4,000 per acre with good management techniques. When fingerlings are stocked in the spring and properly managed, they will reach harvest size of $1^1/_2$ pounds (0.68 kg) by the fall. Survival rates of 80 percent or more are the result of common good management, such as aeration, feeding, and proper handling.

Raceways and tanks with high-water-volume exchange are receiving considerable attention in hybrid striped bass farming. Circular pools or tanks are very good with intensive culture. Plenty of good-quality water must be available. A few producers have access to well water that is about 80°F (26.7°C), which is very good for hybrid striped bass production.

12–58. Hand feeding is used with hybrid striped bass in this tank.

With the very intensive systems, a power failure can pose particular problems. Always have a standby electrical generator.

FEEDING

Hybrid striped bass fingerlings need a feed that is 38 to 52 percent protein, such as salmon or trout feed.

Food fish grow better on a feed with 38 to 44 percent protein. A few manufacturers are making high-protein striped bass feed. If it is not available, trout feed or catfish feed may be used. One drawback with catfish feed is that it has a protein level of about 28 percent, which is somewhat below that needed by hybrid striped bass.

Some producers use automated feeders that provide feed every hour or so. Others may hand feed once or twice a day. The rate of feeding is 3 percent of the fish weight in feed each day for small fingerlings. As the fish grow, the rate should probably be reduced to 1 percent of the weight of fish each day. The rate of feeding also depends on the temperature of the water. Water problems resulting from overfeeding are more likely to occur in warm water.

DISEASES

Good water and nutrition prevent many diseases of hybrid striped bass. The common diseases that affect other cultured fish, caused by bacteria, viruses, or protozoa, can also affect hybrid striped bass. Research has shown that water salinity is helpful in the control of diseases in this fish. There are no approved drugs for use on hybrid striped bass.

The fish are very sensitive to being handled. Minor abrasions can lead to infections. Changing the water can cause problems, particularly if the hybrid striped bass are moved to soft water.

HARVESTING

Hybrid striped bass are typically harvested at a weight of 1 pound (453 g) or more. Harvesting methods depend on the kind of water facility used. In ponds, the fish may be seined. In tanks and raceways, they may be netted. With cages, harvesting is simplified.

With hybrid striped bass, most producers withhold feed beginning about 24 hours before harvest. This allows the fish time to digest the feed that is in their digestive systems. When the fish are shipped on ice without processing, withholding feed is very important.

MARKETING

Marketing opportunities have begun to develop for cultured hybrid striped bass. Restaurant testing has shown that the fish are highly acceptable to consumers. Hybrid striped bass are considered mild-flavored fish with good market appeal.

Current producers are marketing to niche outlets. Ethnic groups in the larger cities of the Midwest and the East like the striped bass. A marketing strategy may involve producers shipping whole fish (with no processing) on ice to distributors, farmers markets, and restaurants in large cities. In the restaurants, the chefs dress the fish and prepare them for customers. Prices paid must reflect the cost of production as well as the cost of transportation.

Market-size hybrid striped bass can be grown in 15 to 18 months.

12–59. A high-quality hybrid striped bass is being packed for shipping as a whole fish. (Courtesy, *Aquaculture Magazine*)

OTHER WARM-FRESHWATER FINFISH

Many other warm-freshwater species could be included. Short sections on sunfish and paddlefish are presented here. Yellow perch, sometimes considered warm-freshwater fish, are covered in Chapter 13 on cool-freshwater species. Some sturgeon will survive in warm fresh water. Chapter 13 also includes sturgeon as a cool-freshwater species.

SUNFISH

Sunfish is a group of about 30 species in the Centrarchidae family. The species are found in North America. The group includes bluegill (*Lepomis macrochirus*), redear (*Lepomis microlophus*), warmouth (*Lepomis gulosus*), and green sunfish (*Lepomis cyanellus*). Collec-

12–60. Four sunfish species are shown here (clockwise from top left): bluegill, redear, warmouth, and green sunfish. (Courtesy, U.S. Fish and Wildlife Service)

tively, these species are commonly known as bream. These are popular game fish but have other uses, such as to consume predators of other species. Black bass and crappie are also among the sunfish species.

The bluegill is stocked throughout North America as a sport fish. It is suited to streams and lakes. The species is identified by a deep, laterally compressed head and a small mouth. Each side has eight to ten double vertical bars. Body color ranges from olive to purple, with white or orange on the ventral side.

The redear is widely found in North America. It is often a companion with the bluegill in managed systems. Redear prefer sluggish water. The body colors are olive and straw yellow, with gray or dusky spots.

Warmouth are also known as goggle-eyes. They inhabit sluggish water where weeds, logs, stumps, and brush are present. The species is a popular sport fish. Warmouth are often used in developing hybrids of other species.

The green sunfish tolerates a wide range of environments, including ponds and streams. It is sometimes used as a baitfish, but this is prohibited in states where it is classified as a game fish. It is blue-green with a yellow or whitish belly. A dark spot is present at the base of the dorsal fin. All fins are yellow or orange, with white occasionally present.

The production of sunfish requires an understanding of their reproductive habits. Spawning begins in early to mid-spring and continues until fall. Geographic location may cause the spawning season to vary. The fish will spawn naturally in ponds or can be manually stripped to remove eggs and milt (sperm) for fertilization in a dish. Water temperature requirements for spawning vary from 70°F (21°C) for warmouth and green sunfish to 80°F (27°C) for bluegills. One female can produce sufficient eggs to have 30,000 to 40,000 fry. Fry in ponds eat natural food materials. Supplemental feeding with a powder or mash designed for fry is often needed. As the fish grow, feeding is required.

12–61. Bluegill are popular sport fish. (Courtesy, U.S. Fish and Wildlife Service)

Market-size sunfish can be produced in ponds, cages, and recirculating systems. Water needs to be of adequate quality. Some will tolerate low levels of salt water. DO should be above 3.0 ppm. Sunfish are hardy but can contract diseases such as columnaris, external fungus, and black, yellow, and white grub parasites. Harvest is usually by seining when sufficient numbers have reached market size.

CONNECTION

WARMING WATER WITH USED OIL

Available water is sometimes too cool for warmwater crops. Heating water a few degrees is costly. With a little extra effort, used engine oil can become a source of heat.

A South Bend, Washington, facility is a good example. These photographs show a small furnace designed to burn used oil. (The furnace is in the small building.) Barrels are near the furnace so that people can leave their used oil. This provides a good way for people to dispose of their oil as well as provides an economical source of fuel for warming the water. A system of pipes moves water to and from the furnace. Controls are used to keep the water at the right temperature.

PADDLEFISH

Only two species of paddlefish exist today. One is found in the Yangtze Valley in China and the other in the Mississippi River Valley of the United States. The paddlefish (*Polyodon spathula*) found in the United States is also called spoonbill and duckbill because of its flattened, paddle-shaped snout.

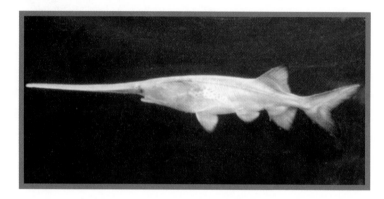

12–62. Paddlefish. (Courtesy, Kentucky Department of Fish and Wildlife Resources)

The paddlefish is a primitive fish, with a cartilage skeleton. The only bone is in the jaw area of the head. Fossil records found show that the paddlefish existed millions of years ago.

Paddlefish have fairly lengthy life spans, with some living 30 years or more. One of the largest paddlefish ever caught by a sport fisher was in Missouri. It weighed 134 pounds 12 ounces (61.1 kg) and was 6 feet 4 inches (1.8 m) long. Records show that paddlefish have reached weights of 200 pounds (90 kg).

Paddlefish are valued for their products. Their grayish-black roe (eggs), which is made into caviar, is most valued. A 40-pound (20-kg) female can yield 4 to 6 pounds (2 to 3 kg) of roe. The boneless, firm, white meat of the paddlefish is also desired. The paddlefish is so valued that destroying the fish to take the eggs is a major cause of the decline in the wild fish population. Destruction of native river habit is another reason for the decline in paddlefish. Research is underway on restoring paddlefish numbers in native streams and on developing cultural methods in tanks and other facilities.

Restoration efforts involve studying the environment needed by paddlefish. To do so, some paddlefish are tagged and released. When later captured, information in the tags is used to track the fish. The tags are very small coded wire about the size of the graphite in a

12–63. Inside view of the mouth of a paddlefish.

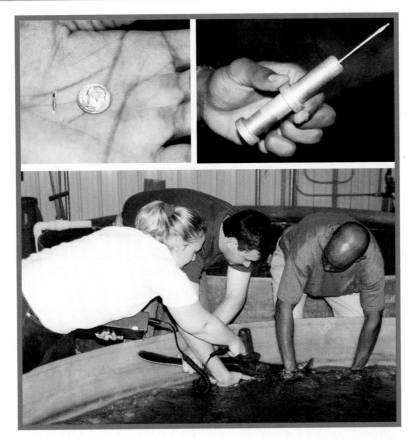

12–64. A tag is implanted to assure future identification of an individual paddlefish. The tag is not as long as the diameter of a dime. It is inserted using a special instrument to minimize injury to the paddlefish. Information in the tag can be read using a special electronic system.

pencil. A tag is placed under the skin near the tip of the rostrum (paddle) without injuring the fish. Its presence and information can be detected without destroying the fish.

Paddlefish are more complex to culture than other common species. Water temperature requirements place them at the lower range of warm water. They cannot tolerate DO below 2.0 ppm. Their preferred foods are zooplankton found naturally in streams and lakes. Paddlefish grow rapidly. They may gain as much as 10 pounds (4.5 kg) in a year. Females must be seven to nine years old to spawn. Because of this age, most female broodfish are captured wild from rivers and lakes when the water temperature is less than 60°F (15.6°C). Males are half to two thirds the size of females. After capturing, paddlefish can be transported in haul tanks much as other species except 0.25 to 0.50 percent salt must be added to the water.

Paddlefish are spawned when the water temperature is 55° to 65°F (13° to 18°C). While the fish are held in tanks, the DO needs to be near 10 ppm. Spawning is induced by injecting the females with a hormone. The injection is made into a female's body cavity in the region

12–65. Improving paddlefish populations requires considerable research. This shows the greatly magnified sperm of a male paddlefish. (Those with tails are considered normal sperm.)

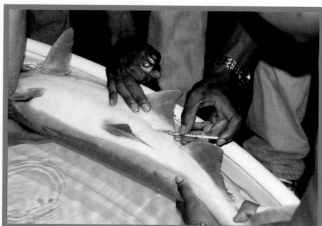

12–66. Injecting a male paddlefish with a hormone to promote sperm development.

of the ovary. Females will ovulate within 24 hours after being injected. Males are also injected with a hormone to promote sperm production 24 hours before the females ovulate. Males will spermiate for three to four days. Both eggs and sperm (milt) are collected for artificial fertilization. Specific skills are needed in collecting eggs and sperm and in assuring fertilization. Eggs hatch in about six days in water that is 64°F (17.8°C).

Young paddlefish need special care to survive. They use food in their residual yolk sacs for the first five to six days. Afterward, zooplankton, particularly the slightly larger species in the *Daphnia* genus, is important in their diets. The gill rakers of young fry are not well developed for filtering.

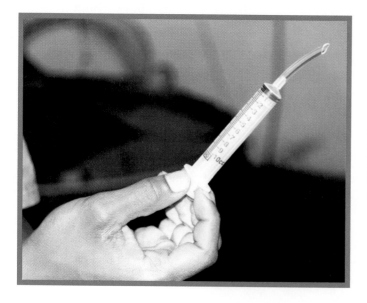

12–67. A device used for collecting sperm from male paddlefish after appropriate hormone injections have been administered. The end of the instrument is inserted into the genital opening of a "ripe" fish.

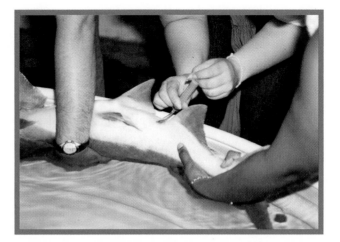

12–68. Sperm are being collected from a male paddlefish.

12–69. A female paddlefish is held in a tank awaiting spawning.

Paddlefish fingerlings are raised in ponds and raceways. Special preparation of ponds is needed to assure a good environment for growth. Water in raceways will need to be about 72°F (22°C). Some research has focused on polyculture of paddlefish with catfish. The filter-feeding paddlefish do not compete with catfish for food.

Individuals considering paddlefish production should carefully study available information and spend time with an experienced paddlefish producer.

12–70. An adult paddlefish being lifted from the water of a tank.

REVIEWING

MAIN IDEAS

Catfish, crawfish, prawns, tilapia, and striped bass are the most widely cultured warm-freshwater food species in the United States. Several species of sunfish are produced for sport fishing as well as food. Paddlefish is also often included as a warm-freshwater species, though it is also found in water that might be considered below the temperature of warm water. Catfish is, by far, the most important species for food production. Some catfish are also used in sport fishing.

When considering which warm-freshwater aquacrops to produce, these basic principles are important:

1. Select only a species adapted to the production system to be used.
2. Select only a species adapted to the warm fresh water available.
3. Feed an aquacrop on the basis of its nutritional needs.
4. Ensure good health by following management practices appropriate to the species being produced.
5. Maintain quality water by using production practices that minimize the possibilities of problems and make water more suitable for the species being produced.
6. Select a species for which there is a market.

Cultural techniques vary with each species. Producers need to be well informed on the successful practices to follow. This information is gained through brochures, books, and Web sites as well as through first-hand contact with current producers and fisheries specialists.

QUESTIONS

Answer the following questions, using complete sentences and correct spelling.

1. What are six important general requirements of aquaculture in warm fresh water? Briefly describe each.

2. What are four warm-freshwater aquacrops? (Include both the common name and the scientific name of each.)

3. Compare catfish, crawfish, tilapia, and hybrid striped bass with regard to the following: environment required, seedstock, culture, feeding, diseases, harvesting, and marketing.

4. Select the species that is (are) best suited to your community. Explain why you made the selection(s).

EVALUATING

Match the term with the correct definition. Write the letter of the term on the line provided.

a. mouthbrooder   e. detritus   i. photoperiod
b. burrow   f. sex reversal   j. manured pond
c. self-perpetuating   g. monosex culture   k. C × B hybrid
d. hapa   h. hollow tail   l. neutral buoyancy

_____1. Amount of light in a day

_____2. Fish that incubates eggs in its mouth

_____3. Pond culture using manure as food for fish

_____4. Small particles of decaying material that float suspended in water

_____5. Condition in crawfish resulting from inadequate food

_____6. The changing of an animal's sex

_____7. Tunnel system made in the earth by crawfish

_____8. Reproducing in adequate numbers, making artificial hatching unnecessary

_____9. Raising batches of fish of the same sex together

_____10. A nylon-type net enclosure that allows fry to escape from larger fish in an aquarium or tank

_____11. The quality of feed to neither float on top nor sink to the bottom

_____12. A hybrid catfish from crossing a female channel catfish with a male blue catfish

EXPLORING

1. Select a species that may be of interest to you. Investigate the biology, production, and marketing of the species. Use this book and other references. Several Web sites will be useful, including AquaNIC at **aquanic.org/**.

2. Select an appropriate species for your climate and water facilities. Begin the production of the species on a small scale in an aquarium, a tank, or a pond. Follow long-term practices to assure success of the aquacrop and provide animal well-being.

3. Prepare a poster or bulletin board that summarizes how to distinguish between the four major species of warm-freshwater aquacrops. If possible, place live species in separate aquariums near the bulletin board, and properly label. Be sure to provide an appropriate environment for each species.

Cool-Freshwater Aquacrops

13–1. A fishery biologist is examining a Lahontan cutthroat trout (*Onchoryhunchus clarki henshawi*). This species is found in an area that is primarily limited to the Lahontan basin of west-central Nevada. It has been placed on the endangered species list by the U.S. Fish and Wildlife Service. The fish is being cultured in a hatchery for stock enhancement purposes. (Courtesy, U.S. Fish and Wildlife Service)

J UST AS SOME species require warm water, others require cool and, sometimes, cold water. These species do not grow well—and may not even survive—in water warmer than their natural habitat.

Species suited to cool water were among the first cultured fish in North America. Trout have been produced longer than any other species. Some of the trout have been used for food; most have been released into streams to enhance wild populations. Many of the trout have later been caught by sport fishers.

The cool-freshwater species are popular in northern areas, where natural water supplies are cool or cold. In some cases, mountain elevations in southern areas also provide water cool enough for some species. Success depends on knowing the requirements of the particular species being raised.

GENERAL REQUIREMENTS FOR COOL-FRESHWATER SPECIES

A *cool-freshwater aquacrop* is a species that survives and grows best in water below 70°F (21°C). The species are sometimes divided into coolwater and coldwater subgroups. When this is done, the species preferring the water with the lowest temperatures are known as coldwater species. In this book, the coldwater species are combined with the coolwater species.

A few species in the coolwater group are very close to preferring water temperatures that would classify them as warmwater species, and vice versa. Some species included in the warmwater group are at the lower edge of the warmwater temperature requirements. An example is the paddlefish. The preferred temperature range results in paddlefish sometimes being classified as a coolwater species. (Paddlefish are covered in Chapter 12.)

Cool water may be a few degrees warmer than 70°F (21°C) for a short time. When this happens, the species may be stressed and fail to grow. Some places where coolwater species grow may get warm in the summer months. Melting snow and springs may tend to keep the water temperature down.

Trout are the most commonly raised coolwater species. Several species of trout are raised, with rainbow trout being most common. Walleye, sturgeon, northern pike, muskellunge, and several sunfishes and perches are also produced.

13–2. Some 50,000 trout are raised in each of these spring-fed raceways in Idaho. (Courtesy, U.S. Department of Agriculture)

The general requirements for the culture of cool-freshwater species are similar to those for the culture of warm-freshwater species except for water temperature. Some species require clear water that is relatively free of suspended tiny pieces of solid materials. Coolwater species often prefer flowing water from springs and melted snow.

Cultural requirements vary from one species to another. The basic requirements tend to be similar.

Table 13–1. Selected Species Produced in Cool Fresh Water

Common Name	Scientific Name	Major Use
Arctic char	*Salvelinus alpinus*	Sport
Arctic grayling	*Thymallus arcticus*	Sport
Chain pickerel	*Esox niger*	Sport
Muskellunge	*Esox masquinongy*	Sport
Pike, northern	*Esox lucius*	Sport
Sturgeon,		
green	*Acipenser medirostris*	Food*
lake	*Acipenser fulvescens*	Food*
Trout,		
brook	*Salvelinus fontinalis*	Sport
brown	*Salmo trutta*	Sport
cutthroat	*Salmo clarki*	Sport
Subpecies of cutthroat include:		
Colorado	*Salmo c. pleuriticus*	Sport
Lahontan	*Salmo c. henshawi*	Sport
Piute	*Salmo c. seleniris*	Sport
Rio Grande	*Salmo c. virginalis*	Sport
Utah	*Salmo c. utah*	Sport
Yellowstone	*Salmo c. lewisi*	Sport
golden	*Salmo aguabonita*	Sport
lake	*Salvelinus namaycush*	Sport
rainbow	*Oncorhynchus mykiss*	Sport, food
Walleye, North American	*Stizostedion vitreum*	Sport
Whitefish, common	*Coregonus lavaretus*	Sport
Yellow perch	*Perca flavescens*	Sport, food

*Caviar and flesh.

Note: Most sport fish are also used as food, but some species are considered game and do not enter the commercial food chain.

SPECIES SELECTION

The cool-freshwater species must be suited to the environment in which they are to grow. Most species have preferences for climates, even within the broad cool-freshwater group. Trout, for example, may die if the water temperature goes above 75°F (24°C). Other coolwater species might be less tolerant of warm temperature. Some species can be raised in warmer climates if a supply of cool water is available. (Refer to Table 13–2 for more information.)

Table 13–2. Principles of Cool-Freshwater Species Selection

1. Select only a species adapted to the production system to be used.
2. Select only a species adapted to the cool fresh water available.
3. Feed an aquacrop on the basis of its nutritional needs.
4. Ensure good health by following management practices appropriate to the species being produced.
5. Maintain quality water by using production practices that minimize the possibilities of problems and make water more suitable for the species being produced.
6. Select a species for which there is a market.

Some species live in fresh water part of the time and in salt water the rest of the time. An example is salmon, which spawn in cool fresh water and grow in the salt water of the ocean.

13–3. Would this water be satisfactory for coolwater species? Why?

AVAILABLE WATER

A dependable, year-round supply of water must be available. Having plenty of the "right" water is essential. The "right" water includes supply as well as characteristics, such as temperature, clarity, dissolved oxygen, freedom from residues, and hardness.

Natural supplies of water often reflect the climate of the area. Streams reflect the temperatures of their water sources. Water originating from melting snow, glaciers, and springs is consistently cooler than water in standing bodies, such as ponds and lakes, which may be warmed in the summer. If all the snow melts in a watershed during the summer, a stream may dry up and not be a dependable source of water.

NUTRITIONAL REQUIREMENTS

Appropriate food is needed for an aquacrop. Flowing streams must contain sufficient wild foods for a population of wild fish. Aquacrops in raceways and tanks must be fed so the nutritional needs of the species are met. Lakes have some natural food supply.

13–4. Cold water from a spring is used at this facility for arctic char production.

The nutritional requirements of fish are not fully understood. Trout have been studied more than the other species. Not just any feed will do. Providing the proper nutrition is essential in aquafarming.

GOOD HEALTH

Keeping cool-freshwater fish healthy is essential for their survival and growth. Diseases reduce growth rate and may cause death. Each species has different health needs. Research has found methods of control and treatment for some diseases. The incidence of disease is reduced if the fish are kept in a proper environment and not stressed.

Some coolwater species are subject to attack by parasites. An example of a parasite is the sea lamprey. A sea lamprey may attach itself to a fish and derive nourishment from its host. A *host* is an organism on which a parasite lives and from which it derives nourishment.

13–5. Demand feeders release feed when activated by fish in the tank. Feeders should be placed 25 to 30 feet apart along tank walls. (The species in this tank is arctic char.)

13–6. An oxygen meter is frequently used to measure the DO level in tank systems.

WATER MANAGEMENT

Proper water management is as important with cool-freshwater species as it is with warm-freshwater species. The aquafarmer begins with clear, cool water. Dissolved oxygen should be maintained at the appropriate level for a species. Ammonia and nitrites may need to be monitored and regulated. Water pH and minerals may need to be controlled. In closed systems, filtration is important to remove suspended solid materials. Other water factors may need to be considered, depending on the species.

Fish stocked at high rates use more oxygen and excrete more wastes than those stocked at lower densities. Systems must be in place to clean and aerate the water. Weather and other organisms growing in the water may also affect water management.

AVAILABLE MARKET

A market should be available before an aquacrop is produced. Success in cool-freshwater aquaculture depends on selecting the appropriate species from a marketing perspective.

Cool-freshwater aquacrops may be marketed in several ways. Some farmers sell directly to consumers; others sell to processors. Trout is the only species with a fairly definite marketing structure in some locations. Fee lakes and natural stream enhancements are major outlets for many cool-freshwater species. Sturgeon are used for caviar, with production depending on niche markets.

TROUT

Trout are, by far, the most important cool-freshwater species in the United States. They have been raised longer than any species of warm- or cool-freshwater fish. The first were raised in New York, Connecticut, and Idaho in the early 1900s. These efforts focused more on restocking streams when the natural supplies were depleted. Most of the early efforts were at government hatcheries.

Commercial trout farming became important in the 1950s. Idaho was an early leading state in trout production. Areas of the state had the advantage of an abundance of water at 55° to 58°F (12.8° to 14.4°C)—ideal for trout.

Some 45 states raise trout, including Pennsylvania, Virginia, North Carolina, Tennessee, and Georgia. Except for Idaho, much of the production is for sport fishing in fee lakes or for stream enhancement. Small niche markets are found in many locations where trout are raised. Idaho currently produces about 75 percent of the nation's commercial trout, or about 40 million pounds a year.

SPECIES GROWN AND IDENTIFICATION

Trout are often referred to as **salmonids**, because they are members of the salmon family. Many characteristics of trout and salmon are similar. A major difference is that trout are adapted to fresh water and salmon are anadromous. Anadromous means that the salmon grow in salt water but return to fresh water to reproduce. Young salmon go from the fresh water to salt water to grow.

Although several species of trout have been cultured, five species are of primary importance: rainbow trout (*Oncorhynchus mykiss*), brown trout (*Salmo trutta*), brook trout (*Salvelinus fontinalis*), cutthroat trout (*Salmo clarki*), and lake trout (*Salvelinus namaycush*). Many vari-

13–7. Trout are often popular for sport fishing. (This shows a pool in a mountain stream with three species of trout. Can you see any trout in the water?)

13–8. Rainbow trout.

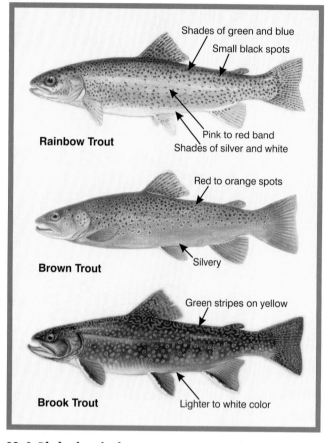

Shades of green and blue

Small black spots

Pink to red band

Shades of silver and white

Rainbow Trout

Red to orange spots

Silvery

Brown Trout

Green stripes on yellow

Lighter to white color

Brook Trout

13–9. Distinctions in three common trout species. (Courtesy, U.S. Fish and Wildlife Service)

ations exist within trout species, with some commercial variants being tried, such as the Dolly Varden trout. Several have subspecies, such as the cutthroat examples in Table 13–1. Of the trout, the rainbow trout is most popular. Besides being adapted to culture, the rainbow trout has strong consumer appeal. The brown trout was the first fish to be artificially reproduced and reared.

Species Identification

All trout have a similar appearance. Identification requires observing minor differences in a species. Even within species, colors and other characteristics can vary depending on age, water characteristics, and other factors.

Rainbow trout vary in color, based on habitat. Various shades of green and blue are found in the dorsal (top) area. A pale pink to brilliant red band usually extends from the gills to the tail. The sides are silvery, with white in the ventral (belly) area. Small black spots are found on the back and sides. Black spots are also present on the dorsal, adipose, caudal, and anal fins.

Brown trout vary somewhat in silvery color but always have red to orange spots. Brook trout have green stripes on a yellow background in the dorsal area and on the sides. Cutthroat trout have one oblong red spot on either side of the throat and are covered with white-encircled black spots, which are somewhat larger than the spots on the rainbow trout.

Size

Trout vary in size depending on nutrition and other conditions of growth. Adult rainbow trout are typically no more than 20 inches (50.8 cm) long. The largest known rainbow trout was considerably longer and weighed 52 pounds (23.6 kg). Harvest-size fish range from 7 to 14 inches (17.8 to 35.6 cm) long and weigh $1/_2$ to 1 pound (227 to 453 g). This size can usually be produced on a farm with favorable conditions in 7 to 14 months. Fingerlings in the 1- to 6-inch (2.5- to 15.2-cm) range can be produced in 1 to 8 months.

13–10. Snake River Canyon trout hatchery. (Courtesy, U.S. Department of Agriculture)

ENVIRONMENT REQUIRED

Trout are coldwater fish. They naturally grow in the streams and freshwater lakes of the northern United States, Canada, Europe, and other parts of the earth. Trout growth tends to be seasonal. In the very cold winter months, the fish become inactive and have slower rates of food assimilation. During this time, trout are essentially maintaining themselves.

Most trout species grow best in water with a temperature range of 50° to 68°F (10° to 20°C). The ideal temperature is considered to be below 64°F (18°C). Below 50°F and above 68°F, the rate of growth slows considerably. Water temperatures in the mid-70s and above are lethal if trout are exposed for more than a short while.

Rainbow trout thrive best in flowing water with a high level of oxygen. The minimum desired dissolved oxygen level is 7 ppm. A water pH of 6.5 to 9.0 is best. The trout will grow (but not spawn) at low stocking levels in ponds with water 10 feet or more deep.

The water environment for trout should be cold, clear, free of pollution, and protected from summer heat and should have plenty of oxygen. Trout are very sensitive to polluted water.

13–11. Clear, rapidly flowing streams with gravel bottoms are preferred by most trout for spawning. (This shows a section of the Soque River, popular trout stream in northeast Georgia.)

SEEDSTOCK

Since trout have been cultured longer than any other species in the United States, improved varieties have been developed. Much of the improvement was through selective breeding of trout species to produce "super trout." Examples include the Donaldson trout and the Dolly Varden trout.

Natural Spawning

In nature, trout spawn in fast-flowing streams with gravel bottoms. Nests are built in the gravel, where the females deposit eggs that are fertilized by the males. The eggs are covered with small gravel for a rather long period of incubation.

Incubation varies among the species and with the water temperature. Rainbow trout eggs hatch in 80 days at 40°F (4.4°C) and in 31 days at 50°F (10.0°C). Brown and brook trout eggs tend to take longer to hatch than those of rainbow trout. Natural spawning of rainbow trout is January to May; natural spawning of brown and brook trout is October to January.

Natural reproduction is not used in trout farming. The eggs may be artificially fertilized and hatched in flowing water.

13–12. Collecting eggs from a female for artificial spawning. (Courtesy, U.S. Fish and Wildlife Service)

Artificial Spawning and Hatching

Artificial spawning and hatching are used in trout production. Streambed spawning results in hatching rates below the level acceptable in commercial aquaculture. Artificial spawning involves removing eggs from the female and **milt** (sperm) from the male. These are mixed in a small pan so that fertilization can occur.

Most trout begin to spawn at two years of age. Water temperature and photoperiod influence the time of spawning. Conditions equivalent to those in natural streams are created to adapt the fish and prepare them for spawning. Most females produce good spawns for about four years.

Brood trout are kept in small tanks or ponds that have flowing water at fairly low stocking density. The sexes must be separated to prevent fighting among the males. Frequent check-

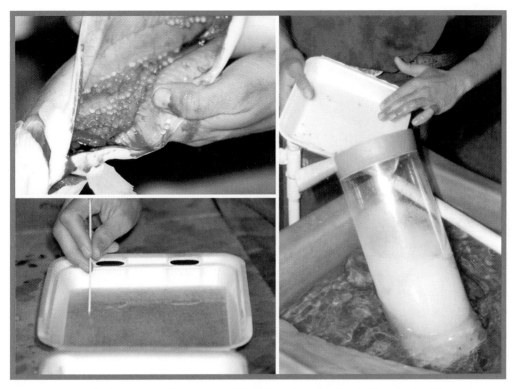

13–13. Eggs are being removed from a sacrificed female trout (top left), mixed with sperm expressed from a male (bottom left), and placed in a hatching jar for artificial hatching.

ing of the broodfish near spawning time is needed to determine when the females are *ripe*—that is, when they have fully developed eggs in their ovaries. Females develop large bellies, and the genital papilla (anus) becomes larger and reddish in color. Readiness of trout to spawn is indicated by the ease with which eggs or milt can be pressed out of the fish. Ripe milt has a creamy white color.

13–14. Incubation trays used with trout eggs at a Virginia hatchery.

13–15. Developing trout eggs with an eyespot.

Eggs and milt are stripped by applying pressure with the hands just in front of the abdominal area. Females are stripped first, and the milt is poured over the eggs. The process must be carried out carefully to avoid breaking eggs and reducing fertilization rates. No water should be in the pan. Water causes the eggs to swell and makes fertilization more difficult.

Fertilized eggs are incubated in baskets in incubation trays. The desired water temperature is 46° to 54°F (8° to 12°C). Most of the systems involve vertical-flow incubators. Water flows from top to bottom in such an incubator. The water comes into each tray so it flows upward through the eggs in the basket. Water may be reused if it is of the desired temperature.

A trout egg goes through three stages in incubation. The first stage is the internal development of the fertilized egg before the appearance of an eyespot. An **eyespot**, or "eye," is a dark spot that shows the developing embryo in each egg. The second stage is the appearance of the eyespot. The third stage is the hatching of the egg through the absorption of the yolk sac.

The fry are kept in the trays until they become active and begin feeding. (The yolk sacs are about 75 percent absorbed by this time.)

Trout eggs are very sensitive during incubation. The amount of time required for hatching is measured in degree days. A **degree day** is the average water temperature (in degrees Celsius) multiplied by the number of days required for hatching. (Eggs hatch more quickly in

13–16. Trout with yolk sac. (Courtesy, U.S. Department of Agriculture)

warm water.) For example, if hatching begins in 32 days at 10°C, the number of degree days is 320. The degree days required is relatively constant among species, with 290 to 330 degree days required for rainbow trout eggs. Brown trout eggs require 400 to 460 degree days.

Eggs need careful observation during incubation. Infertile eggs should be removed by a process known as **egg picking** (removing by hand with large tweezers) or by automated sorting machines or pipettes. An infertile egg turns white, while a fertile egg becomes pink and develops an eyespot.Growers of food-size trout may buy eyed eggs and hatch them or buy fry or fingerlings. This saves having to maintain broodstock and go through the complete cycle. It also allows specialization in artificially spawning trout on other farms.

Caring for Fry

Newly hatched fry are transferred to rearing troughs for growing. Since fry are quite small, dense stocking rates can be used. Some growers put as many as 30,000 fry in a trough containing 5 cubic feet of water. Such a trough would have water 4 inches (10.2 cm) deep and would be 10 feet (3.48 m) long and 18 inches (45.7 cm) wide.

Fry are fed prepared feeds. Effort is sometimes required to get them to start eating, and some natural food materials, such as plankton, may be needed. Commercial feed should be nutritionally complete and in a finely ground meal form.

CONNECTION

RELEASE TODAY TO CATCH TOMORROW

Cool-freshwater species are often raised to "release today to catch tomorrow." Federal, state, and local agencies cooperate to ensure streams have adequate fish. No one wants to go sport fishing and return home without any catch!

"Enhancement" is raising trout and other species in hatcheries and releasing them into streams. This practice enhances the natural population that has survived. The early efforts in aquaculture dealt with enhancement. Without enhancement, many streams would have no fish, and some species and subspecies would become extinct. Examples are the subspecies of cutthroat trout.

A part of enhancement is habitat improvement and the restriction of fishing. Strict regulations are often imposed on streams so that fish will be available.

After fry are eating well, they can be moved to raceways, circular tanks, or ponds for growing. Water should be mechanically moved in ponds to ensure the best possible environment for trout.

As fingerlings grow, they are graded to keep uniform sizes stocked together. Grading is a process of sorting fish by size. Grading reduces cannibalism of larger trout on smaller trout. A larger fingerling can eat a fingerling that is half its size!

CULTURE AND STOCKING

Most trout are cultured in flowing spring or well water. Raceways are typical, but cages and closed-tank systems are sometimes used. Ponds are sometimes used successfully; however, careful water management is needed to keep the water clear and free of pollution. Fingerlings are sometimes placed in cages in flowing streams.

13–17. A raceway used in trout production.

The standard rate of water flow in a raceway should result in a complete exchange of the water every hour. A raceway with a 1 to 3 percent slope will allow water to flow at the proper rate. The water control structure at the end of the raceway segment should provide a drop to re-aerate the water through splashing.

Stocking rates vary with the water facility. Water quality is a major factor in rate of stocking. A general rule is no more than 5 pounds (2.27 kg) of trout per 8 gallons (30 L) of water. Further, 1.8 pounds (0.82 kg) of marketable trout can be produced in 1 gallon (3.8 L) of water flow per minute. With good water management, higher stocking rates can be used.

Stocking rates in low-intensity systems vary from 300 to 750 fingerlings per acre of water. The rate depends on the water flow and other management factors.

FEEDING

Trout must have a high-protein diet. In nature, they are carnivorous, eating insects, fish, fish eggs, and other small animals. Commercially prepared trout feeds are specially designed for the needs of trout. The feeds typically have a protein content of 38 to 45 percent; however, fry and fingerlings may be fed a feed with 48 to 50 percent protein. Fish meal is the primary source of protein in manufactured feeds.

The ratio of protein to energy is important in the efficient use of feed by growing fish. For high-energy feeds, a ratio of 20:1 is recommended. The ratio is interpreted as 20 parts protein to 1 part energy. Ratios above 20:1 often result in wasted feed and excessive feed costs. Ratios below 20:1 may be in feeds with excess fat. Too much fat in the ration of trout results in poor flesh quality and lower dress-out percentages.

Small fingerlings are fed three or four times or more a day. Larger fingerlings and trout approaching harvest size may be fed only twice a day.

Rate of feeding depends on water temperature. The optimum water temperature is 55° to 65°F (12.8° to 18.3°C). Feeding rates for this temperature range vary from 1.5 to 6.0 percent of body weight per day. Rates vary with size of fish and other conditions. Never feed more than the fish will consume in 30 minutes. At temperatures above 68°F (20°C), the digestive systems of trout do not make good use of nutrients. Below 38°F (3.3°C), appetites are suppressed, and trout need only 0.5 to 1.8 percent of body weight each day. Feeding more than the suggested amounts will likely result in wasted feed.

13–18. Hand feeding trout fingerlings in a raceway at a hatchery.

CONNECTION

ALPINE TROUT

Its name may vary with local folks, but the alpine trout is most likely the best example of a cold-freshwater species in North America. Not everyone calls the species alpine trout; many people know it as arctic char (*Salvelinus alpinus*). This species is primarily found in the polar regions of North America . . . some say in all polar areas of the Northern Hemisphere.

Arctic char is sometimes anadromous; other times it is nonanadromous. Scientists are now learning more about it. Taxonomists are still considering its classification and relationships in the trout family. The Freshwater Institute, in West Virginia, has tried to produce arctic char experimentally using cold spring water.

The arctic char is a popular sport fish in Alaska, Canada, and areas of the northern contiguous states. It is very similar to the Dolly Varden (*Salvelinus malma*).

During the summer, the typical rate of feeding is 3 percent of the weight of the fish per day. If fish are fed twice a day, each feeding should provide 1.5 percent of the weight of the fish in the growing facility.

On small farms, feed may be thrown out into the water by hand. Demand feeders or blower feeders may be used on larger farms.

Water temperature is important in the amount of feed that is fed. Reduce the amount when the water temperature is above 68°F (20°C) or below 38°F (3.3°C). Feeding rates should always be adjusted to maintain water quality.

DISEASES

Trout are subject to several diseases. Providing a good growing environment can reduce the incidence of disease. Bacteria, viruses, and protozoa may cause disease.

Trout may have environmental diseases. These result from high levels of nitrogen forms, low dissolved oxygen, or contamination of the water. Factories and other farming operations may contaminate water. Of course, the life processes of fish in the water contribute to lower quality.

Good management is a key to disease control. Bring only clean, disease-free trout onto a fish farm. Healthy fingerlings resist disease. Prevention is the most important part of trout disease control.

13–19. A lake trout with parasitic sea lampreys attached (the two long, black objects just past the gills and midpoint of the fish). (Courtesy, U.S. Fish and Wildlife Service)

HARVESTING

Trout are harvested by seining, trapping, or netting or by draining the water facility. Larger trout may be harvested in the grading process. Trout for food use are harvested when

13–20. Four trout species (clockwise from upper left): lake, brook, brown, and golden. (Courtesy, U.S. Fish and Wildlife Service)

7 to 14 inches (17 to 36 cm) long. Of course, the size at which to harvest depends on market demand.

Marketing

Trout are marketed at several stages in the production process. Some farms specialize in producing for these stages. Marketing may occur in these ways:

- Broodfish, usually of improved stock, are marketed to hatcheries.

- Hatcheries may market eyed eggs to fry and fingerling producers.

- Hatcheries or fingerling growers may market fingerlings to food fish producers.

- Food fish producers may raise fry or fingerlings to the desired food fish size and then market them to processors or directly to consumers.

- Fish producers may market trout to fee-lakes or other recreational operations.

- Live haulers may market trout to processors, fee-lake operators, retail outlets, and others.

- Some producers may process trout and market directly to restaurants or supermarkets.

- Some growers may use combinations of any of the above.

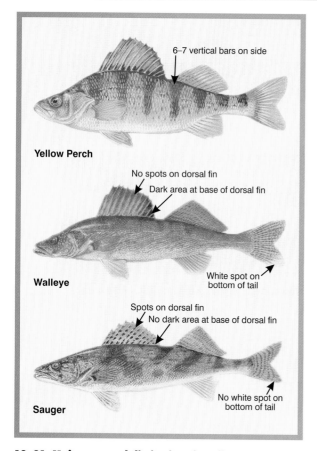

6–7 vertical bars on side

Yellow Perch

No spots on dorsal fin

Dark area at base of dorsal fin

Walleye

White spot on bottom of tail

Spots on dorsal fin

No dark area at base of dorsal fin

Sauger

No white spot on bottom of tail

13–21. Major external distinctions in yellow perch, walleye, and sauger. (Courtesy, U.S. Fish and Wildlife Service)

PERCHES

The perch family (Percidae) contains 170 species, with several widely found in the United States. Most of these are small fish known as darters. Three perch family species predominate: yellow perch, walleye, and sauger. All three are highly regarded as sport fish and for food.

YELLOW PERCH

The yellow perch (*Perca flavescens*) is native to southern Canada and to the northeastern and upper midwestern United States. It is also found in other areas, including coolwater lakes in the upper southern states. The yellow perch is said to be a glacial lake species. Also known as the lake perch, it is a popular sport fish and is also used for food.

Mature yellow perch are typically 6 to 12 inches (15 to 30 cm) long and have a golden yellow color. Young yellow perch are usually whitish. Eyes are green to yellow. Perch have six to eight vertical bars on each side.

Perch form schools of 50 to 200 fish. Schools tend to arrange themselves by size of fish and age. Males and females may form separate schools. Older fish are less likely to school, and some may travel alone.

13–22. A yellow perch. (Courtesy, U.S. Fish and Wildlife Service)

Spawning

In nature, yellow perch spawn in the spring when the water temperature is 45° to 52°F (7.2° to 11.1°C). Spawning will soon follow their movement from deep water, where they overwinter, to shallow water for egg laying. The eggs are laid over submerged tree limbs, sticks, and other vegetation. Perch do not build nests or guard the eggs. The eggs are laid in egg ribbons. An **egg ribbon** is a long, gelatinous strand of eggs that may reach 6 feet (2 m) in length. Males release milt over the eggs. At least two males are usually present to fertilize the eggs. After fertilization, the eggs swell and rapidly harden. They hatch in eight to ten days. The emerging fry are quite small—4 to 7 mm long. The fry feed on zooplankton.

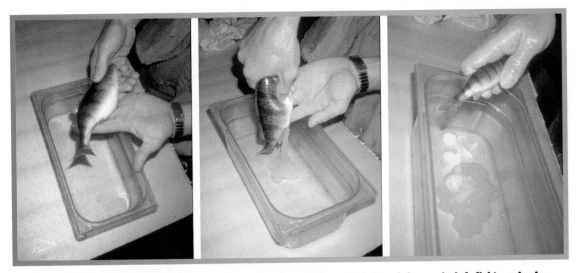

13–23. Artificial spawning involves selecting a ripe female (note bulging abdomen in left fish), stripping the egg ribbon, and stripping milt from a male. (Courtesy, AquaNIC Images)

In hatcheries, yellow perch may spawn in ponds or tanks, or they may be artificially spawned. In ponds, yellow perch may be allowed to spawn much as in the native setting. With tanks, water quality should promote spawning. The temperature should be 53° to 63°F (11.7° to 17.2°C) in flow-through or recirculating water with above 3.0 DO. Broodfish are placed in the tanks in the spring. Feeding is needed to meet nutrient needs of the broodfish. Trout feed is most commonly used. The tanks should be checked each day for the presence of egg ribbons. The egg ribbons are removed and incubated in hatching jars or trays.

Artificial spawning involves stripping eggs from ripe females and milt from males. The eggs and milt are placed together in a pan for fertilization. Afterward, they are moved to a hatching jar or tray.

Once fry hatch, zooplankton food must be available in the water. Using pond water in tanks helps provide this food. Cultured zooplankton or a similar commercial feed may be used.

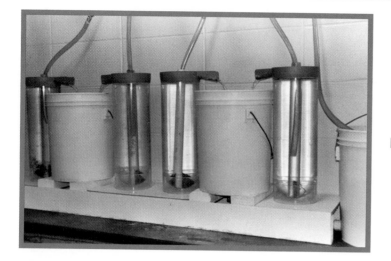

13–24. An incubation system using hatching jars.

Growing

Yellow perch can be grown in ponds, cages, and tanks. Most culture is in ponds. Stocking rates vary considerably, depending on water management, with 2,500 to 10,000 per acre (6,200 to 25,000/ha) being common. Higher stocking rates require water monitoring and aeration. Ponds provide considerable natural food if fertilized. Feeding is needed with increased stocking densities. Many producers use trout feed.

In some ponds, zooplankton inoculation is needed. *Zooplankton inoculation* is the addition of zooplankton to pond water to promote increased zooplankton growth. Water samples from another pond with high zooplankton are collected and moved to the pond where increased zooplankton growth is desired. Zooplankton inoculation is sometimes called seeding.

Growing yellow perch in cages is relatively unproven. Stocking rates are similar to those of other species. In areas where pond surfaces may freeze in the winter, aeration equipment is used to keep the tops of cages from freezing over. Fish in cages also benefit from high amounts of zooplankton.

Intensive culture in tanks and raceways is limited. Water flow-through or recirculation is used. Water DO must be maintained above 3.0. Wastes must be removed from the water with filtration systems.

Marketing

The yellow perch (*Perca flavescens*) is a popular game fish and may be used for fee fishing. The species is also known as lake perch in local markets.

Yellow perch are commercially produced for the food market at weights of 3 to 5 pounds (1.3 to 2.3 kg). The fish are seined or trapped from lakes or ponds. They may be sold live to niche markets or dressed and sold fresh or frozen.

As with all species, a market should be in place before steps are taken to produce a crop.

WALLEYE

Walleye (*Stizostedion vitreum*) have been cultured on a limited basis since the late 1800s. More has been learned about walleye culture in recent years, though the fish is not widely cultured as a commercial food species. The walleye is olive brown to yellowish gold, with sides having brassy flecks. Its fins do not have spots. The lower tip of its tail fin is white.

Walleye are widely used as sport fish in the northern states. They typically grow best in water that is a little too warm for trout and too cool for catfish or tilapia.

Walleye are primarily cultured in ponds. In nature, walleye prefer streams and lakes with gravel or sand bottoms. In many respects, walleye culture is much like yellow perch culture, though some differences exist.

The best water temperature range for walleye is 71° to 77°F (22° to 25°C). Spawning begins naturally in the spring when the water temperature reaches 50°F (10°C). Walleye can survive water temperatures of 34° to 91°F (1° to 33°C). Walleye prefer a dissolved oxygen level of 5 ppm or higher and a pH of 7 to 8.

In the wild, walleye are predatory of other fish. This presents problems in culturing walleye. Most walleye are graded by size to avoid larger fish eating the smaller fish. Even after being trained to eat artificial feed, walleye will eat other fish.

13–25. A walleye. (Courtesy, U.S. Fish and Wildlife Service)

Wild walleye are often used in producing young. As ice disappears, the adult walleye are captured in the wild from lake areas and are moved to holding tanks. Eggs are stripped from ripe females and fertilized with stripped milt from males.

Fertile eggs are usually incubated in hatching jars at a water temperature of 48° to 60°F (9° to 16°C). Hatching occurs in 10 to 25 days, with eggs in warmer water hatching more quickly. Newly hatched fry are reared in ponds for growing into fingerlings. Commercial feed is provided as a fine meal at about 50 percent protein. Due to cannibalism, the number of walleye in a pond may be very unpredictable. The fingerling-size walleye are released into streams to enhance the wild stock.

SAUGER

The sauger (*Stizostedion canadense*) is similar to other members of the perch family. It is somewhat smaller than the walleye, rarely weighing 3 pounds when mature. A characteristic that distinguishes it from the walleye and the yellow perch is the presence of rows of dark spots on its dorsal fin. Its lower tail tip is not white, as is that of the walleye.

Hybrid sauger have shown potential for culture. Crossing a walleye female with a sauger male has resulted in offspring that grow faster and are less stressed by handling than sauger. The hybrid is also less aggressive toward other fish.

Sauger naturally spawn in the spring when the water temperature is 39° to 43°F (3.9° to 6.1°C). One female will lay 15,000 to 40,000 eggs for each pound of body weight. Eggs fall to the bottoms of lakes and streams. Hatching is 25 to 29 days following spawning. Fry feed on zooplankton and aquatic insects. Maturity is reached in two to three years by males and in four to six years by females.

13–26. A sauger. (Courtesy, U.S. Fish and Wildlife Service)

Over the years, the popularity of sauger as a sport fish has declined. As with other perch, cannibalism is a problem with the wild population that is magnified with intensive culture situations. Natural foods are important.

STURGEON

Sturgeon are known for their longevity and size. They are popular as a source of roe, which is used to make caviar (salted roe). One female may produce several million eggs when stripped. Most of the females are quite large and are killed during stripping. The population of sturgeon has been greatly reduced because of the demand for caviar. Further,

13–27. Green sturgeon. (Courtesy, Dan Gotshall, Sea Challengers, Monterey, California)

females do not reach sexual maturity until at least six years of age. Some may not reproduce until they are 20 years old.

A primitive species, sturgeon have a smooth, scaleless body with bony structures along the sides known as *lateral plates*. The number of lateral plates on a fish ranges from 24 to 35. Some sturgeon grow quite large and may reach nearly 10 feet (3 m) long and weigh as much as 265 pounds (120 kg).

Sturgeon have skeletons consisting mostly of cartilage. Their skeletal history dates back about 150 million years.

Twenty-six species of sturgeon are found, with eight in North America. For example, the white sturgeon and the green sturgeon are found on the Pacific Coast. The United Nations Convention on International Trade restricts the import and export of sturgeon because of declining populations caused by great demand for caviar.

SPECIES

As mentioned, eight species of sturgeon are found in North America. The white sturgeon (*Acipenser transmontanus*), green sturgeon (*A. medirostris*), shortnose sturgeon (*A. brevirostrum*), lake sturgeon (*A. fulvescens*), and Atlantic sturgeon (*A. oxyrhynchus*) are most common. Three species are found in the Mississippi River basin. They are the shovelnose (*Scaphirhynchus platorynchus*), pallid (*S. albus*), and Alabama (*S. suttkusi*).

13–28. A shortnose sturgeon. (Courtesy, U.S. Fish and Wildlife Service)

BROODSTOCK

Broodstock are typically captured from the wild, though some efforts at establishing captive broodstock are underway. Broodstock are typically taken from spawning areas during the spawning season, when both eggs and milt are ripe. Handling and transporting sturgeon calls for good equipment and procedures. Some sturgeon may require two or more people to move them. An individual fish may be placed on a stretcher, with two or four people carrying the stretcher. Tanks may be used to hold broodstock for long-term use and study.

Scientists have developed new procedures for removing eggs so the fish is not sacrificed. In the past, many female sturgeon were cut open to get the eggs. The flesh was discarded. This practice of *fish sacrifice* is no longer needed. Using surgery, the female is opened and the eggs are removed. The incision is sutured, and the fish returned to the tank.

13–29. A pallid sturgeon broodfish in a hatchery operated by the U.S. Fish and Wildlife Service. (Courtesy, U.S. Fish and Wildlife Service)

Most broodstock are obtained from hatcheries and transported for spawning. They can be hauled in 300- to 500-gallon tanks at the rate of 2 pounds of fish per gallon of water (1 kg/L). Salt should be added to the water at the rate of 0.2 to 0.4 pound per gallon (25 to 50 g/L). Aeration is essential. Broodfish are moved from water on a stretcher-type canvass to prevent injury. Procedures for determining spawning times and removing eggs for artificial fertilization are detailed and best learned through further study and through practice with an experienced sturgeon producer.

Eggs are incubated in incubation jars, hatching troughs, and other systems. Research is being carried out to identify the best hatching procedures. A water hatching temperature of 60°F (16°C) is considered best. Incubation time is short, with the eggs hatching in two to three days. The yolk sacs are absorbed in five to ten days. Survival rate is low but can be enhanced by keeping sturgeon fry in the rearing facility for several weeks. In some cases, juvenile sturgeon have been kept for two years to assure higher survival rate when released into natural environments.

REARING

Sturgeon are typically anadromous. This means that they spend part of their lives in salt water and return to fresh water to spawn. Other sturgeon remain permanently in fresh water and thrive without ever going into salt water. Some live quite long, such as the Atlantic sturgeon (*Acipenser oxyrhynchus*), which can live up to 80 years. Maturity may take several years. Females may not spawn until 20 years old and only once every 2 to 5 years. Males mature a few years sooner than females. Females typically spawn on the bottoms of flowing streams in rocks and gravel. Females release up to several million eggs at one spawning. Eggs hatch in five days in water that is 68°F (20°C).

13–30. An adult pallid sturgeon being released in efforts to enhance stream populations of sturgeon. (Courtesy, U.S. Fish and Wildlife Service)

Rearing juvenile sturgeon is often thought to be the most difficult step. Careful attention is needed to feeding and to water conditions. Sturgeon are often grown out in circular tanks.

Sturgeon are susceptible to a few diseases. Viruses have posed problems in cultured sturgeon populations. Bacterial infections are rare. Fungi sometimes attack the eggs in incubator environments. Diseased eggs can be removed by a process known as picking. A salt bath of 2.6 milligrams per liter for 30 to 60 minutes is usually effective in controlling egg fungi.

PIKES

Members of the pike family are found in cool or cold fresh water. These include northern pike, chain pickerel, and muskellunge, or muskie. Most of these are cultured on a limited basis primarily to replenish wild stocks in streams and lakes.

Northern Pike

The northern pike (*Esox lucius*) is found in arctic and temperate areas of the Northern Hemisphere. Mature northern pike weigh 22 to 33 pounds (10 to 15 kg), though some as

13–31. Northern pike. (Courtesy, U.S. Fish and Wildlife Service)

large as 44 pounds (20 kg) have been captured. The northern pike may reach a length of 4 feet (1.2 m). It has a bluish- or greenish-gray color, with irregular rows of yellowish or whitish spots.

Commonly, northern pike broodfish are caught in nets in their native habitat and taken to hatcheries for spawning. Knotless nylon netting is used to prevent injury to the fish. Spawning naturally occurs when the water temperature reaches 40° to 52°F (4° to 11°C). Spawning occurs during daylight hours in marshes, bays, and similar low areas. The eggs are spawned scattered about on aquatic vegetation. One female may produce 32,000 eggs that adhere together. Several males may fertilize one female's spawn.

Eggs are incubated in hatching jars. A jar will incubate 30,000 to 68,000 eggs. Flowing water is needed in the jars. Gravel is placed in the bottom

13–32. Preferred habitat for spawning of northern pike. (Courtesy, U.S. Fish and Wildlife Service)

of the jars. Water temperature for incubation should be 48° to 55°F (8.9° to 12.8°C). Treatment with formalin to control fungal disease may be needed.

Eggs hatch in 12 to 14 days. Fry are attached by adhesive glands on their heads to the vegetation where the eggs were. The fry are moved to water a few degrees warmer than the hatching water. The yolk sacs are absorbed in six to ten days, and the fry begin feeding. Zooplankton and aquatic insect larvae are the primary foods. As the fingerlings grow, they switch to a diet of fish. Adult northern pike feed on fish and other available animals. Growth is not efficient, as 5 to 6 pounds (2.26 to 2.72 kg) of food are required for 1 pound (0.45 kg) of gain.

13–33. The Nowitna National Wildlife Refuge in Canada provides an ideal environment for the northern pike. (Courtesy, U.S. Fish and Wildlife Service)

Growth rate depends on the forage available. Supplemental feeding is typically used. Feeders may be used to provide feed manufactured specifically for coolwater fish. Female northern pike grow faster and larger than males, with both males and females reaching lengths of 10 to 12 inches (25 to 27 cm) in one growing season. Predation and cannibalism are particular problems.

CHAIN PICKEREL

The chain pickerel (*Esox niger*) is one of three species of pickerels in the United States. It is a native of slow-moving streams and lakes with dense vegetation. The fish are found in the northern and southern parts of the eastern United States and in Canada. The chain pickerel is a voracious predator of sunfish, catfish, minnows, and pickerel. They may weigh up to 10 pounds (4.5 kg) and reach lengths of 3 feet (91 cm). Overall, the chain pickerel is a long, sleek, yellowish-green fish. The chain pickerel will sometimes naturally hybridize with grass pickerel or redfin pickerel.

A female chain pickerel will produce 8,000 eggs at one spawning. Spawning is naturally in the spring when the water temperature rises to 47° to 52°F (8.3° to 11.1°C). Spawning occurs in the daytime in areas that are 3 to 10 feet (1 to 3 m) deep. Eggs hatch in 6 to 12 days. The fry, similar to northern pike, have adhesive glands on their snouts for attaching to vegetation. After the yolk sacs are absorbed in a few days, the fry begin feeding on tiny invertebrates and larval fish.

Cultural practices are similar to those used with northern pike.

MUSKELLUNGE

Muskellunge (*Esox masquinongy*) are found in pools that form in streams and rivers in the northeastern United States. They eat large amounts of other fish and may destroy a population if accidentally introduced into a lake or stream. During the growing season, muskellunge, or muskies, prefer water that is 64° to 77°F (17.8° to 25°C).

13–34. Muskellunge. (Courtesy, U.S. Fish and Wildlife Service)

Spawning naturally occurs in the spring when water temperature rises to 49° to 59°F (9.4° to 15°C). Eggs are scattered over vegetation in the water. One female can produce 120,000 eggs per spawning. Hatching is in 8 to 14 days when water temperature is 53° to 63°F (11.7° to 17.2°C). In hatcheries, eggs and milt are expressed and mixed for fertilization. Eggs are incubated in hatching jars similar to the eggs of northern pike. Vertical-flow and other kinds of incubators are used with fry. Special techniques are often used, and these are best learned through firsthand experience. Fry are moved to ponds when about nine days old. Zooplankton and other natural foods are consumed.

Muskies do not readily accept artificial food. Fingerlings are very cannibalistic. To avoid population losses, carp, goldfish, and other small species may be stocked with the fingerlings. Muskies make good use of forage fish and have a feed conversion ratio of 1.0 pound (0.45 kg) of gain to 2.75 pounds (1.3 kg) of feed.

Northern pike males are sometimes crossed with muskie females to create a hybrid known as tiger muskellunge. The hybrid has vigorous growth. Research is underway to determine other benefits and to develop commercial approaches to production.

REVIEWING

MAIN IDEAS

Several species of aquacrops are adapted to farming in cool fresh water. The major ones are trout, walleye, and sturgeon. Trout is, by far, the predominant species produced for food and sport uses.

When considering which cool-freshwater aquacrops to produce, these basic principles are important:

1. Select only a species adapted to the production system to be used.
2. Select only a species adapted to the cool fresh water available.
3. Feed an aquacrop on the basis of its nutritional needs.
4. Ensure good health by following management practices appropriate to the species being produced.
5. Maintain quality water by using production practices that minimize the possibilities of problems and make water more suitable for the species being produced.
6. Select a species for which there is a market.

Trout require an abundance of cool, flowing, pollution-free fresh water with a temperature near 55° to 58°F (12.8° to 14.4°C). Several species are grown, with rainbow trout being the most popular for food and sport. Many trout species are quite similar in appearance. In some cases, varieties of trout have been developed over the years by selecting from the species. Artificial spawning and hatching are commonly used with trout. Incubation time is based on degree days, which is the product of the average water temperature (in degrees Celsius) times the number of days required for hatching. Trout eggs hatch more quickly in warmer water, but the temperature usually does not exceed 54°F (12°C).

Yellow perch, walleye, and sauger are popular with sport fishers. These members of the perch family have similar cultural needs.

The sturgeon is a popular source of roe for making caviar. Because female sturgeon are often destroyed to get caviar, wild population numbers are becoming low. Efforts are underway to replenish wild stock with sturgeon produced in hatcheries.

The pike family has three species of particular note in North America. The northern pike, the chain pickerel, and the muskellunge share similar habitats and cultural practices.

QUESTIONS

Answer the following questions, using complete sentences and correct spelling.

1. What are six important fundamentals of cool-freshwater aquaculture? Briefly describe each.
2. What are three cool-freshwater aquacrops? Which is most important? (Include both the common and the scientific names of each.)

3. Describe the trout species as they relate to the following:

    a. Species cultured

    b. Identification

    c. Size

    d. Environment required

    e. Seedstock (Include natural and artificial spawning and hatching.)

    f. Culture and stocking

    g. Feeding

    h. Diseases

    i. Harvesting

    j. Marketing

4. What are the general cultural practices for members of the perch family? Identify three perch species by both common and scientific names.

5. What are the characteristics of three members of the pike family? Include the common and the scientific names of each species.

6. How suited are cool-freshwater species for culture in your community? Write a short paragraph that explains your assessment.

EVALUATING

Match the term with the correct definition. Write the letter of the term on the line provided.

a. cool-freshwater aquacrop
b. host
c. milt
d. ripe
e. eyespot

f. degree days
g. lateral plates
h. fish sacrifice
i. egg ribbon
j. zooplankton inoculation

_____1. The killing of female fish to collect eggs

_____2. Fluid containing sperm

_____3. A fish species that lives in water below 70°F

_____4. An organism on which a parasite lives and from which it derives nourishment

_____5. Condition of female fish with fully developed eggs

_____6. A dark spot that shows the developing embryo in an egg

_____7. A measurement of the amount of time required for eggs to hatch

_____8. Bony structures on the sides of sturgeon

_____9. The addition of water from a source with good zooplankton growth to water with poor zooplankton growth

_____10. The gelatin strip of eggs produced by some female fish

EXPLORING

1. Find a spring or freshwater stream in your community. Assess the potential of the water for growing a cool-freshwater aquacrop. Prepare a report of your findings, including a careful and detailed analysis of the water you selected. Note: Be sure to follow all safety precautions around water.

2. Use a size grader to sort a small batch of fish. Determine the importance of grading with the particular species you have available. Prepare a report on your findings.

3. Prepare a bulletin board or poster that depicts the production of trout.

CHAPTER 14

Saltwater and Brackish-Water Aquacrops

This chapter presents the primary species of aquacrops cultured in salt water and in brackish water in and around the United States. It has the following objectives:

1 Discuss fundamentals of saltwater and brackish-water aquaculture

2 Identify and explain the kinds of facilities and sites used in saltwater and brackish-water aquaculture

3 Identify and explain production considerations in saltwater and brackish-water aquaculture

4 Discuss areas of government regulation in saltwater and brackish-water aquaculture

5 Discuss the culture of shrimp

6 Discuss the culture of salmon

7 Discuss the culture of mollusks, including oysters, clams, mussels, scallops, and gastropods

8 Discuss the culture of lobsters and blue crabs

9 Discuss the culture of other fish, including striped mullet, milkfish, pompano, red drum, cobia, flounder, grouper, threadfin, and mahimahi

TERMS

adductor muscle
alevin
artemia
brine bath
byssus
chlorinity
cultch
depuration
desiccation
diatoms

escargot
estuarine water
eyestalk ablation
fish ladder
gonad releasing
   hormone
gravid
heliciculture
hermaphrodite
hydrometer

intertidal zone
marine water
naiad
natal stream
nauplii
open ocean
redds
refractometer
salinity
salmon farming

salmon ranching
seabed zone
shore
sluice gate
soft crab
spat
sublittoral zone

14–1. Aquacrops are sometimes grown for uses other than food. An example is the oyster cultivated for pearl production. This shows a technician demonstrating how to remove a cultured pearl from an oyster. (Courtesy, National Oceanic and Atmospheric Administration)

AQUACULTURE in salt water and in brackish water has many variations. The types of animals cultured in salt water and in brackish water include several species of fish, mollusks, gastropods, and crustaceans.

In almost all cases, cultured saltwater and brackish-water aquacrops must compete with wild catch. Of course, commercial wild catch operations have the advantage of not spending money on inputs—feed, facilities, and stock. The primary disadvantage of wild catch operations is that the animals are not always readily available—either they are not available at all or they are not available nearby, thus increasing shipping costs. In addition, some areas have been overharvested, and the fish population has been depleted.

Aquaculture has the advantage of producing quality products that are readily available. This is an important advantage for restaurants and retail outlets that want consistently available products.

FUNDAMENTALS OF SALTWATER AND BRACKISH-WATER AQUACULTURE

The United States has considerable saltwater and brackish-water areas that may be suitable for aquaculture. Shorelines along the boundaries of the United States touch about half the states. Major shorelines are along the Atlantic Ocean, the Gulf of Mexico, and the Pacific Ocean. In addition, the Great Lakes and other bodies of water provide opportunities for aquaculture.

Fifteen states have shorelines on the Atlantic Ocean, five states have shorelines on the Gulf of Mexico, and five states have shorelines on the Pacific Ocean. Hawaii, which is made up of islands, is totally surrounded by the Pacific. All together, the United States has 88,633 miles of shoreline. Territories and possessions add even greater shoreline to the total available.

14–2. An exhibit on mahimahi (*Corhyphaena hippurus*) at the Honolulu Aquarium shows the importance of mariculture.

Saltwater and brackish-water aquaculture, known as mariculture, involves the production of aquacrops in marine or estuarine waters. ***Marine water*** is the water in the oceans and gulfs, which is primarily salt water. ***Estuarine water*** is the water in bays, inlets, and mouths of rivers, where salt water and fresh water are mixed. This section describes salinity and production considerations.

Saltwater and brackish-water species make up more than half the imports of fish and seafood into the United States. The potential economic advantage of producing these species is excellent. Fresh and frozen shrimp valued at about $3 billion was imported in a recent year. While ocean catches of shrimp and other seafood remain constant or decrease, the demand for these products has increased. Aquaculture has the potential to fill part of the void.

14–3. Offshore cage near an oil rig in the Gulf of Mexico at sunset. (Courtesy, National Oceanic and Atmospheric Administration)

Salinity

In general terms, *salinity* is the amount of salt in water. The precise definition is more complicated. Salinity is often stated as parts per thousand (ppt). A measure of salinity technically refers to the total amount of solid material in 1 kilogram of water when all carbonates and organic material have been completely oxidized. Under such conditions, the following formula will provide the salinity: salinity = 0.03 + 1.805 × chlorinity.

Chlorinity is the total amount of chlorine, bromine, and iodine, in grams, contained in 1 kilogram of water. A precise definition of salinity is not usually a concern.

Two methods of measuring salinity for aquaculture production are commonly used. These are (1) measuring the density of the water and (2) measuring the refractive index of the water.

The measurement of salinity by density is the least expensive method. A *hydrometer* is used to measure density. The reading is converted to salinity with the use of a conversion table. Readings from hydrometers are very accurate.

The easiest method of measuring salinity is through refractometry, although a refractometer costs more than

14–4. Using a refractometer to test water salinity. (Courtesy, Forestry Suppliers, Jackson, MS)

a hydrometer. A **refractometer** resembles a pocket telescope and requires only one drop of water for salinity measurement. Once the drop of water is placed on the refractometer, the salinity is read from the scale usually provided on the instrument. Some refractometers will require a conversion table. A refractometer is usually accurate to within 0.5 ppt, while a hydrometer is more accurate.

Although various classifications exist, fresh water is typically considered less than 0.5 ppt. Salt water is usually defined as 16.5 ppt or greater. The range between fresh water and salt water is brackish water. The open ocean averages about 35.0 ppt salinity.

The species in this chapter vary widely in the amount and range of salinity needed in the water in which they are raised. Salmon, for example, are anadromous, which means they spend most of their lives in salt water but return to fresh water to spawn. Several species found naturally in salt water or brackish water, such as the red drum and the striped mullet, have the potential for production in fresh water. Conversely, some freshwater species, for example, a few tilapia species and the rainbow trout, have shown tolerance for moderate levels of salinity and could be reared in salt water.

Table 14–1. Examples of Saltwater Species

Common Name	Scientific Name	Use
Cobia	*Rachycentron canadum*	Food
Grouper, Nassau	*Epinephelus striatus*	Food
Milkfish	*Chanos chanos*	Food
Pacific threadfin	*Polydactylus sexfilis*	Food
Pompano	*Trachinotus carolinus*	Food
Red drum	*Sciaenops ocellata*	Food
Salmon,*		
Atlantic	*Salmo salar*	Food
chinook	*Onchorynchus tshawytscha*	Food
coho	*Onchorynchus kisutch*	Food
pink	*Onchorynchus gorbuscha*	Food
sockeye	*Onchorynchus nerka*	Food
Shrimp,		
brown	*Fenneropenaeus aztecus*	Food
pink	*Farfantepenaeus duorarum*	Food
white	*Litopenaeus vannamei*	Food

*Anadromous species.

Table 14–2. Examples of Brackish-Water Species

Common Name	Scientific Name	Use
Bivalve Mollusks:		
Clam,		
quahog	*Mercenaria mercenaria*	Food
soft	*Mya arenaria*	Food
Mussel,		
blue	*Mytilus edulis*	Food
green-lipped	*Perna canaliculus*	Food
Oyster,		
Eastern	*Crassostrea virginica*	Food
European	*Ostrea edulis*	Food
Pacific cupped	*Crassostrea gigas*	Food
Pacific kumamoto	*Crassostrea sikamea*	Food
Scallop,		
bay	*Argopecten irradians*	Food
sea	*Plactopecten magellanicus*	Food
Gastropods:		
Abalone, red	*Haliotis rufescens*	Food
Crustaceans:		
Crab, blue	*Callinectes sapidus*	Food
Lobster, American	*Homarus americanus*	Food
Fish:		
Flounder, southern*	*Paralichthys lethostigma*	Food
Mullet, striped**	*Mugil cephalus*	Manufacturing***

*Will grow in fresh or brackish water.

**One of a few fish cultured in brackish water.

***Species is used in manufacturing fish meal and other products; limited human food use.

SITES AND FACILITIES

The relationship of the site to the ocean or gulf and to the type of facility used is important to the success of saltwater or brackish-water aquaculture. The species produced, the facility used, and the suitability of available land or water for aquaculture are other important factors. The various zones for saltwater and brackish-water aquaculture are the shore, the intertidal, the sublittoral, the seabed, and the open ocean.

14–5. A net pen off the shore of California. (Courtesy, National Oceanic and Atmospheric Administration)

14–6. Mesh netting around the drain pipe keeps the aquacrop from escaping.

SHORE

The **shore** is the land next to the ocean. It is used as the site for most hatcheries in order to reduce transportation costs. The primary advantage of using the shore is that the tides do not affect the water level of the facilities, only the seawater outlet and inlet. The primary disadvantages are that seawater must be pumped into the facilities and that freshwater runoff into the facilities may be a problem in saltwater ponds.

Planning facilities on the shore is simple because, as mentioned, the tides do not affect the facilities. Ponds and tanks are the primary facilities used in the shore zone.

INTERTIDAL

The **intertidal zone** is the area covered with water during a high tide but not during a low tide. The primary advantage of using the intertidal zone is that pumps do not have to be used to pump water into a facility or to pump water out to harvest the crop or treat the pond bottom. Another advantage is the easy access provided to the facility at a low tide. The primary disadvantage is that the tides must be studied. Careful planning is required to build the facility so that the tides will be a help and not a hindrance. Ponds should be built for easy adjustment of the water level during a high tide and easy drainage during a low tide.

The intertidal zone is used primarily to build ponds that hold the water in but that have sluice gates. A **sluice gate** is a structure that allows the flow of seawater in and the flow of fresh water out. It is also used for some culture of mollusks on the bottom, but this requires careful management.

SUBLITTORAL

The **sublittoral zone** includes shallow (usually 5- to 100-feet-deep) inshore areas, such as bays and lagoons. The sublittoral zone has the advantage of always having water. Its primary disadvantages are the reduced access afforded by land and the amount of fresh water that may be introduced into the bays during heavy rains. The fresh water is usually not a concern for brackish-water aquacrops.

When selecting a facility for use in the sublittoral zone, the difference between the water level at a high

14–7. Tank system designed to assure efficient water use.

tide and at a low tide is very important. Ideally, the difference would be as small as possible, while allowing adequate movement of water at low tide. Stocking densities are calculated at the low-tide level. Water movement, however, is important for removing wastes and for providing adequate food for some species, such as shrimp.

The sublittoral is the zone of choice for net enclosures used in the production of many saltwater and brackish-water species, including salmon and shrimp. The nets are placed at the outlet end of the bay to keep the aquacrop in but to allow the movement of water both in and out. Because the nets do not have to be placed around the land edges, the enclosures are inexpensive compared with water available to the contained aquacrop. The major concern is to keep the nets clean so that water movement is not restricted.

Sublittoral facilities are also good choices for floating cages for fish production and rafts for mollusk production. Of course, the fish cages require more intensive management, including daily feeding. When fish cages are used, some regular means of access is necessary. Once mollusks are placed on their rafts or other structures, they require almost no supervision.

SEABED

The **seabed zone** is the ground always covered by the sea. Generally, the seabed offers a constant rate of salinity, its primary advantage. The primary disadvantages are that access to the aquacrop is limited and that the aquacrop must be enclosed to keep it from escaping. This usually limits seabed production to mollusks or crustaceans (in cages moored to the bed).

14–8. An oyster bed in the seabed zone. (Courtesy, National Oceanic and Atmospheric Administration)

14–9. An offshore sea cage is being towed into position. (Courtesy, National Oceanic and Atmospheric Administration)

Before the seabed is selected as a site, the area under consideration must be checked for dissolved oxygen levels and pollutants. Water currents must also be adequate to provide for the removal of wastes and to bring in food for the aquacrop.

The seabed is an excellent choice for mollusk aquaculture, as long as it is not too silty. Also, pens moored to the seabed or to a dock often provide a suitable environment for shrimp.

OPEN OCEAN

The **open ocean** is the area of the ocean that is away from the shore and is not readily affected by tides and the inflow of fresh water. The water may be quite deep and unprotected by land areas. Much of the open ocean is outside the territorial limits of nations and is under control of international law.

14–10. Underwater view of a subsurface sea cage 40 feet below the offshore surface. Note divers on the right side. (Courtesy, National Oceanic and Atmospheric Administration)

14–11. A floating offshore cage. (Courtesy, National Oceanic and Atmospheric Administration)

PRODUCTION CONSIDERATIONS

As with freshwater aquacrops, saltwater species may be produced in several kinds of facilities. Some facilities are practical for large-scale use; others are not. Most emphasis is on using natural areas of oceans and bays rather than tanks, ponds, and raceways.

A major consideration in the production of saltwater and brackish-water species is finding a suitable location. Very few people own parts of the ocean, bays, or other such waterways. Generally, the water used for saltwater and brackish-water aquaculture (the oceans, gulfs, bays, and river mouths) is considered public. States with water in these kinds of areas typically have laws that allow limited leasing for aquaculture production.

The location available must be appropriate for the species to be produced. Oysters and clams require different environments from cobia and salmon. This means that the producer must select a species that will thrive at the site that is available.

If tanks and other manufactured facilities are used for saltwater and brackish-water aquaculture, special considerations must be taken. The higher the salinity of the water, the more corrosive it becomes to metal parts. Any metal parts used with salt water must be protected from the water.

Water-quality management is different in saltwater and brackish-water facilities. If water of the same salinity is added to a closed recirculating system or to a static system, such as a pond, the salinity of the facility will constantly increase as the water evaporates but the salts do not. Fresh water must be added periodically to lower the salinity. If the water coming into a facility is too low in salinity, the salinity may be raised by adding artificial sea salts. This can be expensive if large amounts are needed. If the water used is drawn from a well, its salinity tends to be more stable than if it is drawn from surface water.

REGULATIONS

Laws and other regulations impacting aquaculture are primarily those of federal and state governments. The major federal law is the National Aquaculture Act, which was enacted in 1980 to promote aquaculture in the United States. An interagency coordinating group was established for aquaculture. The U.S. Department of Agriculture is the lead agency. Other agencies are part of gaining permission to carry out aquaculture. Here are a few examples:

- Corps of Engineers—The U.S. Army Corps of Engineers issues permits related to water use, including navigation and water access, international trade and security, and environmental interests.

- Environmental Protection Agency—The Environmental Protection Agency (EPA) issues permits that allows aquaculture under provisions of the Clean Water Act. This includes the issuance of wastewater discharge permits in the open ocean. Provisions of the Ocean Dumping Act of 1999 are enforced by the EPA.

- National Marine Fisheries Service—The National Marine Fisheries Service (NMFS) issues letters of authorization or permits for coastal areas and for parts of oceans within the boundaries of the United States. All commercial fishing operations are under jurisdiction of the NMFS.

- Coast Guard—The U.S. Coast Guard has authority in matters of safety and hazardous situations. It enforces all laws and treaties on the seas and navigable waters of the United States. The Coast Guard is responsible for protecting life and property on the ocean. Beacons, buoys, and other signals, including radio, used in navigating oceans and streams are under jurisdiction of the Coast Guard.

International, federal, and state regulations are in place to protect natural fishing stocks from depletion. These regulations protect endangered species and control the acquisition of stock for culture in salt water and brackish water. Many states have minimum size requirements for the catch or sale of certain species. Sometimes, possessing the size aquacrop needed to stock a facility is illegal. Usually, permits can be obtained either to catch fry for stocking or to buy suitable fry from hatcheries.

Another area of regulation relates to seasons and hours of operation. Many states have closed seasons, which are designed to protect species during times of spawning and to ensure wholesome food products. Normally, this kind of regulation would not affect aquaculture. The laws are problems, however, if they prohibit the sale of species when the seasons are closed. This results in missing marketing opportunities when demand is high and supplies of commercially landed species are gone. Fortunately, several states have recognized aquaculture as agriculture. This makes special permits for sale of protected species unnecessary. States also have regulations on the hours of operation, such as the time of day when commercial fishing may take place. Individuals considering going into aquaculture may get information by contacting the aquaculture coordinator in the department of agriculture for their state.

Though a number of species offer possibilities, the three most important saltwater and brackish-water aquacrops are shrimp, salmon, and mollusks. Several species of these three types of aquacrops are produced in U.S. coastal waters. More information about the species is presented in the following sections.

SHRIMP

The shrimp is the most important and extensively farmed crustacean in the world. Two factors cause shrimp to be ideal for intensive cultivation: (1) they grow rapidly in intensive production facilities, and (2) there is a great demand for shrimp around the world, especially in the United States.

The most common shrimp grown in the United States are penaeid shrimp. Three species most commonly grown are the brown shrimp (*Fenneropenaeus aztecus*), the white shrimp (*Litopenaeus vannamei*), and the pink shrimp (*Farfantepenaeus duorarum*).

Shrimp have been widely cultured in Asia for many years. Their culture is relatively new in the United States. In historic aquaculture operations, shrimp were cultured almost by accident in brackish-water ponds and estuaries as part of a polyculture with fish. The monoculture of shrimp is a relatively new area of aquaculture.

14–12. White shrimp are the most important in North America.

14–13. A crew member on a double-rigged shrimp trawler is preparing to open a net bag of harvested wild shrimp. (Courtesy, National Oceanic and Atmospheric Administration)

Several factors point to an increase in the culture of shrimp. Although the most abundant supply of shrimp in the world is in the Gulf of Mexico, shrimpers (commercial fishing operations) cannot supply even half the demand. Shrimp usually grow well in intensive-culture operations.

Native shrimp provide a large fishery, especially in the Gulf of Mexico. Aquaculture of shrimp, however, is mainly found in Hawaii, Texas, and South Carolina.

GETTING SEEDSTOCK

A major problem in culturing shrimp has been finding a good source of broodstock. Although shrimp are easily spawned in captivity and reared through the larval and juvenile stages, they do not usually produce eggs or copulate under captive conditions in ponds. In the last few years, more shrimp hatcheries have begun using new methods of controlled spawning. One of these is eyestalk ablation. *Eyestalk ablation* involves cutting one eye of a female shrimp, which in turn causes her to produce eggs.

Shrimp are not always available from a hatchery. Two other means of stocking growing facilities are catching larval shrimp for stocking and catching *gravid* (pregnant) females. The captured gravid females are moved to hatcheries, where their offspring can be hatched and grown to stocking size.

Catching larval shrimp for stocking is a difficult venture. Two ways of catching larval shrimp are seining with very fine mesh seines and building tidal ponds with sluice gates. These gates allow larval shrimp to enter the pond with the water from the rising tide. Both ways have serious problems. Catching larval shrimp with the use of seines usually results in a high mortality rate, so many more shrimp must be caught than are needed. Seining by hand is feasible only during certain times of the year when the larval shrimp are most numerous in tidal streams. Tidal ponds constructed so the tides carry larval shrimp into the ponds may also allow larval predators to get into the ponds with the tide. This leads to the loss of shrimp as the predators mature.

Capturing gravid females and moving them to hatcheries may be even more difficult than capturing larval shrimp for stocking. The mortality rate for shrimp caught by seining with a boat is usually 85 percent or greater, no matter how carefully they are handled after being caught. Using cast nets results in fewer deaths but is not very efficient. Even when cast nets are used, not only must the females have eggs, but they

14–14. A facility that uses fiberglass tanks to rear fish.

must also be captured with spermatophores already attached, or they will not spawn. Once gravid females have been supplied to hatcheries, the process of hatching and rearing the shrimp through the larval and juvenile stages is usually successful.

The demand for shrimp and its potential as an aquacrop have led to much research on supplying seedstock. One new method being tried is to drive larval shrimp into tidal ponds or estuaries. Another method is to lure or draw the shrimp into the ponds. Larval shrimp attach themselves to seaweeds to keep from being washed back out to sea. Shrimp cling to these grass "lures." The grass can be pulled up, and the shrimp shaken into a dip net. Research is trying to find ways to provide many more shrimp than by simply opening a sluice gate and letting the tide bring them into a pond.

14–15. Young shrimp feeding on pellet made from soybean materials. (Courtesy, Agricultural Research Service, USDA)

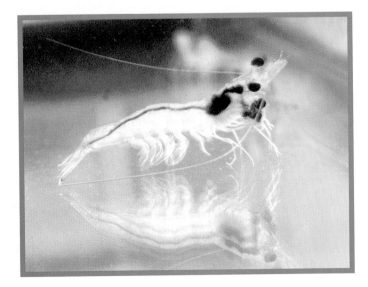

The advances in hatchery techniques, such as those being developed at the Oceanic Institute in Hawaii, will reduce the problem of obtaining seedstock. Hatcheries using these techniques will be able to provide reliable sources of healthy seedstock. This assurance should cause the shrimp aquaculture industry to grow rapidly.

Hatching

The hatchery techniques used in the United States have largely been adapted from those of the Japanese, who have been very successful in hatching shrimp. Once gravid females have been captured, they are placed in tanks of seawater. The seawater is replaced every one or two days. The best salinity for spawning is about 32 to 35 ppt, with the optimum temperature range between 72° and 91°F (22.2° and 32.8°C).

After hatching, the baby shrimp, called *nauplii*, go through several molts within the first three days. At this time, they begin eating microscopic plants and animals and are called larvae. The larvae move rapidly through the growth stages and are considered postlarvae after 10 to 12 days. The postlarvae are kept in tanks until they are between 30 and 40 days old and then are usually moved to nursery ponds.

The postlarvae remain in the nursery ponds for about 50 days or until they reach a weight of about 1 gram (0.035 ounce). The juveniles, called seedlings, are then stocked in the food production ponds at a rate of 30,000 to 40,000 per acre.

During these stages, the shrimp can withstand a wide range of salinity, from 15 to 37 ppt, although the optimum range is 27 to 32 ppt.

Larval shrimp must have an abundant supply of phytoplankton or other food, such as brine shrimp. Some hatcheries supply the phytoplankton by providing a high turnover of seawater in the facilities. Others supplement by adding cultured phytoplankton or brine shrimp to the diets. As the shrimp are moved into nursery and grow-out ponds, their diet may be supplemented with other foods, such as ground fish, chicken blood meal, and similar animal products. Commercially prepared feeds are also available. Some producers feed the shrimp by fertilizing ponds with some type of organic fertilizer to encourage phytoplankton growth.

Production Facilities

Shrimp are most commonly reared in ponds with an abundant supply of seawater nearby, although tanks and other facilities can be used. The facilities must allow for good movement of seawater to maintain a high level of phytoplankton, the shrimp's primary source of food. If intertidal ponds are used, the sluice gates must be large enough to keep the water pressure from becoming too great on the dam. Also, care is needed to find a site with enough clay in the soil to hold water, which is sometimes difficult in coastal areas.

An alternative to intertidal ponds is to use a sublittoral impoundment. This is created by placing a net or a sluice gate at the mouth of the impoundment. However, sublittoral impoundments with the right depth for shrimp production and the ability to keep fresh water out in periods of heavy rainfall are hard to find.

MANAGEMENT CONCERNS

One major concern in producing shrimp is to maintain the desired range of salinity in the water. As the shrimp get older, the range of salinity should be maintained at between 22 and 37 ppt. Older shrimp are not tolerant of lower salinities, so fresh water must be diverted away from the pond or growing facility.

Shrimp also grow best in the 70° to 90°F (21.1° to 32.2°C) temperature range, although they can tolerate higher and lower temperatures. Some mortality may occur, especially in white shrimp, if the air temperature drops quickly below 40°F (4.4°C).

Shrimp can usually grow to market size in about 150 days after stocking. The average facility in the United States produces about 1,000 pounds per acre, but much more can be produced as advanced methods of stocking are developed. The potential for yields of 4,000 to 5,000 pounds per acre under ideal growing conditions is good. These numbers commonly are reached and exceeded by Asian aquafarmers who produce shrimp.

The white shrimp grows best in pond culture. The brown shrimp grows more slowly than the white but is more tolerant of colder water. The pink shrimp does not do well in most

14–16. A high-quality, disease-free shrimp. (Courtesy, National Oceanic and Atmospheric Administration)

pond cultures because of its preference for sandy bottoms. All three species seem to grow well in tank culture. Tank culture is still in the experimental stage.

DISEASES

Because shrimp farming is new in the United States, little is known about the diseases of shrimp grown in intensive culture. Shrimp seem susceptible to a few diseases, with the viral diseases likely of greatest concern. Diseases to which shrimp are susceptible in nature will likely become more serious when shrimp in intensive-culture systems get them. A few of the reported diseases are included here.

Several bacteria species of the genera *Vibrio* and *Pseudomonas* may invade the body fluids and exoskeletons of shrimp. The bacteria do not harm the quality of the meat, but they may make the shrimp unsightly and hard to sell in the shell.

14–17. Grading harvested shrimp in preparation for marketing. (Courtesy, National Oceanic and Atmospheric Administration)

The most dangerous disease for larval shrimp is contracted from fungi of the genus *Lagenidium*. This disease is very contagious and fatal. It can be controlled with malachite green.

The cotton shrimp or milk shrimp disease is caused by a type of protozoan. Other protozoa may cause problems, but the extent is not yet known.

Shrimp may be invaded by cestodes, nematodes, and trematodes, although they are probably an intermediate host and have not suffered severe problems due to these parasites.

HARVESTING

Shrimp are usually harvested by hand with seines or dip nets. In a tidal pond, the sluice gate is opened to drain the water, and the shrimp are caught at the gate or seined from the lower water levels. Therefore, it is important that the pond not have any significant holes on the bottom where the shrimp can congregate and avoid harvesting.

14–18. Fresh shrimp and fish are for sale at this boat dock in Corpus Christi, Texas.

In some areas, the market for fresh shrimp may be such that the facility may need to be partially harvested every day or several times a week. Graded seines are used so the smaller shrimp, not ready for the market, are left to grow. This is a particular concern when shrimp are sold cooked or uncooked at roadside stands.

SALMON

Salmon—wild and cultured—make up an important part of U.S. fisheries. Consumer demand is high. This has led to a significant market for salmon. Salmon products are both exported and imported. More salmon are exported from the United States than any other fish or seafood. The exports are usually frozen or canned salmon. A significant amount of fresh salmon is imported. Aquaculture helps reduce the need to import by providing salmon year-round.

The United States, Japan, Canada, and the Commonwealth of Independent States (CIS) are the major countries with Pacific salmon fisheries. Norway is the largest producer of Atlantic salmon in the world, providing most

14–19. Research has provided considerable information about salmon. A technician is observing a large salmon in migration research. (Courtesy, U.S. Fish and Wildlife Service)

CONNECTION

EGG PICKING

Egg picking is used to remove infertile eggs during incubation. A salmon egg that is fertile turns pink to red as the embryo develops. An egg that is white or yellow is not developing a new salmon. (The darker egg is properly developing; the light-colored egg is not.)

Removing eggs that are not developing keeps down disease and damage to other eggs. Egg picking is a tedious process. Long, wooden tweezers are used to remove white eggs individually. Newer technology is being developed to replace hand egg picking.

14–20. Female (top left) and male (bottom left) sockeye salmon and female (top right) and male (bottom right) coho salmon. (Courtesy, Richard R. Whitney, Leavenworth, WA)

14–21. Chum (top), Atlantic (center), and pink (bottom) salmon. (Courtesy, U.S. Fish and Wildlife Service)

of the salmon imported by the United States that does not come from wild catch. Some salmon culture has developed in the northeastern United States.

Since cultured salmon have strong competition from wild harvest, production costs must be kept down. Products made from the wild catch are mostly exported. Even though the salmon were harvested from the wild, they were most likely hatched and reared as smolts in government and commercial hatcheries.

Because salmon are anadromous fish, their culture follows a particularly interesting process. Overall, two methods of salmon production are used: salmon farming and salmon ranching. Salmon ranching takes advantage of the natural instinct of salmon to return to their place of hatching to spawn. (Note that all salmon and other species closely related to them are sometimes referred to as salmonids.)

SPECIES PRODUCED

Three species of salmon are primarily cultured in the United States. These are the Atlantic salmon (*Salmo salar*), the chinook salmon (*Oncorhynchus tshawytscha*),

14–22. A hatchery in Washington State with the primary goal of replenishing native salmon stocks.

and the coho salmon (*O. kisutch*). The Atlantic salmon is really a trout (same genus as the brown trout). It is widely cultured in northern Europe. In the United States (primarily in Maine) and in Canada (New Brunswick and Prince Edward Island), culture has increased substantially in the last few years. The chinook and coho are cultured in areas of the Pacific Northwest—Washington, Oregon, northern California, and Alaska.

Three other species of Pacific salmon are cultured less extensively in the United States. These are *Oncorhynchus nerka* (sockeye salmon), *O. keta* (chum salmon), and *O. gorbuscha* (pink salmon). The culture of these salmon, also in the Pacific Northwest, is primarily in fish hatcheries used to replenish native stocks.

Government-supported salmon hatcheries have been producing seedstock of salmon for the commercial and sport-fishing industries for many years. Most of this production has been on the Pacific Coast of North America. The fish produced from these hatcheries are later caught, either at sea or on their journey back to their place of origin to spawn.

Fish ladders are often constructed on streams blocked by dams to allow salmon to migrate for natural spawning. A *fish ladder* is a stair-stepped structure that allows salmon to negotiate natal stream waters. The salmon return from the ocean for spawning and go to the ocean to grow into mature fish. Fish ladders help preserve the

14–23. The fish ladder at Rocky Reach Dam in Washington helps salmon negotiate natal stream waters. This ladder has 100 stair-stepped pools of water, each of which is 1 foot higher than the previous pool. The arrangement allows salmon to migrate for spawning and growth.

salmon population and overcome obstacles placed in the salmons' natural way of life by human activity.

Historically, salmon farmers have sometimes had a hard time making a profit for several reasons. The price of salmon may vary widely due to the uncertainty of the wild catch. Even when the wild catch is low, the lower costs of salmon ranching often make it more profitable than salmon farming.

Salmon producers who sell a fresh product to retail markets and restaurants are often more likely to be profitable. The ability to harvest from tanks, cages, and pens helps producers have a continuous supply of product. The salmon runs are so unpredictable that salmon ranchers cannot provide a year-round product.

OBTAINING SEEDSTOCK

Obtaining seedstock for salmon production is not a problem. Salmon that are ripe for spawning are easily caught as they make their way back to their *natal stream* (the place where they were hatched). Then, they are moved to hatcheries with tanks or to artificial spawning channels built into natural streams or rivers.

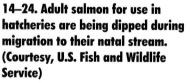

14–24. Adult salmon for use in hatcheries are being dipped during migration to their natal stream. (Courtesy, U.S. Fish and Wildlife Service)

Some artificial channels are built in areas that are near enough to natural spawning grounds to attract females ready to spawn. Other artificial channels are planted with fertilized eggs from hatcheries. These channels typically have beds of medium to fine gravel (approximately 2 to 8 inches in circumference). A steady supply of running water (with dissolved oxygen levels near saturation) is needed. The water temperature should be between 50° and 60°F (10° and 15.6°C). The temperature and flow of water may be managed with water from a dam or a main channel.

14–25. Salmon roe. (Courtesy, U.S. Fish and Wildlife Service)

The time of year when broodstock can be caught varies with the species. The chinook, for example, will enter the river as soon as they reach it and begin to ascend to their natal stream. They will rest in deep pools until fall, their preferred spawning time. The coho will gather in the ocean close to the mouth of the river through the summer, building their fat reserves. In the fall, they will begin their journey upstream.

14–26. Salmon hatchery using egg trays in flowing water.

Hatching

In nature, the female digs a hole, fills it with eggs, and lets the male fertilize the eggs by depositing the sperm, called milt. The female then covers the hole with soil and gravel to complete the process. A female will usually have enough eggs to fill three or more holes, called **redds**, with a total of about 4,000 eggs.

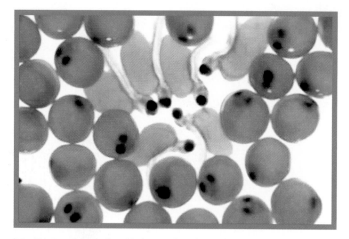

14–27. Eyed eggs beginning to hatch, with a few alevins present. (Courtesy, U.S. Fish and Wildlife Service)

In artificial hatching, the ripe female is usually killed, and the eggs are removed surgically. This poses no real threat to the salmon population since salmon generally die immediately after spawning. The eggs are fertilized with sperm taken from the male, which may or may not be killed in the process. The egg mass is placed in a tray in a trough of flowing water or in an incubator with water dripping over the mass.

The fish hatch in about 60 days with the yolk sacs still attached. The sacs provide the nutrition for the next few days. A newly hatched salmonid with its yolk sac attached is known as an *alevin*. After the yolk sacs are absorbed, the fish are called fry. Once they reach 2 inches in length, they are called fingerlings. At a length of 6 inches, they become smolts.

Chum and pink salmon can be moved to a stream or estuary very soon after they absorb their yolk sacs. In nature, they spend very little time in fresh water. Chinook, coho, and sockeye salmon, on the other hand, must be kept in fresh water for some time. In nature, the chinook, coho, and sockeye may stay in fresh water for up to two years before moving to the open sea.

The main problem with hatchery spawning of salmon is that the average survival rate of adults has been less than 1 percent. In other words, less than 1 percent of the fish hatched from the eggs have returned to spawn in the same location. The rate for natural spawns is between 1 and 10 percent.

Techniques to improve the survival rate of artificially hatched salmon have been studied. One method that seems to improve the rate is to place some type of gravel in the hatchery

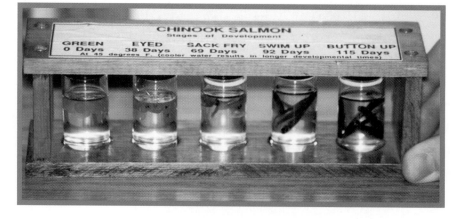

14–28. Stages in the development of chinook salmon.

tank so that the fry spend less energy holding their position. Another is to decrease the stocking rate so that the flow of water can be reduced to a level more like that of the natural spawning streams. Still another method is to move the fish from the hatchery to gravel-bottomed channels at the eyed stage. The use of these and new methods under research should bring the adult survival rate to a level similar to that of natural spawn.

In the past, 50 percent of the salmon returning to spawn were allowed to spawn in order to provide a steady supply of salmon for the commercial fishery. The improved techniques of salmon hatcheries and survival rates require fewer than 50 percent to keep the number of salmon available at an appropriate level.

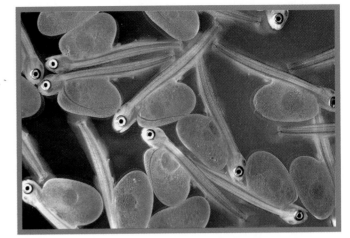

14–29. A magnified image of newly hatched salmon alevins. (Courtesy, U.S. Fish and Wildlife Service)

Feeding

Chinook, coho, and sockeye fry that are being kept in fresh water are usually fed a diet of brine shrimp, ground meat or ground fish, or a combination of these. For fish that are being grown for food production, the diet is similar to that of trout (discussed in Chapter 13). Salmon nutrition has not been studied as much as trout nutrition, so not all the specific requirements are known, especially for adult fish.

14–30. Developing coho salmon sac fry (alevins). Their small size and fragility reduce survival rate.

As carnivorous fish, salmon require a high-protein diet. The protein is obtained through either meat or fish products or through a commercially prepared diet that is high in protein. Start-up feeds are usually 50 to 55 percent protein, fingerling feeds 45 to 50 percent, and grow-out feeds 35 to 40 percent.

The primary source of protein in many salmon diets is from the carcasses of salmon spent from spawning. These carcasses are ground into meal and mixed with a vitamin supplement.

14–31. Round net pen used for rearing salmon near Skagway, Alaska.

Other species of fish and animals may also be used to make the feed. Several commercial nutrient and vitamin supplements are available.

Hatchery fish and smolts are usually fed several times a day. Salmon in net pens are usually fed once or twice a day. Although some automatic feeders are used, most feeding is done by hand.

PRODUCTION PRACTICES

Production of the Pacific salmon species is typically by salmon ranching or salmon farming. In **salmon ranching**, a hatchery releases the fingerlings or smolts to the sea and waits until the fish return. The wait may be from two to five years, depending on the species. Coho and pink usually return within two years, sockeye within three years, chum within three to four years, and chinook within four to five years.

Salmon farming usually involves the use of net pens or sublittoral enclosures. When the smolts or fingerlings are about 6 inches long, they are moved to the enclosures from the hatcheries. Salmon farming in sublittoral enclosures usually involves either the chinook or the coho, since these two species are the most tolerant of fresh water. Chinook and coho are also the predominant species reared in floating net pens moored at sea; however, any species can be cultured.

A concern with net pens is keeping the nets clean so that water can move freely through the pens. Salmon do not tolerate poor water quality. They require a dissolved oxygen (DO) level of around 5 parts per million (ppm), although they can withstand a DO level of 3.5 ppm for a short time. One method of keeping nets clean is to use deeper pens. The tops of the pens can be raised out of the water and cleaned by hand.

Facilities for salmon production must be in waters of suitable temperature. The temperature must be above freezing and below 75°F (23.9°C) for adults and above freezing and below 60°F (15.6°C) for smolts. Salmon require a water pH of between 6 and 8.

14–32. A raceway used in salmon production.

MANAGEMENT CONCERNS

The primary management concern of salmon ranchers is providing a suitable hatchery environment to get a high adult survival rate. The adults can be harvested when they return to their natal stream.

Salmon farmers have the same concerns as aquafarmers growing fish in any enclosure. In net pens or sublittoral enclosures, the dissolved oxygen, nutrition, temperature, wastes, and salinity all are important factors. Pens confine the fish. They cannot move to more suitable waters if one of these factors is unsatisfactory.

In net pens, nutrition is usually the major management concern. Since the fish cannot move about and catch their food, a nutritionally balanced ration must be provided. The site for the pens must be selected carefully, with adequate salinity and proper temperature for maximum growth. Wastes and dissolved oxygen are usually not problems because natural water movement will keep the water oxygenated and wastes moved away from the fish.

In sublittoral enclosures, the stocking rates are usually too high for the facilities to provide enough food for the fish, so their diet must be supplemented. Salinity and temperature are also important factors, especially the runoff of fresh water into the facilities from substantial rains. The stocking rate must be at such a level that wastes do not build up and that dissolved oxygen does not become a problem. Of course, mechanical aeration is possible, but it is normally not used in salmon production. The tides flowing into and out of sublittoral facilities will help oxygenate the water and remove some of the nitrates from fish wastes. Sites must be selected in areas far enough north so the water temperature does not exceed 70°F (21.1°C).

Salmon also perform fairly well in raceways, but the costs of pumping the water through them usually keep raceways from being as profitable as net pens or sublittoral enclosures. The salmon take a longer time to reach market size than other fish commonly grown in raceways, such as trout.

DISEASES AND PREDATORS

Salmon that are artificially spawned or intensively raised are susceptible to a number of bacterial and viral diseases. These include bacterial coldwater disease, columnaris disease, bacterial gill disease, fish tuberculosis, and several others. The most common cause of "sick" salmon is vitamin or mineral deficiency—not a problem when the fish are fed a balanced diet. Providing fish with a nutritionally balanced ration has a major role in reducing the stress on the fish and, subsequently, their susceptibility to disease.

Two methods commonly used to combat disease are drug treatment and genetic improvement. Several approved drugs are available as treatments for the bacterial diseases, but the viral diseases are largely untreatable. Some feed supplements have been developed as vaccinations against certain diseases. Several breeding programs have been successful in developing strains of salmon that are resistant to a number of bacterial and viral diseases.

Two species of phytoplankton are harmful to salmon and can be particular problems with fish raised in net pens. *Chaetoceros convolutus* has spikes that hook together to form long chains of the algae. These sometimes block and damage the gills of salmon, causing them to quit feeding. *Heterosigma akashiwo* produces a mucous-like substance that can be toxic to larger fish.

The seal and the sea lion are two of the most common predators of adult salmon. If salmon are grown in sublittoral enclosures in areas where seals and sea lions are abundant, the facilities must be monitored closely. Bears may also be a problem, but usually are not if the facilities are near populous areas.

The predators of young salmon fingerlings and smolts include numerous carnivorous fish and animals—too many to list here. While in tanks and ponds, the fish can be protected with netting and supervision. Very little can be done to protect them once they are released into the streams or estuaries.

14–33. Seals are predators of salmon in certain environments.

14–34. Feeding salmon in pens on Wilapa Bay, Washington.

HARVESTING

Salmon farmers may harvest the fish from their facilities when the fish are between 1 and 5 pounds. From 1 to 2 pounds, the flavor of salmon compares favorably with that of many other table fish, including trout. Larger fish may be sold to processors who will make salmon steaks for retail markets.

Salmon in net pens are very easy to harvest. The net pens are simply opened and the fish are removed and placed into the boat with dip nets, or the net pens are emptied into the boat.

When salmon are harvested from sublittoral enclosures or from streams, seines are used, as with most fish in ponds or other facilities.

14–35. A biologist inspects a harvested salmon. (Courtesy, U.S. Fish and Wildlife Service)

14–36. Salmon are drying outdoors on racks at Kaltag, Alaska. (Courtesy, U.S. Fish and Wildlife Service)

MOLLUSKS

Several important species are in the mollusk family. Some are bivalved (have hinged shells); others are gastropods (have shells made of one piece). The important bivalve species include oysters, clams, mussels, and scallops. The gastropods include the abalone and snails.

14–37. Mollusks can be identified by the appearance of their shells. Note the features of the Eastern oyster (left), the quahog clam (middle), and the blue mussel (right).

BIVALVE MOLLUSKS

The oyster is the most important mollusk commonly cultured in the United States. Oysters are in high demand as seafood. Many authorities feel that there is excellent market potential for oyster species produced by aquaculture. Cultural practices for clams, mussels, and scallops tend to be similar to those for oysters.

The oysters most commonly cultured in the United States are the Eastern oyster (*Crassostrea virginica*) and the Pacific cupped oyster (*Crassostrea gigas*). The Eastern oyster (also referred to as the American oyster) is farmed in the coastal waters of the Atlantic and Pacific oceans and in the Gulf of Mexico. Production of the Pacific cupped oyster is limited mostly to the Pacific Northwest, with most of the production occurring in Washington State.

The Eastern oyster is found naturally along the Atlantic and Gulf of Mexico coasts of the United States. The species has been successfully introduced along the Pacific Coast as well. The Pacific cupped oyster is cultured along the coasts of the Pacific Northwest. Japanese oystering has had a major influence on the Pacific Northwest.

The culture of oysters in the United States goes back to the late 1800s. Because of the oyster's value as seafood, it has been a popular species for culture. Many aqua-

14–38. A Pacific cupped oyster. Note the curved shape of the shell.

farmers have tried to increase their ability to provide quality oysters—those without irregularities in the shell—for the raw oyster market. Others have simply taken advantage of areas with little natural oyster production but good environment by transplanting oysters to these areas.

Oyster hatcheries are one option for aquafarmers who do not want to participate in the food production of oysters. The number of people who want oyster seed is increasing rapidly, including the oyster farmers and the commercial oyster fishers who want to improve their beds. In many coastal areas, the hatcheries are unable to meet the demand for oyster seed.

14–39. By-products of fish and shellfish production include food for companion animals. (Courtesy, National Oceanic and Atmospheric Administration)

Obtaining Seedstock

In nature, the oyster spawns when the water temperature ranges from 68° to 80°F (20° to 26.7°C). The spawning season lasts for several months. Both the *Crassostrea virginica* and the *C. gigas* are open-water spawners. Fertilization occurs outside the shell. The female releases eggs into the water, which are then fertilized by sperm from the male. As was noted earlier in the book, the same oyster may produce sperm one year and eggs the next. Oysters change genders!

CONNECTION

OYSTER GARDENING

Oyster gardening is the small-scale production of oysters using floats or baskets kept near the surface of the water. The goal is to provide oysters to repopulate areas where the population of oysters has been destroyed by overharvesting or pollution. The line drawing shows how small oyster cages may be suspended from a pier.

The Chesapeake Bay Foundation is one sponsor of a specific program on oyster gardening. The goal is to educate citizens about oyster production as well as enhance natural populations that have been destroyed. Nearly all coastal states have oyster gardening programs.

For information on oyster gardening, use the following Web site at the University of Maryland:

www.mdsg.umd.edu/oysters/garden

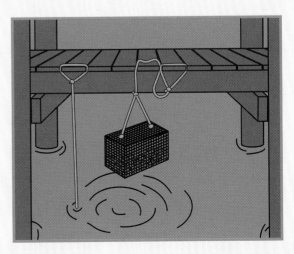

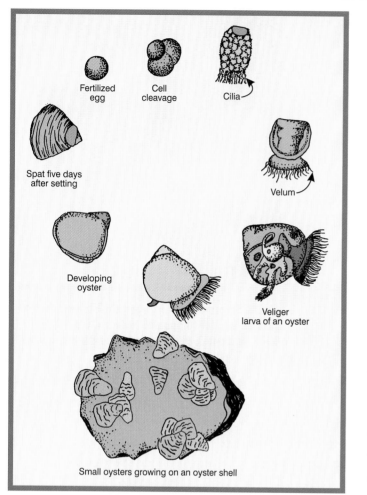

Fertilized egg

Cell cleavage

Cilia

Velum

Spat five days after setting

Developing oyster

Veliger larva of an oyster

Small oysters growing on an oyster shell

14–40. Life cycle of the Eastern (American) oyster, *Crassostrea virginica*. (Source: *Oystering on the Mississippi Coast*, Mississippi Department of Wildlife Conservation)

Accurate counts of the eggs and sperms are not available. The female releases 50 to 100 million or more eggs each spawn, and the male releases more than a billion sperms! Of course, many of the eggs are never fertilized, and many that are fertilized become part of some predator's meal. As a result, only six to ten adult oysters survive from every million eggs released into the water.

Although some hatcheries still collect fertilized eggs from the wild, most try to hatch their own by using sexually mature oysters held in water that is at optimum temperature. Oysters can be induced to spawn by gradually increasing the water temperature to 75° to 77°F (23.9° to 25.0°C).

The fertilized eggs are removed from the water with a fine-mesh sieve and transferred to well-aerated, filtered seawater for hatching. Selecting larvae that demonstrate a rapid growth rate very early in their lives often involves several cullings of the larvae.

14–41. Shells from an oyster plant are bagged and placed on a truck for use as habitat in oyster culture.

14–42. A bay used for oyster culture on the Washington coast has considerable tide fluctuations and inflowing streams from pristine forest areas.

Hatching

Eggs hatch within a few hours after fertilization. From a few days to two weeks, the larvae are free swimmers. This is a delicate time in nature. The larvae may be washed out to sea on even a small current, as they are no larger than a grain of sand.

Within the first two weeks, the oysters develop their two shells and are ready to "settle" into their permanent homes. The oysters, now called *spat*, go to the bottom to look for something to attach themselves to, called *cultch*. Oysters do not move from the cultch for the rest of their lives. Because they do not move, oysters (and other mollusks) are called sessile organisms.

In nature, other oysters, old oyster shells, other shells, and sometimes gravel provide the cultch. In a cultured operation, clam or oyster shells may be spread along the bottom of the facility to provide suitable cultch. The oysters settle on the cultch and attach themselves for life by secreting a concrete-like substance that attaches one-half of their shell. After a few days, the cultch is usually transferred to the area where they will grow until harvest. This may be to an estuary, the open ocean, rafts, or cages.

14–43. Oysters are being cultured using the long-line system. Note that the water in the bay is at low tide. (Courtesy, National Oceanic and Atmospheric Administration)

If the oysters are being seeded into the open water, the timing of the placement of cultch material is very important. If it is placed in the water too early, algae or other materials may form on the cultch and make it unsuitable for the spat, which will then die. If the cultch is not put out before the spat begin to settle, the spat may not find a suitable place and will then settle into the silt and probably die.

Production without cultch is possible, although not as common. The spat may be kept in tanks, in a pond, or on trays in an estuary, although cultch may still be used. Some aquafarmers will keep the oysters indoors throughout the production. This requires a constant source of phytoplankton-rich water.

Feeding

During the hatching process, larvae are fed phytoplankton from flowing seawater or cultured phytoplankton added to the facility. Once the oysters settle, they are provided with seawater that contains phytoplankton, the oysters' primary source of nutrition.

14–44. Oysters are being cultured using the raft culture system. Note that a net is between the stakes to promote algae growth. Algae are a major source of food for the growing oyster crop. (Courtesy, National Oceanic and Atmospheric Administration)

Oysters are filter feeders. They filter seawater through their shells, and the seawater provides them with both oxygen and food. As a result, oysters have little control over what types of organisms are available for them to eat. However, they can reject some food particles.

The primary concern is that their habitat has some phytoplankton but not so much as to choke them. If a strong phytoplankton bloom causes the water to be too thick with the microorganisms, the oysters cannot handle all the food. They will close their shells, sometimes suffocating or starving to death.

Facilities

By far the most likely food production location for oysters is the seabed. Several techniques may be used. The oysters may be sown into an established oyster bed or planted after becoming attached to some cultch material. Sometimes, they are placed just off the seabed on special trays. Other times, they are attached to ropes (usually clam shells on wires) suspended from rafts or tied to poles planted in the seabed. It will take the oysters from two to four years to grow to market size.

The primary concern is selecting a facility that has adequate movement of water, provides phytoplankton, has a bottom that is not too silty, and is free of pollution. The adequate movement of water supplies new oxygen and removes wastes, as well as providing a new source of food for the oysters.

The bottom cannot be silty, as the silt will clog the gills of the oysters. If the bottom becomes too silty, the oysters will close their shells for a while and let the silt settle. Eventually, however, they must breathe, so they will open their shells again. If the bottom is still too silty, they will usually suffocate.

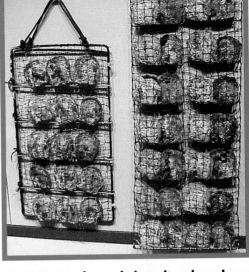

14–45. Oysters for producing cultured pearls are grown in a hanging net system. (Courtesy, National Oceanic and Atmospheric Administration)

Providing pollution-free water is an absolute necessity in oyster production. Because oysters get their food from moving the water through their systems, they usually concentrate any pollution in their meat. Although the oysters may be unharmed, they may be unsuitable for human consumption. Human population increases, with accompanying wastes, and industrial pollution are the two primary reasons for the decline in the harvest of wild oysters. Many beds that were once abundant either have been killed off or are so badly polluted that the oysters are no longer worth harvesting.

Oysters harvested from polluted waters can be purged. This is placing them for a time in clean water, where the oysters expel the pollutants. They are then suitable for the retail market. Because the oysters will move clean water through their systems just as they did polluted water, they can cleanse themselves of most pollutants in one to two weeks.

In these purging systems, the oysters may be moved to raceways that pump running water through the tanks or to the seabed in an unpolluted area. In either case, many oysters that were not suitable can be added to the supply of edible oysters.

14–46. Hand tongs are being used to harvest oysters. (Courtesy, National Oceanic and Atmospheric Administration)

Management Concerns

Once the oysters have settled, they require very little management. Many oyster farmers have full-time jobs in other professions and raise oysters as a source of supplemental income. The low management requirements of oysters make them a good choice as a second occupation in aquaculture.

As was mentioned earlier, the primary work for the aquafarmer comes in the early stages of oyster production. Once a suitable site has been selected and the oysters have been sown, very little management is needed. It is a matter of waiting for the oysters to grow to market size. Market-size oysters are usually at least 3 inches in width. The meat of a mature oyster is usually about 15 percent of its body weight, although higher percentages have been obtained with some culture operations.

Aquafarmers do have some concerns in the two to four years it takes oysters to reach market size, however. Damage from predators, diseases, and pollution must be regularly monitored so that the crop is not wiped out suddenly due to one of these problems. With pollution, removing the source of the pollution is usually the only way to control the problem. Once the source is removed and the water returns to normal, the oysters will usually cleanse themselves and continue their growth. Damage from diseases and predators is discussed in the next section.

The oyster crop may require periodic thinning if the oysters settled well and are growing well. Most oyster farmers thin the crop by using scuba equipment to dive down and remove a certain percentage by hand. The oysters that are thinned out are usually transplanted to another location.

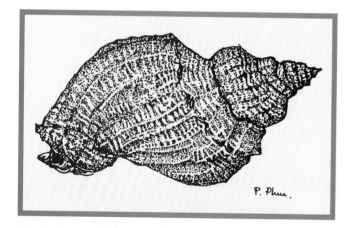

14–47. A common oyster drill. (Source: *Oystering on the Mississippi Coast*, Mississippi Department of Wildlife Conservation)

Diseases and Predators

The most common oyster disease is oyster fungus disease (caused by *Labyrinthomyxa marina*). Oyster fungus disease is found especially in high concentrations of oysters. It is usually not a problem in cool water or in water of low salinity. The oyster slows its growth, then stops growing, then eventually dies. There is no known cure for oyster fungus disease.

Dermo and MSX are two parasitic diseases often found in oysters on the East Coast of the United States. Dermo (*Perkinsus marinus*) causes the oysters to weaken and die. MSX (*Haplosporidium nelsoni*) has similar effects, though it is not fully understood. Use clean oyster seedstock and avoid contamination from diseased oysters, beds, and equipment. Research has shown that lowering salinity of the water has some controlling influence.

The oyster has many predators, including fish, starfish, and gastropods. Perhaps the most serious are the oyster drills—two species of gastropod mollusks, *Urosalpinx cinerea* and *Eupleura caudata*. Oyster drills drill holes in the shells and consume the oysters inside. Control measures include trapping, removal by divers, and chemicals. Oyster drills eat only oysters cultured on the seabed; they are not a problem to oysters raised in baskets or with rope culture.

The starfish, *Asterias forbesi*, can eat up to five oysters per day. The starfish opens the oyster's shell partially by applying constant pulling pressure on the oyster. When the oyster finally opens up just a bit to breathe, the starfish can increase the opening. The starfish then extends its stomach into the shell and consumes the meat inside. Starfish are commonly controlled by lime treatments or by divers. Like oyster drills, starfish are not a problem with rope or basket culture. One method of control that will not work with starfish is cutting them up into pieces. Almost every piece will regenerate and make a new starfish. This increases rather than decreases the population.

Leopard rays also eat oysters. They use their very strong jaws to crush the oyster shells. Then the rays just pick out the meat from the shells. Placing sticks in the ground with sharpened ends pointing upward will usually control them. When the rays drop onto the oyster beds, they impale themselves on the sharpened ends of the sticks.

A pest in many oyster production systems is the oyster flatworm (*Stylochus ellipticus*). Oyster flatworms are a particular problem with young oysters and can wipe out 90 percent of a crop in a couple of weeks. The flatworms are controlled with desiccation. **Desiccation** is

CONNECTION

YOUR HEALTH

Fats! You may hear that you should avoid eating fats. Research is showing that some fats are very important for good health. These are the omega-3 essential fatty acids. Scientists have found that these fats are essential in promoting good health and can sometimes treat illness.

Omega-3 is the name given to a family of polyunsaturated fatty acids. Chemists know them as long-chain substances. Human nutritionists know one of them as DHA (docosahexaenoic acid). Though the human body can synthesize DHA from other fatty acids, including DHA in the diet has major health benefits. The oils in fish are particularly good sources of DHA.

People sometimes want to take dietary supplements for additional DHA. Manufacturers concentrate and purify oil from certain fish, such as the sardine. The product is formulated into oils, softgel capsules, and other forms. According to some authorities, taking a dose each day provides benefits to the brain, eyes, and other human functions.

the process of limitedly drying the shells of oysters. This can be done by lifting the oysters from the water in baskets or by designing facilities so that the natural process of tide movement exposes the shells to dry air for a short time each day.

Oyster farmers must also be wary of human poachers, especially when the oysters near market size. Sometimes groups of oyster farmers organize into patrol groups in regular shifts to discourage thefts by humans.

Harvesting

Oysters cultured on the bottom are typically harvested by tonging, dredging, or diving. Tonging is using a scissor-like device with a rake-like head containing teeth (tongs) that extend into the bottom of the water facility. Moving the two sides along the bottom dislodges the oysters, which are pushed into the basket formed by the two sides of the head. The full tongs are then moved to the surface, either by hand or by power equipment. Hand tonging is very taxing physically and requires a strong person to operate the tongs.

14–48. An oyster dredge at work. (Courtesy, National Oceanic & Atmospheric Administration)

Dredging involves moving an open basket that has a bar with teeth on the bottom of it (the dredge) along the bottom of the water facility to dislodge the oysters. The length of the teeth is dependent on the type of bottom of the facility being harvested. The dredge is pulled by a boat with ropes attached to it. A power winch is used to lift the dredge when it is full.

Diving is using scuba equipment to dive down to the oyster bed with a basket. The basket is filled by hand, and a winch used to pull the basket up to the boat or dock. Some states have regulations prohibiting diving in natural waters, but in aquaculture production facilities, it is permissible. Diving allows the producer to select only the largest oysters and leave the rest for harvesting later.

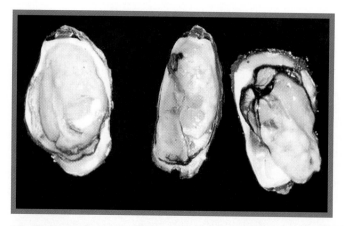

14–49. Opened oysters show a high-quality product. (Courtesy, National Oceanic and Atmospheric Administration)

Divers must be very careful not to get cut by the sharp shells of the oysters. A condi-

14–50. An oyster boat is ready to unload a harvest at a packing facility.

tion commonly called oyster finger may result. Oysters contain a substance that can cause cuts to become badly infected. The cuts remain sore for much longer and leave much worse scars than normal cuts. Experienced oyster fishers' hands will often have telltale scars from oyster finger.

14–51. Oysters are being shucked (removed from shells) at this processing facility. Rapid hand movement is essential.

14–52. Shucked oysters are being cleaned and graded in an automated processing plant.

Depuration

As filter feeders, oysters and other bivalve mollusks contain products of the environment in which they live. The color of a shucked oyster's meat varies with the color and kind of

14–53. Depuration is underway in an oyster processing facility. (Courtesy, National Oceanic and Atmospheric Administration)

14–54. An open quahog clam shell (clam removed) shows the meaning of "bivalve mollusk."

foods the oyster has eaten. If the water is polluted, the oyster may contain pollutants. Color does not reveal the presence of pollutants.

Some oysters become contaminated with bacteria and other organisms that can lead to food poisoning. An example is the *Vibrio parahaemolyticus* bacterium. The bacterium occurs naturally in estuarine waters and is considered one of the leading causes of food-borne illness worldwide. The symptoms are acute gastroenteritis with side effects and, sometimes, death. *V. parahaemolyticus* is particularly a concern with oysters on the half-shell (opened shell with raw meat) and other under-cooked methods of preparation. Cooking, such as frying, usually destroys the bacterium.

Depuration is the process used by some oyster producers and/or processors to cleanse the digestive systems of oysters. Depuration is the removal of impurities from the body. The process includes washing exteriors to remove bacteria that may be present. Depuration can also be used with other species, including mollusks and fish.

Depuration often involves grading oysters, washing them, placing them in warmwater baths followed by ice-cold baths, and using specific depuration equipment. Some depuration processes involve opening oysters; others leave them sealed in their shells. Careful laboratory testing is used to assure that the oysters are free of harmful organisms and substances.

CLAMS

The two species of clams cultured in the United States are the northern quahog (*Mercenaria mercenaria*) and the soft clam (*Mya arenaria*). The northern quahog is also known as the hard clam, the hardshell clam, the littleneck clam, and the cherrystone clam. In addition, there is a southern quahog clam, though it is not widely found. The soft clam is also known as the longneck and

14–55. Clam spat being held in trays in a recirculating tank. (Courtesy, National Oceanic and Atmospheric Administration)

the streamer. The hard clam is found naturally along the Atlantic Coast, while the soft clam's natural range is from North Carolina south along the Atlantic Coast. The soft clam is often used in soups and chowders. Aquafarmers have tended to concentrate on the culture of the hard clam much more than the soft clam, but the culture methods are virtually the same.

Clam culture is relatively new in the United States. Much work with clams is still experimental. Clams are considered to have strong potential as an aquacrop because they will spawn in captivity and they have a sizeable market.

Clams normally spawn only in the summer. Hatching techniques used by oyster hatcheries have proven successful with clams, however. Clams will spawn any time of the year by holding sexually mature pairs in tanks and gradually increasing the temperature to between 70° and 80°F (21.1° to 26.7°C). Today, commercial hatcheries provide nearly all the seedstock used in clam aquaculture.

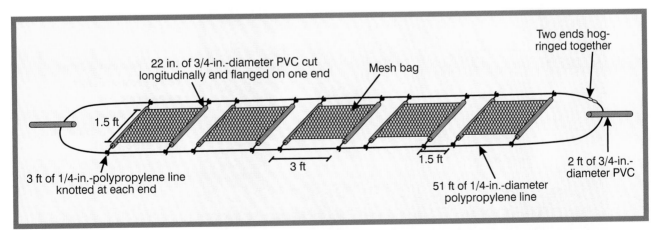

14–56. Drawing of a mesh-bag line system for culturing quahog clams. (Courtesy, Georgia Sea Grant College Program)

14–57. A basket of cultured clams ready for market. (Courtesy, Jimmy L. Avery, Louisiana Cooperative Extension Service)

14–58. Dredging a bay floor for wild clams. (Courtesy, Agricultural Research Service, USDA)

The larval clams are tolerant of temperature changes but require a salinity of at least 20 ppt, with an optimum level of 27 to 30 ppt. Larval clams are fed phytoplankton (microalgae) diets, often cultured by the aquafarmer. Diets of dried microalgae (single-celled algae) have been shown to provide growth rates equal to those from diets of cultured living microalgae.

Clams are cultured for market with techniques similar to those used with oysters. The seed clams are distributed across the beds, where they settle and grow to market size. Some operations put the seed in boxes filled with sand and covered with netting to ward off predators. The clams will reach a marketable size of 2 to 2½ inches in two years in the southern United States and in five to seven years in the northeastern United States.

14–59. Harvested clams being aerated before going to market. (Courtesy, National Oceanic and Atmospheric Administration)

The aquafarmer needs to check periodically for pollution and for predators. Clams occasionally need to be thinned or provided more room in which to grow. As with oysters, clams are susceptible to human predation as they near market size.

Clams feed by drawing in and expelling water through feeding tubes that may look like necks. Millions of cilia (hairlike structures) move the water along. Some cilia strain food from the water. If the clams are in polluted water, they will contain the pollutant. Those from polluted water can be purged or depurated similar to oysters.

14–60. Fresh, live quahog clams are kept on ice in a supermarket.

MUSSELS

Mussels are found in salt water, brackish water, and fresh water. This chapter focuses on saltwater and brackish-water mussels. Nearly all creeks and rivers in the United States have various species of freshwater mussels. A freshwater mussel is sometimes known as a *naiad*.

Many people walk coastal areas when the tide is out searching for wild mussels. Some states have established limits on the number that can be taken. For example, New York State limits the take of mussels to $\frac{1}{2}$ bushel a day. Commercial harvesters are subject to different regulations.

14–61. Quality live blue mussels.

Mussels have not been cultured for very long in the United States. They are widely cultured in Europe and other parts of the world. They are easily cultured, requiring little attention after being placed in the growing facility. The most common species cultured is the blue mussel (*Mytilus edulis*). The blue mussel is also called the common edible mussel and sometimes the black mussel. Blue mussels are found in the coastal areas of North America. Mediterranean mussels (*Mytilus galloprovincialis*) are cultured on a limited basis in the Pacific Northwest. Another species on the West Coast of the United States is the California mussel (*Mytilus californianus*). This mussel is large and can grow as long as 7 inches.

The culture of mussels in the United States has grown very rapidly in the last few years, more than that of any other shellfish. The primary growth has been in Maine and other northeastern Atlantic states.

Mussels are considered a crop with great potential for aquaculture growth for several reasons. First, mussels are very easy to raise. Second, the market for mussels in the United States has increased; thus, growers get a better price for their crop than in the past. Third, several states have developed programs for leasing offshore sites to aquafarmers for mussel production. Maine, for example, has more than 600 acres leased to aquafarmers engaged in mussel production. Fourth, mussels grow faster and yield more meat than other shellfish.

14–62. A blue mussel has been partially encrusted with pesky zebra mussels. (Courtesy, U.S. Fish and Wildlife Service)

Most seedstock for mussel production is obtained from wild beds. The larval mussels may be seined from the water. Structures may be placed in the water and removed with mussels attached. Mussels will spawn at temperatures of 62° to 80°F (16.7° to 26.7°C). Larvae are free swimming, though they may attach several times in an effort to find a suitable location. Most larvae prefer water that is above 65°F (18.3°C) and that has sufficient food. Mussels mature more quickly in these conditions, with two years typically needed.

A mussel attaches to hard substratum by means of a threadlike **byssus** (cluster of filaments, which are chemically similar to silk). Byssus fibers are secreted by the byssal glands. A mussel will attach to almost any structure, including another mussel, another species of shellfish, or a stone. Unlike an oyster, however, a mussel does not usually attach itself to one place for life. It can discard the byssus and move about by crawling, or it can secrete a gas bubble and float to a new location. When a mussel is being transplanted, it is important that its new environment be very much like its old one in terms of temperature, light, and salinity. If not, the mussel may discard its byssus and seek a new home. Mussels sometimes attach themselves in layers, with one mussel attached to another mussel.

Several approaches to mussel production have been studied. Four basic methods are used: raft culture, rope culture, bouchot culture, and beach or bottom culture. Rope culture, similar to that used with oysters, and bottom culture have been the most profitable. The collected seeds are spread over leased areas in the seabed, where they usually attach and remain.

Mussels require water with a salinity of at least 25 ppt. The locations most suitable for mussel growth may not be the best for setting seed. Mussels grow best in locations where the tide changes dramatically, providing the mussels with a strong current of new food. The strong current, however, may carry many of the larval mussels out to sea before they have time to set. If wide tide changes occur, mussels should be set by means of rope culture or pole culture before being placed in the water.

If a good site is selected and the beds are periodically thinned, the mussels will usually grow to a market size of 2 to 3 inches in one year. However, growth to market size may take two years, depending on the size of the seedstock and the climate. In the wild, it usually takes five years for mussels to reach market size. Very little growth occurs in winter months.

Mussels are harvested and stored similarly to clams and oysters. They should not be immersed in water and must be kept cold. Any with broken shells or shells that gape open should be discarded.

SCALLOPS

The scallop is a bivalve mollusk known for its appealing shell and is a popular food. The shell is fan shaped, with radiating ribs or grooves. It flares out near the hinge. The most valued part of a scallop for food is the adductor muscle. The **adductor muscle** is the organ that opens and closes the shell. A scallop has only one adductor muscle. The adductor muscle is sometimes referred to as the "eye." The "eye" is the part normally eaten in the United States, though other parts are eaten in Europe. Scallops are different from oysters and clams in that they move about and glide freely over the sea floor, snapping their shells open and closed.

Scallops are cultured similar to oysters and clams. Wild scallops are harvested with dredges and are shucked soon after harvest. The raw meat is creamy white.

14–63. Scallops. (Courtesy, National Oceanic and Atmospheric Administration)

14–64. Hanging socks of bay scallop spat are being prepared for grow-out in a nearby harbor. (Courtesy, National Oceanic and Atmospheric Administration)

14–65. Cultured scallops have been harvested and are ready for marketing. (Courtesy, National Oceanic and Atmospheric Administration)

The species of scallop that grows the largest (20 per pound) is the sea scallop (*Plactopecten magellanicus*). The bay scallop (*Argopecten irradians*) is most widely cultured. Harvest-size bay scallops may require 50 or more to reach a pound.

Gastropods

Two gastropods are primarily cultured. These are abalones (marine snails) and edible snails, or escargot. Some species are expensive delicacies served in fine restaurants and available in specialized markets or departments.

Abalones

Abalones are snails treated separately here from edible snails because of their importance and appeal. Three species of abalones are commonly found on the West Coast of the United States. The red abalone (*Haliotis rufescens*) is most important. The flat abalone (*H. walallensis*) and the black abalone (*H. cracherodii*) are also natives of the West Coast. The black abalone is rare, and its harvest from the wild is prohibited.

The red abalone is the largest abalone in the world, reaching a weight of more than 3 pounds. Abalones are considered a good aquaculture crop because of the declining commercial catch and their low management requirements.

Red abalones, like other snails, are very slow moving and easy to catch. As a result, they have been overfished to the point that California now has closed seasons and size limits on abalone catches. The commercial catch of abalones, once more than 5 million pounds per year, is now below 1 million pounds per year.

Red abalones are found naturally along the western coast of the United States and Mexico, from southern Oregon to central Baja, California. They prefer well-oxygenated water with a stable salinity and a temperature range between 45° and 65°F (7.2° and 18.3°C).

14–66. An abalone.

A large abalone hatchery in California produces more than 4 million abalones a year. This operation reports a profit margin of 50 percent, almost unheard of in any industry, and expects recent expansion to increase the profit margin within the next few years.

Red abalones will reach sexual maturity and may be ready to spawn when their shell is 1.5 inches (3.5 cm) across. They will spawn throughout the year, but the peak spawning season is in the spring—April and May. When constantly provided with food, red abalones will spawn every 75 to 90 days.

The broodstock are usually harvested from the sea and transported to the hatchery. The male spawns first; the presence of sperm induces the female to shed her eggs. Because of their prolific spawning rate, red abalones are a good choice for hatcheries.

14–67. An abalone farm that uses sheets of corrugated plastic roofing to culture diatoms and algae. (Courtesy, National Oceanic and Atmospheric Administration)

14–68. The inside of an abalone shell has appealing beauty.

In the postlarval stages, red abalones are fed diatoms. **Diatoms** are microalgae usually cultured by the aquafarmer in the tanks in which the larvae are placed. At first, the diatoms grow faster than the postlarvae can eat them, so the tanks are usually covered to inhibit growth of the diatoms. After about 50 days, the tanks are uncovered to encourage growth because of the increased grazing rate of the juveniles.

At six months of age, the abalones are switched to weaning tanks, where kelp (seaweed) is provided, along with the diatoms, for forage. The kelp is the most expensive part of abalone culture because it is mostly water and the food conversion rate is low (10 to 15 percent). In a weaning tank, some structure is provided to give the abalones more surface on which to grow. This is usually accomplished by placing sections of PVC pipe in upright positions in the tank. After the abalones attach to the structure, it can be moved to another location.

After the abalones are one year old, they are moved to grow-out tanks and provided with a diet of giant kelp. They reach harvest size in four to five years. In high-density raceways, with high water flow and filtered water, yields of 200,000 pounds of abalone per surface acre of water are possible. About 30 percent of the body weight is meat.

In all structures used to produce abalones, a constant flow of seawater is necessary. For the grow-out tanks, for example, a flow rate of around 1,000 gallons per minute is recommended.

Snails

Snails are common mollusks. Some live on land, while others live in salt water or fresh water. Of the more than 80,000 different species found, 55,000 live in salt water and are known as marine snails. Only a very few species are cultured.

The snail is a gastropod with a soft body protected by a shell. When the snail is threatened, it withdraws into its shell. Shapes of shells vary from rounded and spiral to flat. A major characteristic is that a snail has a stomach and one foot. Snails have two pairs of tentacles on their heads, with each of the longer tentacles having eyes. The mouths of snails have structures that grind food.

Snails like warm, moist areas and do not do well in dry places. The life span of a snail is five to ten years.

Snails are hermaphrodites. A *hermaphrodite* is an animal that is both male and female. This means that an individual snail produces eggs and sperms at the same time. However, sperms must be exchanged in order for the eggs to be fertilized. After mating, a snail will lay up to 85 eggs in the soil. These will hatch in two to four weeks. Newly hatched snails immediately seek food and will eat the shells they hatched from and other eggs that have not hatched. About two years are needed for a snail to become an adult.

Heliciculture is the process of raising or farming snails. When prepared as food, snails are known as *escargot*. Two species are predominantly referred to as escargot, though other species are also eaten. The small gray snail (*Helix aspersa*) and the apple or Roman snail (*H. pomatia*) are most widely cultured. These are typically $1\frac{1}{2}$ to 2 inches (38.1 to 50.8 mm) across the shell. The larger African snail (*Achatina fulica*) may measure 1 foot (312 mm) long. Snail production is a tedious task that requires some trial and error.

Various systems are used in snail culture. The system chosen depends somewhat on the climate as well as on the resources available to invest in facilities. Snails can be grown in small pens or enclosures within climate-controlled buildings, or they may be grown outside in warm, moist climates. Enclosures are often made similar to wooden troughs and covered

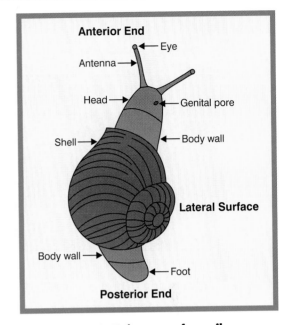

14–69. Major parts of a snail.

14–70. The colors and shapes of snail shells vary, though the shells are similar in many ways.

14–71. Snail on the wall of a culture tank.

with netting to prevent the escape of snails. Escape is a problem in open pens. Stocking rate is approximately eight snails per square foot of pen. The stocking rate is reduced with larger snails.

Snails prefer 59° to 75°F (15° to 23.9°C) and a high humidity of 75 to 95 percent. In temperatures below 45°F (7.2°C), snails hibernate. Between 45° and 55°F (7.2° and 12.8°C), they are inactive and grow very little or none. Much of the activity of a snail is at night. Soil should be available, as snails dig in it, ingest it, and reproduce in it. Fertile soil promotes snail growth.

Growers often use five stages in snail culture: reproduction, hatching, young, fattening, and final fattening. Feed materials vary. Some growers use vegetable trimmings, such as from cabbage or cauliflower. Other growers use a mash similar to that used with chickens that has 16 to 17 percent protein. Snails are subject to some diseases and parasites. Dwarfing is also a problem but is due to culture conditions rather than genetics.

In marketing, snails are typically shipped live but while dormant. Each snail should be visually inspected to be sure it is healthy. Three to four days before shipping to market, snails should be purged to remove grit and other food materials from their bodies. This may involve moving the snails to an area without soil and feeding them cornmeal or bran for a few days. All food materials in their bodies are passed from the digestive system. Snails are shipped in cartons with holes large enough to allow air to enter but small enough to prevent the snails from escaping. Snails are typically canned much as low-acid meats. Improper canning can result in food poisoning.

14–72. Snails are often preserved by canning.

14–73. Snails are typically removed from the shells, cooked, and returned to the shells for serving.

OTHER CRUSTACEANS

Lobsters and crabs are highly prized foods. Some are cultured; others are harvested from the wild. Both are in the phylum Arthropoda and the class Crustacea. Shrimp are also crustaceans.

LOBSTERS

Lobsters are one of the most expensive seafood items and bring premium prices. Some lobsters have claws; others do not. The species with claws are most desired.

The culture of lobsters has long been a goal of aquafarmers. Hatcheries for the American lobster (*Homarus americanus*) have been in production since the late 1800s, but the farming of lobsters from the egg to the market-size adult has not been developed to the point of being practical. Hatcheries have been used in stocking programs to supplement the number of lobsters available from the commercial catch.

Adult lobsters may be captured from the wild and brought to hatcheries. Gravid females (those with eggs) are primarily taken for hatchery use. Careful attention is needed for the eggs to hatch and develop. Young lobsters

14–74. A female lobster with many thousands of incubating eggs attached on her underside.

14–75. Juvenile lobsters are being produced in large jars (round aquariums) at a hatchery where water quality is carefully managed and feed is appropriately provided.

14–76. Brine shrimp eggs may be used to feed newly hatched lobster.

are only about $1/3$ of an inch long and swim about in the water. Only about $1/10$ of 1 percent survive beyond two months if in their natural environment. Hatcheries are able to achieve much higher survival rates, with about 50 percent surviving for six months. Artemia are often used as food. Regular and careful cleaning of facilities is essential to assure a good-quality environment for young lobsters.

The primary drawback of lobster aquaculture is the long period necessary to grow a lobster to market size. Most lobsters require a minimum of five years to mature, with many individuals taking six to eight years. Although keeping lobsters in tanks with warm water can speed up the growth process, this is still not profitable for raising lobsters from the larval stages to the market size. At present, the best chance for culture is to raise juvenile lobsters (two- to three-year-olds) to market size in two to three years.

One problem with intensive production is that lobsters are highly susceptible to crustacean shell disease, a form of exoskeleton necrosis (deterioration). Crustacean shell disease can cause mortality if a lobster does not molt first. Molting usually sheds the disease with the exoskeleton, but the disease is highly contagious, causing problems in the intensive crowding found in aquaculture production.

Most lobsters in the market are captured from the wild. They are often shipped live and demand premium prices based on weight. Lobsters are also processed and frozen. Lobster tails are popular because of convenience of preparation and ability to store the product.

BLUE CRABS

Blue crabs (*Callinectes sapidus*) are primarily a fisheries product and not normally an aquacrop. Ample supplies of crabs to meet the market demands can be caught by commercial fishers, so aquaculture techniques are not usually needed for the general market.

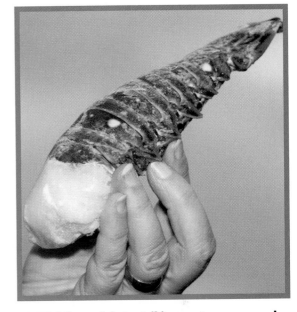

14–77. A frozen lobster tail is easy to prepare and more appealing to a customer than a live lobster.

One market being filled by aquaculture, however, is that for soft crabs (also called softshell crabs). A *soft crab* is one that has molted and has not developed another hard shell. Historically, the crab fishers placed crabs that were about to molt into boxes or fenced pens in the estuaries until they molted. Recently, however, aquafarmers have used indoor recirculating systems for soft crab production.

The production of soft crabs is very intensive. The water must be maintained at about 20 ppt salinity and constantly moved through the system. An upflow sand filter or a combination of an upflow sand filter and a fluidized bed filter is commonly used to maintain water

14–78. Blue crabs are popular brackish-water species in some areas. (Courtesy, Agricultural Research Service, USDA)

14–79. A crab in the process of molting. Immediately after molting, the crab is a delicacy—a soft crab. (Courtesy, Jimmy L. Avery, Louisiana Cooperative Extension Service)

14–80. A female soft crab. It will shed its shell within an hour. (Courtesy, National Oceanic & Atmospheric Administration)

quality. Labor is very important, as the crabs must be constantly watched to keep them from killing the freshly molted crabs. As soon as the crabs molt, they are removed from the facility and usually frozen.

Soft crab production in the United States has largely been concentrated in Louisiana and Florida. The potential for other southeastern and eastern states is good if the market expands and anticipated prices hold at a level that will allow producers to make a profit.

OTHER FINFISH

Several other saltwater finfish species are increasingly being cultured. These include striped mullet, milkfish, pompano, red drum, cobia, flounder, grouper, threadfin, and mahimahi. Culture of some of these species is experimental and long-term procedures have yet to be developed.

STRIPED MULLET

The striped mullet (*Mugil cephalus*) is one of the few fish commonly cultured in brackish water. In nature, the striped mullet is found in tropical and semitropical waters around the world. The mullet is not considered a food fish in much of the United States, except in Hawaii and some southeastern states, but it has potential as such. The wild striped mullet sometimes carries a fluke that is harmful to humans, but this should not be a problem in cultured fish. Small mullets are also used as bait fish.

The striped mullet can be induced to spawn in captivity, leading to an increase in the potential for aquaculture of this species. The rearing of mullet fry to fingerling size, however, has been a major stumbling block of attempted mullet operations. At present, the seedstock for mullet culture is usually obtained from commercial harvests. The mullet may grow as large as 5 pounds, but 1 to 2 pounds is usually the market size.

The striped mullet has several characteristics that make it a good fish for aquaculture production. It can withstand a wide range in salinity, from 0 to 38 ppt. This means it can be cultured in almost any body of water. It can also withstand a wide range in water temperature, from 40° to 95°F (4.4° to 35.0°C). It performs well in polyculture with other fish. As an herbivore, the mullet does not require feeding; its nutritional

14–81. Bait mullets caught by net casting. (Courtesy, National Oceanic and Atmospheric Administration)

needs can be met with a fertilization program. In addition, even though it is not popular as a food fish in most of the United States, its flesh is considered quite good in most countries.

In other countries, the striped mullet is reared in estuarine waters, including brackish-water ponds and sublittoral enclosures. The facilities are stocked either with fish obtained from commercial operations or with fry caught in brackish-water areas, where they spend their first few months of life.

The striped mullet is said to have high aquaculture potential, but little culture exists at this time. Some experimental culture has been conducted in the southeastern United States, particularly Florida, usually with success, but commercial operations are not prevalent.

MILKFISH

The milkfish (*Chanos chanos*) has many of the same characteristics pertaining to brackish-water ponds as the striped mullet. It is herbivorous, grows rapidly, can withstand wide ranges in salinity and temperature, and is very disease resistant.

The milkfish is a popular seafood throughout the tropical Pacific area. Although most of the milkfish sold come from commercial fisheries, the supply is supplemented by aquaculture in many countries. Milkfish grow larger than mullet, sometimes reaching 50 pounds or more, but are usually marketed at 1 to 2 pounds.

Milkfish naturally spawn at sea. The eggs hatch there. The fry make their way to estuaries and brackish water, where they may spend from a few months to a year.

Because milkfish will not spawn in captivity, the facilities used to rear them are stocked either from commercial catches or from fry that have been captured as they move into water near shore. Milkfish production is usually referred to as ranching, because the milkfish are usually held in sublittoral enclosures, where they feed on microalgae until they are harvested. Very little management is necessary.

Milkfish fry can be reared in nurseries for stocking in ponds for grow-out. Once they are moved to grow-out facilities, either ponds or sublittoral enclosures, the primary management needed is fertilizing the facilities to promote algal growth. In other countries, such as the Philippines, the use of ponds is prevalent. In the United States, however, very little milkfish production is carried out, and it is usually in sublittoral enclosures.

14–82. Milkfish are being iced after harvesting. (Courtesy, National Oceanic and Atmospheric Administration)

The potential for milkfish aquaculture is very good for Hawaii and parts of southern California. Although milkfish may grow well in waters of the southeastern United States, these waters are not their natural habitat, and few markets exist for milkfish in the southeastern states.

Pompano

Pompanos are also known as pampanitos and domingo fish. Several species are used as food, with the Florida or common pompano (*Trachinotus carolinus*) being most commonly cultured. These saltwater fish are commonly found along the Atlantic Coast from Massachusetts to Florida. Pompanos bring a premium price because they are not very abundant, they have an excellent flavor, and they are popular in some restaurants.

Pompanos are hardy fish that will thrive in a range of environments. Some of the techniques used with the red drum may be useful with the pompano. Spawning in captivity remains a major obstacle to pompano culture.

Many experimental operations and a few commercial ventures have tried pompano production with various degrees of success.

14–83. Common pompano. (Courtesy, National Oceanic and Atmospheric Administration)

The primary culture of pompanos in the United States has been in waters off the Gulf Coast of Florida. Various facilities have included net pens, tanks, and sublittoral enclosures. Most operations have fed floating commercial feeds, sometimes supplemented with shrimp or frozen codfish.

The operations that have tried pompano production have developed a system of spawning the fish in captivity and rearing the fry. One company had success rearing pompanos from eggs to a weight of about $\frac{1}{2}$ pound, but its tanks were too shallow to allow for further growth. The potential for rearing the fish in net pens or larger tanks after they reach $\frac{1}{4}$ to $\frac{1}{3}$ pound appears to be excellent.

Although the production of pompanos is expensive, the technology exists for commercial production. Several operations are now beginning to realize a profit from pompano production.

RED DRUM

The red drum (*Sciaenops ocellata*) is a very popular fish in restaurants, especially those preparing Cajun-style food, and is popular as a sport fish. Its primary habitat, the coastal waters of Louisiana, Mississippi, Alabama, and Florida, has been overfished. Because of the decline in numbers in the wild population and a substantial increase in the market demand, several experimental efforts have been made to culture red drums.

The culture of red drums, or redfish, is gaining momentum. A drawback has been the relatively slow growth rate. Two seasons are required, which means that the fish must be overwintered.

Many aspects of red drum production have been copied from the catfish industry. Seedstock is generally obtained from commercial fisheries or from the incoming tide by let-

14–84. A red drum, *Sciaenops ocellata*. Note the black spot near the caudal fin, a feature of the red drum. (Local people sometimes call the fish a spottail bass.) (Courtesy, National Oceanic and Atmospheric Administration)

ting it fill saltwater ponds or sublittoral enclosures. Before aquaculture of this species can prosper, more reliable means of obtaining seedstock must be found.

Red drum production is being carried out in small ponds stocked at the rate 2,000 to 4,000 per acre. Higher stocking rates are used where good saline water is available. Begin filling the pond with salt water about 14 days before stocking. Fertilization of the water promotes the growth of natural food organisms, such as zooplankton. Red drum fingerlings are stocked when about 6 inches (15 cm) long. Water temperature should be at least 50°F (10°C). A dense plankton growth is needed at the time of stocking that includes an abundance of rotifers and copepods. Feeding a floating pellet that is 35 percent protein is recommended. Pellet size must be small enough for fingerlings to eat. As the fish grow, larger pellets can be used. The DO level of the water must be at least 4.0 ppm.

Harvesting of food-size red drum begins by withholding feed 24 to 48 hours before harvest. Cooler water should be pumped into the pond if possible. Seining is used to capture the fish. Be sure that the water provides a quality environment and that stress and injury to the fish are kept to a minimum.

As soon as reliable sources of seedstock can be developed, the potential for red drum aquaculture will increase substantially. Red drums appear to be relatively easy to raise in salt water and brackish water in warm climates.

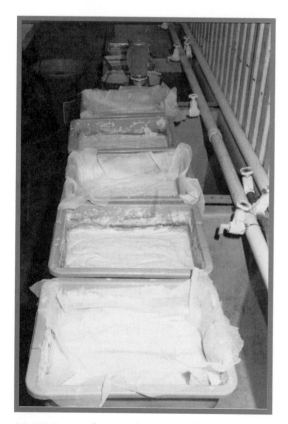

14–85. System for growing nematodes (*Panagrellus redivivus*) as feed for larval fish. (Courtesy, Red Ewald, Inc.)

COBIA

Interest in cobia (*Rachycentron canadum*) production has increased considerably since the late 1990s. The cobia produces white flesh that is highly desired. The species is naturally found in tropical and subtropical ocean waters, though it is also found in other areas.

14–86. Cobia in an offshore cage. (Courtesy, National Oceanic and Atmospheric Administration)

14–87. Juvenile cobia being dipped to move to a grow-out pond. (Courtesy, National Oceanic and Atmospheric Administration)

The cobia grows fast, reaching 1 foot (0.3 m) long in four months. It can obtain a weight of 10 pounds (4.5 kg) in about a year and 20 pounds (9 kg) by the end of its second year. Most interest in cobia culture involves open-ocean cages in ocean areas with warm water. Hatcheries use ponds and tanks for incubation and for growth of fingerlings to 3 to 4 inches (7.6 to 10.2 cm) long. Broodstock may be injected with hormones to promote spawning.

14–88. A cobia broodfish is being carefully moved to prevent injury. (Courtesy, National Oceanic and Atmospheric Administration)

14–89. A southern flounder. (Courtesy, National Oceanic and Atmospheric Administration)

14–90. A recirculating raceway is being used to culture southern flounder. (Courtesy, National Oceanic and Atmospheric Administration)

FLOUNDER

Flounder is a popular food fish. Several species are captured wild by commercial fishers and marketed as flounder. Turbot and sole are similar and sometimes called flounder.

The southern flounder (*Paralichthys lethostigma*) is likely the species with the greatest potential in aquaculture. Other flounder species cultured include the summer flounder (*Paralichthys dentatus*) and the Japanese flounder (*Paralichthys olivaceous*).

Adult flounder have a markedly different appearance from other finfish. They do not swim about in an upright position. Flounder appear to lie on their sides on the bottom of the water. Because of this, they are sometimes known as flatfish. The underside of a flounder is white; the side facing upward is dark. Both eyes are on the top side. The mouth is turned toward the topside.

Adult southern flounder swim away from the shore into salt water in the fall to spawn in late winter. They return to the shore to be in the brackish water of estuaries and rivers immediately after spawning. Larval flounder remain in the salt water and feed on zooplankton for 30 to 60 days. After metamorphosis, the juveniles begin migrating toward the shore and into rivers and estuaries.

Flounder are capable of reproduction at about two years of age. A female can produce 45,000 eggs per pound (100,000/kg) of body weight at spawning. Spawning is influenced by water temperature and number of the daylight hours. Flounder prefer water that is 60°F (16°C) and need nine to ten hours of light. In hatcheries, spawning is promoted with captured wild broodfish by using an implant containing **gonad releasing hormone**. The gonad releasing hormone is usually a synthetic form given at a rate based on fish size. Eggs are released and float in the water where males have released sperm. Fertilization rate can be low, partly because male flounder produce a much smaller volume of sperm than males of other fish species. In hatcheries, eggs are often stripped from females and artificially fertilized with sperm.

Eggs hatch in about 55 hours at an incubation temperature of 63°F (17°C). Newly hatched larvae do not have eyes, mouths, or fins. These develop within five days with energy from the yolk sacs. At that time, they begin to consume food, such as rotifers and artemia. Water temperature should remain at 63°F (17°C). The salinity should be 33 ppt. At about 30 days of age, metamorphosis begins and is complete in two weeks. Afterward, the juveniles can consume dry nutritionally complete commercial feed with a protein content of 50 to 55 percent. The juveniles are graded by size and moved to culture tanks. Uniformity of size helps prevent cannibalism. Juveniles are fed to market size much as other finfish.

With the decline of wild catch, greater demand will develop for cultured flounder.

GROUPER

Some 250 species in the Serranidae family are known as groupers. They are sometimes called serranids. Groupers are highly valued as food fish and as ornamentals. Efforts to culture groupers are continuing, with the practices needed for a successful grouper crop increasingly being refined. Species cultured include Nassau grouper (*Epinephelus striatus*), gag grouper (*Mycteroperca microlepis*), black grouper (*Mycteroperca bonaci*), and jewfish (*Epinephelus itajara*).

Groupers mature in two to six years, though most reach food size in less time. Grouper culture has primarily involved catching wild juveniles. In some cases, broodfish have been used that reproduce either naturally or with hormone-induced treatments. Natural spawning appears to be related in some way to moon phases. Grouper larvae are small and fragile.

Nassau groupers are hardy fish. They have thick skin and can withstand short intervals out of water. They require water with sufficient oxygen, with 4.0 ppm being an acceptable minimum. A female Nassau grouper weighing 13 pounds (6 kg) will spawn 900,000 eggs a day and 3.3 million eggs over a four-day period. The eggs are sometimes quite small. Spawning is best near a full moon in March or April in tropical or subtropical climates. Approaches for

14–91. The Nassau grouper is a cultured species that is hardy and can tolerate relatively low salinity for short intervals.

incubating eggs are similar to those used with other species. Since larvae have small mouths, food materials must be very small. Groupers need live food for 35 to 70 days after hatching. Juveniles are fed **artemia** (brine shrimp), but gorging can occur, resulting in death. Larvae grow best in water 75° to 81°F (23.9° to 27.2°C). Seawater salinity of 35 ppt provides the best environment. The Nassau grouper can tolerate salinity as low as 15 ppt for a few days. As groupers grow, manufactured feeds that are nutritionally complete can be fed. Ponds, cages, and tanks are used in growing groupers.

THREADFIN

The Pacific threadfin (*Polydactylus sexfilis*), also known as moi, is one of several species marketed as threadfin. It is a prized fish in restaurants because of ease and variety of preparation. Most interest in culture of the species has been with the Pacific threadfin. This fish makes an attractive meal presentation in whole-fish form.

Moi are produced in tanks and raceways, fish ponds, and submerged sea cages in Hawaii. Pond culture may include seaweed, milkfish, and mullet in the same pond as the moi. In recent years, most interest has focused on large sea cages that allow a considerable quantity to be produced in one cage.

Grow-out takes six to eight months after juveniles are stocked. Market size is 0.5 to 1.0 pound (225 to 50 g). In a year, moi may weigh 1.5 pounds (700 g). The typical feed conversion ratio is 1.5:1, which is excellent. Feed should be nutritionally complete with a 50 percent protein content and contain fish meal as one of its ingredients. Pellet forms are typically used, with juvenile moi started on smaller pellet sizes.

At harvest, care should be taken to avoid injury to the fish. Because of visual appeal, small injuries detract from quality and the price paid. Moi are often packed for shipping

14–92. Pacific threadfin (moi) harvested from an offshore cage. (Courtesy, National Oceanic and Atmospheric Administration)

14–93. Pacific threadfin being cultured in an offshore cage. (Courtesy, National Oceanic and Atmospheric Administration)

using a brine bath. A *brine bath* is a medium used to chill live fish to an inactive state. The fish reach the market alive, but all life processes have been greatly reduced. A brine bath is a 2:1 mix of ice and seawater with salt (NaCl) added at the rate of 8.8 pounds to 265 gallons (4 kg/1,000 L) of ice and seawater.

MAHIMAHI

Mahimahi (*Coryphaena hippurus*) is a fish with brilliant colors that has gained a great deal of popularity for food. The flesh of mahimahi is dense and moist, with a mild, slightly sweet flavor. The fish naturally prefer tropical and subtropical seawater. The name *mahimahi* is a Hawaiian word meaning "strong-strong." Mahimahi are sometimes known as dolphinfish but are not dolphins (porpoises). Mahimahi are fish; dolphins are mammals. Mahimahi are sometimes referred to as dorado. They have a very aggressive behavior.

14–94. Mahimahi have distinct head features.

14–95. Mahimahi caught by a sport fisher. (Courtesy, National Oceanic and Atmospheric Administration)

Mahimahi are naturally distributed in tropical and subtropical ocean water. Culture is generally limited to water that is 64° to 86°F (18° to 30°C). They grow best when water temperature is 79° to 82°F (26° to 28°C) and prefer open-ocean environments. Mahimahi can be cultured in captivity.

Sexual maturity is reached by six months of age. Under good conditions, the female mahimahi spawns 100,000 to 250,000 eggs every other day (usually at night). Broodstock are easily stressed and can make sudden swimming bursts resulting in injury by banging into walls of tanks and other structures. Egg quality is often poor. Eggs will hatch in about 40 hours after fertilization. Water salinity should be 30 to 35 ppt, and water temperature 77° to 82°F (25° to 28°C). Larval forms have high mortality. Once the yolk sacs have been used, larval artemia or rotifers can be fed. As the fish develop, nutritionally complete dry feed with 55 to 60 percent protein is fed. Mahimahi can weigh 10 pounds (4.5 kg) in eight months if properly managed.

REVIEWING

MAIN IDEAS

Saltwater and brackish-water aquaculture includes varied species. Aquacrops cultured in salt water and brackish water include several types of fish, mollusks and gastropods, and crustaceans. As a general rule, the species that are widely cultured became popular as food taken from wild catches. Often, the early culture practices of these species were not aimed at food production but at replenishing wild stocks for commercial and recreational harvests.

Success depends on knowing the habitat requirements of the aquacrop being produced and how to provide that habitat in a cost-efficient manner. Salinity and other water-quality factors must be monitored and adjusted to maintain the optimum levels for production. The five major categories of water facilities for saltwater and brackish-water aquaculture production are the shore, intertidal, sublittoral, seabed, and open ocean. All permits must be obtained and regulations followed when culturing fish in ocean and shore areas.

Three aquacrops dominate saltwater and brackish-water aquaculture around the world. Shrimp, salmon, and oysters make up more than 80 percent of all saltwater and brackish-water aquaculture. Practices in culturing these species are continuing to emerge to assure successful cropping.

In the United States, aquaculture of saltwater and brackish-water species has not progressed as rapidly as that of some freshwater species, such as trout and catfish. Saltwater and brackish-water aquaculture should increase in scope within the next several years. The cultural practices for many species have been well established. The culture of these species is needed to provide food sources and to replenish wild stocks.

Practices to culture a number of species are being studied, and proven approaches are emerging. Red drum, striped mullet, milkfish, pompano, Pacific threadfin, cobia, flounder, mahimahi, and other species are included.

QUESTIONS

Answer the following questions, using complete sentences and correct spelling.

1. Name and describe the two most common methods of measuring water salinity.

2. If water salinity is too high, how can it be lowered? If it is too low, how can it be raised?

3. Why must metal parts be protected from salt water or brackish water?

4. What are the three most important saltwater and brackish-water aquacrops?

5. What three factors determine if a site is suitable for saltwater or brackish-water production?

6. Give the primary advantage and primary disadvantage of shore facilities.

7. Why is the sublittoral zone used so often for net pens and cage culture?

8. What precautions must be taken in the selection of a seabed site?

9. How is seedstock obtained for shrimp production?

10. Describe the process for hatching shrimp.

11. Describe the spawning of salmon.

12. Differentiate between salmon farming and salmon ranching.

13. What are some management concerns in rearing salmon in net pens?

14. What diseases and predators cause problems in salmon production?

15. Where is seedstock for oyster production usually obtained?

16. How do oysters obtain nutrients from the seawater?

17. What predators cause problems for oyster farmers?

18. What are the two species of clams cultured in the United States?

19. List the common names of five species of saltwater fish and/or shellfish that are most appealing to you. Write the scientific name of each by the common name. Write one sentence that best describes the species.

20. What is open-ocean aquaculture?

21. What is the role of the interagency coordinating group for aquaculture established by the National Aquaculture Act?

22. What is oyster depuration? Why is it used?

EVALUATING

Match the term with the correct definition. Write the letter of the term on the line provided.

a. cultch
b. gravid
c. diatom
d. natal stream

e. nauplii
f. redds
g. sluice gate
h. spat

i. desiccation
j. byssus
k. adductor
l. heliciculture

_____ 1. Larval oysters

_____ 2. Material to which oysters attach themselves

_____ 3. Larval shrimp

_____ 4. Holes filled with fertilized salmon eggs

_____ 5. Water movement device for sublittoral enclosures

_____ 6. Pregnant

_____ 7. Microalgae

_____ 8. Place of hatching

_____ 9. Process of drying oyster shells for short intervals to help control disease

_____ 10. Snail farming

_____ 11. Cluster of threads mussels use to attach themselves to surfaces

_____ 12. Strong muscle that opens and closes the shell of a mollusk

EXPLORING

1. Assess a local area based on its potential as a site for saltwater or brackish-water aquaculture production. Include the advantages and disadvantages of the site, and list the steps that would be necessary to bring the site into production.

2. Create a mini salmon hatchery in your classroom or laboratory. Obtain a male salmon and a female salmon ripe for spawning. Strip the eggs from the female and fertilize with the milt from the male. Observe regularly and report on the survival rate. Release the smolts into a suitable stream (or continue to raise them if facilities permit).

3. Determine the prices of salmon, shrimp, and oysters at a local seafood store or supermarket. Compare the prices weekly throughout the year, both in and out of season. What do the differences in prices mean to aquafarmers who might produce these crops?

4. Obtain some female and male shrimp and keep them in a saltwater aquarium. Practice eyestalk ablation on the females to see if it will cause them to become gravid. Prepare a written report of your findings.

CHAPTER 15

Ornamental Aquaculture

OBJECTIVES

This chapter covers ornamental species as related to aquaculture. It has the following objectives:

1 Discuss the meaning and nature of ornamental aquacrops

2 Identify the components of an ornamental aquaculture system

3 Explain the management of an ornamental aquaculture system

4 List and explain factors in selecting ornamental species

5 Explain how ornamental fish are produced

6 Discuss ornamental plant selection and culture

7 Discuss ornamental fish marketing

8 Explain the meaning and role of well-being in relation to ornamental species

TERMS

air stone	fancy	labyrinth fish
aquarium heater	fish keeping	mechanical filtration
biological filtration	floating aquatic plant	rooted aquatic plant
bunched aquatic plant	hardy	therapeutic benefit
chemical filtration	hospital tank	thermostated heater
color enhancer	isolation tank	water aging
euthanasia	keeping ease	well-being

15–1. Maintaining an aquarium with an oscar (*Astronotus ocellatus*) is educational and fun. Another common name for the oscar is the velvet cichlid.

AQUACULTURE is far more than food fish production! Though food fish production is a large share of aquaculture, ornamental fish production can be a highly profitable enterprise. Further, some closely related aquatic species are produced for research and educational purposes.

Ornamentals (as ornamental species are often called) are sources of pleasure for many people. As an attractive aquarium shows us, ornamental species come in many colors, shapes, and sizes. They have varied environmental requirements, depending on their natural habitats. A large number of ornamental species are kept, including a few of the same species used in food and bait production.

Nearly everyone admires an attractive aquarium. Time and effort are needed to care for an aquarium so that it is in good condition and provides a good environment for the fish.

ORNAMENTAL AQUACROPS

Millions of dollars are spent each year in the United States on ornamental fish and related aquaculture species. In most cases, ornamental species are for recreational purposes. They bring pleasure to those who have or use them. Related species used for research and educational purposes are sometimes included as ornamentals.

Ornamental aquaculture is the raising or keeping of aquatic species for their appearance and gracefulness. People enjoy observing the behavior and growth of ornamental species. Two main areas of ornamental aquaculture are fish keeping and commercial production.

15–2. A large aquarium with both live rock and invertebrates and finfish that are products of a commercial ornamental marine culture facility in Florida. (Courtesy, National Oceanic & Atmospheric Administration)

FISH KEEPING

Fish keeping is caring for ornamental fish species as a hobby or an avocation. Fish keepers enjoy watching the species grow and enjoy maintaining a good environment for them.

Keeping ornamental fish often has therapeutic benefits. A *therapeutic benefit* is something that provides enjoyment, relaxation, and a feeling of personal well-being. Some people find keeping ornamentals a relaxing activity. It is an escape from the stress of everyday life. People enjoy the challenge of maintaining the ecosystems in the aquariums for ornamentals.

Table 15–1. Examples of Freshwater Ornamental Fish

Common Name	Scientific Name
Angelfish	Pterophyllum scalare
Amur catfish	Pelteobagrus fulvidraco
Banded gourami	Colisa fasciata
Barred loach	Nemacheilus fasciatus
Betta	Betta splendens
Black molly	Platypoecilus mentalis
Black piranha	Serrasalmus niger
Bleeding heart tetra	Hyphessobrycon erythrostigma
Butterfly fish	Pantodon buchholzi
Cardinal tetra	Cheirodon axelrodi
Clown loach	Botia macracantha
Dwarf gourami	Colisa lalia
Electric catfish	Malapterurus electricus
Flame tetra	Hyphessobrycon flammeus
Giant gourami	Osphronemus goramy
Goldfish	Carassius auratus
Guppy	Poecilia reticulata
Hyena cichlid	Nimbochromis polystigma
Jewel cichlid	Hemichromis bimaculatus
Koi*	Cyprinus carpio
Longnose gar	Lepisosteus osseus
Molly	Poecilia latipinna
Neon tetra	Hyphessobrycon innesi
Pale barb	Hypsibarabus wetmorei
Pearl cichlid	Cichla ocellaris
Pearl gourami	Trichogaster leeri
Platy	Xiphophorus maculatus
Red-eyed tetra	Arnoldichthys spilopterus
Sailfin molly	Poecilia velifera
Silvertip tetra	Hasemania nana
Spotted barb	Barbus binotatus
Swordtail	Xiphophorus hellerii
Tiger barb	Barbus pentazona hexazona
Upside-down catfish	Synodontis nigriventris
Zebra loach	Botia striata

*Koi is a subspecies of *Cyprinus carpio*; several varieties of the subspecies are available.

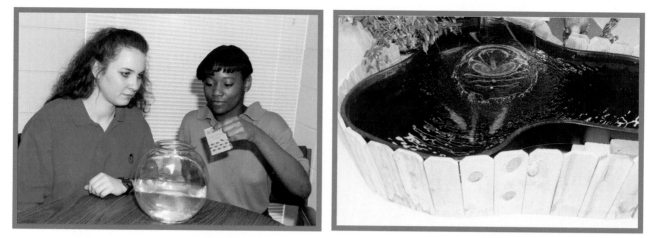

15–3. Fish bowl with a goldfish.

15–4. Koi in a decorative interior water garden.

Aquatic species are often more economical than other types of pets. They do not make noise, run away, or destroy property. Many species of ornamentals can be kept in a small amount of space and without much training in how to maintain them. Owners of small aquariums do not meet with the objections of neighbors, as owners of cats or dogs sometimes do.

Ornamental aquaculture is diverse. Sometimes, it consists of tropical or fancy fish; other times, it includes pet or hobby aquatic species. Some species prefer fresh water; others prefer salt water or brackish water. Providing the right environment is a challenge. The one common element is that all the species are maintained in a water environment that is usually in an aquarium.

15–5. An interesting mix of plants and fish has been achieved in this aquarium. (Growing plants and animals in this manner is sometimes referred to as aquaponics.)

Ornamental aquaculture adds to the decor of homes, offices, and businesses. An attractive aquarium stocked with fish, plants, and other aquatic species can serve as the focal point in many places. Schools use ornamentals for educational purposes in teaching many areas of science and ecology. Offices and businesses may employ custom-care services to maintain their aquariums.

Some ornamentals live in simple aquatic systems, such as common fish bowls. Others require sophisticated water management systems in aquariums. Beginners should start with the species that are easy to grow. As skill is gained, they can advance to species that are more difficult. Mixing species, or polyculture, can help maintain a quality ecosystem (community of organisms).

Ornamental plants and animals, and the supplies needed, are sold through pet stores, discount stores, and other retail outlets. All these provide career opportunities for qualified people. Some pet stores may have a third or more of their business in ornamental aquaculture. The value of ornamental species, equipment, and supplies runs into hundreds of millions of dollars each year in the United States.

15–6. Complete aquarium outfits can be purchased by beginning ornamental fish enthusiasts.

COMMERCIAL PRODUCTION

Fish keepers need dependable sources of ornamental fish and other species. Commercial producers breed and market species to meet the demand. Florida is the leading state in ornamental production. California, Maryland, and several other states have significant production. All states have some production.

Ornamental stocks may be cultured or captured in the wild. Some are imported into the United States. Most of the imported ornamentals are from Singa-

15–7. A commercial producer uses tank systems to raise goldfish.

pore, Thailand, the Philippines, Indonesia, and Hong Kong. The South American countries of Colombia and Peru provide some ornamentals.

Ornamentals are usually sold in small quantities with a higher price markup than baitfish species. The value of the imported ornamentals is many millions of dollars a year. Since these ornamentals pass through several wholesalers and brokers, the retail value is much greater.

The United States exports several million dollars of cultured ornamentals each year. The top recipients of ornamentals from the United States are Canada, Mexico, Hong Kong, Japan, and Taiwan.

RELATED SPECIES

Educational and research programs may use aquaculture species similar to those kept by ornamental fish enthusiasts. Biology students in high school and college frequently use fish and other aquatic animals in their laboratory study of anatomy. Various species of fish are used in teaching morphology and anatomy.

Research programs may use fish to solve important problems. Not only does the research deal with improving efficiency in aquaculture, but it also seeks answers for the betterment of human life.

One example of a species used in research is the Japanese medaka (*Oryzias latipes*). This species of fish is 1 to $1\frac{1}{2}$ inches (2.54 to 3.81 cm) long at maturity. It is hardy in a wide range of environments and will spawn any time of the year. The female is very prolific and will produce 3,000 or more eggs in a single breeding season. The eggs are excellent for studying embryo development. The small fish are excellent for physiology and genetic research. Millions of these fish can be economically produced for research and educational purposes.

15–8. An aquarium can be used to produce ornamental fish, such as gouramis.

ORNAMENTAL AQUACULTURE SYSTEMS

Many species (perhaps 100 or more) may be used for ornamental purposes. Each species has its unique requirements for culture and growth. Some species can share the same environment with other species. Knowing the general needs of ornamental aquaculture is essential for success in fish keeping.

This chapter primarily focuses on freshwater aquariums. Saltwater and brackish-water aquariums require materials compatible with the water and environment needed for the species kept.

The water system needed for ornamental species is roughly the same whether the species are being raised by the hobbyist or the commercial producer. The major difference is the size of the venture. An ornamental aquaculture system must have a water container, a satisfactory source of water, and equipment to maintain water quality. The size and/or quantity of these depend on the scope of the ornamental hobby or business.

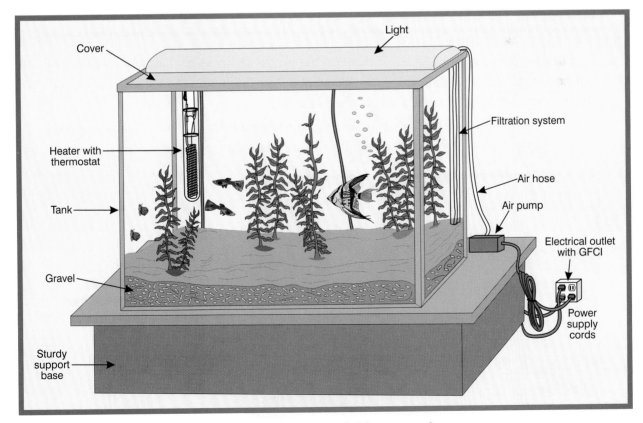

15–9. Basic equipment needed for an aquarium.

15–10. A special aquarium facility is maintained at the Warm Springs National Fish Hatchery.

The hobbyist may have one aquarium with a few pieces of equipment. Commercial ornamental producers often have large systems of water tanks and other facilities. Some growers of fancy, expensive fish have set up production in specially constructed buildings or in garages at their homes.

WATER CONTAINERS

Various water containers and attachments are used with ornamentals. Water containers may be aquariums, tanks, ponds, or other facilities. The hobbyist will likely have an aquarium with a capacity of 15 to 40 gallons (56.85 to 151.6 L).

An aquarium is a glass container for establishing a habitat for ornamental fish and other species. Aquariums are typically rectangular and are designed for viewing of the ornamental

15–11. Aquariums on sturdy wooden stands constructed from lumber.

15–12. Multiple aquariums for keeping individual or small groups of fish separately have been conveniently arranged.

species and for easy cleaning. Common dimensions are 36 × 18 × 15 inches (capacity is 42 gallons if filled entirely with water) and 24 × 15 × 12 inches (capacity is 18 gallons if filled entirely with water). (Note: These dimensions and capacities, as well as other measures in this chapter, can be easily converted to the metric system using Appendix A.)

The commercial ornamental grower may have a number of larger aquariums. Sometimes, round glass bowls, bottles, or other items are used. Plastic materials may be substituted for glass. Sizes and shapes should be convenient to use and not so large that reaching some areas of the containers is difficult.

Construction

Construction materials and design are important. All-glass materials are preferable; however, metal or plastic frames with the glass cemented in place are sometimes used.

All-glass aquariums are held together with a durable silicone-rubber cement. Scratched glass indicates a flaw that could later result in a break and water leak. Glass thickness should be at least $^1/_4$ inch (0.64 cm) for a small aquarium, except for the bottom, which should be $^3/_8$ inch (0.95 cm) thick.

Any new aquarium or one that has been unused for a while should be tested for water leaks. It can be partially filled in a location where leaked water will not be a problem and where emptying it will be easy.

Installation

Careful consideration should be given to selecting the site for an aquarium or tank. Once in place, an aquarium is not easy to move. Water sources, electricity, and water drains should be convenient. The aquarium should be set up and ready before the fish arrive. This

15–13. A glass aquarium should be placed on a sturdy stand.

15–14. Adding a commercial substrate to a tank.

means that water is in the tank and the heater has been used to obtain the desired temperature.

Electrical needs must be considered in selecting a location and installing an aquarium. One aquarium may have at least three electrical devices that need 110-volt power. These devices include pump/aerator, heater, and light. Every outlet used with an aquarium should be protected with a ground fault circuit interrupter (GFCI). Avoid using extension cords and makeshift wiring. These can be dangerous as well as fail to provide the needed electricity. Commercial producers may have standby electric generators as backup in case of a power failure.

Water containers must be set on strong stands or other supports. Weight of water adds up quickly. For example, a filled 18-gallon aquarium weighs about 155 pounds. The weight of an aquarium, in pounds, can be calculated by multiplying 0.036 (the weight of a cubic inch of water, in pounds) × the number of cubic inches in the aquarium. The number of cubic inches is found by multiplying length × width × height. For example, an aquarium that is 24 × 15 × 12 inches contains 4,320 cubic inches. The weight is 0.036 × 4,320, or about 155 pounds. And this is a small aquarium!

An aquarium should also have a Styrofoam® or plastic cushion between the bottom and the surface on which it sits. Using a wooden frame that would not require a cushion may be possible.

After the aquarium has been placed on its stand, substrate should be added. Substrate is the solid material on the bottom made of crushed rock or other matter. This material may be a part of the filtration system. Substrate helps anchor plants and decorative structures in the tank. Substrate also serves as a nesting and spawning place for some species. It is best to buy gravel made especially for substrate use.

The filtration system should be installed. Several kinds are available, and these are described later in this chapter. A system to oxygenate the water is also needed. This may be

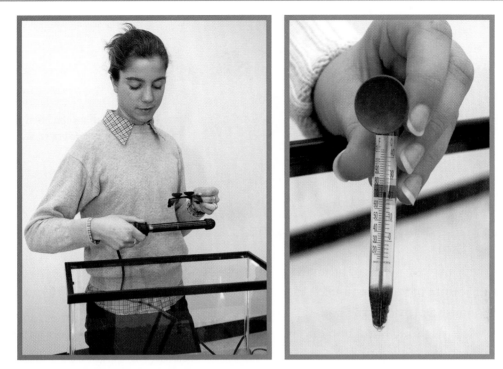

15–15. A bayonet-type heater may be used on an aquarium.

15–16. A thermometer for an aquarium.

a part of the filtration system or be installed separately. The sizes of filters and aerators depend on the size of the aquarium.

A heater will most likely be necessary. An *aquarium heater* is a specially designed device for warming water in an aquarium. The need for a heater depends on the species kept and on the temperature of the surrounding environment. Many fish keepers use bayonet-type heaters. Select a heater large enough to maintain the appropriate temperature in the aquarium. Do not turn a heater on until it is in the aquarium and water has been added. Use care in handling the heater to prevent breakage. A thermometer will be needed to go along with the heater. It may take some time to get the heater adjusted so that it heats the water to the desired temperature.

ACCESSORIES

Several accessories may be used. These provide for the welfare of the system as well as promote enjoyment. Water containers may have covers, hoods, and lighting attached to them.

Covers serve several useful purposes: keep fish and other aquatic animals from jumping out, keep water from splashing out, and keep unwanted items from being dropped in. Covers

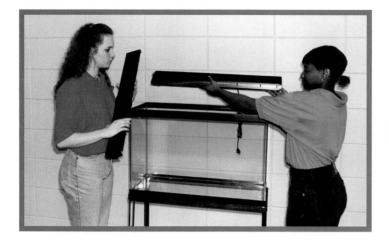

15–17. Installing the hood and light on an aquarium tank.

may be made of glass, metal, or other material. A glass cover is often of thinner glass than the walls and bottom of the aquarium. A metal cover should be of material that will not rust or corrode and is nontoxic to the aquatic species.

Fluorescent lighting is the standard in aquariums because it is cooler and more economical than incandescent lighting. It consists of tubes that enhance the growth of aquatic plants and organisms. Individual aquariums may be fitted with lights, or, in the case of several aquariums in the same room, the room may be lighted appropriately.

Generally, aquarium lights should provide 10 watts per cubic foot of aquarium. To determine the watts needed, calculate the number of cubic inches in the aquarium and divide by 1,728, which is the number of cubic inches in a cubic foot. This gives the number of cubic feet. Multiply the number of cubic feet times 10 to determine the wattage needed. Tubes should be positioned lengthwise in the tank and about 1 inch (2.54 cm) above the water level. Commercially available hoods often have built-in lighting. (Note that some species may grow best in aquariums with low levels of light.)

15–18. A cover of hardware cloth attached to a wooden frame protects koi.

15–19. A chainlink fence is being used to protect from poachers and large predators.

Covers in commercial growing operations may be made of wire, sheets of Styrofoam® construction material, thin plywood, or other materials. Covers prevent the loss of fish caused by their jumping out and keep predators from getting into the tanks. Covers also keep debris, such as leaves, from falling into tanks.

WATER QUALITIES

Several factors are important in assessing water needs and sources. The kind of water environment the species needs should be a first consideration. Water salinity, temperature, and treatment are major factors. A "match" of species and available water is essential for success with ornamentals.

Salinity

Aquariums can be established for species adapted to salt water, brackish water, or fresh water. Some species have low tolerance of water that is different from their natural habitat. A few species have high tolerance of variations in water.

Water for a freshwater aquarium may need to be checked for the presence of salt. Some species can tolerate low-level salinity; others cannot. The presence of

15–20. Salinity is measured with a hydrometer. (Water in a marine aquarium should have a specific gravity of 1.020 to 1.025. Fresh water should be near 1.0.)

salt in water intended for a freshwater aquarium may make the water unfit. Another source of water may be needed.

Other properties of water may also be important in its suitability for ornamental production. These include the presence of calcium, iron, and other minerals. (See Chapter 7, "Water Environments.")

The species selected must be adapted to the water that is to be used. In some cases, the salinity of small quantities of water can be modified to suit the species to be grown. This is an expensive process for a large-scale aquarium operation.

Temperature

Water temperature must be appropriate for the species. Some species need cold water, while others must have warm water. Heaters and coolers can be used to regulate the water temperature needed by a particular species. Changing the temperature of water is expensive; therefore, selecting a species adapted to the available water temperature is best.

15–21. Collecting tap water for aging.

Treatment

Many aquarium producers use tap or well water that has been prepared for use in fish culture. Municipal water systems often treat water with chlorine or other chemicals. This treatment makes the water unfit for use directly in aquariums. Water may need to be aged.

Water aging is collecting an open container of water and allowing it to stand for 24 hours exposed to the open air. This will result in the escape of chlorine and some other additives from the water. Some growers keep a supply of aged water on hand. Water from lakes and streams, rain water, and water stored in caustic containers should not be used in aquariums.

Growers who produce ornamentals in ponds or raceways often use well water, much as food fish growers do. Goldfish producers are a good example. The goldfish, a prolific fish used for both ornamental and bait purposes, is more tolerant of a wide range of environments than most ornamentals.

MANAGING ORNAMENTAL SYSTEMS

The keeper or commercial producer of ornamental aquaculture must consider the same basic areas as the commercial producer of food fish. The nature of the areas varies somewhat.

Aquariums, tanks, pools, and other facilities should be observed at least each day, with most growers observing them several times a day. Written records or computer logs should be kept of various factors, such as temperature and behavior of the species.

Several of the basic areas to be considered are presented here, with particular application to the production of ornamentals.

WATER MANAGEMENT

The water of aquariums, pools, and other ornamental water structures must be managed just as carefully as that in large food fish farms. This may involve monitoring oxygen, ammonia, pH, mineral content, and other water-quality and chemistry factors.

Water quality is maintained in aquariums by both mechanical and biological means. Several factors to be considered are aeration, temperature control, filtration, cleaning, water analysis, wastewater disposal, and adding water.

Aeration

Aeration in aquariums is often accomplished with devices that inject air or pure oxygen into the water. Flexible plastic tubing carries air from an air pump to an *air stone*, a porous material in the bottom of the aquariums. Air bubbles from the air stone into the water, diffuses throughout, and rises to the top of the water.

Aquatic plants can produce some oxygen through photosynthesis. In most cases, however, the amount they produce is inadequate for a heavily stocked aquarium. Without aeration, oxygen can enter the water only from the surface. This occurs at a very slow rate in still water. Splashing increases the diffusion of oxygen into water.

15–22. Attaching tubing to an air stone for an aquarium.

15–23. Checking a new bayonet-type aquarium heater.

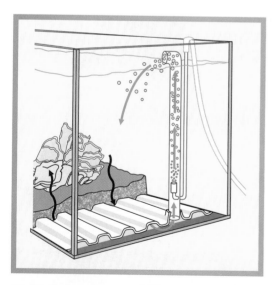

15–24. Underwater gravel filters are sometimes used with aquariums.

Temperature Control

Ornamental species usually have definite temperature requirements. Water temperature should be kept constant throughout the day. Ornamentals should be protected from rapid warming and cooling. Drops of more than 2°F or increases of more than 5°F in one day should be avoided.

Aquariums inside buildings usually need to have a water temperature higher than the temperature of the air surrounding the aquariums. Various ways of warming the water may be used. A ***thermostated heater*** is a warmer with a thermostat that is suspended in the water. A thermostat is a device that senses temperature and turns the heater on and off as needed. A thermostated heater should control the temperature within a range of 1.5°F of the thermostat setting. Most heaters are powered by electricity.

A heater has a wattage rating. The wattage needed depends on the size of the aquarium and the amount of heat necessary to keep the water within the desired range. As a general rule, a 75-watt heater is adequate for an aquarium holding 18 gallons (68 L) of water. A 100- to 150-watt heater is adequate for an aquarium holding 40 gallons (152 L). Use good electrical wiring; avoid extension cords and other dangerous makeshift wiring. Large users of heated water may have gas-fired boilers to warm the water.

Adding cold water or ice (for a drastic change) or using a refrigeration process will cool water that is too warm. Water is much more likely to need warming than cooling.

Filtration

Water filtration is used to maintain water quality. Filtration removes excess feed, feces, gases, and other substances from the water. Three kinds of filtration may be used: mechanical, biological, and chemical.

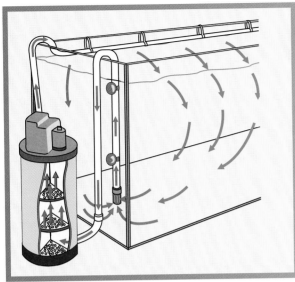

15–25. Direction of water flow with a nonattached cannister filter located outside and near an aquarium.

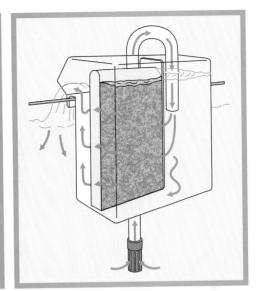

15–26. Direction of water flow with an outside floss filter attached to an aquarium.

Mechanical filtration is the passing of aquarium water through materials that remove suspended solids. The water is cleared of small solid particles of excess feed, feces, and decaying organic matter. Filters may be made of gravel, sand, charcoal, metal or plastic screens, or floss (a fibrous material). Mechanical filtration materials must be regularly cleaned or replaced. Clogged filters do little good and can result in damage to the system or fish. Floss, underwater gravel, and outside cannister mechanical filters are most common. In small aquariums, mechanical filtration often includes aeration of the water.

15–27. In a mechanical filtration system, floss filters must be regularly checked and cleaned or replaced.

15–28. A snail is used in biological filtration and to remove algae. (One snail will not be sufficient for a tank of more than a few gallons. Snails are always used in conjunction with other methods of filtration.)

Biological filtration is the use of bacteria and other living organisms to convert harmful substances to less harmful forms. These organisms feed on solid wastes and gases in the system and convert them to other forms.

Crawfish, snails, and other organisms often serve useful roles in keeping an aquarium clean. Crawfish scavenge food particles from the bottom of the tank. Snails eat (remove) organic material from the water. Organisms promote the nitrogen cycle. They convert harmful nitrogen forms into less harmful forms. For example, ammonia can form in an aquarium as a result of biological processes. Bacteria denitrify the ammonia. A variety of aquatic plants may be used in an aquarium to remove waste materials left by the fish or other species.

Chemical filtration is the use of chemical processes to filter water. Chemicals, ozone, and ultraviolet light may be used. Charcoal is often used with the chemical filtration to help keep water clear and prevent yellowing.

Filtration kits that fit inside or attach to the outside of aquariums are often used by hobbyists. Large producers may have filtration systems outside the aquariums to remove undesirable materials from the water.

15–29. A system that uses plants to help clean water. (The lower tank contains fish. Water is pumped to the upper tanks, which have plants growing in gravel. The plants use nutrients excreted by the fish from the water. Water returning to the fish tank has been cleaned.)

Overall, combinations of filtration methods are used. Mechanical filters may use nylon threads, plastic mats, charcoal, or gravel to remove solid particles from the water. A hobbyist may use a gravel-covered bottom in an aquarium to filter the water. Charcoal is an excellent filtration material because it can absorb a large amount of unwanted substances. Glasswool filtration material should not be used because of possible danger to the species and to the person who handles it. Most filtration systems use combinations of materials. Different materials filter different substances from the water.

In recent years, gravel filtration has grown in popularity with hobbyists. This usually involves covering a commercially available kit with 2 to 3 inches (5.0 to 7.6 cm) of fine gravel in the bottom of the aquarium. A benefit of this type of filtration is that it makes use of biological filtration. This means that in the gravel many bacteria are present that consume some of the harmful materials and convert them to other forms. For example, bacteria convert ammonia to less toxic forms of nitrogen.

Cleaning

An aquarium needs regular attention. Cleaning should be done to prevent the buildup of wastes and the growth of algae. The walls may need to be scrubbed to remove algae and

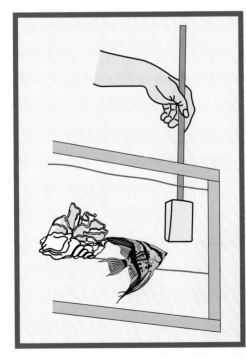

15–30. Scrubbing the sides of an aquarium removes algae and other materials and helps keep it attractive.

15–31. How siphoning works.

15–32. Using siphoning to clean the bottom of an aquarium.

other material. Afterward, siphoning can be used to lift and remove materials from the bottom. As water is removed, additional water should be gradually added.

Water Analysis

Quality water is needed for ornamentals to live and grow. The same principles apply with ornamentals as with species produced as food and sport fish. Water quality and analysis was covered in detail earlier in the book.

With ornamentals, six indicators of water quality are important. If out of balance, these may require corrective action. To some extent, the importance of water quality is related to the species chosen. For example, goldfish are more tolerant of poor-quality water than are mollies and bettas.

The six water qualities to assess and regulate with aquariums are

- pH—As the measure of acidity or basicity of water, pH also influences the presence of other substances, such as ammonia and nitrite. Kits are available, or a pH meter can be used. Most fish will do well at a pH range of 6.0 to 8.0. Various products are available to raise or lower pH. (A pH of 7.0 is neutral; readings below 7.0 are acidic and those above are basic.)

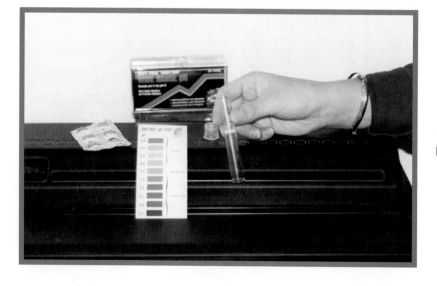

15–33. A kit for testing pH.

- Ammonia—Excess ammonia is the main killer of ornamentals. It is caused by the decomposition of wastes in the water. Several kits for testing ammonia are available. These may use test tubes or paper strips. Read the instructions that accompany a kit. A perfect aquarium will have no ammonia (tests will show 0.0 ppm ammonia). Some fish show stress with 0.5 ppm ammonia. If the test shows a water level of 2.0 ppm or higher, take immediate steps to lower the ammonia level. One step is to replace some of the water in the aquarium. This reduces the concentration of ammonia. Clean wastes from the aquarium and see that the filtration system is properly operating. Aquarium stores have products that will help prevent the buildup of ammonia.

- Nitrite—Nitrite is produced by nitrifying bacteria as they break down ammonia. Nitrite is very dangerous to ornamentals. It destroys the ability of blood to carry oxygen. Low levels cause stress and lowered disease resistance. Death can result. A commercial test kit should be obtained and used. An ideal nitrite test reading is 0.0 ppm. Nitrite levels tend to be higher in new aquariums and decline as the biological filter develops.

- Nitrate—Bacteria in the biological filter break down ammonia and nitrite into nitrate. Test kits are available for assessing the presence of nitrate. Nitrate levels should be below 40.0 ppm. Good overall water management reduces nitrate content. High levels can be reduced by adding water or using commercially available products.

- Chlorine—Chlorine is typically a problem with water obtained from a municipal system that adds chlorine. Test kits can be used to determine the presence of chlorine. Ideally, the chlorine level should be 0.0 ppm. Tap water can be aged by letting it stand before use in an aquarium. Products can be purchased that will rid water of chlorine.

CONNECTION

EXPERIENCE COUNTS

Aquaculture is learned in several ways. Background technical information comes from books and classes. The nature of aquatic species in a given environment is learned through experience. Combining books, classes, and experience provides the best education.

Experience with aquariums and different species is important in learning how to raise your favorite ornamentals. The experience can also help in selecting the species to include in an aquarium. This tank has exotic catfish and prawns, among other species.

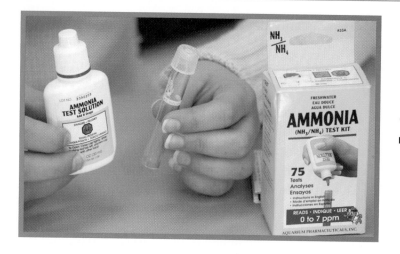

15–34. A kit for testing ammonia, nitrites, and nitrates.

- Hardness—Calcium, magnesium, and, to a lesser extent, heavy metals in water lead to hardness. These can affect the pH and other balances in the aquatic environment. Test kits can be used to test for hardness. Most aquatic species prefer hardness of 50 to 150 ppm. Below 50 ppm, pH may become a concern. Products can be added to an aquarium to eliminate hardness problems by removing calcium, magnesium, and heavy metals.

15–35. A bank of aquariums with a manifold system of wastewater disposal.

Wastewater Disposal

Growers of ornamental species must also consider how to dispose of water. Large volumes of water cannot usually be dumped into sewage systems, creeks, or lakes. Holding and treatment facilities may be needed. The hobbyist with one aquarium produces very little used water, and this does not usually pose a problem. Care must be taken in disposing of wastewater to assure that no organisms get released from the tank. For example, a couple of escaping fish can get into a native stream and create havoc in the natural environment.

Adding Water

New water will need to be added periodically to aquariums. (Of course, only conditioned, or aged, water should be added.) Hobbyists are reminded that at least one-fourth of the water in an aquarium should be replaced each month. This accounts for that lost to evaporation.

NUTRITION AND FEEDING

Ornamental species require nutrients for growth. Both plants and animals must have the nutrients available. Nutrients should be provided in the right amounts, never more than can be used. Normally, fish should be fed no more than they will eat in 10 minutes when feed is given one to three times a day. Uneaten feed fouls the water.

Commercially prepared feeds are available for many ornamental fish. These feeds tend to provide a reasonably balanced diet. The diet needs of many ornamental species are unknown. Variety in the diet is usually a good idea.

Feeds may be manufactured for general use with ornamental species. In some cases, feeds may be manufactured for specific species of fish because of unique differences and nutrient needs. An interesting additive to feed for some species is a substance to promote color. Most fish feeds have at least some portion of fish meal or fish oil as well as grains and mixes

15–36. Many specialized kinds of commercial feeds are available for ornamental fish.

15–37. Flakes are commonly used with goldfish and other ornamentals.

of vitamins and minerals. Protein content is particularly important. Many ornamental fish feeds have 35 percent protein, 7 percent crude fat, and 5 percent fiber. Younger fish may need higher protein content.

Size of feed particle is also important. Small fish cannot readily consume large-size feed particles. Very small fish need finely ground meals. They may also consume plankton, rotifers, or other material. Artemia are sometimes used. Small fish can consume $1/8$-inch pellets. As the fish grow, pellet size can be increased to $1/4$-inch. Some fish never grow large enough for pellets and are fed flakes, crumbles, or other forms.

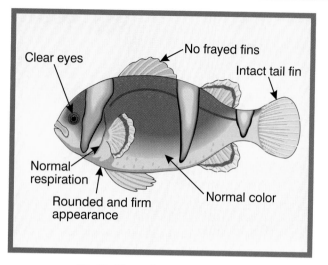

Clear eyes

No frayed fins

Intact tail fin

Normal respiration

Rounded and firm appearance

Normal color

15–38. Signs of good fish health.

HEALTH

Good health is important with ornamental species. Diseases can cause problems, and some fish may die. Sanitation, quarantine, and isolation are good practices. New fish should never be put into an established aquarium without being observed for a while for the presence of disease. One diseased fish put into an aquarium of healthy fish can result in the loss of the entire population!

Some fish keepers have small isolation tanks. An *isolation tank* is an aquarium where new fish are kept for a few days before being put into a large aquarium with other fish. This allows time to observe the new fish for health condition.

In a well-designed aquarium stocked with healthy species and well-maintained water, disease problems seldom occur. Entire aquariums should rarely be medicated. Diseased fish should be moved to a separate small aquarium, known as a *hospital tank*, for treatment.

15–39. A therapeutant may be added to the water to help control disease.

HANDLING

Ornamental fish may be handled when the tanks are being cleaned, reproduction is being encouraged, or the fish are being shipped to market.

Ornamental fish are often shipped in plastic bags in Styrofoam® chests. The bags are partially filled with water. Pure oxygen is added to ensure safe delivery. The Styrofoam® chests are usually placed in a cardboard box for air shipment. Fish shipped long distances may be placed in new water with new oxygen while en route. Use care to prevent stress and injury.

SELECTING ORNAMENTAL SPECIES

Both animal and plant species may be grown in aquariums. These may be suited to fresh water, salt water, or brackish water. Knowing the required environment for a species before trying to grow it in an aquarium is important. The proper environment must be provided.

Deciding which species to grow depends on your goals as the producer. If the species is to be grown for marketing, produce a species for which there is good demand. Never produce a species for which there is no demand. Your aquaculture business will fail! If your goal is to keep fish for fun and enjoyment, make your selection based on the requirements of the species, available water, and other needed resources. Your knowledge and skill are important. If you are a novice, begin with species that are hardy and require only minimal skill to keep them growing. As experience is gained, more difficult species may be grown.

FACTORS IN SELECTION

There are many ways of looking at ornamental fish. Most all species can be assessed on several criteria. Important criteria are

- Water temperature—Fish can be classified on the basis of water temperature. Most species have a temperature range in which they grow best. The ornamentals known as "tropicals" require warmer water than other species. Tropicals typically prefer water in the range of 72° to 80°F (22.2° to 26.7°C).

- Water salinity—Water salinity refers to the salt content of the water required for growth. Salt water (as in the ocean) is approximately 35 ppt salt, whereas fresh water contains virtually no salt. Brackish water has a salt level between that of fresh water and salt water. Large exhibits in museums may have separate aquariums showing aquatic species in all three water environments. Many of the favored aquarium species are best adapted to fresh water.

- Reproduction—Some ornamental fish are livebearers, meaning that the young are born ready to swim and take food. Others are egg-layers, meaning that the female

15–40. Size of a fish may be a factor in selection. This shows measuring the length of a koi.

expels eggs, which are fertilized by sperm from the male. A period of incubation is required for the eggs to hatch. Many of the favored aquarium species are livebearers.

- Size—Ornamental fish range from less than an inch long to a foot or more at maturity. Of course, as length increases, weight also increases. Small aquariums are best suited to the smaller species of fish. In addition, smaller fish usually eat less food and require less water and oxygen.

- Feeding habits—Fish species vary in their diet requirements. Some are carnivorous; others are herbivorous. The grower needs to know the general dietary requirements of fish in order to provide for their needs.

- Behavior—Some species of fish are very aggressive toward other species and other individuals within their species. Aggressive species must often be grown in isolation to

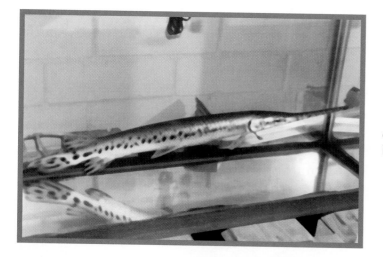

15–41. A longnose gar (*Lepisosteus osseus*) has interesting appeal, but is it practical for your aquarium?

prevent them from destroying the other fish. Many ornamental producers prefer the species that are less aggressive.

- Physical appearance—*Fancy* is the term used to describe ornamentals that have characteristics which are particularly appealing to people. Variations include color, body shape, fin shape and size, and presence of barbels (feelers about the mouth, as on catfish). Personal preference has much to do with the selection of species on the basis of physical appearance.

- Scientific classification—Various schemes of scientific classification have been used over the years. These are intended to show relationships among the species on the basis of anatomy (structure of the species) and morphology (form and structure).

EASE OF KEEPING

Keeping ease is the ease with which a particular species is produced. Some species are more difficult than others. The beginner or the individual who wants only to devote minimal time to fish keeping should select those that are easy to grow.

In this book, ornamental fish are classified into three groups based on keeping ease: easy, medium, and difficult. The easy-to-grow species will survive in a range of conditions. The medium-care will need more attention. The difficult-to-grow will require the most attention to water environment and other needs.

PRODUCING ORNAMENTAL SPECIES

Some species are very difficult to grow and should be attempted only by experienced growers. In selecting a species or a combination of species, consider the available water, the species requirements, and the knowledge of the grower about the species and aquaculture.

EASY-TO-GROW ORNAMENTALS

Some ornamental fish are *hardy*. This means they will survive in a wide range of conditions. They do not stress easily when water temperature varies. They are not extremely sensitive to fouled water or water that is low in oxygen. A few examples are presented here.

Goldfish

The goldfish (*Carassius auratus*) is a popular, hardy species of ornamental fish originally developed by the Chinese and Japanese. New varieties are continually being developed. The

15–42. Goldfish in a well-maintained aquarium.

new varieties feature fancy fins, colors, and eye sizes. Some fancy varieties are the bubble-eye, black moor, comet, lionhead, veiltail, and fantail. Of course, the most popular is the common goldfish.

Goldfish will grow in water that is a little cooler than that preferred by the tropicals. Goldfish do not do well in water above 80°F (26.7°C). They will survive in backyard ponds, aquariums, and bowls or jars. The size they will reach depends on the food provided, the water quality, and the amount of water area available. At least 2 gallons (7.6 L) of water are needed for a goldfish to reach a length of 2 inches (5.1 cm) and survive. Some goldfish will live as long as 15 years. Heaters are not often used in aquariums with goldfish.

A variety of commercial foods are available for goldfish. In outside pools, goldfish eat insects, algae, and water plants; however, most also require supplemental food.

Goldfish that lose their color need some vegetation to nibble on. More direct sunlight on the water in their container may be used to try to restore color. All goldfish tend to lose some color as they age. Goldfish are considered to be messy fish and require water exchange in bowls and aquariums.

Goldfish reproduce by laying eggs, with the eggs hatching two to four days after spawning and fertilization. As mentioned, the size attained by goldfish is determined by the amount of water, quality of the water, and nutrition. In ponds, they may reach a length of 2 feet (61 cm)! Most are marketed by the commercial grower at a length of 2 inches (5.1 cm) or less.

15–43. Brightly colored goldfish in an outdoor pool. Can you see any dark-colored fish?

Koi

Koi are increasing in popularity in the United States. Koi originated from the common carp (*Cyprinus carpio*) over a period of several hundred years. Several subspecies (varieties) are kept for their fancy colors and appeal. Examples of subspecies include the kohaku, tancho, butterfly, and koromo koi.

As the national fish of Japan, koi were first used for food. Individual koi with bright colors were not eaten, but were used to breed koi, which have brilliant colors and appealing features. Today, koi-keeping clubs are found in Japan and other nations.

Koi are similar to goldfish, but are larger and have barbels about their mouths. Koi varieties are classified on the basis of their color and arrangement of color. Koi may be solid black, red, yellow, brown, gold, or silver, or they may have spots of different colors in various patterns. The presence of scales also varies, from the fish being completely covered to having no visible scales. Koi may grow to 3 feet (91 cm) long and live for 60 years. Size and life span depend on care and protection from hazards.

Koi are often kept in small outdoor pools. However, they can also be kept in other water structures, such as tanks and aquariums. Outdoor pools or water gardens are often designed into landscapes and building features.

Koi breeders carefully select broodstock. A male should be at least two years old and a female three years old at the time of first spawning. Before spawning, females have rounder bodies than the males. A female may produce 100,000 to 750,000 eggs at one spawning, depending on size and condition.

15–44. Kyoto koi have variable color patterns. Koi are popular in larger aquariums and water gardens, such as this Japanese garden.

15–45. This koi shows a wide range of colors.

15–46. Dip netting koi from a culture tank.

15–47. Seining koi from an outdoor plastic-lined pool.

Koi can often spawn in the pool where they are kept, but special breeding pools are preferred. The eggs should be removed as soon as possible after fertilization because the adult koi will eat them. At 70° to 75°F (21° to 24°C), the eggs hatch in four to seven days.

Fry lose their egg sacs in two to three days and will freely swim in the water. Koi fry are fed newly hatched brine shrimp (artemia) or a commercial feed. At a month of age, the koi should be eating dry feed in meal or small-pellet form. Culling may begin at two to four weeks of age. Weak, deformed koi are removed first. Koi with the desired colors are selected as ornamentals.

Good management can prevent disease and other problems. Koi need water quality similar to that needed by most warmwater, medium-hardy species. The water should be free of pollution and contain sufficient oxygen. Feeding should be at the same location and time each day. Small to medium-size floating pellets are used. Some commercial koi foods contain color enhancer. A *color enhancer* is a feed additive that intensifies the brilliance of the fish colors. Carotene is a common color enhancer.

15–48. Testing water in an outdoor pool is an important part of managing koi environments.

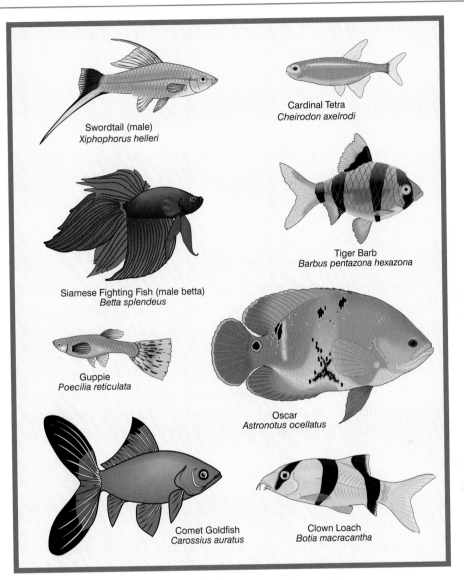

15–49. Common freshwater-aquarium species.

Barbs

The barbs include several species in the same family as the goldfish (Cyprinidae). The name *barbs* is derived from the barbels about the fishes' mouths; however, some barbs have no barbels, while others have two pairs, and still others have four pairs.

Barbs prefer well-lighted aquariums. The larger barbs may be aggressive toward the smaller barbs. Barbs prefer water that is 70° to 80°F (21.1° to 26.7°C). Most barbs reach a maximum size of 2 to 4 inches in length. They are egg-layers with behavior similar to that of goldfish. Some species will eat their eggs after spawning. The most common species are the following.

Spotted Barb. The spotted barb (*Barbus binotatus*) reaches a maximum length of 4½ inches (11.4 cm) and prefers water 75° to 78°F (23.9° to 25.6°C).

Rosy Barb. The rosy barb (*Barbus conchonius*) has a rosy color, reaches a maximum length of 3 inches (7.6 cm), and prefers cool water of 64° to 74°F (17.8° to 23.3°C).

Tinfoil Barb. The tinfoil barb (*Barbus schwanenfeldi*) is the largest—reaching 9 inches (22.9 cm) in length—and the most active barb. It is the color of aluminum foil, except for the fins, which may be orange and black.

Guppies

Guppies (*Poecilia reticulata*) are the most popular tropical fish. They are livebearers that reproduce profusely. A female guppy 2½ inches (6.6 cm) long may give birth to as many as 200 baby fish at a time; the average number is 40 to 50. One adult pair of guppies can fill an aquarium with young guppies in a few weeks.

Several varieties of guppies are kept, with some growers developing guppies that have fancy colors and fins. Varieties include red deltatail, blue veiltail, gold flamingo, and half-back veiltail. A guppy may live about two years under good conditions. Guppies should be fed a basic diet of commercial tropical fish food. They will also eat mosquito larvae and other natural foods.

Gouramis

Gouramis are a large group of easy-to-grow ornamentals. They are known as *labyrinth fish* because of an air storage chamber above the gills. This chamber is called a labyrinth and is filled with air by the fish gulping at the surface of the water. The oxygen in this chamber supplements that absorbed by the gills.

The air temperature should be similar to that of the water, because much colder air can contribute to the development of respiratory disease in the fish. Gouramis are well suited to aquariums and may live for five years or more. Most prefer a water temperature of about 75°F (23.9°C) and need a complete commercial pet-fish food. Three popular ornamental gouramis are discussed here.

Kissing Gouramis. Kissing gouramis (*Helostoma temmincki*) are known for their trait of extending their thick, fleshy lips and kissing. Kissing gouramis require aquariums of at least 20 gallons (75.8 L) and should be fed twice daily, with additional vegetable matter included with one of the feedings. They may reach a length of 12 inches (30.5 cm).

15–50. Kissing gouramis are probably the most interesting species of gourami.

Blue Gouramis. Blue gouramis (*Trichogaster trichopterus*) are very hardy and easy-to-raise ornamentals. Blue gouramis reproduce by the female laying eggs in a foamy bubble nest constructed by the male, who also fertilizes the eggs. The fish may reach a length of 6 inches (15.2 cm).

Pearl Gouramis. Pearl gouramis (*Trichogaster leeri*) are pleasing pets. They are quiet fish that seldom attack others and do best in medium-size aquariums. Pearl gouramis may reach a length of 4 inches (10.2 cm).

MEDIUM-CARE ORNAMENTALS

The fish described here require medium care to be successfully grown. Varieties within species may vary in the amount of care required. Water conditions, nutrition, reproduction, and temperature need careful attention. A few examples of medium-care ornamentals are presented here.

Tetras

This group of tropical fish includes several species in the Characidae family. The tetras make up one of the largest families of freshwater-aquarium fish. They reproduce by scattering eggs throughout the aquarium and, in general, do not care for either their eggs or their young. They tend to swim in small schools (also known as shoals).

Tetras have bright colors and a peaceful temperament. They are hardy and easy to handle. They do best in aquariums with soft, slightly acid water, under low-light conditions. Most prefer a water temperature of 72° to 85°F (22.2° to 29.4°C). They range from 1½ to 3 inches (3.8 to 7.6 cm) in length. Tetras tend to grow better if several are kept in the same aquarium so they can swim in schools of six or eight. Four species of tetras are discussed here.

15–51. Children enjoy watching easy-to-keep and medium-care ornamentals.

Neon Tetra. The neon tetra (*Hyphessobrycon innesi*) reaches a maximum length of 1¹/₂ inches (3.8 cm) and prefers dimly lit areas in the aquarium.

Cardinal Tetra. The cardinal tetra (*Cheirodon axelrodi*) has a brilliant reddish color and is less common than the neon, with a maximum length of 1¹/₂ inches (3.8 cm).

Black Tetra. The black tetra (*Gymnocorymbus ternetzi*) is peaceful when young but becomes more aggressive with age. Its black color fades to gray as it ages.

Golden Tetra. The golden tetra (*Hemigrammus armstrongi*) has a bright, golden shine and grows better in groups of four to eight fish.

Catfish

This is a large group of fish having barbels about their mouths. Often characterized as scavengers among the ornamental species, they bear no relationship to the cultured, farm-raised channel catfish and other species grown for human consumption that receive specific rations. Most ornamental catfish have unique features that justify their designation as ornamentals. Most prefer water in the 70° to 80°F (21.1° to 26.7°C) range. They reproduce by laying eggs. Three common ornamental catfish are listed here.

Glass Catfish. The glass catfish (*Kryptoptereus bicirrhis*) may grow up to 4 inches (10.2 cm) long. It is opalescent, showing rainbow colors in the right light.

Upside-Down Catfish. The upside-down catfish (*Synodontis nigriventris*) has the unique characteristic of swimming inverted and prefers a dimly lit aquarium.

15–52. The upside-down catfish is an interesting aquarium species. Even the coloration is reversed from other catfish—the belly side is dark, and the back is white.

Electric Catfish. The electric catfish (*Malapterurus electricus*) has the ability to produce an electric shock that will kill small fish and keep larger ones away. The species must be isolated in an aquarium.

DIFFICULT-TO-GROW ORNAMENTALS

The ornamentals that are more difficult to grow are less common, require a higher level of knowledge and skill to culture successfully, and may sell for a higher price. Some of these fish are capable of inflicting injury when they are being tended. A few examples are presented here.

Piranhas

Piranhas (*Rooseveltiella nattereri*) are best known as fish with razor-sharp teeth that will take bites out of other fish and aquatic animals, as well as the humans who tend them.

Piranhas prefer water that is about 78°F (25.6°C). Their diet should include chunks of beef heart, kidney, or liver; raw fish; earthworms; and goldfish. They may reach lengths of 10 to 12 inches (25.4 to 30.5 cm).

Piranhas should be isolated from other fish, including other piranhas, as they will attack, kill, and consume the fish. Not much is known about the culture of piranhas. Their importation and possession may be illegal in some states.

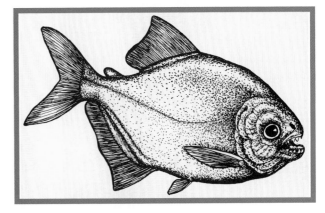

15–53. The piranha is a rare, interesting, dangerous, and often illegal aquarium species.

Hatchetfish

This group has several species of fish in the Gasteropelecidae family. Hatchetfish are peaceful fish but often do not live long in captivity. The aquariums must be kept covered, as hatchetfish will tend to "fly" out by using their winglike pectoral fins. Hatchetfish need long aquariums with considerable surface water. The aquariums should have protected or shaded areas, as the fish are easily frightened and may injure themselves by crashing into the glass.

Hatchetfish do best in groups of three to six fish at a water temperature of 75° to 85°F (23.9° to 29.4°C). They should be fed floating feeds or food that remains near the surface of the water. Two examples of hatchetfish are included here.

Marbled Hatchetfish. The marbled hatchetfish (*Carnegiella strigata*) reaches a maximum length of 2¼ inches (15.7 cm) and has irregular streaks of dark color on the pearl-like ventral side, with a golden dorsal side.

Silver Hatchetfish. Silver hatchetfish (*Gastropelecus levis*) are very sensitive to their environment. They are slightly larger than marbled hatchetfish.

15–54. Turtles are sometimes kept in aquariums.

OTHER AQUATIC ORNAMENTAL SPECIES

Aquariums may also contain other aquatic ornamental species. Some of these may be saltwater species that are popular with people who keep saltwater aquariums. Animals that are aquatic or water loving may be a part of some aquariums.

Fresh Water

Common freshwater animal species include salamanders, tadpoles, freshwater ghost shrimp, African aquatic frogs, snails, and turtles. Each species has specific requirements for growth. Some species contribute to keeping a balanced aquarium. For example, the snail helps to keep the glass and decorations in an aquarium clean. Of course, it also contributes its own wastes to the water. Some species are the food of fish. For example, the ghost shrimp will be readily eaten by some fish.

Salt Water

Some saltwater species are very popular. The species are often brightly colored. A saltwater environment is needed to provide for their well-being. Details on their culture are available from reference materials, via the Internet, and at stores that sell saltwater species.

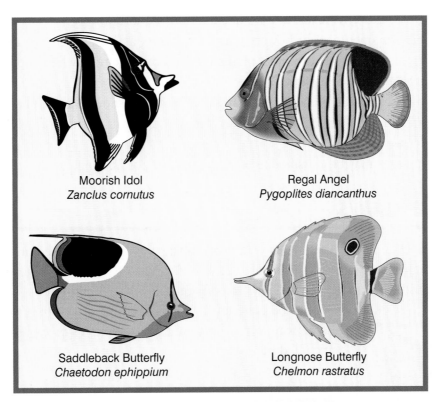

Moorish Idol
Zanclus cornutus

Regal Angel
Pygoplites diancanthus

Saddleback Butterfly
Chaetodon ephippium

Longnose Butterfly
Chelmon rastratus

15–55. Examples of saltwater fish kept in aquariums.

15–56. An attractive saltwater aquarium.

ORNAMENTAL AQUARIUM PLANTS

Plants are used to make an aquarium more attractive and help maintain water quality. Commercial growers of plants keep pet stores and other retail outlets stocked with various plants for hobbyists. The volume of production for the retail market is small. A few plants will quickly grow and provide all that are needed in an aquarium.

Commercial ornamental fish growers may view plants as pests in the management of their production systems. For example, plants interfere with seining when capturing ornamental fish grown in ponds or large tanks.

Some plants are considered pests in streams and lakes and should not be placed in them. Regulations may make the stocking of these plants a violation of the law, with fines and other penalties for doing so.

Aquarium plants may be classified as rooted, bunched, or floating.

ROOTED PLANTS

A *rooted aquatic plant* grows with roots in the gravel or other medium at the bottom of an aquarium. Rooted plants are attractive but can cause problems if their roots grow into the filtration system in the gravel. When an aquarium is set up, the roots of the plants should be covered in the gravel and, if possible, anchored in some way to the bottom. Some examples of rooted plants are included here.

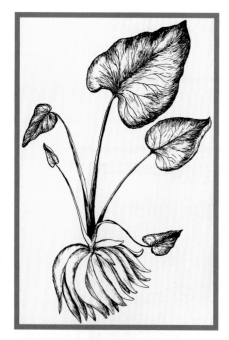

15–57. The banana plant gets its common name from its banana-shaped tuberous roots.

Hygrophila

The hygrophila (*Hygrophila polysperma*) tends to grow well but requires good light. It is planted in small bunches. The narrow leaves, which are about 2 inches (5.1 cm) long, grow on stems that may be several inches long. Propagation is by cuttings or leaves. Hygrophila typically grows in fresh water.

Banana Plant

The banana plant (*Nymphoides aquatica*) produces banana-shaped tuberous roots that lie on top of the gravel in the bottom of an aquarium. The leaves may be 2 inches (5.1 cm) across and grow on stems that are 3 to 4 inches (7.6 to 10.2 cm) long. The plant grows best in fresh water with a temperature of 70° to 82°F (21° to 28°C). Plant-eating fish often prefer it.

Amazon Sword

The Amazon sword plant (*Echinadorus paniculatus*) is suited only to larger aquariums because it may reach a height of 2 feet (61 cm). A smaller variety, the pigmy Amazon sword (*Echinadorus tenellus*), may be used in smaller aquariums. The pigmy grows about 4 inches (10.2 cm) high. New plants are developed from runners and should be cut off and removed to keep from overcrowding the aquarium. Both are attractive plants. Inadequate light may result in discolored leaves.

Bunched plants

A *bunched aquatic plant* is one that grows so that a bunch shape is formed. Bunched plants are probably more popular in aquariums than rooted or floating plants. They are propagated from cuttings that may or may not produce roots. They typically grow quickly in bunches and need cutting back to keep them from taking over the aquarium. Some examples of bunched plants are included here.

Fanwort

The fanwort (*Cabomba caroliniana*) grows fine leaves in a fan-shaped arrangement on a stem that may reach several inches in length. The fanwort is sensitive and can be killed by sudden changes in water temperature. It prefers water of about 72°F (22.2°C). Light and aeration are necessary. Some species of ornamental fish eat the foliage, with goldfish being an example.

Elodea

The elodea (*Elodea densa*) is a hardy plant that thrives in water 72° to 85°F (22.2° to 29.4°C). Some species of fish nibble on the foliage. Since it grows rapidly and quite long (up to 10 feet, or 3 m), it should be located at the back of an aquarium and pruned often.

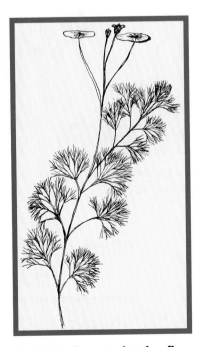

15–58. The fanwort plant has fine underwater leaves and may have flowers and floating leaves.

Milfoil

Several species of milfoil (*Myriophyllum spicatum*), also known as foxtail, may be used in aquariums. They are similar to hornwort and fanwort. The plants will have a deep, bright green color if they receive eight hours of light each day. Many small leaves grow along the stems and form attractive aquarium plants. Milfoil often does best in cooler water.

FLOATING PLANTS

A ***floating aquatic plant*** is one that floats on the water. Floating plants are the least desirable plants in an aquarium with other species that need light. They block the light from passing into the water and to the bottom of the aquarium. Floating plants are best in an aquarium where lighting is low. Examples of floating plants are included here.

15–59. Water hyacinths may be used in large outdoor tanks.

Duckweed

Duckweed (*Lemna minor*) is popular for shading aquariums from strong light. Larger species of fish will eat duckweed. The tiny, $1/2$-inch (1.27 cm) round leaves can quickly cover the surface of the water in an aquarium. Duckweed is considered a pest in pond aquaculture. **It should never be released into ponds, lakes, or streams!**

Crystalwort

Crystalwort (*Riccia fluitans*) forms a mass of short, narrow leaves. It must be kept thinned to no more than 1 inch thick at the surface of the water of an aquarium. Some species of fish spawn in the mass that is formed.

MARKETING ORNAMENTALS

Marketing is connecting the seller or producer with a buyer or fish keeper. Large producers use sophisticated systems of wholesalers or jobbers to reach buyers. Small producers may sell directly to fish keepers.

15–60. The ornamental fish department of a pet store.

A wise commercial producer will develop a marketing plan before any fish are produced. A marketing plan is a written statement that guides the marketing process. Research is needed to assess market potential and ways of reaching the final consumer. A marketing plan forces an individual to assess marketing opportunities and determine if there is a demand for a product. It identifies how the fish will be marketed and the channels they will pass through. A plan also helps determine if the product will be profitable.

A marketing plan will help identify other products that can be carried along with the ornamentals produced. Other products include feeds, therapeutants, and aquarium equipment.

MARKETING CHANNELS

Ornamental marketing may involve several approaches or channels. They are

- Direct marketing—This involves selling at retail prices directly to the fish keeper. In most cases, only a small volume of fish can be sold in this manner. The producer may maintain a retail store in addition to the production facilities. This is similar to the on-farm sales of fruit and vegetables by some growers.

- Internet marketing—This involves having a Web site to advertise the products available and take orders. A method of receiving payment must be in place. Orders must be shipped to assure prompt arrival of a quality ornamental fish.

- Retail stores—This involves selling directly to retail fish stores. Such stores may specialize in ornamental fish or have a full line of companion animals and pet-care products. A list of such stores must be developed, and the stores contacted to solicit orders. The orders must be taken and delivered.

- Discount stores—Large discount stores often have ornamental fish departments. Sales to the stores may be arranged through a jobber or fish hauler. In some cases, direct deliveries are made. Regardless, cultivating contacts with store buyers is essential to gain sales.

Marketing Functions

Marketing ornamental species involves several functions or procedures. These are

- Identifying outlets—This involves identifying and cultivating relationships with potential buyers. The buyers may be representatives of large stores, haulers, or exporters.

- Harvesting—Harvesting is seining, dip netting, trapping, or otherwise capturing fish for selling. Care must be taken not to injure the fish. Conditions must be calm to minimize stress.

15–61. Ornamentals are separated by species in marketing.

- Grading—Grading is used to assure uniformity of a batch of fish. Defective, diseased, or injured fish are removed. Color, size, and other factors may be parts of the grading process. Grading may also involve counting or weighing fish.

- Packing—Fish may be placed in tanks, plastic bags, or other containers for transporting. The approach used must assure that the product arrives in good condition. Some ornamentals are placed in plastic bags with water and pure oxygen. The bags are kept

15–62. Grading involves sorting fish based on color, size, and defects.

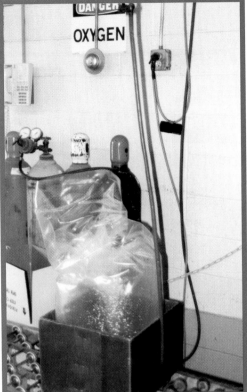

at an appropriate temperature. The bags are sometimes placed in Styrofoam® or paper boxes for shipment.

- Transporting—Ornamental fish may be transported in producer-owned trucks or by carrier. Next-day deliveries are possible with public carriers, such as UPS and FedEx. All regulations for shipping should be met.

- Pricing—Pricing is establishing the amount for which the ornamentals will be sold. It is

15–63. The packing department at an ornamental fish producer shows boxes that hold plastic bags with water and pure oxygen added from the bottles in the background.

determined through discussion with buyers and knowledge of prices generally paid for the product. Pricing should be at a level that provides a profit to the fish producer.

15–64. These boxes are used to hold plastic bags for ornamentals. (Note the labels with information about the product.)

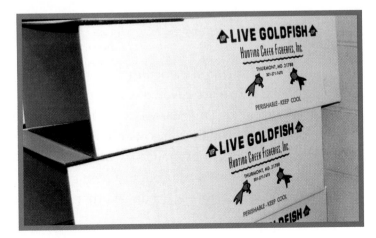

WELL-BEING

Well-being is the state in which an animal's needs are met and it does not suffer. Needs vary by species. These variances should be taken into consideration.

Providing for well-being means being sure conditions are met that best meet an animal's needs and promote its health and growth. A producer or keeper would never mistreat a fish, snail, turtle, or other animal. A producer would care for an animal's needs by providing a good environment and proper feed and by minimizing disease and injury. Animals are harvested, moved, and handled in ways that minimize injury.

Animal well-being is sometimes known as animal welfare or animal rights. Since these terms conjure up emotions and do not necessarily reflect the situations of production and keeping, the term *well-being* is more appropriate to use, though it might not be as popular.

15–65. Quality water in this tank helps provide for the well-being of these ornamentals.

The U.S. Department of Agriculture operates the Animal Welfare Information Center (AWIC). Specific areas are devoted to aquatic animals, including those used for laboratory research, as companion animals, and for food production. For more information, go to the AWIC Web site: **www.nal.usda.gov/awic/.**

Sometimes an animal must undergo euthanasia. *Euthanasia* is the killing of an animal that is suffering. Death is carried out in a humane way. An animal that is euthanized might have been injured or might have a disease that cannot be cured.

REVIEWING

MAIN IDEAS

Ornamentals consist of both plant and animal species, with fish being the predominant crop. The two major areas involved are fish keeping and commercial production. Fish keepers are people who have ornamental fish for fun and relaxation. Commercial producers are those who produce aquaculture crops for sale.

Aquariums are often used to grow the fanciest, highest-priced ornamentals. Some ornamentals, such as goldfish and koi, are adapted to pond or large-tank culture. Hobbyists get enjoyment from establishing and maintaining aquariums of mixed plant and animal species. Meeting the needs of each species requires studying the adaptations of the species. Water systems must be established and controlled to ensure that the species are in a suitable environment.

Ornamentals can be classified into three categories on the basis of difficulty in growing: easy-to-grow, medium-care, and difficult-to-grow. Hundreds of species of ornamentals can be put into these categories. Easy-to-grow species include goldfish, koi, barbs, guppies, and gouramis. Medium-care ornamentals include the tetras and catfish. Some difficult-to-grow ornamentals are the piranhas and hatchetfish. Inexperienced individuals should begin with the easy-to-grow species; as the growers develop skills, they can advance to the more difficult species.

Marketing is an important part of a successful business. It must be considered when selecting the species to be produced. The producer must also be able to establish a marketing channel and carry out the marketing functions. A written marketing plan is very useful in an ornamentals enterprise.

Well-being is providing for the needs of animals so that they do not suffer and their needs are met. The U.S. Department of Agriculture has the Animal Welfare Information Center, which addresses the well-being of aquatic animals.

QUESTIONS

Answer the following questions, using complete sentences and correct spelling.

1. Define ornamental aquaculture.

2. Why are ornamentals popular?

3. What are the system needs for ornamental aquaculture? Briefly describe each of the components.

4. What is the weight of the water in an aquarium that is 36 × 18 × 15 inches?

5. Describe water for an aquarium.

6. How is water quality maintained in an aquarium?

7. What are three classifications of aquarium plants? Distinguish between the classifications and name examples of plants in each.

8. What are some ways of classifying ornamental fish? Briefly describe each of the ways.

9. Ornamental fish are classified into three groups on the basis of how easy they are to grow. Name the three groups and give an example of a species in each group.

10. Select one species of ornamental fish and provide some details on its cultural requirements.

11. What are the channels in marketing ornamentals? Briefly explain each.

12. What are the functions in marketing ornamentals? Briefly explain each.

13. What is well-being? How is it related to animal aquaculture?

14. What are the signs of good health with ornamental fish?

EVALUATING

Match the term with the correct definition. Write the letter of the term on the line provided.

a. hospital tank
b. well-being
c. fish keeping
d. water aging

e. thermostated heater
f. rooted aquatic plants
g. floating aquatic plants
h. fancy

i. color enhancer
j. labyrinth fish

_____1. Fish with air storage chamber above the gills

_____2. Aquatic plants with roots in the soil or gravel at the bottom of water

_____3. A separate tank where diseased fish are kept

_____4. A feed additive to make ornamental fish more colorful

_____5. The state in which an animal's needs are met and it does not suffer

_____6. Characteristic of appealing ornamental fish

_____7. Aquatic plants that float on the surface of water

_____8. Heater with thermostat suspended in the aquarium water

_____9. Allowing water to stand in the open air so that substances may escape

_____10. Caring for ornamental fish as a hobby

EXPLORING

1. Select and set up an aquarium in your classroom or home. Determine the species to be kept, the source and quality of water, and the steps to be taken to meet the habitat requirements of the species selected. Prepare a report on your activities.

2. Manage an aquarium for a week. Keep careful records of all observations, feedings, and other events. Give a report in class on your experiences.

3. Tour a local pet store or other facility with an ornamental fish department. Determine the species that are for sale. Identify the fish-keeping equipment, including costs for getting a beginning aquarium system underway. Prepare a report on your observations.

4. Investigate the contents of one of the following Web sites and prepare a short report on your findings:

Aquariums Central—**www.aquariumscentral.com**

Virtual Aquarium—**www.cnr.vt.edu/efish/families/**

Koi Colorado—**www.koicolorado.com**

CHAPTER 16

Baitfish

OBJECTIVES

This chapter covers the fundamentals of baitfish production. It has the following objectives:

1 Identify common species of baitfish

2 Explain how golden shiners are produced

3 Explain how fathead minnows are produced

4 Explain how goldfish used for bait are produced

5 Discuss baitfish marketing

TERMS

bait	feeder fish	spawning board
baitfish	female:male ratio	spawning mat
breeding tubercle	formalin	
egg transfer	fry transfer	

16–1. A baitfish producer checks the oxygen system on a haul truck.

FISHERS use baitfish to catch fish and a few other aquatic species. A baitfish is typically placed on a hook to lure a larger fish into biting. The larger fish views the bait as food. When the larger fish bites, the hook and barb are taken into the mouth along with the baitfish. In some cases, the bait is put into a net or box trap.

Baitfish are chosen because the fisher wants to use live bait rather than artificial lures or other attractants. Fishers typically view baitfish produced on baitfish farms as superior to those caught wild.

Baitfish production can be a profitable venture. As with all enterprises, profit is not guaranteed. Good management and the production of a desired product help assure a profitable baitfish enterprise.

BAITFISH SPECIES

16–2. Pouring harvested baitfish into a haul tank.

A *baitfish* is a species of fish used as bait to catch desired species for pleasure or food. The use may be as part of a hobby or as part of a fishing enterprise.

Bait is anything used to lure or attract an animal onto a hook or into a net or trap. Besides baitfish, products used as bait include cut-up scraps of large fish, chicken parts, crawfish or shrimp, insects, worms, and various manufactured concoctions. Artificial look-alike baits, such as plastic worms, are also used. (Chapter 19 has more detail on baits and how to use them in recreational fishing.)

Baitfish may be captured wild or produced on fish farms. They may be freshwater, brackish-water, or salt-water species. The cultured species typically require an environment with fresh water and conditions similar to those of food fish or ornamental fish.

Some baitfish species are used as feeder fish. A *feeder fish* is a species used as live food for the production of other species. The feeder fish supplement naturally available food and may replace manufactured feed in the diets of the species being fed. At present, feeder fish are mostly used in striped bass and hybrid striped bass culture.

PRODUCTION

Some 20 species are grown for bait in the United States. Most are produced in ponds, with more than 30,000 acres (12,146 hectares) of freshwater ponds currently in baitfish production.

The volume produced per acre may reach 1,000 pounds (453.6 kg) or more each year. Since most baitfish are small—often no more than 2 inches (5.1 cm) long—the production is 250 to 300 pounds (113 to 136 kg) at market size. An acre of pond with 1,000 pounds (453.6 kg) of 2-inch (5.1-cm) baitfish would contain approximately 285,700 fish. Four acres would produce more than a million baitfish—enough to satisfy the sport-fishing requirements of many fishers.

Demand for baitfish is tied to the number of sport fishers and the extent of their fishing activity. Baitfish authorities are continually observing the practices of sport fishers. In recent years, the number of sport-fishing licenses sold has declined somewhat. Could this lead to an overall decrease in demand for baitfish?

16–3. A baitfish of desired size for bass sport fishing.

Another factor in demand is the extent to which sport fishers capture and use baitfish. Some sport fishers routinely seine pools or creeks to get bait before they go fishing. This tends to be a declining practice. Reducing the harvest of baitfish from the wild increases demand for cultured baitfish.

Cultured baitfish are typically grown in a manner similar to the pond production of food fish. Important areas are selecting and culturing the species, managing water, feeding, controlling diseases and predators, and marketing. Marketing includes harvesting, grading, holding, hauling, and selling.

PECIES

A few species of baitfish account for the vast majority of the production. Preferences vary by region of the country. Golden shiners are, by far, the leading baitfish in the Southeast, Southwest, and West. Fathead minnows are dominant in the Midwest and Northeast. Goldfish, green sunfish, and white sucker are also cultured as baitfish.

Table 16–1. Examples of Cultured Baitfish

Common Name	Scientific Name
Fathead minnow	*Pimephales promelas*
Golden shiner	*Notemigonus crysoleucas*
Goldfish	*Carassius auratus*
Green sunfish	*Lepomis cyanellus*
White sucker	*Catostomus commersoni*

As with food fish, baitfish species have certain characteristics that the potential grower should consider. Primary among these is the market demand, as this is the major factor in determining whether the crop produced can be sold for a profit. Some baitfish are used exclusively by sport fishers; others are used to grow other fish, such as goldfish, which are sometimes used as food for catfish broodfish.

The three major species of baitfish are the golden shiner, the fathead minnow, and the goldfish. Each has advantages and disadvantages for the baitfish producer. All three are grown in fresh water.

GOLDEN SHINER

The golden shiner (*Notemigonus crysoleucas*) has a bright, flashy appearance that supposedly attracts game fish. This has made it very popular among sport fishers because they feel that a game fish is more likely to be attracted to a "flashy" baitfish. The dorsal fin on the golden shiner is pointed. The body has large, loosely attached, gold- or silver-colored scales.

Golden shiners are somewhat delicate and sensitive to handling and hot weather. Handling may result in the loss of scales. When excited, the fish may leap from tanks or other containers holding them. They are very lively when properly baited onto hooks. Most are marketed at 2 to 3 inches (5.1 to 7.6 cm) in length; however, they may reach a maximum length of 10 inches (25.4 cm).

Golden shiners have been cultured long enough for domesticated stocks to be developed. Wild broodstock should be avoided. Female golden shiners may become infected with an ovarian protozoan that impairs reproduction. This organism can be transmitted by wild fish.

16–4. A golden shiner. (Note the coloring, fin shapes, and overall body conformation.) (Courtesy, U.S. Fish and Wildlife Service)

REPRODUCTION

Sexual maturity of golden shiners is reached in one year, when the fish are about $2^{1}/_{2}$ inches (6.4 cm) long. Females grow faster than males. Females begin spawning in the spring when the water temperature reaches 70°F (21.1°C), and they continue into the summer. Spawning ends when the water reaches a temperature of 85°F (29.4°C). A female golden shiner may produce up to 10,000 eggs in one season.

Spawning mats are used in managing the spawning process. A *spawning mat* is a mat of fibrous material used to control spawning. The material is sold as Spawntex®. Mats are typically 21 × 30 inches (53.3 × 76.2 cm) each and placed end-to-end along the edge of a pond about 1 inch (2.5 cm) below the water surface. The material may be sandwiched between concrete reinforcing wire the same dimensions as the mats. A 1-acre pond may have 500 spawning mats. The Spawntex® encourages the females to deposit their eggs on the mats. Without mats, the females may release their eggs randomly above the living plants, rocks, or other debris in the water. Females deposit eggs on the spawning mats within 12 to 24 hours of being placed in a pond during spawning season. Do not leave mats in a pond longer than 24 hours.

Once eggs have been deposited on the mats, one of two approaches can be followed: egg transfer or fry transfer.

16–5. Spawning mats used in reproducing golden shiners.

Egg transfer is the approach of removing the mats from the broodfish pond and placing them in a rearing pond. Once the eggs hatch, the fry live and grow in the rearing pond. In transporting egg-covered mats, stack and wrap them with burlap to prevent drying. Mats can be kept out of the water for up to one hour. Fifty to 75 egg-covered mats are placed per acre of rearing pond. The mats are placed 6 to 12 inches (15.3 to 30.5 cm) below the water surface. Hatching occurs at a water temperature of 75° to 80°F (23.9° to 26.7°C) in four to eight days after spawning. The mats are left in place for about one week after the eggs have hatched. This brief time allows fry to seek protection in the mat material. The mats are then removed and stored until next needed for spawning.

Fry transfer is the approach of allowing the spawning mats with eggs to remain in the broodfish pond for hatching. The fry are moved to grow-out ponds when they are about $^3/_4$ inch (2.0 cm) long. Fry are captured using fine-mesh seines and various trapping devices.

Grow-out ponds are typically stocked with 50,000 to 200,000 fry per acre. Feed, water management, and protection from diseases and pests are needed to assure a good crop at time of harvesting.

FEEDING

In ponds, golden shiners may be grown extensively (at low-population density) or intensively (at high-population density). With extensive culture, natural plankton bloom is a pri-

16–6. A finely ground feed for baitfish young.

16–7. Water in baitfish ponds is assessed for DO and other conditions much as with food fish production.

mary feed. The water may be fertilized to encourage plankton growth. (Pond fertilization was covered in a previous chapter.)

With intensive culture, the golden shiners must be fed. Most growers use a high-protein, commercially manufactured feed. Fry are fed a finely ground feed when they first come to the surface of the water. They will grow faster if fed several times a day. As they grow, the particle size of their food may be increased, and the number of times they are fed each day reduced. They should not be fed more at one time than they will consume in a few minutes. A general rule is to give no more than 40 pounds (18.1 kg) of feed per acre each day.

ATER QUALITY

Water quality is just as important in the production of golden shiners as it is in the production of food fish and ornamental fish. Each species of baitfish may have its own water-quality needs. Producers should study the needs of a species as related to the water available. Only species suited to the available water should be grown. Growers must regularly monitor water to ensure that the oxygen level is satisfactory. An oxygen level of 3 ppm or higher is usually appropriate for baitfish.

HEALTH

Golden shiners may have various predators and diseases. The major predators are turtles, wild fish, frogs and tadpoles, snakes, and birds. The eggs are attacked by turtles, snails, crawfish, insects, wild fish, frogs and tadpoles, and certain zooplankton. Various methods will control the predators and diseases. Because some predators are protected by law, the aquafarmer should be careful to use only those methods of control that are legal. Careful sanitation and quarantine procedures should always be practiced with new fish.

Common parasites and diseases with golden shiners and other baitfish are

- Protozoa—These are small external parasites that are identified only with a microscopic examination. Ich, trichodina, chilodonella, and spore-forming protozoa are examples.

- Grubs—Also known as flukes, grubs infect gills, skin, and internal organs.

- Worms—Tapeworms and roundworms are the most common internal worm parasites of baitfish.

- Bacterial diseases—Baitfish are subject to several bacterial diseases. Columnaris and *Aeromonas hydrophilla* are two examples.

- Others—Other parasites and diseases of baitfish involve crustaceans, fungi, and viruses.

The health problems of baitfish are quite similar to those of food fish. More details on fish diseases are presented in Chapter 6.

Always get the latest information on therapeutants from a local aquaculture specialist or the land-grant university in your state. Regulations change. An example is the approval of formalin as a parasite treatment on finfish. ***Formalin*** is an aqueous solution of 37 percent formaldehyde that can be used in water for the control of external protozoa and

CONNECTION

CHECK THOSE VALVES

Valves on tanks need to be in good condition and properly closed when fish are being hauled. Suppose a valve came open just after you left the farm in a truck with 20,000 minnows in a tank. You might have water and baitfish lost along the highway for many miles. When you reach your destination, the tank might be empty. Also, you would go home with an empty pocket because you had no baitfish to sell.

Preventing the loss of a tank of baitfish is easy. Know how to operate the valves. Be sure they are in good working condition. Double-check each value to see that it is properly closed before leaving with a load of fish. You may also want to lock valves closed to prevent accidental opening or a wasteful prank by a thoughtless person.

16–8. A fathead minnow. (Note the blunt head and small mouth; also, note the thick body, with dark olive color on the upper portion and silvery color below and with the black strip down the side.) (Courtesy, U.S. Fish and Wildlife Service)

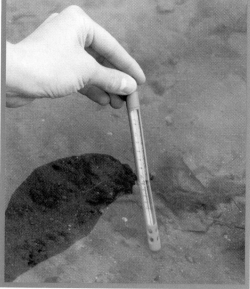

16–9. A thermometer can be used to determine water temperature.

monogenetic trematodes. The use of formalin was broadened by the Food and Drug Administration in 1998. Formalin can be used in tank water to treat baitfish at a rate of up to 250 ppm.

Some water treatments can be used with baitfish that are not approved for use with food fish. With all treatments, trying approved products on a small sample of fish is a good idea just in case there is any unusual sensitivity.

FATHEAD MINNOW

The fathead minnow (*Pimephales promelas*) is very similar to the golden shiner except that it is somewhat hardier. The body is streamlined, with a rounded dorsal fin, and is covered with small scales. The fathead minnow has a duller color than the golden shiner. The males tend to be darker and larger than the females. The maximum length is about 3 inches (7.6 cm). Broodfish should be about 2.5 inches (6.3 cm) long.

The spawning season begins when the water reaches 65°F (18.3°C) in the spring. It may end during the warm summer months and start again as the weather cools in the fall. It ceases when the water temperature goes below 65°F (18.3°C).

Fathead minnows reach sexual maturity in one year. Spawning is typically in small ponds. The number of females and males to be placed in a pond can be stated as a ratio. The ***female:male ratio*** is the number of females that can be stocked in a broodfish pond for each male. A spawning pond may be stocked with 2,000 brood females and 400 males per acre if the fathead young are left to grow in the pond. (A ratio of 5:1 is used; five

16–10. A spawning board floats on the surface of a fathead brood pond.

females are stocked for each male.) If the fry are transferred to another pond, 25,000 brood females and 5,000 males may be stocked in a pond.

A female will produce 200 to 500 eggs at each of several spawnings. The male fathead minnow develops numerous breeding tubercles. A *breeding tubercle* is a hornlike projection that develops on the head at the beginning of the breeding season. A pad develops just back of the head, which the male uses in preparing the nesting site and caring for the eggs.

Fathead minnows spawn on the underside of objects in the water. Spawning boards are often placed in ponds. A *spawning board* is a flat board that floats or is suspended on the surface of the brood pond so that fathead minnows can spawn underneath. Spawning boards are typically standard lumber, such as 1 × 12 × 4 (1 inch thick, 12 inches wide, and 4 feet long). Board dimensions (especially length) can vary, though wide and thin lumber is best. The boards are attached with wire to stakes on the bank of the pond. This keeps them from

16–11. A large trash fish is being removed from inside a seine during harvest. The carp has competed with the fish and reduced yield of the desired crop.

floating around the pond. The male fathead minnow guards the eggs until fry emerge in five to six days after spawning and fertilization.

Fathead minnows are fed much the same as golden shiners. As with any aquatic animal, proper nutrition is essential for growth and well-being.

Somewhat more tolerant of handling than golden shiners, fathead minnows can be handled in warm weather. As bait, they are frequently used on casting rods. Specialized varieties of fathead minnows have been developed. One example is the rosy red, which is used as a feeder fish for other, larger species. Producers often obtain more production per acre with fathead minnows than with golden shiners.

The water management problems, diseases, and predators of fathead minnows are similar to those of golden shiners.

GOLDFISH

The production of goldfish for bait is somewhat different from their production for ornamental use. Goldfish (*Carassius auratus*) are heavy-bodied fish with colors ranging from white, gold, red, and dark olive brown to black. They usually have long, graceful fins. Goldfish can grow to weights of 2 pounds (0.9 kg) if allowed plenty of space. They are hardier than golden shiners and fathead minnows.

As baitfish, goldfish are not as popular as golden shiners and fathead minnows because they are not as active. They are used on trotlines and as feeder fish for bass, brood catfish, and larger aquarium fish.

Goldfish may begin to spawn when the water temperature reaches 60°F (15.6°C). A female will produce 2,000 to 4,000 eggs during each of several spawns in a growing season. The eggs are released randomly and attach themselves to living plants and other objects in the water. Culturists may place spawning mats in the water. Incubation lasts two to eight days, depending on the temperature of the water. Adults give the eggs and fry no protection.

Feeding is similar to that of golden shiners. Proper fertilization of the water and proper feeding can result in yields of 3,000 pounds (1,361 kg) or more per acre.

The water management problems, diseases, and predators of goldfish are similar to those of golden shiners.

16–12. Goldfish. (Courtesy, U.S. Fish and Wildlife Service)

MARKETING BAITFISH

Marketing includes several steps in getting the baitfish to the consumer: harvesting, grading, holding, hauling, and selling. Selling involves establishing a price and changing ownership. Marketing is a major factor in the success of a baitfish enterprise.

Growers have several market alternatives: (1) producers can sell the baitfish to wholesalers, who in turn sell them to retail outlets, such as bait shops; (2) growers can sell the baitfish directly to local retail outlets; (3) producers can operate retail bait sales stores themselves for selling directly to sport fishers; and (4) producers can sell via the Internet. The use of the Internet in marketing baitfish continues to be developmental, though its role will likely be substantial in the future.

The demand for baitfish depends on the interests of sport fishers. The market is quite seasonal and is poor when weather is not good for outdoor activities, such as sport fishing. The market increases near holidays during warm months of the year. Baitfish cannot be stored for long periods and, therefore, may be lost if the demand of sport fishers is weak when the crop is ready. Holding baitfish even for short periods requires appropriate facilities to keep them alive.

Sport fishers want baitfish that are healthy and attractive to game fish. Bait that dies before reaching the fishing site is not desirable.

HARVESTING

Harvesting usually involves seining the baitfish from the small ponds in which they are grown. Seines typically have a mesh of $^3/_{16}$ inch (0.48 cm). After the baitfish are confined with the seines, they are lifted from the ponds with dip nets or boxes made of screen wire. Some are harvested with traps.

16–13. Seining is typically used to harvest baitfish in ponds.

16–14. A box-type grader may be used at the harvest site with baitfish.

Withholding feed for about 24 hours before harvest is usually a good idea to reduce fouling the water. In warm weather, when the surface water temperature is above 75°F (23.9°C), harvesting should be done in the early morning hours, when it is cooler. In small ponds, cool water can be added to lower the water temperature.

GRADING

Baitfish are graded to ensure uniform size. Various screens and devices with bars are used to grade baitfish. The graders allow the smaller fish to pass through holes or between bars. They then retain the larger fish. Most bait shops want to get baitfish of uniform size and species.

Prices are established based on length, species, and overall condition of the baitfish. Larger baitfish typically bring higher prices. If larger baitfish fail to bring higher prices, the producer is financially shortchanged. This is because of the increased investment in feeding and otherwise caring for the product to get it to market.

Injured or diseased baitfish are culled during grading. Retail outlets and sport fishers will not buy poor-quality baitfish.

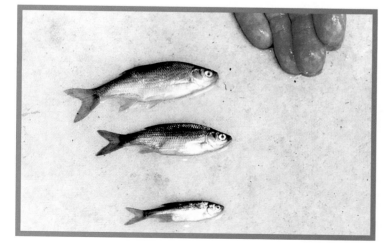

16–15. Three sizes of baitfish are shown here: 1-, 2-, and 3-inch grades.

HOLDING

Storing baitfish until they are sold or moved requires maintaining a healthful environment. Tanks, vats, and other water facilities may be used for holding baitfish. Oxygen must be maintained in the water. A water temperature of approximately 70°F (21°C) is best. Some haulers and jobbers use refrigeration to keep water in holding and transport tanks cool during the warm season of the year.

16–16. Baitfish may be held in aerated vats or tanks for wholesaling or retailing.

Only quality water should be used in holding facilities. Some experts recommend returning any baitfish that have been held for more than a week to the pond. Emptied storage tanks should be scrubbed with chlorinated chemicals, such as household bleach, and rinsed well before they are used again. Baitfish should not be put into water with cleaning chemicals or into water from municipal systems that contains chlorine or other chemicals.

16–17. A thermometer is being used to check water temperature in a tank.

16–18. Vats in this baitfish facility are equipped with coolers to keep the water from getting too warm in summer weather.

16–19. A flatbed semitrailer truck with several tanks.

Hauling

Hauling is done in tanks on trucks that are equipped to aerate the water and keep it at an appropriate temperature. Baitfish should not be subjected to sudden changes in temperature or hauled in tanks at temperatures to which the fish are not adapted.

Haul trucks usually have tanks with compartments or individual tanks stationed next to each other. The tanks are on flatbed

16–20. A device has been placed at the bottom of each tank to bubble oxygen from a cylinder into the water.

semitrailers or bob trucks. Smaller haul tanks have several advantages. Each tank can be managed independently. Species and quantities of baitfish can be kept isolated. Oxygen may be injected directly into tank water through various devices. Pumps may circulate the water and help with aeration.

SELLING

Selling occurs when the buyer and the seller agree on a price and when ownership of the baitfish changes. The buyer pays the seller in cash, with a check, or in some other way.

It is a good idea to leave baitfish in the pond until a buyer is found. A rule of thumb is never harvest any fish crop unless there is a buyer. Written agreements may be used in buying and selling to spell out the qualities of the product to be exchanged and the payment involved.

16–21. Two 12-volt motors are used to operate aerators on this small haul tank. (The electrical system of the truck provides the power for the motors.)

REVIEWING

MAIN IDEAS

Baitfish are often cultured in ponds, much as food fish. The predominant species are golden shiners, fathead minnows, and goldfish. Stocking rates can be much greater than with food fish because the baitfish are harvested at a much smaller size—often no more than 2 inches (5.1 cm) long.

Water management, disease and predator control, feeding, and marketing are important considerations in the production of baitfish. The grower tries to produce a baitfish that is attractive to sport fishers.

Marketing is an important part of financial success in baitfish production. Quality baitfish are harvested, graded, stored, hauled, and otherwise handled to minimize injury and assure quality.

QUESTIONS

Answer the following questions, using complete sentences and correct spelling.

1. What is a baitfish? A feeder fish? Distinguish between the two.

2. What is bait? Why is it used?

3. What is the relationship between demand for baitfish and interest in sport fishing?

4. What are the most popular baitfish? List their common and scientific names.

5. What is the desired market size of golden shiners?

6. Why are spawning mats used with golden shiners?

7. Name and distinguish between the two approaches in hatching golden shiners.

8. Distinguish between feeding practices with extensive and intensive golden shiner production.

9. How is spawning promoted with fathead minnows?

10. What ratio of females to males is used in brood ponds with fathead minnows?

11. What market alternatives may be available to baitfish producers?

12. How does weather (temperature) influence baitfish harvesting?

13. Why are baitfish graded?

14. What is the preferred water temperature for baitfish in holding tanks?

EVALUATING

Match the term with the correct definition. Write the letter of the term on the line provided.

a. spawning mat
b. egg transfer
c. baitfish
d. fry transfer
e. feeder fish
f. spawning board
g. formalin
h. female:male ratio

_____1. The number of females stocked with each male in a brood pond

_____2. A species of fish used as bait

_____3. A fish used as live food for other species

_____4. An aqueous solution of formaldehyde

_____5. The moving of spawning mats with eggs from the broodfish pond for hatching

_____6. The process of leaving spawning mats in the pond and moving the fry after hatching

_____7. A broad board that floats on the surface water of a broodfish pond

_____8. A fibrous material placed in broodfish ponds at the onset of spawning season

EXPLORING

1. Grade a sample of 25 baitfish. Visually observe each baitfish, and remove the fish with defects. Measure each fish, and sort the fish by length. Be sure to follow practices that protect the baitfish from injury. Afterward, prepare a report on your experiences.

2. Estimate the number of fry in a tank or trough. Using a small tea strainer, collect a small sample of fry. Fill the strainer and quickly count the number of fry in the strainer. Future quantities of fry can be estimated with the strainer without counting. How many fry did you estimate in the tank or trough?

CHAPTER 17

Water Gardens, Plants, and Algae

This chapter covers the primary species of plant and algae aquacrops produced in the United States and some that have potential for production. It has the following objectives:

1 Identify common plant and algae aquacrops

2 Explain principles of aquatic plant and algae production

3 Discuss the installation and management of water gardens

4 Describe the culture of saltwater and brackish-water food algae

5 Describe the culture of freshwater food plants

6 Describe the culture of aquatic plants and algae for animal feeds

7 Describe the culture of specialty aquaculture plants

TERMS

aquatic plant
benthic
carrageenan
corm
gamete
hulis

hydroponics
koi pond
ornamental aquatic plant
paddy taro
phycocolloid
rhizome

spore
substrate
thalli
water garden
zygote

17–1. An interior water garden adds charm to a fine restaurant in a hotel.

THE PRODUCTION of plants and algae has an important role in aquaculture. More emphasis is on animal aquaculture, for good reason. Whether in terms of acres or pounds or dollar value, the production of aquatic plants and algae in the United States is small when compared with animal aquaculture. But, it is an expanding area!

Of the many plants and algae that grow in water, only a few are used for food. Several aquatic plants are used as ornamentals in water gardens. Very few of these are widely cultured in the United States, though the production of ornamental aquatic plants is increasing. The future could hold a significant increase in production and income from plant and algae aquaculture.

Plant and algae aquaculture may involve the production of products for consumption by humans or other animals or the production of products for specialty purposes, such as ornamentation or wastewater treatment. Plant and algae aquaculture may be in salt water, brackish water, or fresh water.

COMMON PLANT AND ALGAE AQUACULTURE SPECIES

17–2. A can of Chinese water chestnuts, as commonly found in a supermarket.

17–3. A commercial producer of ornamental aquatic plants uses modified hanging flower baskets in the water growing facilities. (Lifting the baskets by their handles makes harvest easy.)

Five categories of aquatic plants and algae are introduced here. They are ornamental plants for water gardens, saltwater and brackish-water food algae, freshwater food plants, plants cultured for use as animal feeds, and specialty plants.

An **aquatic plant** is a plant that grows in water. Most aquatic plants would not survive in terrestrial (land) environments. Some aquatic plants may grow in land areas covered with water some or most of the year.

ORNAMENTAL AQUATIC PLANTS

Several species of aquatic plants are grown for ornamental purposes. An **ornamental aquatic plant** is a plant grown in water for its aesthetic appeal. Such species are used in water gardens or other water areas where attractive plants are desired. Some ornamental aquatic plants are also cultured for secondary uses, such as wildlife food and water purification.

Ornamental aquatic plants are grouped in several ways. Commonly, they are grouped by climate as hardy or tropical. A hardy plant can survive some or even a great deal of cold weather. A tropical plant cannot survive with frost and freezing conditions. Some species that will tolerate cold climates will also tolerate tropical climates.

Ornamental aquatic plants may be grouped by their relative growth position in the water. Some are floaters; others are shallow-water plants, lilies, and underwater plants. A floating plant fairly well floats on the surface of the water. It does not have roots connected to soil. Other plants may have roots attached to soil or other media at the bottom of the water.

Ornamental aquatic plants are further grouped by their tolerance to shade or their requirement for full sun. Selecting plants that tolerate shade is important if the pond or water garden is in a shady area. Examples of tropical floaters that tolerate shade are water hyacinth and water lettuce. Hardy floaters that tolerate shade include butterfly fern, fairy moss, and frog bit.

Many varieties of water lilies are included as ornamentals. These are chosen for flower

17–4. A lotus flower. (Courtesy, Vernie Thomas, Danville, IL)

color and shape as well as climate adaptation. Some varieties of water lilies are suited only to tropical climates. Water lilies are also chosen for their adaptation to shade.

Table 17–1. Examples of Freshwater Ornamental Aquatic Plants

Common Name	Scientific Name	Position in Water	Shade or Sun*
Hardy Plants:			
Water Hawthorne	*Aponogeton distachyox*	Attached to bottom	Shade tolerant
Yellow floating heart	*Nymphoides peltata*	Attached to bottom	Shade tolerant
Butterfly fern	*Salvinia rotundifolia*	Floater	Shade tolerant
Frog bit	*Limnobium spongia*	Floater	Shade tolerant
Fairy moss	*Azolla caroliniana*	Floater	Shade tolerant
Dwarf cattail	*Typha minima*	Shallow water	Shade tolerant
Canna longwood hybrids	*Canna longwood hybrids*	Shallow water	Shade tolerant
Arrowhead	*Sagittaria latifolia*	Shallow water	Shade tolerant
Lotus**	*Nelumbo nucifera*	Attached to bottom	Full sun best
Tropical Plants:			
Mosaic plant	*Ludwegia sedioides*	Attached to bottom	Shade tolerant
Water poppy	*Hydrocleys nymphoides*	Attached to bottom	Shade tolerant
Aquatic morning glory	*Ipomea batatas*	Shallow water	Shade tolerant
Dwarf papyrus	*Cyperus haspans*	Shallow water	Shade tolerant
Tropical banana plant	*Musa zebrina*	Bog	Prefers sun

*Some are listed as shade tolerant but will perform best in full sun.

**Included as hardy though not suited in the northern Plains and the northeastern United States.

A popular plant with many water gardeners is the lotus (*Nelumbo nucifera*). It can grow 4 to 8 feet across, is rooted in medium at the bottom, and has appealing blossoms in the summer.

FOOD ALGAE

The saltwater and brackish-water food products are all algae. These include brown algae (kelp), red algae (nori), and green algae (aunori). Two species of brown algae are most widely cultured as giant kelp: *Macrocystis pyrifera* and *M. integrifolia*. Five species of red algae are cultured (*Porphyra angusta*, *P. kuniedai*, *P. pseudolinearis*, *P. tenera*, and *P. yezoensis*). One species of green algae (*Monostroma enteromorpha*) is cultured.

Table 17–2. Examples of Non-ornamental Cultured Aquatic Plants and Algae

Common Name	Scientific Name	Uses	Location
Brown algae	*Macrocystis integrifolia*	Food, mulch, fertilizer	Salt water
	Macrocystis pyrifera	Food, mulch, fertilizer	Salt water
Red algae	*Porphyra yezoensis*	Food, mulch, fertilizer, phycocolloids	Salt water
	Porphyra pseudolinearis	Food, mulch, fertilizer, phycocolloids	Salt water (tolerates higher salinity)
	Porphyra tenera	Food, mulch, fertilizer, phycocolloids	Salt water
	Porphyra angusta	Food, mulch, fertilizer, phycocolloids	Salt water
	Porphyra kuniedai	Food, mulch, fertilizer, phycocolloids	Salt water
Green algae	*Monostroma enteromorpha*	Food, mulch, fertilizer	Salt water, fresh water
Watercress	*Nasturtium officinale*	Food	Fresh water
Chinese water chestnut	*Eleocharis dulcis*	Food	Fresh water
Water spinach	*Ipomoea reptans*	Animal feed	Fresh water
Duckweed	*Lemna* spp.	Wastewater treatment, animal feed	Fresh water
	Spirodela spp.	Wastewater treatment, animal feed	Fresh water
	Wolffia spp.	Wastewater treatment, animal feed	Fresh water
	Wolffiella spp.	Wastewater treatment, animal feed	Fresh water
Water hyacinth	*Eichhornia crassipes*	Wastewater treatment	Fresh water

FOOD PLANTS

The three primary species of freshwater food plants cultured are watercress (*Nasturtium officinale*), Chinese water chestnut (*Eleocharis dulcis*), and taro (*Colocasia esculenta*). Taro is a tropical plant that can become a pest if it gets out of control. Other freshwater plants that have been cultured, but to a much lesser extent, are water spinach (*Ipomoea reptans*) and arrowhead, which includes several species of the genus *Sagittaria*.

FEED PLANTS

Several species of aquatic plants are cultured for use as animal feeds. These can be divided into two groups: those used to feed livestock, particularly cattle, and those used to feed other aquacrops, usually phytoplankton for consumption by filter feeders and by the larvae of several species.

The primary aquacrop suitable for use as livestock feed is duckweed, which includes several species from the genera *Lemna*, *Spirodela*, *Wolffia*, and *Wolffiella*. Water spinach is sometimes used as livestock feed as well. Numerous species of algae and microalgae are cultured for use in aquaculture operations, such as those involving oyster or shrimp larvae, or in ponds, where filter feeders, such as mullet, are reared.

SPECIALTY PLANTS

A few aquatic plants are cultured for specialty purposes. These include duckweed and water hyacinth (*Eichhornia crassipes*) for wastewater treatment and certain red algae for the extraction of phycocolloids. A phycocolloid is a gel-like substance with many uses. Other specialty plants are used as ornamental plants or for making fuel.

17–5. A papyrus plant cultured in a greenhouse in association with an aquaculture tank system. It is felt that the presence of papyrus in the water system promotes tilapia growth.

PRINCIPLES OF PLANT AND ALGAE AQUACULTURE

Plants that grow in water share many characteristics of terrestrial plants. Some characteristics, however, are unique to aquatic plants. Some basic principles of plant biology, functions, and culture are presented in this section.

PHOTOSYNTHESIS

Most plants make their own food starches through a process called photosynthesis. Photosynthesis, simply defined, is the process by which a plant uses light energy, in the presence of chlorophyll, to convert carbon dioxide and water into carbohydrates, which provide energy. By-products of photosynthesis include water and oxygen. This is the source for the common statement that plants "give off" oxygen. The equation for photosynthesis is

$$6CO_2 + 12H_2O \xrightarrow[\text{chlorophyll}]{\text{light}} C_6H_{12}O_6 + 6O_2 + 6H_2O$$

17–6. Leaves on these water hyacinths carry out photosynthesis.

Chlorophyll allows photosynthesis to occur. Several types of chlorophyll are found in plants, including chlorophyll a, b, c, and d. Chlorophyll a is recognized as giving plants their green color. Other pigments in plants include xanthophylls, phycobilins, and carotenes. Some of these cause certain plants to be reddish or brownish in color.

RESPIRATION

To utilize the carbohydrates formed by photosynthesis, plants convert the carbohydrates to energy in the form of ATP, adenosine triphosphate. Plants accomplish this by the process of respiration. Respiration involves the conversion of carbohydrates and oxygen to energy, with by-products of carbon dioxide and water. The energy released can then be used for the various processes of the plants, including growth and reproduction. The chemical equation for respiration is

$$C_6H_{12}O_6 + 6O_2 \longrightarrow 6CO_2 + 6H_2O + energy$$

NUTRIENT UPTAKE

Aquatic plants obtain most of their nutrients from the water in which they are grown. This function makes aquatic plants very useful for removing ammonia and nitrite wastes from the water. Removing wastes greatly enhances the cleaning of water in wastewater treatment facilities. This will be discussed later in this chapter.

Removal of wastes also makes polyculture of plant and animal aquacrops profitable. Because the plants will remove excessive wastes that may be harmful to the animal aquacrop, higher stocking rates of animals can be used. The wastes produced by the animal aquacrop usually provide enough nutrients to the plants that commercial fertilizer does not need to be applied. When aquatic plants and animals are produced in the same system, the species must be compatible. Plants cannot be grown with species of fish that forage on plant materials and destroy the plants. Although little polyculture of this type has been practiced with freshwater aquacrops, the potential is excellent.

Water from animal aquaculture production facilities can also be used for hydroponics or for irrigation of pastures and row crops. *Hydroponics* involves the culture of terrestrial plants whose roots grow in gravel or some other substrate where a shallow current of water constantly flows. Hydroponic production is not generally considered aquaculture but has become popular with many aquafarmers as a source of additional income. These aquafarmers use the wastewater from animal aquacrops, which is high in nitrogen compounds, to provide the nutrients for plants grown hydroponically. This practice can reap excellent profits for the aquafarmers while providing a means of cleaning up the water from their operations.

FOOD QUALITIES

Saltwater and brackish-water food plants and the various algae are excellent sources of nutrients. These plants are primarily available to the public through commercial health food stores, where they are recognized as health foods.

Human taste for these seaweeds is an acquired one. Consumption is not much in the United States. It is much greater in Asian countries, most notably Japan, China, and South Korea.

17–7. A nutrition supplement prepared using blue-green algae.

The algae are an excellent source of vitamin A, found in the beta carotene in the plants. Most of the algae have a higher percentage of vitamin A than eggs, a common source of the vitamin in the United States. They are also good sources of vitamins B_2 and B_{12}, as well as vitamin C, although the amounts vary with the season. Historically, red algae have been an important part of Inuit diets, as the major provider of vitamin C.

Compared with other plants, some algae are also high in protein, ranging from 15 percent to almost 50 percent for some red algae and green algae. Algae contain energy-providing carbohydrates. These plants also serve as excellent sources of iodine and other essential micronutrients.

Of the freshwater food plants, watercress is high in vitamins A, B, and C, similar to the salad greens commonly eaten in this country. It is also high in iron and iodine.

Chinese water chestnuts are high in carbohydrates (about 30 percent). They are low in protein, however, with less than 2 percent. Chinese water chestnuts are widely used in cooking because they keep their firm texture, even when cooked. Chefs like them because they provide a "crunchy" addition to casseroles, salads, and other dishes.

Habitat

The primary concerns for the production of aquatic plants are water temperature, salinity, and substrate material. For most algae, the desired salinity is at saltwater levels of 35 ppt or just below. Some species can survive lower salinities but will not reproduce. Brown algae will not produce gametophytes or sporophytes at salinities lower than 27 ppt, for example. Some algae, in particular the green algae, have freshwater species and other species that are more tolerant of brackish water. The freshwater species mentioned in this chapter require water with a salinity at or near 0 ppt.

In general, the algae can survive a wide variety of temperatures, but different species have particular temperature ranges in which they grow best. For example, brown algae grow and reproduce best between 50° and 70°F (10° and 21°C) but can withstand cooler and warmer temperatures. Watercress requires cool, flowing water with a temperature of less than 78°F (25.6°C) but grows best when air temperatures are between 70° and 85°F (21° and

29°C). Chinese water chestnuts are tropical plants in nature and grow best in warm climates and warm water above 70°F (21°C).

Aquatic plants that attach themselves to the ground or bottom of the water facility are called **benthic**. Algae, watercress, and Chinese water chestnuts are all benthic plants. Floating plants, such as duckweed and many of the microalgae, are called planktonic. For benthic plants, the **substrate** (material that makes up the bottom of the growing facility) is very important. Many species of algae require mollusk shells or some other solid surface to which the **spores** (small, seedlike parts) can attach. Watercress requires a firm growing bed because of the large amounts of water circulated across it. Sometimes, gravel or crushed rock is added for firmness to beds that are too soft.

SIZE

Size varies widely among the different aquaculture plants, and even within the different orders of plants, such as algae. Brown algae (such as kelp) are often called macroalgae. Giant kelp **thalli** (the stems) can reach 200 feet or more in length. Other species of algae, however, are unicellular (one-celled) plants that are very small. These plants can be seen only when they attach themselves to each other to form chains.

Watercress is usually harvested when the plants reach a height of 12 to 14 inches above water level. They may grow much larger if they are not harvested. Chinese water chestnuts are a type of sedge and grow to a maximum height of 3 to 6 feet during one growing season; they will die back if they are not harvested before the first frost.

17–8. Plants in a newly established water garden are being examined for growth.

REPRODUCTION

Plants may reproduce either sexually or asexually. Many of the aquatic plants discussed in this chapter reproduce by both means at different times, with some mechanical reproduction techniques also used.

Sexual reproduction involves the fusion of **gametes** (sex cells), followed by meiosis (sex cell division). The process may result in a seed or in a **zygote**, a new plant. Asexual reproduction refers to any means of reproduction other than sexual reproduction.

17–9. Water hyacinths are being reproduced asexually by dividing plants.

In nature, algae reproduce by both sexual and asexual means. Mature plants, called sporophytes, release spores that become microscopic plants. The spores then produce gametes, which fuse and begin the process again. Accessory reproduction occurs when asexual spores are produced by young plants. These spores, called monospores, then become new plants.

Watercress naturally reproduces sexually. The fusion of the gametes results in a seed. Watercress can also reproduce by sprouting shoots, which grow into new plants. In commercial operations, however, most reproduction is mechanical, with terminal cuttings used to start new plants. This method allows for a more uniform crop and a shorter growing period.

Chinese water chestnuts reproduce by producing *corms*, fleshy underground vertical stems that are parts of rhizomes. *Rhizomes* are horizontally creeping, below-the-ground structures that send up shoots for the reproduction of some plants. During a good growing season, each parent corm can produce hundreds of new corms, all of which can split from the parent corm and become new plants. This is the part harvested for food. Some corms are kept for reproduction purposes.

WATER GARDENS

A *water garden* is a decorative water area that has a variety of plants and, typically, goldfish. Water gardens usually hold no more than a few hundred gallons of water and are typically 12 to 24 inches deep. Water gardens are used in landscapes of commercial buildings and residences to add interest and to create an appealing interactive environment of water, plants, and animals.

17–10. A small water garden.

Water gardens are sometimes equated with koi ponds, but there are some differences. A *koi pond* is an ornamental water area used for keeping koi. Very few plants grow in a koi pond because koi eat the plants. Koi ponds are also usually larger than water gardens. Except for being larger and deeper, koi ponds are often designed similar to water gardens.

In this book, the water facility used for water gardens and koi ponds is referred to as a pool.

ESTABLISHMENT

Several decisions must be made in establishing a water garden or koi pond. Overall, an individual must have a strong commitment to maintaining such a facility after it has been constructed. Regular care is essential. Otherwise, the water garden or koi pond will deteriorate, the plants and fish will die, and the pool will be unattractive. Keep in mind that water in an abandoned pool is a breeding area for mosquitoes.

Before you begin, visit water gardens and koi ponds. One source would be stores that sell materials used in their construction. Another source would be the Internet and Web sites on design, maintenance, and supplies. Get as much information as you can on design and construction. You may want to prepare a sketch of

17–11. A koi pond at a resort hotel in Hawaii has no aquatic plants. Note that the surrounding area is nicely landscaped.

17–12. A tub-type water facility of rigid plastic.

your planned pool, including waterfalls and streams as well as the location of plumbing, pumps, and electrical devices.

Water gardens are rarely constructed with earth bottoms. Most are made of rigid plastic material or flexible rubber liners. Concrete and other materials are sometimes used. Rigid plastic gardens have specific shapes and designs. They are placed in the ground or in other locations to accommodate their shapes. Rigid plastic water gardens tend to be smaller and more economical than those made with flexible rubber liners.

The major steps in establishing a new facility using a flexible rubber liner are as follows:

1. Determine the kind of facility—Decide whether you are going to have a water garden or a koi pond. Note: In some locations, a building permit and/or a water-use permit may be needed.

17–13. A small water facility made with a flexible rubber liner.

2. Select an appropriate location—The site should be easy to see and be located where runoff from rain will not get into the pool. The usual recommendation is that the location provide at least four hours of sunlight a day. A pool should be near sources of water and electric power. Also consider safety and accessibility by small children, who might accidentally fall into the pool.

3. Determine the construction to be used—A pool may be made with a preformed plastic basin, or it may use a flexible rubber liner cut to the size of the pool. The latter is the type of construction assumed here. Also, consider the kinds and sizes of pumps to be used. (Note: Assistance may be needed from a qualified water garden or koi pond installer or supplier.)

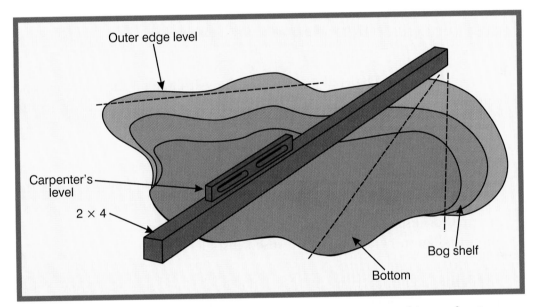

17–14. The outer edge of a water garden should be level all the way around (except for streams and waterfalls). (A carpenter's level can be placed on a 2 × 4 across the pond to assure that the edges are level.)

4. Determine the size of the pool—Tentatively lay out the pool shape with a rope or water hose. Small pools are no more than 10 to 20 feet (3 to 6 m) across and may be rectangular, circular, or irregular in shape. Use a level on a long board to plan a pool with level edges. Make measurements to determine the area to be included and the depth. Water gardens for goldfish and plants need be no more than 2 feet (0.6 m) deep. Koi ponds need to be at least 3 feet (1.0 m) deep, and some may be up to 5 feet (1.5 m) deep. Remember, the larger the pool, the more water it will hold. Large water gardens and koi ponds are more stable and often easier to keep. (The volume of a pool can be determined by multiplying surface area by average depth.)

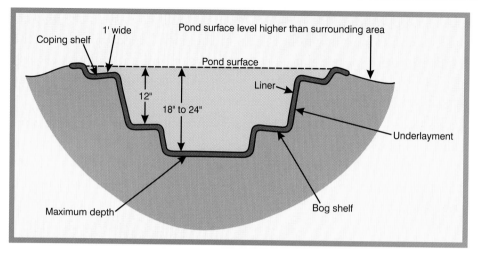

17–15. Overall excavation for a water garden.

5. Dig out the area—The pool area may be dug with a hand shovel or with power equipment. Shape the dug area to include shelves for different plant materials. For example, bog plants will not thrive in deep water.

6. Install plumbing—Pipes to supply water as well as remove water should be installed. Plumbing will include pumps, skimmers, and other features to maintain the system. (Note: You will need to get more information from books, the Internet, or discussions with water gardeners. In some cases, you may wish to hire installation by a qualified licensed installer.)

7. Install the liner underlayment—Underlayment is material placed over the soil or rocks to act as a buffer between the soil or rocks and the liner. Underlayment helps protect the liner from damage and give the desired shape.

17–16. Rocks are being added to create a natural appearance.

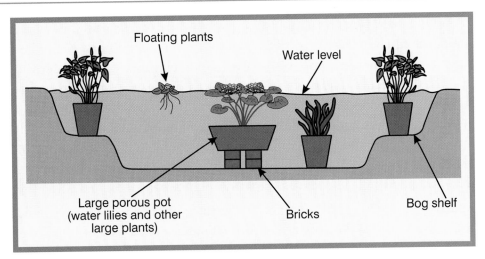

17–17. Placing plants in a water garden.

8. Install the liner—Installing the rubber liner involves placing it in the hole with underlayment and unfolding it in the excavation. Be careful not to puncture the liner.

9. Install accessories—Waterfalls, streams, and other features should be installed after the liner is in place.

10. Make connections—Connect pipes (PVC, etc.) and electrical wires. (Note: Local codes may require the use of licensed plumbers and electricians to handle plumbing and wiring work.)

11. Place edge materials—Stones and other materials may be installed around the edge of the pool. These may be used to hold the liner in place.

12. Add water—Water should be added until the pool is within a few inches of being full. This will help work out wrinkles in the flexible rubber liner. After the wrinkles are out, complete filling the pool with water.

17–18. A water garden covered with netting to keep leaves and other debris out. (Courtesy, Vernie Thomas, Danville, IL)

13. Add plants—Most plants should be installed before fish are added. Attached plants are anchored with roots in special fibrous containers. Many authorities indicate that the most important plant is anacharis. It is an underwater plant that uses nutrients that promote the growth of algae. Anacharis will therefore help limit the growth of algae in the pool. One bunch of anacharis (elodea) should be used for approximately every 3 square feet of surface area. (If koi are to be added, the anacharis will need to be protected with netting to prevent destruction by the koi.) Water lilies are added so that two thirds of the surface area is shaded by their leaves. Floating plants can be added after the fish.

14. Add fish—Some people prefer water gardens with only plants. If goldfish are desired, add them once water conditions have settled from adding plants. The number to add depends on the size of the pool and water conditions.

Maintenance

A water garden requires daily care to assure that proper water conditions and nutrients are present. Control of algae is essential. Water testing may be needed to detect potential

17–19. Removing the cover to service a pump.

17–20. An attractive koi pond with a waterfall and terrestrial landscaping.

problems and to make needed corrections, such as aerating and fertilizing the water. Pumps need to be checked for proper operation. Water may need to be added if the design does not include automatic water level maintenance. Dead leaves, stems, and other materials should be removed from the pond. The goldfish will need to be fed a commercial fish food. Netting may be placed around the water garden to prevent access of raccoons and other small animals.

Seasonal maintenance is particularly important. Water gardens may need to be winterized by partially covering, adding heaters to prevent freezing, and removing fallen leaves and other debris. Seasonal needs vary with the climate. Seek the assistance of individuals qualified in your local area.

CULTURE OF SALTWATER AND BRACKISH-WATER FOOD ALGAE

The culture of the three types of seaweeds used for food—brown algae, red algae, and green algae—is not common in the United States. Brown algae are the only algae cultured in any significant amount, with most of this culture occurring off the Pacific coast of California. Red algae and green algae are abundant in certain coastal waters of the United States, but there is little harvesting of these plants for human consumption.

Japan leads the world in the culture of seaweeds. Most of the available waters suitable for growing these plants in Japan are already in production, but the demand still exceeds the supply. The potential exists for a market for seaweeds cultured in the United States for export to Japan, China, and other Asian countries.

BROWN ALGAE

The culture of brown algae of the division Phaephyta is common in Japan and other Asian countries. The primary species cultured is *Undaria pinnatifida,* called wakame in Japan and kelp in Europe and the United States.

Brown algae contain chlorophyll *a* and chlorophyll *c,* as well as alpha and beta carotene. The brownish or olive green color comes from the xanthophyll called fucoxanthin.

The culture of kelp is an involved process. Mature sporophyte plants are brought into the laboratory and kept in concrete and plastic tanks. The salinity is maintained between 30 and 33 ppt. Wooden or metal frames with cotton strings are placed in the tanks. The released spores attach themselves to the strings. During the summer, the spores develop gametes, which fuse to become sporophytes, the plants that are eaten.

The strings, with the sporophytes attached, are tied to rafts or buoys in the open ocean. This is usually done in September or October.

The mature sporophytes are ready to harvest in January or February. Although the whole plant is sometimes harvested, usually only part of the plant is cut off for harvesting. The plants are then dried and chopped into small pieces. The most common use is as a salad green.

The most common culture of brown algae in the United States is that of *Macrocystis pyrifera* and *M. integrifolia,* two species of giant kelp. These "plants" may reach heights of 200 feet or more.

Compared with the intensive culture of *Undaria pinnatifida,* the culture of giant kelp is more of a harvesting practice. Aquafarmers locate a bed of giant kelp and cut the kelp near the ocean floor with underwater mowers. The cut thalli are then raked to the shore. Some are eaten, but most are used for mulch or fertilizer. Some aquafarmers extract phycocolloids from the kelp, as is discussed later in this chapter.

RED ALGAE

Red algae are in the division Rhodophyta. The red algae of the genus *Porphyra* are the most commonly cultured seaweeds in the world, although little culture occurs in the United States. The common name is *laver* in Europe and the United States and *nori* in Japan. Some

CONNECTION

KELP FORESTS

Large forests of kelp naturally grow in some ocean waters, such as the Monterey Bay. Groves of waving and branching kelp are found beneath the surface. The exhibits at the nearby Monterey Bay Aquarium and materials washed up on the shore help explain these forests.

What are the implications in aquaculture? Kelp is now harvested for a wide range of uses, such as to make algin, which is used in ice cream and other foods. Growing kelp that meets market demand certainly has potential.

Note: Kelp is not a plant. It is in the Protista kingdom, which contains algae and other species.

reports of nori culture in Japan date back to 1570. In Japan, nori is the most valuable aquacrop cultured in salt water or brackish water.

Red algae contain chlorophyll *a* and phycobilins, which give them their red color. The phycobilins are especially suited for absorption of the green, violet, and blue light that penetrates the depths of the ocean. They allow the red algae to grow in deeper water than either brown or green algae.

In Japan, extensive culture of red algae is done on nets placed horizontally in the open ocean. The seedstock for the nets comes from commercial laboratories. The mature plants are put in tanks with mollusk shells placed on the bottom. The released spores attach to the mollusk shells. The spores grow into microscopic plants that release monospores that grow into thalli.

Temperature is used to control the release of the monospores. When an aquafarmer brings nets into the laboratory to catch monospores for seedstock, the temperature is lowered, and the plants release the monospores. After a short time, from less than an hour to several hours, the nets are removed and placed in the open ocean, attached to poles so that they are parallel to the surface of the water.

Nets are usually placed in the water in early September. The growing season lasts from September to early April. The artificial spawning of the monospores allows for a longer growing season. Each net may be harvested three or four times before the end of the growing season, whereas with natural spawning, only two harvests are possible.

Harvesting red algae involves cutting the thalli and leaving stocks for further growth. The harvest is then washed and cut into small pieces. After it has been washed again in a freshwater barrel, it is placed on a wooden frame and allowed to dry into mats. The dried product is very high in protein, from 30 to 50 percent, but is expensive and usually eaten in small amounts.

Although several species of red algae are common off both the Atlantic and Pacific coasts of the United States, very little food production occurs. Some food production of red algae occurs in Hawaii and in Alaska.

Some experimental culture of red algae from the genus *Gracilaria* has been conducted. Up to 50 dry tons per acre per year have been produced in highly intensive systems. The systems, however, have not been energy efficient and have required too much water to be prof-

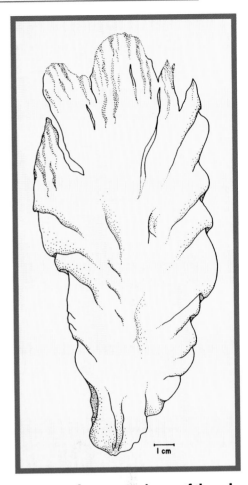

17–21. Porphyra yezoensis, one of the red algae commonly eaten by humans. (Courtesy, J. E. Hansen, J. E. Packard, and W. T. Doyle, California Sea Grant College Program)

itable. Less-intensive production of this species, found all along the eastern coast of the United States, should be profitable.

GREEN ALGAE

Green algae are in the division Chlorophyta. They are the least cultured of the three primary types of algae, although some production occurs, again mostly in Asia. The species most commonly cultured are from the genera *Monostroma* and *Enteromorpha*. Called aonori in Japan, *Monostroma* is the most expensive seaweed cultured. Cultural practices in the open ocean are similar to those of red algae, but the spore-gathering process is not as advanced. Also, the production levels are not as great as with red or brown algae because green algae have a slower growth rate.

Some experimental culture of other green algae has shown promising results. *Chlorella*, one of the freshwater green algae, has been grown in the United States with impressive production numbers. *Chlorella* is about 50 percent protein, but it does not sell well, except in some specialty markets, such as health-food stores. The primary reason for the poor sales is that the flour made from *Chlorella* turns the food in which it is cooked either black or dark green, so many people do not like its appearance.

CULTURE OF FRESHWATER FOOD PLANTS

Other than the production of rice, which is generally considered an agronomic crop, very little freshwater plant aquaculture takes place in the United States. The primary aquacrop produced in the United States is watercress (*Nasturtium officinale*). Most of its production takes place in Hawaii. The other important freshwater aquacrop is Chinese water chestnuts (*Eleocharis dulcis*), a specialty crop not grown commercially in large quantities in the United States. Although several other aquacrops are grown in very small quantities, none of them have been shown to be profitable as commercial products.

WATERCRESS

About 1.5 million pounds of watercress are produced in Hawaii each year, with the rest of the United States producing less than 100,000 pounds. That doesn't sound like much compared with catfish production, but watercress is the leading freshwater plant aquacrop in the

United States. The farm value of watercress is about $1.1 million annually. Some people harvest wild watercress from local streams, and many people grow it in small quantities for private use.

Watercress has two primary habitat requirements. One requirement is an abundant supply of continuously flowing water—about 1 million gallons per acre per day. The other requirement is many sunny days during the growing season.

Watercress is cultured in 1 to 2 inches of water in shallow ponds or beds. The water must be relatively high in nitrates, about 4 ppm, for optimum growth. The nitrates must be in the water because, like many aquatic plants, watercress obtains most of its nutrients from the water.

The best growth of watercress occurs when the air temperature is between 70° and 85°F. As a result, the prime production period in Hawaii is in the winter months. Watercress will sustain growth throughout the year, however. The plant is also suited well to most climates in North America and will grow in all but the coldest months.

Watercress beds require firm bottoms because of the amount of running water that must flow through them. The beds have a slope of 100:1 to 200:1, which means that they are nearly level. The slope is just enough to allow for complete drainage and adequate flow-through of water. Although the size of beds may vary, most beds in Hawaii are 40 feet wide and 80 feet long. Concrete tile dikes are constructed around the beds to allow water to flow through and to provide foot access to the beds.

Although watercress can be planted from seeds, the normal method of propagation is by terminal shoot cuttings. Four to six shoots are placed in bunches about 1 foot apart and parallel with the flow of water so they are less likely to be washed away. The water level is kept at about $\frac{1}{4}$ inch until the roots anchoring the plants develop properly. The water is then gradually increased to the depth of 1 to 2 inches for growing.

17–22. A bunch of living watercress as sold at a supermarket. Consumers use watercress in salads or as a cooked salad green, much like spinach or other greens.

17–23. A watercress cutting ready for planting. When the cutting is planted, the basal end is placed in the direction of the current.

About 45 days after planting, the watercress is ready for harvesting, at a height of about 12 to 14 inches. The crop is harvested by hand, with the harvester grasping a bunch and cutting the stems with a sickle. The stubble is left to continue to produce, and more cuttings are usually added after harvesting to replace damaged stems. In another 45 days or so, depending on the time of year, the crop will be ready to harvest again. Plants will usually yield three or four cuttings before being replaced. Obviously, the harvesting process is very labor intensive.

The harvested watercress is vacuum cooled and stored in a refrigerator. The shelf life is very short, usually only about one week. The consumer may use watercress as a salad green or as a cooked green vegetable, much like spinach.

17–24. A Chinese water chestnut corm that is ready for planting. Note the sprout that is beginning to grow.

CHINESE WATER CHESTNUTS

In Asian countries, Chinese water chestnut production is an important part of aquaculture and of international commerce. In the United States, however, production is usually small scale and not as efficient as that in Asian countries. The supply of water chestnuts produced in the United States does not meet the demand, although the markets are relatively small.

The part of the water chestnut that is eaten is the corm, the fleshy underground stem. It is firm and white and remains so even after being cooked.

The best location in the United States for Chinese water chestnut production appears to be in the Southeast, with its warm, humid climate.

Water chestnuts require sandy soil. Corms are planted 2 to 3 inches deep and about 3 feet apart. Planting is usually done in March. Water chestnuts need about 1 ton of balanced fertilizer per acre, which is usually applied at three different times. The first application is at planting, with one following in May and another in August.

Water chestnuts may be grown in raceways, flooded fields, or indoor troughs. They are warmwater plants, with their best growth occurring in the summer months.

About 220 days after planting, in late October or early November, the corms are ready for harvest. Each planted corm will have produced about 20 pounds of new corms by this time. In a good growing season, 15 to 20 tons of corms per acre can be produced.

The corms are usually harvested with rakes or small plows covered with rubber to prevent damage to the corms. The harvesting is extremely labor intensive. Spading forks are used to work the beds, and the soil is often screened to collect all the corms. Although most corms are between 2 and 4 inches deep, some may be found as deep as 10 inches. The aquafarmer usually keeps enough corms to restock the beds the next year and then sells the rest. Keeping seedstock is necessary because supplies are both hard to obtain and expensive.

After the corms have been harvested, their tough outer skin must be removed. The corms are cleaned and bleached, and then they are ready for market. Corms sold in large quantities as food vary in price from 10 to 20 cents each. In specialty ornamental sales, prices may be much higher. The water chestnuts are used in a variety of casseroles and other dishes and as a garnish. They are crunchy and add a mild taste to these dishes.

Chinese water chestnuts are also an excellent choice for polyculture with animal aquacrops. In raceway culture, for example, the water can be used to fertilize the plants after it has moved through the animal production facility. Water chestnuts also make an excellent biofilter for intensive indoor systems. Polyculture uses are not common practices at present; however, the potential for polyculture with water chestnuts is excellent.

TARO

Taro is a tropical plant produced for its large underground stems (corms), which are used to prepare a starchy-type food. Taro will grow as a terrestrial plant, though it most widely cultivated as an aquatic or wetland plant. The plant is similar to elephant's-ear and caladium, two ornamentals.

Aquatic taro is sometimes called *paddy taro*. Taro breeding has resulted in improved varieties adapted to a range of cultural environments. The paddy-taro varieties are grown in wetland areas using the lo'i system in Hawaii. Paddy production eliminates most problems with weeds. In south Florida, taro may be produced on land.

Taro is propagated using hulis. A *hulis* is a cutting made of a piece of stem 12 to 18 inches (0.3 to 0.5 m) long and a 2- to 3-inch (5- to 8-cm) section of the corm. Cuttings are often washed in a 10 percent bleach solution for 30 seconds to kill any disease organisms that may be present. The cuttings are placed

17–25. Paddy taro growing in Hawaii.

18 inches (0.4 m) apart in 36- to 48-inch (0.9- to 1.2-m) rows in flooded areas. Fertilizer may be needed, depending on soil analysis results. Maturity is typically reached in six to ten months.

CULTURE OF AQUATIC PLANTS AND ALGAE FOR ANIMAL FEEDS

Several types of unicellular algae have been successfully cultured for use as feed for larval stages of certain aquacrops and for herbivorous fish and mollusks. Some algae are suitable as feed for livestock. Other aquacrops, such as duckweed and water spinach, also have been cultured for use as livestock feed. The cost of production is usually low, and the nutritional value of these aquatic plants is usually quite high. Some of the more common uses are given here.

ALGAE

Several species of green algae from the genus *Spirulina* grow very rapidly in fresh water and will work well as feed for some animal aquacrops. The protein content of some species is 70 percent. *Spirulina* are found in fresh waters all over North America. When used as feed for an animal aquacrop, some mature plants are placed in the water facility and allowed to begin reproduction before the aquacrop is stocked.

Some experts believe that green algae of this type will someday be used more for human consumption, but very little is used that way now. Although humans can digest the algae, most people do not like the distinct flavor. In Mexico and some Asian countries, however, *Spirulina* is gathered and dried into patties to be added to other foods. It provides a nutritious supplement to other foods but is almost never eaten by itself.

Numerous types of algae and diatoms are cultured as phytoplankton (floating or suspended plant material) for feeding to several animal aquacrops. Most of this culture is of blue-green algae from the family Cyanophyta, diatoms from the family Crysophyta, and green algae from the family Chlorophyta.

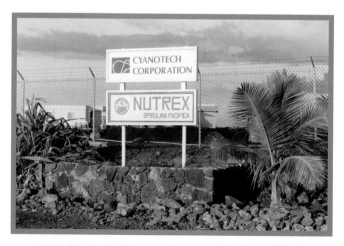

17–26. A Spirulina production facility in Hawaii.

Some species of red algae and brown algae are also harvested as livestock feed supplements. In Japan and Europe, this is a common practice. Off the coasts of Scotland and Ireland, some livestock producers have reduced the labor in this effort by letting their sheep and cattle graze in the intertidal zone, where they can eat the algae washed up on the shore. In some areas of Scotland and Ireland, these animals feed almost exclusively on *Palmaria palmata* (one of the red algae) and the brown algae of the genus *Alaria*.

DUCKWEED

Several species of common duckweed from the genera *Lemna*, *Spirodela*, *Wolffia*, and *Wolffiella* are found in ponds all across North America. Duckweed is considered a weed in many aquaculture systems because its rapid growth may choke out other plants and bother some animal species. Duckweed can usually cover the surface of a pond by the end of a growing season if it is not harvested in some way.

17–27. Duckweed.

Duckweed plants are made of floating fronds (leaflike parts) and stems that develop mats over the surface of freshwater ponds. The mats may get as thick as 2 inches, although the stems are usually less than $1/4$ inch thick.

Duckweed is a favorite food of herbivorous fish and waterfowl. It can be harvested and used in cattle, swine, and poultry feeds. Duckweed grown in ponds that are well fertilized is high in protein—about 40 percent. It also provides some essential amino acids and xanthophyll, a necessary ingredient in poultry rations.

With very little input required, duckweed is one of the least expensive aquacrops to produce. The growth rate is so rapid that weekly harvesting is common. The plants are harvested by skimming the surface of the water. The duckweed plants are dried and then added to livestock feeds.

WATER SPINACH

Water spinach (*Ipomoea reptans*) is more commonly cultured in Thailand, Malaysia, and Singapore than in the United States. It is often used in polyculture with fish or freshwater prawns. It is eaten as a green vegetable in a few areas but is much more commonly used as livestock feed.

Water spinach grows very rapidly, producing more than 20 pounds of green matter per acre per day. The reason it is not cultured more extensively is that it provides very little protein and few carbohydrates. The protein content is about 2 percent, and the carbohydrate content is about 3 percent.

CULTURE OF SPECIALTY AQUACULTURE PLANTS

A few specialty aquacrops are included here. Some are also harvested wild, though emphasis is increasingly on their culture.

PHYCOCOLLOIDS

The most important use of seaweeds in the United States is the extraction of phycocolloids. A *phycocolloid* is a gel-like substance that has many applications in science and the food industry. The two most commonly used phycocolloids are agars and carrageenans. Agar is soluble in hot water but not in cold. Some carrageenans are soluble in cold water, and all are soluble in hot water.

High-quality agar comes primarily from red algae of the genus *Gelidium*. Its most important use is as a culture medium. Almost every hospital, college, research institute, and public health agency uses agar to culture bacteria, viruses, and small plants. Agar used as a culture medium requires a high degree of purification before it is suitable.

Agar from the genus *Gracilaria*, which is of a somewhat lower quality, is widely used in printing, brewing, canning and preserving, gel chromatography, and the making of dental impressions. Japan is the leading producer of agar, but there is some production in the United States, with considerable increases in the last 20 years.

Carrageenan is actually a collection of phycocolloids from agar-producing plants. It may be extracted from numerous species of red algae and some brown algae, but its characteristics may change, based on the plant from which it was extracted.

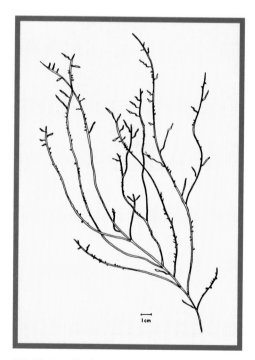

17–28. Gracilaria verrucosa, one of the red algae commonly harvested for extraction of phycocolloids. (Courtesy, J. E. Hansen, J. E. Packard, and W. T. Doyle, California Sea Grant College Program)

The United States leads the world in carrageenan production. About 75 percent of the carrageenan produced in the United States is used in the food industry, as water gels and as dairy protein applications. The water-gel uses include dessert gels, pet foods, jellies, barbecue sauces, imitation milks and creamers, whipped toppings, and puddings. The dairy applications include ice cream, egg nog, evaporated milk, infant formulas, and custards. Carrageenan is also found in the hamburger patties produced by some hamburger chains.

WASTEWATER TREATMENT

Because of their ability to remove wastes from the water in which they grow, many aquatic plants are used in wastewater treatment lagoons to clean the water. The idea behind the lagoons is that the organic matter provides nutrients for unicellular algae to grow, the algae provide oxygen for bacteria, and the bacteria break down the organic matter so it can be used by the algae.

The only problem with the system is that the algae must be removed from the system periodically, or the system will have the same amount of organic matter, in the form of algae, that it had with the wastes. The treatment facilities are not very cost effective because the collection of the algae is expensive. Some costs can be recovered through the sale of the collected algae as mulch, cattle feed, or fertilizer. However, a more cost-effective system would be beneficial.

Some wastewater treatment facilities have solved the problem somewhat by using higher plants, such as duckweed and water hyacinth. These plants are just as effective as the algae in removing wastes, and they are much easier to harvest.

ORNAMENTALS

Aquatic plants grown for their aesthetic value are called ornamentals. The ornamentals included here are often used in aquatic gardens and dried flower arrangements.

One of the most common of these aquacrops is the cattail (*Typha latifolia* or *T. angustifolia*). The cattail is often used in flower arrangements. It is also grown in water gardens.

Arrowheads are also used in ornamental gardens. These include several species of the genus *Sagittaria,* as well as many other species found naturally in the United States.

The cattail and the arrowhead also have edible parts, although they are not cultured for food as a general rule.

FUEL SOURCES

When fossil fuels are in abundant supply and prices stable, very little attention is paid to other means of producing fuel. The fuel produced by alternative sources is not nearly as cost efficient. However, when supplies run low or prices increase because of trade problems, alternative sources of fuel may be necessary. Two types of aquatic plants have shown promise in the production of fuel. These are the water hyacinth and some species of algae.

The water hyacinth has been used in experiments to produce methane gas, a clean, economical fuel. The method of using the water hyacinths from wastewater treatment facilities might make both operations more economically feasible.

Some species of algae have the ability to break down seawater into hydrogen and oxygen. The hydrogen is a waste product that could be used as fuel. Hydrogen fuel, used in jet airplanes, is another clean, economical fuel.

REVIEWING

MAIN IDEAS

Although most aquaculture in the United States has focused on animal production, there is good potential for plant and algae aquaculture as well. All the environmental factors are in place for significant plant aquaculture production. Freshwater supplies are abundant in many areas. Access to salt water and brackish water is adequate in the areas where production would occur. Suitable climates exist for many aquaculture plants. Proven culture techniques have been established by aquafarmers in the United States and other countries.

The greatest increase in production of aquatic plants has been for water gardens. Several species are widely used for their beauty and appeal. Water gardens are carefully designed to provide good habitat for the species produced. Koi are usually not kept in a water facility with plants because of their nibbling on the plants.

Although the possibilities for increased production of aquatic plants exist, several factors have inhibited the growth of plant aquaculture. For the most part, Americans are not accustomed to including aquatic plants in their diets. Except in Hawaii, aquatic plants historically have not been standard table fare. Also, the methods of producing aquatic plants for commercial purposes are unknown to most aquafarmers.

Many species of aquatic plants can be cultured. The uses for these plants include food for human consumption, animal feeds, wastewater treatment, scientific culture material, food additives, and fuel.

When aquafarmers become aware of the possibility of polyculture as a means of increasing income from existing facilities, they will begin to take notice. Some promotion to inform the public of the nutritional benefits of aquacrops should also help increase production. As improved techniques for the culture of freshwater aquacrops are developed and markets are expanded, plant aquaculture in the United States should grow significantly.

QUESTIONS

Answer the following questions, using complete sentences and correct spelling.

1. What are the five categories of aquatic plants and algae? Name and define each.
2. What are the most commonly grown saltwater and brackish-water algae aquacrops?
3. What are the three most commonly grown freshwater food plants?
4. Define photosynthesis.
5. Define respiration.
6. What is the purpose of chlorophyll?
7. What are the three common habitat concerns of aquatic plants?
8. What is sexual reproduction in plants?
9. What is a water garden? How does a water garden differ from a koi pond?
10. How are water garden plants grouped? Identify and briefly explain each group.
11. Describe the reproductive process of algae.
12. Describe the reproductive process of the Chinese water chestnut.
13. Where do brown algae get their olive brown color?
14. Describe the spore collection process for brown algae.
15. How do aquafarmers obtain seedstock for the production of red algae?
16. What are the two primary habitat considerations for watercress?
17. Describe the commercial propagation procedure for watercress.
18. How is taro propagated?
19. What are some specialty uses of aquatic plants?
20. What should be considered in selecting a location for a water garden?

EVALUATING

Match the term with the correct definition. Write the letter of the term on the line provided.

a. water garden
b. benthic
c. koi pond
d. corm
e. gametes
f. phycocolloids
g. hydroponics
h. spores
i. thalli
j. hulis

_____ 1. The growing of terrestrial plants in water

_____ 2. Stems of algae

_____ 3. A decorative water area that has a variety of plants and, typically, goldfish

_____ 4. Characteristic of aquatic plants that attach to the bottom or substrate

_____ 5. The reproductive part of an underground stem

_____ 6. Plant sex cells

_____ 7. Gel-like substances, such a agar and carrageenan

_____ 8. An ornamental pond for keeping koi

_____ 9. Small, seedlike plant parts

_____ 10. Vegetative cutting of stem and corm of a taro plant

EXPLORING

1. Make a trip to a local supermarket to identify aquatic plants and algae. See if watercress and fresh Chinese water chestnuts are available in the produce section. Find a can of Chinese water chestnuts. Find a vegetable mix in the frozen food section that has water chestnuts. Ask the manager if the store has any seaweed for sale. Get the prices for all the items you find. Give an oral report to the class.

2. Take a trip to a local aquafarm involved in plant aquaculture. Ask the county extension agent for possible locations. Give a report to the class.

3. Set up a mini Chinese water chestnut growing facility in the school greenhouse or lab. Any container that will hold 6 to 8 inches of sandy soil (and will hold water after flooding) will be fine. If the climate is suitable, the Chinese water chestnuts can be planted outside. Remember to fertilize at planting, at two months after planting, and at four months after planting. Starting at four months, dig up one corm every two months. Count the number of smaller corms and record their size. Compare the early diggings with the corms that are grown a full growing season.

4. Develop a poster depicting the growing stages of each of the three most common types of algae (seaweed) grown.

5. Find an animal aquafarm in your community. Conduct an assessment of the feasibility of including some type of plant aquaculture as part of the operation.

6. Design a water garden for your home or school. Use information from Web sites and other sources to guide your plan. Present your plan in class. Suggested Web sites are

The Water Garden—**www.watergarden.com**

The Pond Professor—**www.practical-water-gardens.com**

SRAC—**http://srac.tamu.edu/435fs.pdf**

PART SIX

Aquaculture and People

CHAPTER 18

Sustainable Aquaculture

OBJECTIVES

This chapter introduces the concept of sustainable aquaculture. It has the following objectives:

1 Discuss sustainable aquaculture in a historical context

2 Describe how inputs of resources can efficiently and safely produce aquaculture products

3 Explain how to integrate aquaculture with other economic activities

4 Describe the positive and negative environmental impacts of aquaculture

5 Explain how aquaculture can utilize or change the human resource

6 Define organic aquaculture and explain how it can help sustain the future of aquaculture

TERMS

by-product
carnivorous fish
detritivorous fish
food chain
integrated aquaculture-
   agriculture

niche
omnivorous fish
organic aquaculture
phytate
planktivorous fish
restricted feeding

rice-fish culture
sustainable aquaculture
water reuse

18–1. Watershed ponds add value to agricultural enterprises as a productive use of low or unproductive cropland.

THE FUTURE of aquaculture will depend on a successful mix of conservation and efficient business management. The inputs of feed, seedstock, labor, and energy should come from sustainable resources.

Aquaculture can and should be combined with other agricultural and industrial enterprises to improve efficiency and profitability. Ponds can be constructed to fit within the landscape of watersheds to achieve water and soil conservation goals.

Human resources should benefit from aquaculture enterprises. Future aquaculture businesses will fit into existing cultural, environmental, and economic practices.

THE PRACTICE OF SUSTAINABLE AQUACULTURE

In the future, aquaculture businesses will successfully combine natural resource conservation with efficient business management. **Sustainable aquaculture** is the production of aquatic organisms using efficient and cost-effective methods to improve human capacity, utilize and conserve available resources, and protect the environment. The inputs of feed, seedstock, labor, and energy must come from sustainable sources.

18–2. The mirror strain of common carp can be used in polyculture with other carp species.

HISTORY OF SUSTAINABILITY

Aquaculture has been practiced since ancient times. Chinese aquaculture methods were the earliest recorded and were also very sustainable. Ponds in China were stocked with a variety of fish species that each ate different things. Five or more species of carp were raised in the same pond to better use the food that was offered or the food that was produced by fertilizing the water.

Crops were planted near the ponds that could be utilized as food for the fish directly or as by-products. By-products such as leaves, husks, or bran were not used by humans and were added to the ponds directly, composted to release nutrients, or fed to livestock to produce manure fertilizer. The water from the fish ponds was used to water crops and livestock. This type of integrated aquaculture is still practiced in China and has been used in many developing countries around the world.

Other countries have developed aquaculture in different ways. Europe has cultured trout and carp for many centuries in monoculture, where only one species was grown in the pond at one time. Trout and carp were introduced into the United States soon after colonization, but the most important U.S. aquaculture species, catfish, gained importance in the late 1900s, again in monoculture.

Shrimp and tilapia farms in Central and South America, as well as in Asia, have also developed monoculture systems. However, other fish and shellfish species are now being added to these systems to provide biological control of weeds or diseases or to utilize more

18–3. Fish ponds use nutrients from animal waste on this tropical integrated farm.

parts of the culture system. Chinese polyculture, in which more than one aquatic species is raised in a system at one time, is a concept that may soon be used by many aquaculture enterprises.

EXAMPLES OF SUSTAINABLE AQUACULTURE

Agricultural crops can benefit from aquaculture, and the producer adds a profit center to the farm. Rice-fish culture has been used as a type of sustainable aquaculture that also helps agriculture sustainability. *Rice-fish culture* is the stocking of fish into rice fields to eat the golden snail. Since the golden snail can harm the rice, rice-fish farming boosts the rice yield and gives a fish harvest as a bonus. In Zambia, farmers build small ponds in their vegetable

18–4. Traps have been placed to harvest crawfish from a rice field in Louisiana.

gardens so that pond water can be used for irrigation and pond mud can be used as organic fertilizer for their vegetable crops.

Fish and shellfish can be raised in nets or pens in lakes, estuaries, or coastal bays, where they can feed on natural food produced by available nutrients. In some cases, the diets for these fish are supplemented with **by-products** (secondary products) from agriculture or industry. Mussels are raised in nets off the coast of Spain. Tilapia are placed in net pens in Central America. Trout are raised in nets in Peru. Salmon are placed in off-shore pens in the United States and several other countries.

Pond construction allows aquaculture to be located near the agricultural crop. In Arkansas, in the mid-1900s, large ponds were built to store water for crop irrigation. It seemed natural to stock that water with buffalo carp and catfish. Today, the catfish industry still uses catfish pond water to irrigate rice fields in Arkansas and Mississippi. However, large concentrations of fish ponds make integration with agricultural crops difficult.

Aquaculture as a Sustainable Cropping System

Culture system design and system management can make aquaculture as sustainable as any other cropping system. Species that are low on the food chain fit the sustainable crops definition most easily. The **food chain** is the sequence in which organisms feed. It starts with the smallest organisms that use dissolved or suspended nutrients and ends at the highest levels with animals that eat meat from other animals.

Some species may be sustainable in culture at low densities or in special systems that allow reduced inputs or that control the release of wastes. The importance of natural food increases as fish densities decrease in earthen ponds.

Natural food organisms are located in a certain part of the environment called a niche. A **niche** is the location of an organism within a pond and the function of the organism. Identification and filling of niches within the culture system can improve sustainability while inputs are reduced in proportion to aquaculture production.

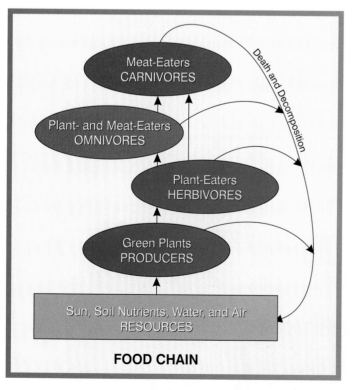

18–5. How the food chain works.

Fish need water for growth, and conservation of that water is important to sustainable production. One form of water conservation involves the reuse of water used to culture fish. **Water reuse** is the directing of water to other aquaculture or plant culture systems, which allows for more value to be obtained per unit of water. Cage culture and raceway culture can allow water to be used for aquaculture without substantially reducing its use by natural ecosystems. The more efficient the reuse of aquaculture water, the better the aquaculture system fits the sustainable definition.

Aquaculture products are high-quality and high-value products. Systems that allow for economical culture of these products are important sources of nutritional products for our world population. For example, catfish contain 81 percent lean meat, compared with pork, beef, and poultry, which are 54 to 65 percent lean. Catfish have fat content of 5 percent, and chicken are relatively low in fat at 9 percent. However, the beef carcass contains 25 percent fat, and the pork carcass has 26 percent fat.

18–6. Biofiltration promotes efficient use of water. (This shows biofiltration media being examined in a newly installed system.)

Table 18–1. Dressed Carcass Characteristics of Food Animals

Source of Flesh	Dressing Percentage	Lean (%)	Fat (%)	Unused Trimmings (%)
Catfish	60	81	5	14
Beef	61	60	25	15
Pork	72	54	26	21
Chicken	72	65	9	30

Source: Tom Lovell. *Nutrition and Feeding of Fish*. New York: Van Nostrand Reinhold, 1989.

Fish products also contain vitamins and minerals that are valuable in the human diet. Only calcium, vitamin A, and vitamin C are low in fish, relative to the daily recommended allowance for humans. Calcium contributed by salmon and sardines is higher because of the bones included in the processed product. Vitamin A is higher in oily fish species. Vitamin C is low in all fish and must be obtained from other food sources, such as fruits and vegetables.

Fish products are adaptable to a variety of recipes and can appeal to households of different income levels or cultures. Traditional recipes for fried, bone-in fish have been replaced by recipes for fillets that are broiled or baked. Convenience products that are pre-breaded, pre-cooked, or marinated have recently become popular as younger-generation cooks start to buy aquaculture products. This adaptability contributes to sustaining the market for aquaculture products during shifts in cultural preferences for food types.

BALANCING INPUTS AND PRODUCTS

High yields of aquaculture products can be achieved with careful management of land, water, nutrients, and energy inputs. It is economically and environmentally important to avoid waste in production aquaculture. Careful planning can prepare aquaculture projects to be sustainable by choosing good locations and managing resources efficiently.

LAND USE FOR AQUACULTURE

Sites selected for aquaculture projects should be compatible with neighboring land uses. Aquaculture can complement other agricultural uses and, in some cases, recreational activities.

18–7. Aquaculture land use should be compatible with other agricultural uses. (Aquaculture, livestock production, forestry, and field crops are evident in this scene.)

Pond construction near existing cropland and pastures can provide dual-use opportunities and improve farm profitability. Low-fertility or acid soils not suitable for crops can be well suited for pond construction. Heavy soils lead to excessive soil moisture for most crops during wet weather. However, soils of high clay content make good pond dams and help conserve water used for aquaculture.

Avoid locations that interfere with water drainage, destroy wetlands, or alter productive cropland. Fragile ecosystems can be destroyed by the construction that accompanies land development, and this can be true with aquaculture. Existing social and economic customs should be considered before aquaculture projects are developed. Local regulations may already be in place to discourage improper land use. Consult local soil and water conservation authorities early in the site-planning process.

High productivity from aquaculture farms makes them attractive alternatives to many other types of agricultural production. Catfish ponds located next to rice fields, for example, can provide water to irrigate the rice crop. Ponds in cattle pastures can add 4,000 to 6,000 pounds of fish production per acre on land that would be unsuitable for good forage production. In areas that have potential for recreational enterprises, fish ponds can provide attractive alternatives for tourists by providing fishing, picnicking, and wildlife enjoyment opportunities.

WATER USE, CONSERVATION, AND REUSE

Ponds retain and contain water from precipitation and runoff that would otherwise leave the area. In some cases this water can be utilized for irrigation of crops or as drinking water for livestock. Groundwater use can be reduced by constructing ponds that capture rainfall. Pond management to regulate pond depth can improve water conservation for aquaculture. The practice of keeping ponds less than full, at least 6 inches low, can allow rainfall to be captured and to replace evaporation. During heavy rainfall, ponds can store water that could otherwise increase flooding downstream from the ponds. Alluvial soils and sediments in runoff are retained by ponds so that streams are less turbid and watershed erosion is reduced.

Ponds should not be constructed without careful consideration of downstream water uses. Dam construction in areas near navigable waters is regulated by the Army Corps of Engineers in the United States. Reducing water flow into certain streams that contain fragile fish can have damaging effects on the ecosystem that sustains the threatened fish population.

Water capture can be improved by using watertight soils, collection aprons, reservoirs, and diversion ditches. Ponds should be constructed with heavy clay that is prop-

18–8. Careful pond construction reduces water losses from ponds when clay is packed into the core trench.

18–9. Water used for aquaculture can be more sustainable when it is recirculated.

erly compacted to limit seepage. Water collection aprons constructed of concrete, plastic, or other impervious materials can provide water for small aquaculture systems or fill reservoirs for future use. Ponds have been used as reservoirs for crop irrigation, and the fish crops are an added benefit. Reservoirs filled during the rainy season provide water for the fish and plant crops later. Reservoirs are planned to be deep enough to hold the water needed plus the expected loss to evaporation. Those built in dry climates are deeper than those built in humid climates.

Recirculating water through aquaculture systems can reduce the amount of water used. Efficiency of water reuse can be as high as 99 percent, but systems with 90 percent water reuse may utilize less energy or require simpler design. Filters are used to remove fish waste and to prepare the water to be returned to the culture system. Biological or mechanical filters can be integrated with vegetables, herbs, algae, or filter-feeding aquatic animals to recover waste feed and fish wastes.

FEEDS FOR EFFICIENT NUTRIENT USE

Aquaculture feeds should be both very easy to digest and economical. Most fish species are best at using protein from animal products and energy from oils. However, plant proteins can be less expensive. A balance can be made between the cost of the feed and the efficiency of nutrient use. To make the decisions necessary to balance a diet, a great deal of knowledge is needed about the characteristics of each part of the diet.

Some diet ingredients have anti-nutritional factors that can slow fish growth or cause nutritional diseases. Trypsin inhibitor is found in soybeans and can cause poor protein utilization unless the soybeans are heated to destroy the inhibitor. Cottonseed contains a toxic chemical called gossypol that can reduce fish growth when a large amount of cottonseed meal is added to fish diets.

Most feed ingredients that are products of grains have *phytate*, a chemical that contains phosphorus. However, fish cannot digest the phosphorus from phytate very well. The result is that they release the undigested phytate phosphorus into the environment. Recently, enzymes that help the fish digest phytate phosphorus have been added to fish feed to improve the conservation of dietary phosphorus.

ALTERNATIVE FEEDING METHODS

Natural food is an alternative to commercial fish feeds. In polyculture systems, fish use natural foods very efficiently when the right fish species are selected. Combining a species of carnivorous fish, two or more types of planktivorous fish, a species of omnivorous fish, and a species of detritivorous fish can make feed use very efficient. In this case, the **carnivorous fish** eat insects, worms, or small fish. The **planktivorous fish** eat algae or zooplankton. The **omnivorous fish** eat foods of both animal and plant origin. Living plants, fish eggs, insects, and aquatic invertebrates are foods of omnivores. The **detritivorous fish** eat decaying leaves, fish waste, and other nonliving organic materials. For example, largemouth bass are often stocked with bluegill sunfish, redear sunfish, and catfish in ponds in the United States, and no supplemental feed is necessary.

When fish feed is offered in a limited or restricted feeding fashion, the feeding efficiency is better. **Restricted feeding** is supplementing the fish diet by providing only what the fish need beyond the natural food available. Restricted feeding is most effective when fish stocking density is low. Catfish stocked at less than 4,000 fish per acre can still use natural food as an important part of their diet. However, at a higher stocking density, the feed must contain all the nutrients the catfish need for good health and growth.

ENERGY REQUIREMENTS IN AQUACULTURE

The ideal and sustainable source of energy for aquaculture is the sun. Sunlight can warm the water, provide energy for plant and animal growth, and power photosynthesis to produce oxygen in pond water. Aquaculture systems that have effectively used the sun include watershed pond fish production, algae culture, and most forms of extensive aquaculture.

As the intensity of aquaculture increases, more energy is needed to produce a crop. Water must be pumped to fill the culture system and to replace water losses. Aerators may be used continuously or only when needed to prevent low dissolved oxygen concentrations that could harm the fish. Tractors and trucks used to harvest fish in many aquaculture enterprises consume energy.

18–10. Energy is required when harvesting large ponds with seines and tractors.

18–11. Aerators use a major portion of the energy in aquaculture enterprises.

Energy use increases as the stocking density and the scale of the farm increase. There are many ways, however, to decrease energy use. For example, harvesting effort can be reduced by using cages or net pens to eliminate the need to seine large ponds. Catch basins can reduce the energy needed to harvest by reducing the area of a pond that must be seined. Fish can be captured as a pond is emptied, and the water reused. Monitors of dissolved oxygen in aquaculture systems can control aeration to optimize energy use.

Recirculating aquaculture systems must be carefully designed to conserve energy. Pumps and aerators operate continuously in most recirculating systems. Since the amount of water movement in a recirculating system depends on the density of fish in the system, a close balance should exist between system design, stocking rate, feeding rate, and water exchange. Heat is conserved in a recirculating system, but a heat source may be needed during cool seasons. When the system is located near a waste heat source, such as a power plant, the recirculating system can recycle energy for mutual benefits. Greenhouses can be used to extend the season for growing warmwater fish species.

SELECTING THE BEST SPECIES FOR CULTURE

Fish growth is very efficient in terms of weight gain per unit of food eaten. Some fish species can convert more than 84 percent of their food to weight gain. Among the reasons for this efficiency are the way fish suspend themselves in water with little effort and the fact that they are "coldblooded" so that they do not heat their own bodies. Also, the conversion of food to fish weight includes a change from a very dry feed to fish flesh that contains more than 25 percent water. Therefore, some of the weight gain in fish is actually water.

Monoculture of tilapia, bait minnows, clams, oysters, and other filter feeders can be sustainable. These species can thrive from nutrients and food organisms found naturally in water. Fertility in the water provides the nutrients that are necessary for natural food organisms to grow. Compost, manure, and other fertilizer can be used to increase natural food production when these and other planktivorous fish are cultured. Baitfish producers prefer their enterprise because of relatively low inputs required to produce a crop compared with those required to produce food-size catfish.

Polyculture of tilapia and carp or of bass and bream is an example of efficient use of pond area for aquaculture. The actual species used for polyculture systems can depend on the market potential, cultural preferences, climate, salinity, and producer preferences (see Table 18–2).

Table 18–2. Combinations of Fish Used in Selected Polyculture Systems

Species Combination	Yearly Production per Acre
Largemouth bass Bluegill sunfish Redear sunfish Catfish Grass carp (exotic)	300–500 lb (fertilization only)
Channel catfish Freshwater prawn	3,000–4,000 lb
Freshwater prawn Rainbow trout (winter)	2,000–2,500 lb
Catfish Rainbow trout (winter)	4,000–5,000 lb
Catfish Fathead minnow Threadfin shad	4,000–10,000 lb
Tilapia (exotic) Grass carp (exotic) Silver carp (exotic) Bighead carp (exotic)	3,000–5,000 lb (fertilization only)
Tilapia (exotic) Catfish (in earthen ponds)	4,000–5,000 lb
Tilapia (exotic) Catfish (partitioned aquaculture system)	14,000–15,000 lb

18–12. Hybrid tilapia are highly productive in either pond or tank systems.

While a Chinese polyculture system uses only carp species, a comparable system in the United States might use one carp species (the grass carp) in combination with sunfish, catfish, and bass. Careful planning is needed to keep inputs at a minimum. Improper species selection will cause underproduction of one or more species and usually requires more feed input.

18–13. Hybrid sunfish utilize zooplankton for rapid growth in polyculture with bass, catfish, and grass carp.

INTEGRATING AQUACULTURE WITH OTHER CROPS

The combination of two or more economic activities on a farm can make the farm more efficient and profitable. Combining aquaculture with plant or livestock production is a good way to lower input costs, conserve resources, and increase net return on investment (see Table 18–3).

Table 18–3. Some Impacts of Integrated Fish and Plant Culture

Before Aquaculture Was Added	*After* Aquaculture Was Added
Low land was not used.	Poorly drained land is productive.
No resources were shared.	Resources are centered around the pond because of its water.
Crop by-products were not used.	Agricultural by-products are used as fish food.
Water was not always available for plant production.	Nearby ponds provide water for agricultural crops.
Water supply was uncertain.	Pond water is used to water livestock, to provide fire protection, and provide recreation.
Inorganic fertilizer was used for crops.	Pond mud can be used as fertilizer.
Fish were a small part of the family diet.	Fish provide family food and income.
Only a few crops were grown.	More crops, including water-sensitive crops, can be grown.

When a fish farm is started, for example, the tractors, trucks, and other farm equipment can be shared with the new fish enterprise. The same is true for water wells, office equipment, roadways, and some farm buildings.

Integrated aquaculture-agriculture is practiced to some extent on many fish farms. It is the combination of practices to produce traditional crops and livestock products as well as aquaculture crops and products. The amount of integration depends on the amount of resources shared among the different parts of the farm.

CONNECTION

GIVING OYSTERS A LIFT

Native wild oysters are often damaged by overharvesting and polluted water. Oyster populations have declined rapidly in some locations. A number of approaches have been used in turning the situation around.

Improving oyster habitat often involves restoring sites where oysters live and grow. Since oyster young cling to old shells, placing shells in areas where oysters should grow helps improve their habitat. The young now have old shells to attach themselves to.

This photo shows a helicopter dumping a load of oyster shells on a site that is being restored. (Photo courtesy, U.S. Fish and Wildlife Service)

FISH AND PLANT SYSTEMS

The basis for integrating aquaculture and plant culture is sharing water used in aquaculture. Both aquaculture and plant production become more sustainable when water is shared, because water from every source except rainfall has a cost. In one form of plant and fish culture, rice-fish culture, water is used to raise both crops at the same time. However, most integrated systems use two separate locations, one for aquaculture and one for plant production, with water exchange between the two.

18–14. Discarded fish-tank water is being used to irrigate these tomatoes under red plastic mulch. No wastewater is discharged from the system.

Recirculating aquaculture systems and plant culture are good matches because the concentrated systems use a relatively small amount of water. The area of plant production can be small and still be able to utilize the aquaculture water efficiently. For example, a single tank of 20,000 tilapia can support a single greenhouse of tomatoes without water loss. However, two acres of pond water stocked with 20,000 tilapia could supply water to eight or more acres of crop at the rate of 12 inches of irrigation per unit of crop area per year.

USING AQUACULTURE EFFLUENTS

18–15. Discharged water from a fish tank goes to a nearby greenhouse and carries nutrients for a tomato crop.

Discharge of wastewater (effluents) from aquaculture can pollute natural waters. Nitrogen, phosphorus, and particles of organic material contained in the effluent would be wasted if not reused on agricultural land. Some aquaculture systems have greatly reduced the amount of effluent they release. All aquaculture systems have nutrients to get rid of, either in the water or in the sediments. By integrating with agricultural crops, 26 to 44 times less nitrogen and 12 to 15 times less phosphorus is released into the environment.

Integrated aquaculture-agriculture systems are more efficient but also concentrate nutrient use in a certain area. Comparing a natural area with an area of farming or integrated aquaculture will show that nutrient pollution occurs in any farming system. However, when systems of food production are compared, the integrated aquaculture-agriculture system is preferred to aquaculture or crop production alone.

BY-PRODUCTS USED IN AQUACULTURE

Sustainable aquaculture uses agricultural by-products rather than products that could be used as human food. With traditional aquaculture, fish feeds are often made with grains and other materials that could be used as human food.

In developing countries, garden waste can be added to fish ponds directly or indirectly after composting. In manufactured diets, by-products include rice bran, wheat middlings, cottonseed meal, and distillers' grains, to name a few. Each by-product has individual characteristics that define its value as a food or fertilizer to produce a particular species of aquatic animal. Alligators, for example, can utilize

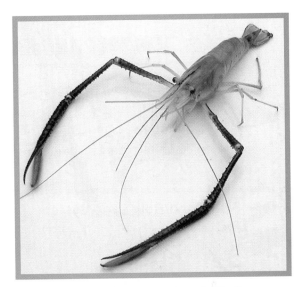

18–16. Freshwater prawns can be raised using agricultural by-products and natural foods.

salvaged chickens from poultry farms as a large part of their diet. Grass carp can use grass clippings or vegetable leaves for growth. Freshwater prawns can benefit from pond fertilization with high-fiber distillers' grains.

AQUACULTURE BY-PRODUCTS

Integrated systems can increase the value of the by-products of aquaculture. Fish waste, after fish have been processed for human food, is sometimes buried or burned. However, fish waste can be used directly as fertilizer for plants. It can also be composted after mixing with other by-products of agriculture. The resulting compost has a high value as a plant fertilizer.

Aquaculture in ponds produces aquatic plants and algae that can be considered by-products. These plants and algae are sometimes called green manure. They can add fertility to a rice field or be utilized by herbivorous or planktivorous fish.

ENVIRONMENTAL IMPACT OF AQUACULTURE

Aquaculture has a definite impact on the environment. Aquaculture facilities must be planned carefully to avoid damage to the environment. Earth moving, water pumping, and pond draining can have positive or negative effects.

AQUACULTURE AND HABITAT CHANGE

Pond construction changes the landscape. Ponds can be used to manage flooding or soil erosion, but in doing so, the natural contours of the land are changed forever. With soil erosion control, soil is moved by humans rather than by nature. The construction of ponds, when carefully planned, can improve conditions in a watershed.

Nonproductive areas can be made productive by the addition of aquaculture ponds. The definition of nonproductive areas varies according to the goals of each person. In general, areas of poor fertility or poorly drained soils are considered nonproductive for agricultural purposes. Pond construction can help make those areas productive so that they contribute to the well-being of the farmer.

In some areas, aquaculture development destroys important natural habitat. The importance of wetlands has been determined, and wetlands have been protected in the recent past. Current government regulations limit the amount of wetland area that can be changed to other uses, like aquaculture. It is usually a better idea to locate aquaculture facilities outside the areas determined to be wetlands.

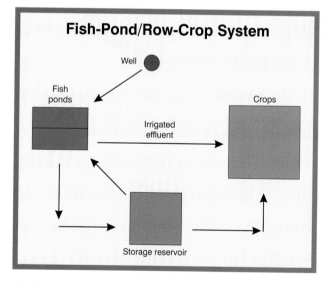

Fish-Pond/Row-Crop System

Well

Fish ponds

Crops

Irrigated effluent

Storage reservoir

18–17. Water discharged from fish ponds can be stored in reservoirs. Later it can be used in irrigating row crops or be reused in fish ponds.

IMPACT OF AQUACULTURE EFFLUENTS

Aquaculture changes the water it uses. Nutrients, soil, and organic matter are added to the water during aquaculture activities. In most cases, water warms up when it passes through an aquaculture facility. These changes can greatly affect the natural environment if the aquaculture effluent is discharged without consideration.

Trout streams are particularly fragile environments that should be protected from aquaculture discharge. However, slow-moving temperate streams may not be adversely affected by nearby aquaculture. To improve sustainability, aquaculture effluent discharge should be limited.

CULTURED FISH AFFECT NATIVE FISH

Although cultured fish originated from native fish, many changes have been made by humans as the aquaculture industry has developed. Aquatic animals have been moved from place to place so that they may no longer represent the genetic profile of native animals of the same species.

Selecting aquatic animals for survival and growth within aquaculture systems has changed their behavior and genetics. A debate exists about whether the changes are good or bad for native populations. Regulatory protection of native aquatic environments against exotic introductions may increase in the future.

HUMAN RESOURCE CHANGE BY AQUACULTURE

Aquaculture development adds new jobs and improves farm income in most cases. Aquaculture products have a high value, and the money returned to the farm has an impact on many parts of the rural economy. However, traditional lifestyles have been lost when large aquaculture projects have been developed without regard for the environment or competing land uses.

ENHANCING OR DISPLACING LIFESTYLES

Fish farming creates a new lifestyle for most farmers. Aquaculture is more management and capital intensive than most forms of agriculture. For this reason, higher economic returns are possible, but risks are also high. In sustainable aquaculture, the systems should be less intensive so that risks are lower, less capital is required, and impacts are positive. Regulation of aquaculture development is usually needed to encourage farmers to build sustainable systems.

Conflicts can develop between aquaculture and traditional occupations. Commercial fishers have complained that aquaculture products lower the price for their fish. Native land own-

18–18. Shrimp ponds in mangrove areas may have adverse effects on local environments if not properly designed.

ers have been displaced by fish farm development. However, aquaculture can provide jobs for fishers who are no longer able to make their living from commercial fishing. A balance between aquaculture development for economic gains and the impact on society is important.

Fish and seafood are highly desirable food products that are also part of the cultures of most human populations. Fish fillets are comparable in price to the highest-quality cut of beef, pork, or chicken. Retail value of large shrimp, red snapper fillets, and other marine fish fillets often exceeds the price of high-quality red meat cuts. Aquaculture of species like shrimp, tilapia, and hybrid striped bass has increased the availability and lowered the price so that more consumers can enjoy these seafood products. Asian cultures are noted for their love of many types of seafood, and European cultures prize species like trout and salmon as delicacies.

Some religions value fish as a preferred food during certain periods of their religious year. Fish-eating traditions are characteristic of the Jewish and Roman Catholic cultures, for example. Certain regions in the United States have preferences for different fish species or product forms. New England is noted for its cod industry and has recently become a market for large catfish fillets. The mid-Atlantic states are the primary market for hybrid striped bass because of traditional striped bass fishing in that area. Catfish markets in the southern United States and along the Mississippi and Ohio Rivers sustained that industry for years while acceptance in other areas was being developed.

LABOR REQUIREMENTS IN AQUACULTURE

Labor is not a major input for production of most aquaculture products. In sustainable aquaculture systems, plans to limit labor should be made before facilities are constructed. Less-intensive fish production requires less labor. In many cases, one person can manage most of the work on a small integrated fish farm. Training fish farm workers is a very impor-

18–19. A fish pond constructed with many laborers in a developing country provides needed employment.

tant part of aquaculture, and responsible workers must be able to perform diverse duties, including fish feeding, water-quality management, and fish health management.

Part-time labor is usually needed at harvest time. For this reason, many catfish farms use custom harvest crews to seine their ponds. Pay lakes are aquaculture businesses where fish farmers charge people for the opportunity to harvest fish from the ponds. Fish can be grown in cages or nets to make harvesting easier.

INDUSTRIES ASSOCIATED WITH AQUACULTURE

Jobs are created off the farm by aquaculture. The processing and marketing of aquaculture products results in many jobs. Feed manufacture is also a major benefactor of aquaculture development. Service industries can also benefit from aquaculture because of the new source of income it represents to a rural community.

ORGANIC AQUACULTURE

The organic concept is gaining popularity as a distinct product quality. Organic production seeks to reduce inputs and may improve sustainability of aquaculture production. Strict guidelines are required for truly organic fish product certification.

A DEFINITION

Organic products in agriculture are produced without any off-farm inputs and without harm to the environment. *Organic aquaculture* is the production of fish and other aquacrops without off-farm inputs. Organic aquaculture is an integrated system that uses management practices rather than synthetic materials to provide for the needs of the aquaculture system. The organic concept looks at the whole system, and every part of the system must be organic.

BALANCING ECONOMICS WITH LOW INPUTS

All inputs must be 100 percent organic all the time to produce an organic product. National standards are available for many agricultural products and are reviewed by the National Organic Standards Board. Organic livestock cannot receive therapeutic chemicals or feed additives. Genetic engineering and cloning are not allowed in organic production. For these reasons, animals that are highly resistant to disease and naturally fast growing are best suited for organic production.

The tools developed to make production more efficient may not be available in organic aquaculture. Therefore, yields may be lower with organic aquaculture. The loss in yields must be balanced by lower and less costly inputs. Managing the aquaculture system to reduce stress on the aquatic animals is important in organic production. A polyculture pond with natural fertilization, such as a bass-bluegill-catfish pond, may be a good example of organic fish production if no inorganic fertilizer is used. It is important to remember that medical treatment to diseased animals cannot be withheld in order keep the animals organic.

Integrated aquaculture has better potential to be certified as organic because of its low environmental impact. Discharge of fish waste into the environment must be avoided. Outside contaminants must be kept from the water supply. The water supply for aquaculture must be used in a manner that is ecologically sound.

18–20. Can crawfish raised on aquatic vegetation be certified as an organic product?

SPECIES FOR ORGANIC SYSTEMS

Aquatic species that do not require a manufactured diet may be the best choices for organic production. Species that need pelleted feed may not be the best choices. The feed manufacturing process is almost always an off-farm activity, and organic feed ingredients are difficult to find. There might be opportunities for development of certified organic fish feed mills if the needed volume of organic feed sales could be justified.

Many of the same species used in polyculture systems could be adapted to organic aquaculture. However, many of the carp species are spawned artificially by using hormones that would prevent their use in organic systems. Crawfish grown with aquatic vegetation could easily be certified as organic if natural resource conservation practices were followed.

MARKETING ORGANIC AQUACULTURE PRODUCTS

Prices for organic aquaculture products should be higher than for nonorganics. The lower yields require higher prices.

Consumer demand should determine the need for organic aquaculture products and therefore influence the prices. Local sales may not be the best option for organic products. Access to big-city markets may provide a better way to sell organic fish. There are simply more people who have unique food requirements in population centers than in the rural communities.

REVIEWING

MAIN IDEAS

Sustainable aquaculture systems use efficient and cost-effective methods to improve human capacity, utilize and conserve available resources, and protect the environment. Feed, seedstock, labor, and energy used to produce the aquacrops must come from sustainable sources.

Aquatic species that are low on the food chain fit the sustainable crops definition most easily. Other aquatic species may be sustainable when raised at low densities or when special systems allow reduced inputs. Natural food can be important in sustainable aquaculture systems and can be managed to improve the economy of production. Identifying and filling niches within the culture system can improve sustainability while inputs are reduced in proportion to aquaculture production.

Economical and sustainable yields of aquacrops can be achieved with careful management of land, water, nutrient, and energy inputs. Avoiding waste in production aquaculture is economically and environmentally important. Carefully plan the location and resource needs of aquaculture projects so that they can be sustainable.

Integrating aquaculture with plant or livestock production is a good way to lower input costs, conserve resources, and increase net return on investment. Sharing tractors, trucks, and other farm equipment between the farm and the new fish enterprise makes the whole farm more efficient. Integration makes better use of most farm facilities, including water wells, office equipment, roadways, and some farm buildings.

Aquaculture facilities must be planned carefully to avoid damage to the environment. Earth moving, water pumping, and pond draining can have positive or negative effects. Cultured fish sometimes harm native fish populations if they escape or transfer a disease.

Aquaculture development adds new jobs and improves farm income in most cases. The money returned to the farm from aquaculture has an impact on many parts of the rural economy. Diversifying into aquaculture can help a farmer maintain a farming lifestyle or improve the standard of living. However, traditional lifestyles have been lost in underdeveloped areas when large aquaculture projects have been created without regard for the environment or existing cultural activities.

Organic production seeks to reduce inputs and may result in sustainable aquaculture. Strict guidelines are required for organic fish product certification. Truly organic aquacrops may be difficult to produce.

QUESTIONS

Answer the following questions, using complete sentences and correct spelling.

1. What makes aquaculture sustainable? Give two examples of sustainable aquaculture systems.

2. What are three ways to reuse water used in aquaculture?

3. How can aquacrops and agriculture be integrated so that farmland can be used more efficiently? Give an example.

4. How can restricted feeding allow more efficient use of feed inputs?

5. List and explain three ways aquaculture may negatively affect the natural environment.

6. Describe three ways that aquaculture can enhance the lifestyle of people.

7. In what ways can aquaculture benefit nearby agricultural crops?

8. What agricultural by-products can be used in aquaculture? Name four.

9. Explain how monoculture of aquatic species can be sustainable.

10. Define organic aquaculture.

EVALUATING

Match the term with the correct definition. Write the letter of the term on the line provided.

a. carnivorous fish
b. detritivorous fish
c. planktivorous fish
d. phytate
e. organic aquaculture

f. food chain
g. restricted feeding
h. water reuse
i. integrated aquaculture-agriculture
j. niche

_____1. A certain part of the environment that is described by the location within a pond and the function of an organism

_____2. The directing of the water to other aquaculture or plant culture systems so that more value can be obtained per unit of water

_____3. The sequence in which organisms feed, starting with the smallest organisms that use dissolved or suspended nutrients and ending at the highest levels with animals that eat meat from other animals

_____4. A substance in feed ingredients that contains phosphorus

_____5. A fish that eats decaying leaves or fish waste

_____6. A combination of two or more economic activities on a farm to make the farm more efficient and profitable

_____7. Supplementing the fish diet by providing only what the fish need beyond the natural food available

_____8. A fish that eats insects, worms, or small fish

_____9. The production of fish without off-farm inputs

_____10. A fish that eats algae or zooplankton

EXPLORING

1. Set up a tank of tilapia (or other suitable species of fish). Feed the fish a diet of pelleted fish feed. Check the ammonia and nitrite concentrations in the fish tank water. Exchange the tank water for fresh water and use the tank water to irrigate tomato plants planted in a bale of peat moss or other organic material. In a warm climate, this can be done outside; elsewhere use a greenhouse or grow lights in an enclosed room. Compare the tomatoes grown with fish water to some fertilized the conventional way.

2. Create a poster that shows how aquaculture can be integrated with the production of row crops and livestock. Use arrows and labels to show where the nutrients go.

3. Visit a local office of the Natural Resource Conservation Service and ask about using ponds to conserve water and soil. Give an oral report in class.

4. Visit a local pet store that has many kinds of tropical fish. Ask the pet store owner about the eating habits of the fish. Try to identify a carnivore, a planktivore, and an omnivore. See if you can also identify other types of niche behavior in the fish. Give an oral report in class.

CHAPTER 19

Recreational Aquaculture

This chapter focuses on the operation of recreational aquabusinesses. It has the following objectives:

1 Explain the meaning and kinds of recreational aquaculture
2 Describe how to establish a recreational aquabusiness
3 Describe considerations in operating a recreational aquabusiness
4 Identify legal and risk situations in recreational aquaculture
5 Discuss ways of pleasing customers
6 Identify sport fishing equipment and supplies
7 Relate recreational aquaculture to agritourism

TERMS

agritourism
angler
bait-and-tackle store
business plan
cane pole
catch-out pond
customer assistance

daily fee
facility plan
fishing hook
fishing tackle
float
line
lure

put-and-take pond
season fee
sinker
sport fishing
weight-of-catch fee

19–1. Sport fishing on the bank of a fee-lake.

MANY PEOPLE like to go fishing! They especially enjoy making a big catch; some enjoy talking about the big one that got away. Recreational aquaculture helps satisfy the interests people have in sport fishing.

Operating a successful recreational aquabusiness requires good management. Knowing some of the fundamentals can help ensure success. Customers must come first. Without customers, a recreational business cannot be profitable. Just as with other areas of aquaculture, profit is the measure of success. Customers will spend their money for something they enjoy. This means that the recreational business should provide a comfortable, rewarding experience for the sport fisher.

RECREATION IN AQUACULTURE

Recreational aquaculture is the area of aquaculture that provides people with enjoyable relaxation through sport fishing. It is a way for them to escape from the routines of work and life. It helps them renew their energy and refresh their physical and mental well-being. The enterprising aquabusiness operator will find ways to help people enjoy themselves.

19–2. A good catch is rewarding to the sport fisher. (Courtesy, U.S. Fish and Wildlife Service)

19–3. A young sport fisher with a nice stringer of fish.

Sport fishing is an avocational activity of catching fish for fun and relaxation. Part of the fun is the challenge of landing a prized fish. The fish may be wild or cultured. If the fish is game fish, a license may be required. Sport fishing may be on a creek, lake, pond, river, or ocean. The equipment used may be simple or elaborate.

An *angler* is an individual who fishes with a hook. The term is typically applied to a sport fisher.

Many opportunities exist to operate a successful aquabusiness and, at the same time, help people enjoy sport fishing. Possible businesses include fee-lakes, bait-and-tackle stores, boat and accessory stores, tour guide services, and related areas, such as food and lodging.

FEE-LAKES

Fee-lakes are small lakes or ponds where the public can pay fees to fish. Fees may be assessed in several ways.

Fee Assessment

Several methods of charging customers for fishing in fee-lakes are used. Three are most popular, along with one combination method.

Daily Fee. A *daily fee* is a fixed amount a fee-lake user pays to fish all day. No guarantee is made that any fish will be caught. No charges are made for fish caught.

The daily-fee method is often used with a low-density pond, where the person fishing is not likely to catch many fish. However, with a well-stocked pond, where the fisher is likely to catch several pounds, the daily-fee method is probably not the best type to use.

One advantage of charging a daily fee is that no one has to be present all the time to monitor catches. A disadvantage is that some catches could be large, which would soon deplete the supply of fish. The owner tends not to get adequate pay for large catches when a daily fee is charged, unless the fee is large. A large fee might deter patronage by the fishing public. Fees typically range from $1 to $5 a day.

19–4. A sign advertising a fee-lake.

19–5. Relaxing at the edge of a clean fee-lake. (Courtesy, James Tidwell, Kentucky State University)

Season Fee. A *season fee* is a fee a fee-lake user pays for a full fishing season or a year. This is sometimes known as an annual fee. An individual who pays the fee may fish as often and as long as he or she likes during the season or year. Sometimes this method is used in conjunction with a fishing club.

The season fee should be adequate to cover expenses and provide a profit to the owner of the fee-lake. The season or annual fee may range from $25 to $150 or more, depending on the services provided.

Weight-of-Catch Fee. The *weight-of-catch fee* is a fee a fee-lake user pays based on the pounds of fish caught. This method helps ensure that the owner is compensated for the fish removed from the pond. The per pound rate depends on the kind of fish, the rate needed for profit, and the level the fishing public will pay. Rates range from $0.50 to $1.50 or more per pound.

Some weight-of-catch operations provide dressing services for the fish caught. A per pound dressing fee of 25 to 50 cents is charged, based on the weight of the fish before dressing. Equipment and an attendant to dress the fish must be supplied. With this method, someone must always be on duty to weigh the fish and provide services.

19–6. Weighing a catch of trout. (The fish are in a plastic bag.)

Combination Fee. Some fee-lakes charge a combination fee. It involves both a daily fee and a weight-of-catch fee. Customers are charged for both the opportunity to fish and the pounds of fish they catch. This is probably the most common method. Someone must be present at all times to collect fees, weigh fish, and assist in other ways.

Types of Fee Facilities

Put-and-Take Ponds. A *put-and-take pond* is a fee facility stocked with catchable-size fish grown elsewhere. The stock of fish is kept replenished. The operator of the put-and-take facility buys the fish for stocking from a live hauler or a fish farmer. In some cases, the owner of a put-and-take may have production ponds located elsewhere to provide the needed stock. The stocking density is heavy because the owner wants the fishing public to make good catches.

19–7. A fish stocking truck is being loaded with fish for restocking ponds and streams. (Courtesy, U.S. Fish and Wildlife Service)

Only quality, disease-free fish should be stocked in a put-and-take facility. The presence of sick and dead fish has a negative effect on the public. Careful water management is needed at high-stocking densities. Put-and-take facilities typically involve charging the public on a weight-of-catch or combination basis.

Put-and-take operations frequently use ponds, but they may also use large tanks, raceways, or other facilities. Sometimes large, transportable tanks are moved to shopping malls or other locations. Careful and constant attention is needed in the operation of a put-and-take facility.

Catch-Out Ponds. A *catch-out pond* is a fee facility where the fish are raised in the pond where they are to be caught. The amount of fee fishing that can occur is no greater than the amount of fish that will grow in the pond. The stocking rate, feeding, aeration, and other production factors influence the volume of fish produced.

Catch-out ponds are not very popular because the fish supply may be depleted and returns to the owner may be less than with put-and-take ponds. Sport fishers like to go to fee-lakes where they can expect to make good catches. Catch-out ponds may not always provide enough fish for this to occur.

BAIT-AND-TACKLE STORES

The fishing public must have certain equipment and supplies. These items may be available on site as part of the fee-lake operation, or they may be available at a separately established business near the recreational lake.

A *bait-and-tackle store* is a retail business that specializes in meeting the equipment and supplies needs of sport fishers. The operation of a bait-and-tackle store is much

19–8. Bait-and-tackle stores near fee-lakes fill important sport fishing needs. (Courtesy, National Oceanic & Atmospheric Administration)

like the operation of any retail store. Convenience, good prices, quality merchandise, courteous employees, and good management are essential. The business must be conveniently located and properly advertised.

Bait-and-tackle stores typically handle a wide range of fishing gear and baits. The items stocked should be appropriate for the fish in the area. The interests of the fishing public must be considered.

Bait-and-tackle stores may offer services to the fishing public. Selling licenses to individuals that permit them to fish in public streams and lakes is frequently a part of the business. In most cases, licenses are not needed to fish in fee-lakes. The stores may also offer other services, such as dressing the catch and preparing it for shipping.

Besides selling items for fishing, bait-and-tackle stores often sell food, fuel, books and magazines, clothing, and camping supplies. A few also have restaurant services. In areas with considerable sport fishing, lodging accommodations may be available near bait-and-tackle stores.

The people who work in bait-and-tackle stores must be qualified to assist sport fishers with their needs. They must be able to offer advice on where the fish are biting and how to catch them. Good assistance in selecting appropriate equipment can result in more sales to satisfied customers.

BOAT AND ACCESSORY STORES

Boat and accessory stores provide boats and related items to the public. These stores typically sell boats, trailers, and other types of recreational equipment and supplies. In some cases, the stores may also rent equipment on an hourly, daily, or weekly basis. Storage space

19–9. Boat and accessory stores handle a wide range of equipment for sport fishing. (Courtesy, National Oceanic & Atmospheric Administration)

may be available for rent to owners of boats and other recreational equipment. Repair services for engines may also be provided.

Many fee-lakes do not allow fishing boats. Boat and accessory stores are often located near large public lakes, streams, or seashores. Considerable investment may be needed to establish and operate such businesses. Qualified employees are very important.

TOUR GUIDE SERVICES

The fishing public often needs assistance in knowing where and how to fish. In some cases, charter boat services take people where they can fish. Although few fee-lakes have tour guide services, the employees must be able to provide advice to the fishing public.

Tour guide services may help groups or individuals gain access to good fishing in remote areas of streams and lakes. Guides may provide only information, or they may also provide the complete equipment and supplies needed to fish. The fee is often on a daily or weekly basis.

Charter boat services are usually offered for fishing in oceans, large lakes, and other large bodies of water. A boat operator may take one individual or a small group out for a few hours or for a day or more of fishing. Tackle, bait, and other supplies are provided

19–10. Several sport fishing and site-seeing charter boat services are available from this small port in Lahina, Maui.

by the boat operator. Fees vary considerably, depending on the services and length of time involved. Charter boat services may also be offered for fish watching, such as the whale-watching excursions off the coasts of Hawaii and the western states.

HOW TO ESTABLISH A RECREATIONAL AQUABUSINESS

Establishing a successful recreational aquabusiness will require attention to a number of factors. Some major considerations in establishing a recreational aquabusiness are

- Determining the kind of recreational aquabusiness—Determining the best kind of aquabusiness to establish will involve studying the kind of recreational aquaculture available in the area and the demand for it by the public. A fee-lake must have customers to be successful. Enough people interested in recreational aquaculture must be in the area to provide sufficient business. Certainly, climate and its possibilities with various aquacrops is a consideration.

- Determining the site for a recreational aquabusiness—A good site is one that will attract enough customers to make the aquabusiness profitable. A location easily accessed from highways and near centers of population holds the best potential. The site should also have the natural advantages of good terrain and should have access to public utilities, such as electricity. The location must comply with zoning regulations. The site must be available at an affordable price. Paying too much for the land can result in a debt that will be too large for the operation.

19–11. Setting a crab trap in the Gulf of Mexico is refreshing recreation.

- Determining the development needed for the site—Ponds, buildings, water wells, parking areas and driveways, fences, and other construction may be needed to prepare a site for a recreational aquabusiness. Of course, the facilities should be constructed according to the intended use of the property. Cost estimates must be a part of assessing needed site work.

- Developing a facility plan—A *facility plan* describes how the site is to be prepared for the recreational aquabusiness. It includes how the earth is to be excavated, what buildings will be needed, where access roads and parking areas will be built,

19–12. Collaborating with state agencies can help build a recreational aquabusiness. (This shows a mobile urban fishing facility operated by the Illinois Department of Natural Resources.) (Courtesy, Vernie Thomas, Danville, IL)

where ponds will be located, and other features. Ponds are typically small, ranging from one acre or less to a few acres. The design of a pond should provide a maximum of bank or land area for the fisher to access the pond. A small building with a weighing area, supplies area, dressing area, restrooms, concessions, and public telephone is often constructed. Sometimes, a small office may be included. Scales, cleaning equipment, a cash register, an ice machine, soft-drink and snack concessions, and any other supplies and equipment deemed necessary should be readily available. A first-aid kit and a fire extinguisher are essential.

19–13. A few public fishing facilities have boat ramps to attract sport fishers. (Courtesy, National Oceanic & Atmospheric Administration)

- Preparing a written business plan—A written plan requires attention to details that might be overlooked when no such plan is prepared. The written **business plan** is a document that contains short-range, intermediate-range, and long-range plans for the business. Short-range plans focus on what can be done in the near future to ready the site. Intermediate plans focus on one to five years, while long-range plans are typically for more than five years. Good plans include estimates of costs and returns. A detailed site preparation plan should be prepared. Assistance from the agencies of the U.S. Department of Agriculture may be needed.

- Obtaining the needed finances—Adequate money to support the establishment and initial operation of the recreational aquabusiness must be secured. Risks are involved. Lending agencies need some assurance that the business will be operated profitably so that loans can be repaid.

19–14. Providing a place for sport fishers to display their catch for photography is good promotion.

OPERATING A RECREATIONAL AQUABUSINESS

Daily management is needed once a recreational aquabusiness has been established. This is to assure that the business is operated efficiently. Some management duties related to a successful recreational aquabusiness are

- Having good on-site management—The owner, or someone designated by the owner, must be available to manage the recreational aquabusiness. The manager is responsible for seeing that things get done efficiently and effectively. Attention to day-to-day details is a must.

- Handling income and disbursements—A way to handle income and the payment of charges must be established. Fees charged to customers must be properly accounted for and deposited in the bank account. Employees must be paid. Utilities, supplies for resale, fish for the pond, and other items must be paid for in a timely manner. Careful and accurate records must be kept.

- Having dependable employees—A fee-lake operation typically has only a few employees. In this small business, employees must be qualified to do their work. Often, the owner is also the manager, who may rely on family members to help out. All employees must relate well to the public, be able to offer assistance to those who fish, and responsibly handle the details. Larger aquabusinesses dealing with boats, equipment, and other areas may need a wide range of qualified employees. Some fee-lakes are open only during certain hours or on certain days of the week. When they are open, personnel must be on duty to run the operations.

- Advertising—Advertising is used to get customers to the fee-lake. The public must be informed about a business if the business is to be patronized. Advertisements in local newspapers or on local radio stations may be helpful. An attractive sign identifying the aquabusiness will help the public in locating the business. A recreational aquabusiness may use the Internet to promote its services. A Web site may be established. The site may describe the species of fish, identify the location of the fee-lake, and explain the services available. Reservations for day and time of fishing may be taken through the Web site. One of the best forms of advertising is by word of mouth. Individuals who have patronized a recreational aquabusiness tell others about their experiences. Good experiences result in positive comments about the aquabusiness; bad experiences result in negative comments about the aquabusiness.

- Maintaining the facilities—Once constructed, facilities must be kept in good condition. Dilapidated facilities are not attractive to the public. The grounds must

19–15. Good signs promote fee-lakes and help attract customers. (Four different signs are shown here. Which one do you like best? Why?)

19–16. Besides a regular pond, this operation has a bonus pond. This is where tagged fish or trophy-size fish are kept.

be kept clean and free of trash, such as cans, bottles, and paper. Buildings will need to be painted and kept presentable. Pond dams must be covered with sod and appropriately mowed. Erosion to dams or other areas must be controlled. Broken equipment or discarded fishing tackle should be removed. Trash cans should be conveniently located. Safety and health hazards must be removed.

- Keeping records—As with any business, good records must be kept. These include records of income and expenses. Computer systems are available to help. The records must be analyzed regularly to determine the profit status of the operation. Some aquabusinesses use the services of accountants to assist in keeping records.

- Submitting reports—Regular reports must be sent to various federal, state, and local agencies. These pertain to taxes, employee benefits, and other requirements. Most of these are due at the same time each year. A routine schedule of preparing and submitting reports can be established and followed. As with record keeping, accountants may be engaged to help with reports.

LEGAL AND RISK SITUATIONS IN RECREATIONAL AQUACULTURE

When setting up and operating a recreational aquabusiness, appropriate regulations must be observed. Ways of protecting against liability are needed.

GOVERNMENT REGULATIONS

Laws have been enacted to protect the consumer and the environment. The operator of a recreational aquabusiness needs to be aware of legal requirements and comply with them.

Obtaining permits to operate a recreational aquabusiness is a time-consuming, but important, activity. Major changes in the natural water reservoirs require permits from the

U.S. Army Corps of Engineers and the U.S. Environmental Protection Agency. Permits may be required from state agencies responsible for wildlife conservation, particularly if exotic species of fish, such as tilapia, are to be stocked. Permits to drill water wells and to dispose of water may be needed.

From a retail business standpoint, licenses may be required for operating the aquabusiness. For example, some fee-lakes have soft-drink and snack vending machines, which must have licenses or decals attached, indicating that fees have been paid to operate them.

LIABILITY

A recreational aquabusiness should provide a safe, comfortable environment for customers. The owner may be held responsible for accidents or losses that occur to customers. Posting warning signs about dangers is helpful but is inadequate by itself. Facilities should be kept free of hazards.

Legal action may be taken by individuals who have suffered injury. This involves their going to court to try to prove that the aquabusiness owner was negligent. Not correcting dangers that are obvious may be sufficient grounds for negligence. So may failure to provide safety equipment, such as life preservers and rescue equipment.

Some fee-lake operators try to protect themselves by carrying liability insurance. Such insurance can be expensive and can cut into the profit of a business. Regardless, having some insurance coverage is a good idea. A fish producer is often able to get general liability

CONNECTION

POPULAR FEE-LAKES

People go to a fee-lake to have fun. They want to catch fish and relax. You see more people at some fee-lakes than at others. Here are a few reasons:

- Fish are plentiful.
- Fees are reasonable.
- Location is convenient.
- Surroundings are clean.
- Suitable safety practices are enforced.
- Fee-lake operators are courteous.
- Parking areas are nearby.
- Grass is neatly-mowed.
- Restrooms, water, and other facilities are provided.

This photo shows a fee-lake that meets all these criteria. (Photo courtesy, James Tidwell, Kentucky State University)

coverage for an entire farm. Local agricultural organizations can often provide fee-lake operators with lists of sources of liability insurance.

SAFETY FEATURES

The owners of recreational aquabusinesses must follow practices that help to make their facilities safer. A few safety suggestions are listed here.

1. *Put up warning signs near places of danger.* These should state that individuals use the facilities at their own risk. Install signs reminding adults that children should be supervised.

2. *Post a notice that gives emergency telephone numbers.* The numbers of emergency officials, as well as a telephone, should be readily available. A public telephone is an added convenience of a fee-lake operation.

3. *Provide life-saving equipment near water areas.* A life ring with a 100-foot rope is probably sufficient.

4. *Do not allow swimming in the same area as fee fishing.* If swimming is allowed, it should be in a separate area. A lifeguard may be needed.

5. *Fence ponds to keep out children, animals, and unauthorized persons.* Fencing also keeps individuals from trespassing and from not paying the fees.

6. *Keep all boats and other equipment in safe operating condition.* Most fee-lakes do not permit boats. A few, however, will rent boats. Only those boats that are in good condition should be available for rent.

19–17. Tethered ring buoys may be placed on the banks of fee-lakes.

7. *Allow only trained employees to operate equipment.* 3Fee-lakes that have fish-cleaning equipment should provide personnel to operate the equipment. Most customers would have little training in how to use it. The customers would likely damage the equipment and possibly injure themselves. They might waste their catch or damage its suitability.

8. *Train employees in emergency procedures.* Local hospitals often have training courses to prepare people for emergencies.

SOURCES OF INFORMATION

The area of legal regulations and liability often involves locally specific laws and regulations. Individuals are advised to get in touch with specialists of their Cooperative Extension Service for assistance. Local chambers of commerce, economic development officials, and others involved with recreational aquaculture are also good potential sources of information.

KEEPING CUSTOMERS HAPPY

Success in recreational aquaculture requires customers. First, customers must be attracted to a fee-lake facility. Second, customers must have a good experience if they are to return.

Treating customers with respect and providing the information they need can go a long way toward building a successful recreational aquabusiness. Besides being friendly and considerate, workers should offer assistance that will help customers in catching the fish. When the customers have a good time, they are more likely to repeat their visits.

KEEPING THINGS CONVENIENT

Providing for the convenience and comfort of customers is important. Locating parking, concessions, and weighing areas near the ponds helps people get more enjoyment from their outing. Providing picnic tables, chairs, and other conveniences is beneficial. Customers are more likely to return if they enjoyed themselves, and they will tell others!

Some fee-lake operations have vending areas for soft drinks and snacks. These should be kept attractive and clean. Only fresh, wholesome products should be sold. Such services can add to income.

19–18. A covered picnic table is provided at this trout fee-lake in Virginia.

KEEPING THE PLACE ATTRACTIVE

Recreational customers like to visit clean, attractive places. Owners are reminded that a few simple practices can enhance attractiveness.

- Fish weighing and cleaning areas should be kept clean. Keep down bad odors and properly dispose of wastes.
- Flies, ants, and other insect pests should be controlled, as should dogs and cats.
- Scales should be accurate.
- Weeds should be kept mowed.
- Fences should be maintained.

19–19. Fee-lake operators may help customers with taxidermy services for trophy-size fish. (This white bass has been used in an office as decoration.)

ASSISTING CUSTOMERS

Fee-lakes often have customers who know very little about fishing. *Customer assistance* is helping customers select tackle and bait, use fishing techniques that will lead to good catches, and handle the live fish in ways that prevent injury. Some fee-lakes maintain small supplies of bait and equipment for sale. Many customers need instruction in how to prepare the tackle, bait the hook, remove the fish from the hook, place the fish on a stringer, and prepare the fish for cooking. Where and how to fish are frequent areas of concern.

Happy customers help to build a successful recreational aquabusiness.

EQUIPMENT AND SUPPLIES

Fishing equipment and supplies are needed to assure a good catch. Operators of fee-lakes may have some equipment and supplies available and must be able to advise customers on how to use equipment, bait hooks, and handle fish. What customers want varies. One may enjoy a simple pole, line, hook, and bait. Another may want an elaborate rod with expensive artificial bait.

Usually, a fee-lake provides a basic pole or rod and reel and bait. A net, dressing facilities, and ice are typically included with the fee. Coolers for transporting iced fish may be for sale. A few fee-lakes do not allow fishers to bring their own equipment.

Some fundamental equipment and supplies are discussed here.

FISHING TACKLE

Fishing tackle is the equipment used when sport fishing. It includes a variety of devices for attracting fish, getting the fish to bite or attack a baited hook, and landing the fish from the water after it bites. It may also include items to keep the fish fresh until it is dressed and even afterward.

19–20. This fee-lake provides a rod and reel, bait, and a net for capturing fish.

The simplest tackle is a *line* (string) attached to a pole on one end and with a hook attached to the other. Lines may be monofilament or braided nylon, dacron, or silk. Lines are sized based on diameter of the string and weight of the material they are designed to lift, known as test weight. A line should be about the same length as the pole. A line longer than the pole is hard to use and get the hook placed out in the water.

Cane poles are the most common types of poles, though metal and glass poles are used. A *cane pole* is a fishing pole made of the hollow, flexible, jointed stem of bamboo or another reed plant. Poles range from 7 to 15 feet long.

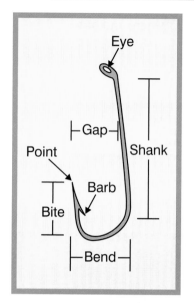

19–21. Parts of a hook.

A small float is attached to the line. A *float* is a small piece of cork, plastic, or other material lighter than water used to let the fisher see movement of the fishing line. The float is usually attached so it can be moved up and down the line to hold the hook at the desired depth below the water surface. A *sinker*, or small weight, may be on the line near the hook. Some sort of bait or attractant is used on the hook.

A *fishing hook* is a curved piece of metal for holding bait and for sticking into and holding fish. The hook may have a barb that securely holds a fish that takes the baited hook into its mouth. Up-and-down or sideways movement of the float on the water is evidence of a bite—a fish is taking, or has taken, the baited hook. The pole is sharply moved upward to "set" the hook, and the line lifted from the water to remove the fish.

Hooks vary in size and design. Most are single hooks, though some are double and treble. The kind of hook needed depends on the species and size of the fish. Hooks are made of various metal wire materials that have been shaped for the best success in fishing. The better hooks cost a little more because they may be coated to prevent rust.

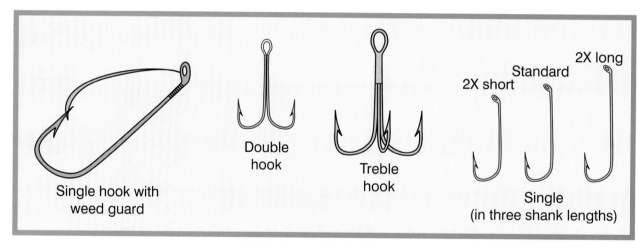

19–22. Common kinds of hooks.

Hooks are sized by number and length of shank. Two numbering systems are used, though the systems merge. Sizes range from 32 to 13/0 or larger. Generally, the smaller hooks and lighter lines and rods are used with freshwater fish, because they are intended to catch smaller fish. Small hooks are sized with larger numbers. Numbers for large hooks are given as numerators. Larger hooks have larger numerators. Table 19–1 shows common hook sizes and the species they are used to catch.

Table 19–1. Common Hook Sizes

Hook Size (No.)	Length (In.)	Species of Fish	
		Freshwater	Saltwater
Small Hooks			
14	$^{11}/_{32}$		
12	$^{7}/_{16}$	Sunfish	
10	$^{9}/_{19}$	Bluegill	
8	$^{11}/_{16}$	Crappie	Smelt
6	$^{13}/_{16}$	Trout	Snapper
4	$^{15}/_{16}$	Perch	Kelp bass
Medium Hooks			
2	$1^{1}/_{8}$	Bullhead	
1	$1^{1}/_{4}$	Bullhead	
$1^{1}/_{2}$	$1^{3}/_{8}$	Pickerel	Pompano
1/0	$1^{1}/_{2}$	Channel catfish	Flounder
2/0	$1^{5}/_{8}$	Walleye	Croaker
3/0	$1^{3}/_{4}$	Walleye	Croaker
4/0	$1^{7}/_{8}$	Bass	Bluefish
5/0	2	Pike	Striped bass
6/0	$2^{1}/_{4}$	Muskie	Channel bass
Large Hooks**			
7/0	$2^{1}/_{2}$		Barracuda
8/0	$2^{3}/_{4}$		Tarpon
10/0	$3^{1}/_{4}$		Marlin
12/0	$3^{3}/_{4}$		Tuna

*Round hooks with standard-length shanks. Shanks vary in length from short to long.

**Large hooks are primarily used in deep-sea fishing.

Some sport fishers use more expensive poles or rods. Many rods are made of graphite and have been carefully manufactured to withstand force in landing fish. Rods may be in various lengths, but 6 feet is most common. A reel is often attached to a rod near the rod handle. A reel has a winding of several feet of line that can be used to reach a distance out into the water. Some reels may have 100 or more yards of thin monofilament line. Skills in casting or fly fishing are needed to make the most efficient use of reels.

Both expensive equipment and economical equipment rely on similar hook designs. As mentioned, a hook usually has a barb that ensures that the hook is "set" and does not come loose from the fish. The hook may also be designed with a weed guard to keep the hook from getting caught in vegetation in the water. A hook must be securely tied to the line. Several kinds of knots are used, with the improved clinch knot being popular.

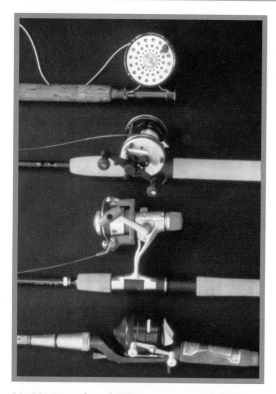

19–23. Examples of different types of fishing reels are shown here (from the top): fly reel, bait-casting reel, open-face spinning reel, and closed-face spinning reel. (Courtesy, Charles Stutzenbaker, Port Arthur, TX)

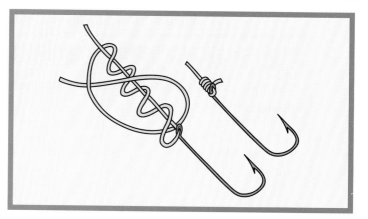

19–24. Attaching a hook to a line requires the ability to tie a knot that will hold. This shows an improved clinch knot.

Tackle includes tools and equipment to make fishing comfortable. Examples are cord or chain stringers, creels, live bags, bait containers, tackle boxes, pliers, dressing knives and other cleaning equipment, insect repellant, and safety equipment.

BAIT AND LURES

Bait is live or dead material put on a hook to entice fish to bite. Bait may be natural or artificial. Natural bait is used more often to catch fish than is artificial bait. Artificial baits are also known as lures.

19–25. Roe (fish egg mass) may be used as bait. This shows trout roe from fish caught at a fee-lake being used as bait to catch trout. The roe is cut into $\frac{1}{2}$- to $\frac{3}{4}$-inch pieces and placed on a hook.

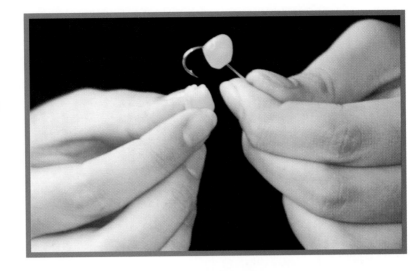

19–26. Whole kernels of corn can be used as bait in some fee-lake situations. (It may be illegal with game fish in streams and lakes.)

Bait is a material that is attractive to the fish being sought. The nature of bait varies with the species of fish. Worms, minnows, and crickets may be used for bass and other sunfish. Chicken livers and stink-bait may be used for catfish. Salmon eggs, small pieces of fish, and frozen squid, shrimp, or crawfish are sometimes used as bait. With some fish, cut-up pieces of wiener are all that they need to bite. The most common live bait is minnows. They are widely used because they are the principal natural food of many fish.

A *lure* is an artificial bait pulled through the water with the notion that the fish will mistake it for something to eat. The fish will strike the lure, which has one or more hooks on or around it. Lures are made of wood, metal, feathers, or plastic. Various kinds of lures are used, with flies, spoons, spinners, plugs, and jigs being common. Lures are typically used with rods and reels and cast a distance out into the water. Some lures stay near

19–27. Worms are common fish bait. (Courtesy, Buford Bait Company, Georgia)

19–28. Manufactured bait may be used with some fish. This bait is especially for trout fishing. A small ball is formed and placed on the hook.

or on the surface; other lures sink into the water. Lures are selected for their particular appeal to certain species of fish. Some have moving parts to give added appeal in attracting a striking fish.

19–29. How to attach bait securely to the hook.

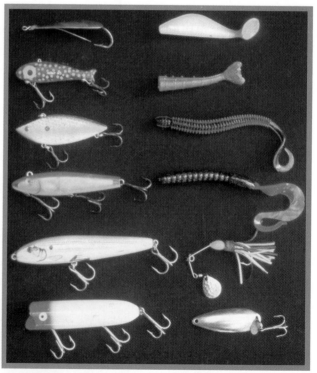

19–30. Different types of lures are used to entice fish to strike and bite. (Courtesy, Charles Stutzenbaker, Port Arthur, TX)

AGRITOURISM

Recreational aquaculture is part of the larger area of agritourism. *Agritourism* is tourism that attracts tourists and vacationers to a commercial venture on a farm for enjoyment, education, active involvement, and relaxation. The owner charges them to stay and provides activities for their entertainment.

ACTIVITIES

Agritourism can involve a number of activities. Various approaches can be used with aquaculture to create interest. A few activities and other aspects related to aquaculture enterprises are

- Fee fishing in ponds or streams
- Guided fishing in natural streams
- Competitive fishing, such as catching tagged fish, the largest fish, or albino fish
- Camping and picnicking
- Bed and breakfast lodging
- Hiking and guided walks
- Horseback riding
- Birding (bird watching)
- Roadside stands and U-pick operations

The kinds of activities provided depend on interests and the facilities available. Some activities add new dimensions to an aquaculture fee-lake enterprise.

ESTABLISHING AND MANAGING

Agritourism on a fish farm is a business venture. It should create income for the owner. It will also bring about the need for additional planning and management.

Before establishing an agritourism enterprise, make a careful assessment of the demand for such a venture. A good location is needed. The environment of the facility must be appealing. Accommodations must be provided to make guests comfortable and safe.

The basic management considerations are similar to those for establishing a fee-lake operation. The bottom line is whether the venture will produce a profit. If it will not, seek alternatives to agritourism.

REVIEWING

MAIN IDEAS

Recreational aquaculture has much potential in some locations. Careful planning and management are essential for a successful fee-lake.

Fee-lakes are of two main kinds: put-and-take and catch-out. With put-and-take, the fish are raised elsewhere and moved to the facilities where they are caught. With catch-out, the fish are raised in the facilities where they are caught. Fees may be assessed on a daily, seasonal, weight-of-catch, or combination basis.

Careful planning and operation are essential. Customer convenience and safety are of high importance. Some conveniences, such as soft-drink vending machines, can increase profits.

Convenience, comfort, good catches, fair fees, courteous treatment of customers, and pleasant surroundings all go into making a successful fee-lake operation.

Fishing supplies and equipment will be needed. Hooks, rods and reels, bait, nets, and a few other basic items may be provided by the fee-lake. The operator should be able to advise and assist customers in having an enjoyable fishing experience.

Fee fishing is a part of the broader area of agritourism. Agritourism can provide additional income from a fee-lake operation, but it will also require additional investment in equipment, facilities, and management.

QUESTIONS

Answer the following questions, using complete sentences and correct spelling.

1. Why are customers important to a recreational aquaculture business?
2. What are some business opportunities in recreational aquaculture?
3. How are fees assessed in fee-lakes?
4. Distinguish between a catch-out pond and a put-and-take facility.
5. What factors should be considered in the establishment of a recreational aquaculture business?
6. What are the important considerations in the operation of a recreational aquabusiness?
7. What legal and risk situations must be addressed in a recreational aquabusiness?
8. List and briefly explain several safety practices that might be implemented at a fee-lake.
9. What are three areas that are important in keeping customers happy? Why are these important?
10. What is fishing tackle? What are the common kinds of tackle?
11. What is bait? What kinds of bait are used?
12. What is an agritourism enterprise?

EVALUATING

Match the term with the correct definition. Write the letter of the term on the line provided.

a. agritourism
b. season fee
c. business plan
d. weight-of-catch fee

e. put-and-take pond
f. daily fee
g. catch-out pond
h. bait-and-tackle store

i. lure
j. facility plan

_____1. A fee charged for fishing for one day without regard to catch

_____2. Tourism that attracts tourists and vacationers to a commercial venture on a farm

_____3. A fee charged based on the weight of the fish caught

_____4. A retail store that specializes in supplies for sport fishing

_____5. A type of fee-lake where the fish are raised elsewhere and hauled in

_____6. A fee charged to a customer to fish for a season in a lake

_____7. A type of fee-lake where the fish are raised in the facility

_____8. A document that contains short-range, intermediate-range, and long-range plans for a business

_____9. A plan that describes how a site is to be prepared for a recreational aquabusiness

_____10. Artificial bait

EXPLORING

1. Visit a fee-lake. Interview the manager to determine the way fees are assessed, the source of the fish, and the services provided to customers. Prepare a report on your observations.

2. Plan a hypothetical fee-lake in your community. Select a site and choose the type of water facility, the species and source of fish, and the services to be provided. Examine other details, such as local laws. Prepare a written report on your proposal.

3. Go fishing at a fee-lake. Use fishing tackle, bait, and other items appropriate to the species in the lake. Clean and cook your catch. Prepare a report on your experiences.

CHAPTER 20

Career Success in Aquaculture

This chapter focuses on understanding the nature and types of aquaculture careers. It has the following objectives:

1 Describe the career decision-making process

2 Identify characteristics of good employees

3 Name types of aquaculture careers

4 Describe the nature of the work in selected aquaculture careers and discuss the education required

5 Describe career ladders in aquaculture

6 Select an appropriate career in aquaculture

TERMS

career
career ladder
driver
employee
employer

general worker
large-equipment operator
manager
owner
salesperson

service technician
supervised experience
supervisor

20–1. A molecular biologist and an aquaculture scientist collect samples of tissue for use in developing a genetic map of rainbow trout. (Courtesy, Agricultural Research Service, USDA)

AQUACULTURE offers many career opportunities. Careers are in production, management, research, sales, supplies and services, education, and other areas. The work varies widely. It may involve much hands-on outdoor activity or be mostly indoors with the emphasis on thinking and making management decisions. Occupations in aquaculture often include both indoor and outdoor work.

The nature of work in aquaculture is changing. New types of occupations are emerging. Yet, traditional contact with water and living species continues as the major emphasis. Success depends on being productive. This applies equally to working for another person and to running an aquabusiness of your own.

No doubt, there is a career for you. Explore and gain experiences so that you can make good choices. Achievement in school classes, attendance at field days, and participation in other activities will help you enter an aquaculture occupation and be successful in it.

MAKING CAREER DECISIONS IN AQUACULTURE

The choice of a career should not be taken lightly. A *career* is the general direction of a person's life as related to work. The career a person chooses will affect his or her lifestyle, friends, amount of money earned, and status in the community. A good career choice should take into account personal interests, the stability of the work, the likely places of employment, the education required, and many other factors.

One of the best ways to begin choosing a career is to talk to people who work in an area of your tentative interest. Find out if they like what they do for a living. Ask about both the advantages and the disadvantages of their jobs. Find out if you can work part time to see if you are really interested. You may want to shadow the workers for a few days. (Shadowing involves going with a person to work and observing what he or she does on the job.)

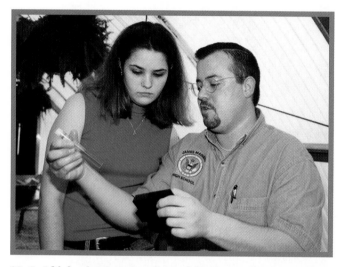

20–2. A high school student is receiving instruction in properly testing water. Learning skills early gets a person off to a good start.

Another important step is to talk to people who know you and your abilities. Your agriculture teacher should be able to answer many of your questions. Your school guidance counselor can also help. Ask about the schools where you can get the necessary education for the career in which you are interested. Also ask about the admission requirements and how to get admitted. The counselor can help you match your abilities with a career and the education required to be successful in that career.

As with any major decision, your parents should be consulted for advice and encouragement about the career you choose. They may be able to finance the necessary education or help you find a way to finance it. They may also provide land and other capital for you to start your own aquafarm. You may need their support to be successful!

Once you have chosen a general area, seek experience with the different aspects of aquaculture. Working within the different areas of aquaculture will help you decide what you like and do not like about different jobs. Developing a supervised experience (SE) program in aquaculture will help you to make wise career decisions. More experience may be

20–3. Talking with your school counselor can help you in making career decisions.

required, however. You may obtain this experience by working full time during the summer months when you are not in school or by working for someone else while you save money and gain experience to start your own aquafarm or aquabusiness.

An excellent way to become an entrepreneur (someone who owns his or her own business) is by observing problems faced while you are gaining experience. You may find that a needed service is lacking in your area. If so, that may open the door for you to start a business by providing that service. Many small-business loans and entrepreneurship training programs are available for those interested in providing a useful service to an industry. Check with your local chamber of commerce for details if you have an idea and need help getting started.

A career decision is one of the most important decisions you will ever make. Many questions must be answered before the decision can be made. Select an area of study with some flexibility. Develop skills in communications and human relations. A good career decision sometimes comes after finding out what you do *not* want to spend your life doing.

20–4. Learning how to conduct laboratory tests develops job skills needed in some areas of aquaculture.

CHARACTERISTICS OF GOOD EMPLOYEES

Regardless of the type of work performed, good employees have several characteristics in common. An **employee** is an individual who works for another person, a business, or an agency. An **employer** is a person, a business, or an agency that hires other people in order to achieve particular goals through their efforts.

Hiring a person is an important task. Employers want productive employees who exhibit a wide range of desired characteristics. It usually doesn't take long to find out whether an employee possesses or lacks these characteristics. Some of those things an employer will look for in a good employee are discussed below. You will want to develop these characteristics.

20–5. Developing the ability to get along with people is a part of social skills.

ABILITY TO GET ALONG WELL WITH OTHERS

Good employees have positive attitudes about their work and the people they work with. They show respect and concern for others. A kind word will go a long way with co-workers. Remember that you rely on others and that they rely on you to get the job done. Not getting along with others is one way to lose a job. Show some understanding, be friendly, help others when possible, and try to be flexible about work schedules and sharing of tasks.

APPROPRIATE KNOWLEDGE AND SKILLS

Try to prepare yourself for your job as well as possible. Know the extent of your abilities. Do not expect to know everything from the beginning, however. Employers would much rather take a little time to explain a task properly than to spend much time making up for mistakes that result from lack of knowledge or skill. Good employees may not have all the necessary skills, but they will try to learn quickly and thoroughly. Do not be afraid to ask questions!

20–6. Completing the needed education is a big step in the right direction.

MOTIVATION

Good employees motivate themselves to come to work on time, to work enthusiastically, and to perform tasks as well as they can. They focus on the pleasurable aspects of their jobs and do not complain about the not-so-pleasurable parts. Encourage others, and they will share the enthusiasm.

20–7. Motivation to do the job right is important. (This aquafarm worker is checking DO in a pond.)

DEDICATION

Work hard to do each task as well as possible. This benefits the employer and may lead to promotions and raises. Employers appreciate employees who contribute to the profitability of the operations. This dedication makes the employers look good, and they, in turn, will provide rewards when possible.

20–8. Follow safe practices in doing work. Here, safety glasses are worn while using a bandsaw to cut PVC for a tank system.

SAFETY CONSCIOUSNESS

Many occupations in aquaculture involve equipment, facilities, and tasks that can be dangerous if an employee is careless. Injuries due to carelessness not only harm the person involved, but they also slow down operations and cost money. Employees whose carelessness puts them and their co-workers in danger cannot be tolerated.

HONESTY

An employee must be trustworthy. Dishonesty will get an employee fired very quickly. Each time an employee is assigned a task or left in charge of an operation, the employer must be able to trust that the employee will get the job done and will be honest about the work.

In many cases, employees are trusted with money or checks to pay for goods. They may be asked to handle sales transactions in the absence of the employer. They are also trusted with the health of an aquacrop and with the operation of expensive equipment. The employer expects this trust will be rewarded with honest, responsible behavior.

20–9. The ability to work together is important to success. This shows researchers investigating the genetic structure of paddlefish.

FREEDOM FROM SUBSTANCE ABUSE

Good employees are always free of substances that impair their judgment and their ability to think clearly and work. Likewise, a good employer never shows up for work under the influence of drugs or alcohol. Substance abuse by either an employee or the employer could endanger others at the work site.

Employees are expected to get plenty of rest before coming to work and to refrain from using drugs or alcohol beforehand. Employers expect workers to maintain certain standards of behavior outside work hours as well as on the job. Alcoholism and drug abuse, along with their side effects, are common causes of dismissal.

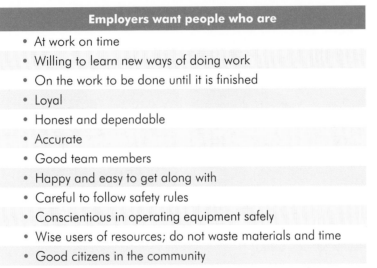

Table 20-1. General Employer Expectations

Employers want people who are
• At work on time
• Willing to learn new ways of doing work
• On the work to be done until it is finished
• Loyal
• Honest and dependable
• Accurate
• Good team members
• Happy and easy to get along with
• Careful to follow safety rules
• Conscientious in operating equipment safely
• Wise users of resources; do not waste materials and time
• Good citizens in the community
• Careful to lead lives that promote health and well-being

TYPES OF AQUACULTURE CAREERS

The most common type of career in aquaculture involves working on an aquafarm as the owner, the manager, or a general worker. Several types of careers may be found in other areas of aquaculture or in the many service and support industries related to aquaculture. The occupations vary greatly in the amount of physical labor involved, the education required to perform the work, and the amount of responsibility of the worker.

A common occupation in aquaculture is that of a *general worker*. This worker is expected to handle a wide variety of tasks rather than specializing in a specific type of job. The occupation may be at an animal aquafarm, such as a catfish farm or trout farm. It may be at a plant aquafarm. Fish hatcheries, processing plants, and aquabusinesses also employ general workers.

20–10. A fish biologist is examining a market-size sunshine bass. (Courtesy, Agricultural Research Service, USDA)

20–11. A processing plant manager is involved in all areas of providing a quality food product.

Supervisors may be employed on large aquafarms or at aquabusinesses. A *supervisor* is an individual who oversees, directs, and evaluates the work of employees. Plants that add value to aquacrops through further processing often have several supervisors. Also, large farms may have night supervisors responsible for crews that check water for dissolved oxygen and that prevent poaching.

Many aquafarms are run by their owners. An *owner*, of course, is the person who owns the business. Some aquafarms employ managers. A *manager* is an individual who is in charge of the everyday operations of a business. Often on an aquafarm, the owner wears several hats, including that of supervisor and manager, as well as general worker. Owners sometimes work off their farms and employ managers.

Service technicians are needed in several kinds of businesses that provide goods and services to aquafarmers. A *service technician* is a skilled individual who provides a variety of services in setting up, adjusting, operating, and servicing equipment and processes. Feeding equipment, tractors, water testing equipment, processing equipment, and electronic controls, just to name a few items, must be installed, serviced, and repaired to keep aquafarms in production.

Many of the businesses that support aquaculture by providing goods and services will employ salespersons. A *salesperson* is an individual who promotes products to customers, takes orders for products, and sees that products are sold efficiently and accurately. Feed, chemicals, feeding equipment, general supplies, and specialized clothing are examples of products with which a salesperson may be involved. Processing plants will also need sales staffs to move processed products to retailers. Large aquafarms may have sales staffs that sell to retailers and restaurants, while many large- and small-scale operations sell directly from the farms.

Hauling fish from location to location, transporting feed to the aquafarms, and moving processed products to market usually require trucking. Drivers must be hired for the trucks. A *driver* is an individual trained and licensed in the efficient and safe operation of trucks and other vehicles.

Many general workers at aquafarms must have the ability to handle large equipment, at least around the farms or for short distances on the road. Some aquafarms require large-equipment operators on a nearly full time basis, but operating tractors, bulldozers, and other large equipment is usually just part of the

20–12. A sales manager is explaining the high quality of these fish fillets.

work involved. A *large-equipment operator* is a person skilled in the efficient and safe operation of bulldozers, front-end loaders, and other heavy equipment. Such an operator usually has specific training in operating certain kinds of equipment.

20–13. A tractor operator uses a power feed blower to feed fish in a pond.

Researchers, educators, veterinarians, engineers, and others are also part of aquaculture. They may spend all their time doing aquaculture work or share their time with other areas. For example, a veterinarian may serve the health needs of fish as well as of other animals.

NATURE OF THE WORK AND THE EDUCATIONAL REQUIREMENTS

Most careers in aquaculture require a combination of physical labor and thinking skills. Workers at each level have to work hard physically, but they also have to make decisions regarding the health and well-being of the aquacrop. These decisions may concern water quality, nutrition, diseases, harvesting, and so on.

The majority of jobs in aquaculture are outdoors. One of the attractions of aquaculture, like many other occupations in agriculture, is the satisfaction people get from working outside with their hands and getting physically tired from their work.

At times, inclement weather makes the outdoors part of aquaculture less appealing. The goal of making a quality aquaculture product always available means that processing must occur year-round. This requires harvesting of the aquacrops during all times of the year. Wading in a pond in 4 feet of water on a cold winter day is not as pleasant as it is on a warm summer day.

As with other types of agriculture, however, the physical labor is just part of the job. Successful aquafarms require sound management. This includes keeping records, analyzing expenses, developing marketing plans, making production decisions, and engaging in other

20–14. Many aquaculture jobs are outdoors. Here workers are feeding fish in cages on Willapa Bay, Washington.

thinking-type activities that are not usually accomplished outdoors. The use of computers and consultants may reduce the time spent on these activities, but not their importance.

Some common careers in aquaculture and a description of the activities performed as part of those careers are discussed below.

AQUAFARMER

An aquafarmer may be the owner of an aquafarm or someone who is hired as the manager. While the responsibility of managers and even owners varies from farm to farm, it is assumed that the person running an aquafarm takes responsibility for all the processes that determine whether the aquafarm makes a profit. As you read about aquafarmers, remember that they are sometimes referred to as aquaculture producers.

An aquafarmer performs many tasks. Some of the more important are making sure adequate facilities for producing the aquacrop are in place and that an abundant supply of clean water is available. The aquafarmer must select a site for facilities and then plan the layout of the different facilities. He or she may also be involved in constructing facilities, such as ponds, tanks, raceways, cages, and pens. Of course, if one of the ponds or other facilities

20–15. This hatchery worker is placing spawns for proper incubation. (Courtesy, *Progressive Farmer Magazine*)

20–16. Testing water for dissolved oxygen is a routine part of aquaculture.

20–17. Harvesting may involve operating equipment, wading in water, and carefully handling large numbers of fish. (Courtesy, U.S. Department of Agriculture)

becomes damaged, the aquafarmer is responsible for repairing it or hiring someone to repair it.

Being able to secure an adequate supply of water will determine the site of a facility. The aquafarmer must determine the source of the water and the amount of water needed. He or she must also be responsible for testing the water to make sure it is suitable for the aquacrop. (Chapter 8 presents more information on water quality.)

To make sure the water is adequate, the aquafarmer may have to establish a systematic testing program to monitor dissolved oxygen and to use aerators or other means to correct oxygen problems. This program will usually be required for ponds and tanks that keep the same water for long periods. Flow-through systems and raceways that continuously bring in fresh, oxygenated water will not require constant monitoring. Other systems also have to be checked, just not as often. The water must be checked for chemical contamination, nitrates, and excessive weed growth.

As with any farm, the aquafarmer must secure adequate finances to employ general workers, purchase equipment, construct facilities, and maintain an adequate inventory of supplies and aquacrops. Appropriate stocking rates must be determined. High-quality fingerlings must be selected. The management of an

20–18. This shows a fish farmer adding feed to a demand feeder. (Courtesy, U.S. Department of Agriculture)

aquafarm will require complying with government regulations and budgeting financial resources.

With any aquacrop, nutrition is very important. To maximize profits, the aquafarmer must feed the fish or other aquacrop the right type and the right amount of feed. The aquafarmer must also select which method of feeding is best for a particular aquacrop and facility. Feeding by truck, by demand, and by hand are the common methods used.

To ensure that the aquacrop completes the growth process and makes it to a market, pests and diseases must be controlled. The aquafarmer must recognize symptoms, select treatments, calculate treatment rates, and treat fish. **It is very important to follow label directions and to use only chemicals approved by the EPA for aquaculture.** Predators, such as snakes, birds, and turtles, must also be controlled. This may involve a number of scare tactics, besides shooting, netting, and other means. Careful consideration must be given to predators on the endangered species list or otherwise protected by state and federal laws.

GENERAL WORKER

The general worker on an aquafarm will often be engaged in the same tasks as the aquafarmer. He or she will often be more involved in the hands-on work on the aquafarm. For example, the general worker will have the responsibility of actually feeding the aquacrop, operating feeding equipment, and checking the aquacrop for behaviors that might signal disease or injury.

The general worker will often be directly involved in the harvesting of fish or other aquacrops. This involvement may include setting the seine, making sure the seine stays on the bottom of the pond or other facility, and removing undesirable species from the species collected. The general worker on an aquafarm that grows plants will also be heavily involved in harvesting, either operating the equipment or harvesting the aquacrop by hand, depending on the aquacrop grown.

While the aquafarmer or aquafarm manager will usually make the "big" decisions, the general worker who is checking the dissolved oxygen in a pond often has to make decisions that immediately affect the well-being of the aquacrop. The general worker must have some knowledge of the growth process of the aquacrop and of factors that influence this growth process. The general

20–19. Construction workers are preparing to install new equipment at a processing plant.

20–20. Monitoring and maintaining equipment is an essential duty in aquaculture.

worker's knowledge and reactions to problems often mean the difference between whether an aquacrop survives or dies.

An aquafarm general worker will usually get his or her training through experience working on an aquafarm and through a high school or community college agricultural education program. The agricultural education program provides classroom instruction, supervised experience, and leadership training.

SUPERVISOR

Supervisors are usually found in two types of on-farm aquaculture operations. Large aquafarms may have supervisors for crews that perform particular tasks either exclusively or very frequently. Custom operations may have supervisors for crews that harvest aquacrops, construct ponds or other facilities, feed aquacrops, apply chemicals, test for water quality, or diagnose diseases or causes of death in aquacrops.

Many aquaculture-related industries, including those that add value to aquacrops through further processing and those that provide inputs to the aquafarmer, employ supervisors.

A supervisor often participates in the same activities as the workers being supervised. However, the supervisor has been given the authority to assign tasks to see that the overall

20–21. The manager of an aquabusiness must be an effective communicator.

goals of the work are accomplished. The supervisor should try to utilize the talents of the members of the group as fully as possible.

The supervisor should motivate employees to be more efficient and to complete their work conscientiously. Often, the supervisor has some incentive, such as a pay bonus or vacation time, to keep his or her crew producing as much or as well as possible. For example, a supervisor of a night crew that monitors dissolved oxygen in catfish ponds may be offered a bonus as an incentive. If, because of the crew's performance, no fish are lost during a certain period, then the supervisor will receive the bonus.

20–22. Important work in a processing plant is trimming fillets for final inspection.

Incentives are common in processing plants. Here, supervisors may get bonuses if their crews produce at a rate higher than expected and do so safely.

Supervisors must be trained not only in the processes their workers perform but also in human relations and management. They usually need some college work in these areas to be effective, but extensive experience may serve as a substitute.

SERVICE TECHNICIAN

Service technicians help the aquaculture industry by making sure that the numerous pieces of equipment used on aquafarms or in processing plants work consistently. The types of equipment may include feeding machines, processing plant equipment, portable monitoring equipment used to test for water quality, and electronic devices that monitor ponds and control aeration or feeding machines.

Service technicians usually help install the equipment or machines and often have the job of servicing the equipment and repairing it when it breaks down. They must have skills in all these areas. The work is usually outdoors, although this may depend on the type of equipment. The service technician is usually on an aquafarm making a service call. However, some machines and equipment are brought in to a service center for repair and maintenance.

Service technicians must get along well with the people who use their products. Once a product is sold, the service technician is often the only person from the company to interact

20–23. A technician services an automated conveyor in a processing plant.

with the aquafarmer. The quality of service often determines if the company will get repeat business.

A service technician may work with an experienced technician in an apprentice-type situation to learn the job. More often, a vocational or technical program will provide the necessary skills. This training will probably be in electronics, mechanics, or other areas and will not be directly related to aquaculture.

SALESPERSON

Salespersons work in many areas involved in aquaculture, both directly and indirectly. Any large business will have one or more salespersons who service existing customers and try to find new customers. The primary purpose of a salesperson is to find out the customer's or potential customer's needs and to provide a product that meets those needs.

Many of the businesses that support aquaculture employ salespersons. These include feed companies, specialized aquaculture equipment manufacturers (such as makers of seines, feeders, and water-monitoring devices), general suppliers, tractor companies, and makers of specialized clothing, such as boots and waders.

As a rule, salespersons have two types of customers. One is the actual aquafarmer,

20–24. Selling involves relating well to people in promoting a product—crawfish in this photograph. (Courtesy, U.S. Department of Agriculture)

who buys products directly from the manufacturer. Items sold to this customer may include feed, seines and seine reels, and feeders. These items may be sold through on-the-farm visits or through direct marketing, such as by sending the potential customer a catalog.

The other type of customer is a general aquaculture supplier, who buys goods to resell to aquafarmers. Much specialized equipment is sold to the aquaculture supplier. In turn, the aquaculture supplier will employ salespersons to sell directly to aquafarmers. These salespersons will usually wait for the aquafarmers to come into the business, but they may also make on-the-farm visits or send catalogs to potential customers.

Salespersons who work for suppliers must have a general knowledge of many different types of products and how they are used. Aquafarmers will depend on them to provide solutions to problems. Salespersons may have to recommend feeds and feed rations, chemicals to control diseases and pests, types of equipment, and many other products. How well an aquafarmer feels a salesperson met his or her needs will probably determine whether he or she will repeat as a customer. The salesperson has a responsibility to help meet the aquafarmer's needs in a way that is cost-effective to the aquafarmer.

A good salesperson must meet two basic requirements. The first is a knowledge of the products being sold and how they are used. The second is the ability to interact with people so as to make a customer feel comfortable with the product and the person selling it.

Salespersons may receive training for their work in several ways. Some large companies hire college graduates for their sales positions. Smaller companies with local markets will hire people with less education, provided these individuals have extensive experience working with or for the clients and working with the products. Many salespersons start by work-

CONNECTION

LIKING YOUR WORK

People who work in aquaculture should like their work. Of course, this is true with any occupation. Liking your work involves many areas that vary with the kind of aquaculture and where it is located.

How about the work in this photograph? This person is examining a catfish grown in 90°F (32°C) thermal water in a raceway in Idaho. Though the air temperature is cold, the water is warm.

The warm water results in rapid year-round fish growth. This is a distinct advantage to the producer of warmwater species. Having water of the right temperature and quality is a major factor in deciding on the species to raise. (Photo courtesy, U.S. Department of Agriculture)

ing for an aquaculture supplier or on an aquafarm while they are attending school. Despite a salesperson's education and experience, an employer often requires participation in a company training program and may require a probationary period of employment.

DRIVER

Processing plants and feed companies are the two aquaculture-related businesses that employ the most drivers. A processing plant usually has a fleet of live-haul trucks that go to the farms to pick up the aquacrops and haul them back to the plant for processing. A feed company usually has a fleet of trucks to haul feed to the aquafarms.

20–25. Drivers are needed to haul fish to restocking locations. (Courtesy, U.S. Fish and Wildlife Service)

The drivers have an important job within the industry. Like service technicians, they are the ones from their company most likely to come in contact with the customers—the aquafarmers. As a result, the drivers must have good interpersonal skills to maintain good relations with the aquafarmers.

Drivers often handle billing and receiving procedures for their companies. For example, a driver for a processing plant must weigh the aquacrop as it is loaded in the truck and then give the aquafarmer a receipt. Other requirements for a driver include a safe driving record and a commercial driver's license.

Drivers usually do not need to have a college degree. Some companies hire drivers from driving schools, while others try to hire drivers who already have experience driving for other companies. A few companies provide their own training programs.

EQUIPMENT OPERATOR

Nearly all aquafarms have some equipment that requires careful operation. Only large aquafarms will employ persons to operate large equipment on a regular basis. Large-equipment operators usually work for custom service providers, such as people who construct ponds or raceways for aquafarms or help aquafarmers maintain pond levees. The work is outdoors and requires a great deal of skill and experience in using the equipment. Earth movers and bulldozers are the two primary types of large equipment used in aquaculture. Large tractors with special equipment are also used.

A large-equipment operator must do more than just sit in the driver's seat and operate the equipment. When constructing a pond, for example, the operator must be able to read the maps, follow the surveyor's stakes, and judge the transformation of the earth very accurately. The operator may also be required to assist with the surveying and layout of the pond. Constructing the pond to the right specifications in the minimum amount of time is the main goal.

Operators are usually responsible for the service of the equipment and must often make minor repairs. They may also have other jobs, such as transporting the equipment from one farm to the other.

20–26. One example of equipment that must be operated on an aquafarm is a tractor with a seine reel.

The primary skill necessary for the job is the ability to operate the equipment efficiently and safely. This equipment is very expensive and requires care. Carelessness in the operation or maintenance of the equipment should not be tolerated. Of course, the operator must also be concerned with his or her own safety.

Most operators learn to use the equipment as apprentices to experienced operators. Some technical schools provide training in large-equipment operation.

OTHER OCCUPATIONS

Like any industry, aquaculture is supported by a wide range of important occupations. Some of the jobs may not be directly related to fish production. Others require considerable skill in many areas.

Researcher

Research and education are important to the advancement of aquaculture. Researchers are trained in biology, chemistry, genetics, molecular biology, aquaculture, agricultural engineering, and related areas. The kind of training needed depends on the research being done.

20–27. Researchers investigating offshore cobia production are loading gear on a boat in preparation for their work. (Courtesy, National Oceanic and Atmospheric Administration)

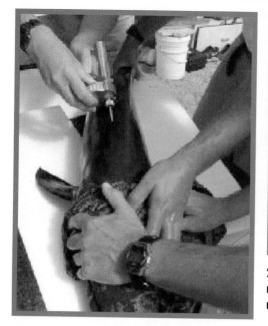

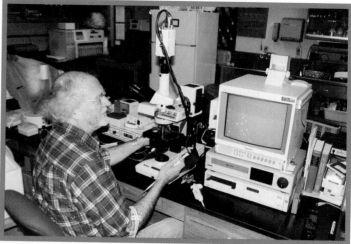

20–29. A research scientist at Kentucky State University is using microscopy to observe greatly enlarged paddlefish sperm on a monitor.

20–28. Scientists and assisting technicians must have considerable skill with instruments and in handling fish. This shows an adult fish being given a hormone injection to stimulate spawning. (Courtesy, National Oceanic and Atmospheric Administration)

The nature of research work varies widely. Some work is in a bench laboratory; other work is outside or in water. Considerable skill is needed in designing research, testing treatments, and observing findings.

Educator

Many people have occupations in providing education about aquaculture. Some of these teach in public schools, colleges, and universities. Others carry out nonformal education through the Extension Service and other state and federal agencies. Educators typically

20–30. An Extension Specialist uses digital photography to record on-site images for use in educational presentations.

have college degrees in aquaculture, agriculture, or related areas. The baccalaureate degree is essential for entry level. Master's and doctor's degrees are often needed for advancement.

Engineer

Engineers design and build special equipment and structures. Ponds, processing plants, and hatcheries involve engineers. Their role is to assure that the facilities are well constructed to serve long and useful lives. Engineers also design equipment to carry out certain functions, such as processing fish. Engineers have college degrees in mechanical, electrical, or other areas of engineering.

Aquaculture Health Worker

Individuals in aquaculture health occupations promote the well-being of aquatic species. Some are trained as veterinarians. Veterinarians determine methods of controlling disease and ways of improving health. Other aquaculture health workers are trained in biology, microbiology, and related areas.

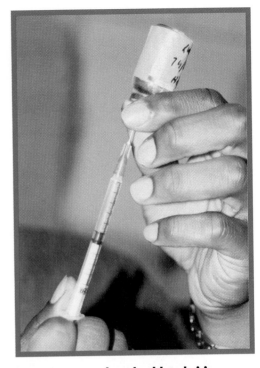

20–31. An aquaculture health technician prepares an injection.

CAREER LADDERS IN AQUACULTURE

A *career ladder* is a series of steps involved in moving from a lower-level occupation, usually with lower pay, to a better occupation. Career ladders may be vertical or horizontal.

Moving on a vertical career ladder would involve moving to a better occupation doing similar work. For example, an aquafarm general worker might move to a position as a supervisor of several general workers, or a manager of an aquafarm might decide to leave the aquafarm and start one of his or her own.

Moving on a horizontal career ladder would consist of moving to a better occupation doing work that is not similar, though it is usually somewhat related. An example would be an aquafarm general worker leaving his or her job to go to work as a feed salesperson.

20–32. Developing skills in aquaculture requires careful observation of the work of trained specialists and educators.

In aquaculture, moving on a vertical ladder usually involves lower-level workers on aquafarms, in processing plants, and in aquaculture supply companies becoming supervisors, managers, or salespersons.

Moving on a horizontal ladder in aquaculture may necessitate that workers move to and from several different occupations. The most common type of move is from jobs as aquafarm general workers to other jobs with suppliers or processors. Many of the moves on a horizontal career ladder require obtaining more education or training.

SELECTING A CAREER IN AQUACULTURE

Once you decide aquaculture is the career for you, think about the career opportunities discussed earlier in this chapter. Talk to people who work in aquaculture. Find out the advantages and disadvantages of their occupations.

20–33. Agricultural education programs can provide many students with opportunities to learn more about aquaculture. (These students are testing water in the outdoor lab at their school.)

Use the *supervised experience* (SE) program offered by your school to find out more by getting some experience. The SE program is that part of agricultural education that allows you to practice what you have learned in the classroom and the laboratory. With your parent(s) or guardian(s) and your agriculture teacher, plan some activities to answer your questions. If you have a specific job picked out, plan to spend some time working at that job after school and in the summer to find out if the work is really what you want to do for the rest of your life. If you have not decided on a particular job, set up an exploratory SE program to help you learn about as many different jobs as possible.

Remember to find out what abilities and education are required to be successful. Do not pick a job that requires more education than you can handle or finance.

If the occupation you select involves owning your own operation, do some investigating. Locate sources from which you can obtain the necessary capital to start the business. Give yourself a chance to be successful as your own boss. Remember that entrepreneurs share in the risks as well as the rewards. This responsibility cannot be handled by everyone.

Choose a career in aquaculture that meets your requirements. Does it allow you to work where you want? Will you enjoy the nature of the work? Can you successfully complete the work required with your present mental and physical abilities? Will you need to go to college or complete a vocational-technical program to perform well? Do you have the necessary experience or the means of getting it? Will you be able to provide a stable, adequate income for yourself and your possible dependents? Will you have to change your lifestyle? These and many other questions will have to be answered before you make your final choice.

REVIEWING

MAIN IDEAS

Aquaculture has many exciting careers. Opportunities abound in this fairly young industry. However, many opportunities for success often mean many opportunities for failure. A career decision should be made carefully because it is so important.

The career opportunities in aquaculture range from those as general workers with limited requirements in entry-level skills to owners/managers with high requirements in both ability and education. Most young people with interests in aquaculture can find occupations that fit their needs, abilities, and education. The nature of the work and the opportunities to move up career ladders must also be considered.

To be successful in an aquaculture career, a person should acquire the necessary experience and training, as well as develop the personal characteristics of successful employees in any occupation.

QUESTIONS

Answer the following questions, using complete sentences and correct spelling.

1. Why is the career decision-making process so important?
2. What are some important factors that must be considered when a person is making a career decision?
3. Outline the steps in the career decision-making process.
4. What are the seven characteristics of good employees? Briefly discuss each.
5. List eight types of aquaculture careers.
6. What is a career ladder?

REVIEWING

Match the term with the correct definition. Write the letter of the term on the line provided.

a. aquafarmer   d. large-equipment operator   g. service technician
b. career ladder   e. manager   h. supervised agricultural experience
c. driver   f. salesperson

_____1. A person who operates tractors, bulldozers, etc.

_____2. Someone who owns or manages an aquafarm

_____3. A series of steps involved when someone moves to a better job, either vertically or horizontally

_____4. The part of the agricultural education program in which a student learns about a job by working in it

_____5. Someone who tries to get people to buy a product

_____6. A person who is in charge of an operation but does not own it

_____7. Someone who takes care of equipment

_____8. Someone who operates a truck, usually for a processing plant or a feed company

EXPLORING

1. Select the occupation in aquaculture in which you would most like to work. Interview someone who works in that occupation to find out what that person likes and does not like about his or her job. Prepare a written report describing the nature of the work and the education required.

2. Develop a supervised experience program for an aquaculture occupation. Include the skills you would like to develop and the amount of time you will spend in the program. Identify an employer or resources necessary to help you get started.

3. Identify some career ladders in aquaculture in your community. Identify one person who has moved on a vertical or horizontal career ladder in your community. Give an oral report to the class.

4. Use the book *Developing Leadership and Communication Skills* to help you improve your abilities in interpersonal relationships, team building, communicating, and other areas. (*Developing Leadership and Communication Skills* is available from Pearson Prentice Hall Interstate.)

Appendixes

TABLE OF EQUIVALENTS FOR AQUACULTURE

$$1 \text{ inch} = 2.54 \text{ centimeters}$$

$$1 \text{ foot} = 30.48 \text{ centimeters}$$
$$= 0.305 \text{ meter}$$
$$= 12 \text{ inches}$$

$$1 \text{ cubic foot} = 7.481 \text{ gallons}$$
$$= 62.4 \text{ pounds of water}$$
$$= 28,354.6 \text{ grams of water}$$

$$1 \text{ yard} = 36 \text{ inches}$$

$$1 \text{ cubic yard} = 27 \text{ cubic feet}$$
$$= 0.76 \text{ cubic meter}$$

$$1 \text{ acre-foot} = \text{acre of surface area covered by 1 foot of water}$$
$$= 43,560 \text{ cubic feet}$$
$$= 2,718,144 \text{ pounds of water}$$
$$= 325,851 \text{ gallons of water}$$

$$1 \text{ gallon} = 8.34 \text{ pounds of water}$$
$$= 3,800 \text{ cubic centimeters}$$

1 quart = 950 cubic centimeters

= 950 grams of water

1 pound = 453.6 grams

= 16 ounces

1 ounce = 28.35 grams

1 meter = 39.37 inches

1 cubic meter = 35.135 cubic feet

1 ppm requires: 2.72 pounds per acre-foot

0.0038 gram per gallon

0.0283 gram per cubic foot

0.0000623 pound per cubic foot

1.0 milligram per liter

8.34 pounds per million gallons of water

1 ppt requires: 2,718 pounds per acre-foot

3.80 grams per gallon

28.30 grams per cubic foot

APPENDIX B

REGIONAL AQUACULTURE CENTERS

The U.S. Department of Agriculture has established five regional aquaculture centers. Each region comprises several states. A contact person is designated in each state to work with the regional centers. For additional information, contact the nearest center. The centers are listed below.

Northeastern Regional Aquaculture Center (NRAC)
University of Massachusetts Dartmouth
285 Old Westport Road, Research Building 201
North Dartmouth, MA 02747-2300
www.umassd.edu/specialprograms/nrac/

Western Regional Aquaculture Center (WRAC)
School of Fisheries
Box 357980
University of Washington
Seattle, WA 98195-7980
www.fish.washington.edu/sofunits/wrac/

Center for Tropical and Subtropical Aquaculture (CTSA)
University of Hawaii and The Oceanic Institute
Makapuu Point
41-202 Kalanianaole
Waimanalo, HI 96795-1820
http://library.kcc.hawaii.edu/CTSA/

North Central Regional Aquaculture Center (NCRAC)
Fisheries and Wildlife Department
13 Natural Resources Building
Michigan State University
East Lansing, MI 48824-1222
http://ag.ansc.purdue.edu/aquanic/ncrac

Southern Regional Aquaculture Center (SRAC)
Delta Research and Extension Center
P.O. Box 197
Stoneville, MS 38776-0197
www.msstate.edu/dept/srac/

Glossary

abscess—a swollen area in the tissue of the body.

additive—a substance placed with the feed ingredients during manufacture.

adductor muscle—the organ that opens and closes the shell of a bivalve mollusk.

advertising—calling the attention of possible consumers to a product and encouraging them to buy it.

aeration—exposure of water to the air so that it will pick up oxygen from the air.

aerator—any device designed to add oxygen to water.

agricultural education—programs in agriculture that usually focus on formal classroom instruction in high schools, vocational centers, and community colleges.

agritourism—tourism that attracts tourists and vacationers to a commercial venture on a farm for enjoyment, education, active involvement, and relaxation.

air stone—a porous material in the bottom of an aquarium from which air bubbles into the water, diffuses throughout, and rises to the top of the water.

alevin—a newly hatched salmonid with its yolk sac attached.

allele—a different form of a gene.

ammonia toxicity—a level of ammonia that injures or kills an aquatic species.

anadromous—living mostly in salt water but returning to fresh water to spawn.

anatomy—the study of the structure of whole organisms, including form, shape, and appearance.

angler—an individual who fishes with a hook. The term is typically applied to a sport fisher.

annual fixed cost—a cost that occurs every year, no matter the level of production.

aquacrop—a crop grown in water.

aquaculture—the production of aquatic plants and animals.

aquarium—an impoundment similar to a tank, typically made of glass, and with a capacity of from 5 to 50 gallons or more of water.

aquarium heater—a specially designed device for warming water in an aquarium.

aquatic plant—a plant that grows in water.

aquifer—an underground formation of sand, gravel, or rock that contains water.

artemia—brine shrimp.

arteries—vessels that carry blood from the heart.

artesian well—a well in which natural pressures in the earth cause the water to flow like a fountain.

asexual reproduction—the production of a new individual without the union of a male sex cell and a female sex cell; the same as cloning.

B

backflushing—forcing water to flow in reverse through a filter and/or system.

bacterial disease—a disease caused by bacteria.

bait—anything used to lure or attract an animal onto a hook or into a net or trap.

bait-and-tackle store—a retail business that specializes in meeting the equipment and supplies needs of sport fishers.

bait aquaculture—the raising of small fish and other aquatic species for use as bait.

baitfish—a species of fish used as bait to catch desired species for pleasure or food.

basic processing—deheading, eviscerating, and skinning or scaling fish; essentially the same as dressing.

bathing—adding chemicals to the water where fish are being kept or placing the fish in chemically treated water, in either case exposing the fish to the chemicals for a longer time than with dipping.

benthic—characteristic of aquatic plants that attach to the bottom or substrate.

bilaterally symmetrical—divided into two mirror-identical halves.

biofilter—any structure or material that uses natural organisms to improve water quality.

biofilter media—in a biofilter, the surface to which the microbes attach.

biological filtration—the use of bacteria and other living organisms to convert harmful substances to less harmful forms.

biological oxygen demand—the amount of oxygen used in the water for many natural purposes: decay of uneaten feed and vegetation, decay of plankton, respiration by the aquacrop and phytoplankton, and use by trash fish. Abbreviated *BOD*.

biological weed control—the use of plant-eating fish or other animals to control weeds and algae.

biomass—the amount of living and nonliving biological material in a given location.

bivalve mollusk—a mollusk with two shell parts hinged together.

brackish water—the water where fresh water and salt water run together.

breed—a group of animals of the same species with distinct and similar features that are passed on to offspring.

breeding—the process of helping organisms reproduce so that the offspring have desired qualities.

breeding tubercle—a hornlike projection that develops on the head of a male fathead minnow at the beginning of the breeding season.

brine bath—a medium used to chill live fish to an inactive state.

B-to-B marketing—business-to-business marketing; a World Wide Web approach that connects businesses that have fish and seafood to sell with those that wish to buy fish and seafood.

bunched aquatic plant—a plant that grows so that a bunch shape is formed.

buoyancy—the characteristics of food particles in water as related to position.

burrow—a tunnel system made in the earth by mature female crawfish that connects to the surface with a hole that may be capped with a mound, or "chimney"; used for hiding and reproduction.

business plan—a document that contains short-range, intermediate-range, and long-range plans for an aquabusiness.

by-product—a secondary product.

byssus—a cluster of threads, chemically similar to silk, that mussels use to attach themselves to surfaces.

C

C × B hybrid—a catfish produced by crossing the female channel catfish with the male blue catfish.

cage—a container for aquacrops that floats in the water.

cage culture—aquaculture that involves placing a cage made of netting on a metal, plastic, or wood frame in an existing water structure.

cane pole—a fishing pole made of the hollow, flexible, jointed stem of bamboo or another reed plant.

captured aquafood—a plant or animal that grows wild in a body of water and is caught by a commercial fisher.

carbohydrates—substances that come from sugars, starches, and celluloses.

career—the general direction of a person's life as related to work.

career ladder—a series of steps involved in moving from a lower-level occupation, usually with lower pay, to a better occupation.

carnivorous fish—fish that eat insects, worms, or small fish.

carrageenan—a collection of phycocolloids from agar-producing plants.

catadromous—living mostly in fresh water but returning to salt water to spawn.

catch-out pond—a fee facility where the fish are raised in the pond where they are to be caught.

caviar—fish eggs, usually the roe (egg mass) of large fish, such as the sturgeon, eaten by humans as a rather expensive appetizer or entree.

cell—the basic unit of a living thing.

cell specialization—the development of cells for a particular purpose or function.

cell structure—the general pattern of organization and relationship in a cell.

chelas—the two front legs of a crawfish that form pincers (sharp claws).

chemical disease—a disease that results when the amount of a chemical in the water injures or kills the fish.

chemical filtration—the use of chemical processes to filter water.

chemical weed control—the use of herbicides for weeds and algicides for algae.

chlorinity—the total amount of chlorine, bromine, and iodine, in grams, contained in 1 kilogram of water.

chromosome—a tiny threadlike part in a cell that contains the genetic material.

cloning—the production of one or more exact genetic copies of an organism.

closed raceway—a raceway in which the water is recycled.

closed system—a system in which no new water is added.

color enhancer—a feed additive that intensifies the brilliance of fish colors.

commercial landing—wild fish caught in their natural habitat but not cultured.

commercial producer—one who raises fish and other crops for the money obtained when the crops are sold.

conchiolin—an organic material that makes up the periostracum of a shell.

consumption—the amount of a food people eat and of other products they use.

cool-freshwater aquacrop—a species that survives and grows best in water below 70°F (21°C).

cooperative—an association formed to provide certain services to its members.

corm—a fleshy underground vertical stem that is part of a rhizome.

corporation—a business formed by creating an "artificial person," or a legal entity.

crustacean—an arthropod with a relatively hard exterior skeleton.

cultch—material to which oysters attach themselves.

cultured aquacrop—a species raised or grown with human care.

customer assistance—with regard to an aquabusiness, help to customers in selecting tackle and bait, using fishing techniques that will lead to good catches, and handling the live fish in ways that prevent injury.

D

daily fee—a fixed amount a fee-lake user pays to fish all day.

decapod—a shortened form of "decapod crustacean," which is a crustacean that has five pairs of appendages on the thorax. At least one pair is modified as pincers.

decision making—the act of choosing among alternatives for an aquabusiness.

degree day—a measurement of the amount of time required for eggs to hatch obtained by multiplying the average water temperature (in degrees Celsius) by the number of days required for hatching.

deheading—removing the head of fish.

depuration—the process used by some oyster producers and/or processors to cleanse the digestive systems of oysters.

desiccation—the process of drying oyster shells for short intervals to help control disease.

detritivorous fish—fish that eat decaying leaves, fish waste, and other nonliving organic materials.

detritus—small particles of decaying material, primarily from plants.

deveining—removing the vein under the dorsal side of the shell of a crustacean or mollusk.

development—the use of information to create something new.

diagnostic laboratory—a place specially equipped to examine both live and dead fish.

diatoms—microalgae.

diet—the type and amount of feed in a ration.

dipping—immersing fish into a concentrated solution for a few seconds.

direct loss—a loss that occurs when an aquacrop is attacked or injured.

disease—a condition that develops in an organism and then damages it in some way.

dissolved oxygen—oxygen that is in water and available to aquatic organisms. Abbreviated *DO*.

division—the duplication process in which one cell splits into two cells.

DNA—deoxyribonucleic acid; a protein-like nucleic acid on genes that controls inheritance.

DNA sequencing—determining the order of nucleotides on a DNA fragment.

dominant trait—a trait that covers up or masks the allele for a recessive trait.

dormancy—a state of rest or inactivity when an organism does not eat or grow.

driver—an individual trained and licensed in the efficient and safe operation of trucks and other vehicles.

E

economic deception—the substitution of a less expensive species for a more expensive species.

economy of scale—a concept relating the size of a fish farm and the marketing alternatives to the profit made.

ectothermic animal—an animal whose body temperature adjusts to that of its environment.

effluent—used water from aquafarms, processing plants, or other sources.

egg picking—removing eggs by hand with large tweezers.

egg ribbon—a long, gelatinous strand of eggs produced by some female fish.

egg transfer—the approach of removing the spawning mats from the broodfish pond and placing them in the rearing pond.

employee—an individual who works for another person, a business, or an agency.

employer—a person, a business, or an agency that hires other people in order to achieve particular goals through their efforts.

environmental disease—a disease caused by the water environment in which fish and other aquacrops grow.

environmental weed control—the creation of conditions unfavorable to weed and algae growth.

escargot—snails prepared as food.

estuarine water—the water in bays, inlets, and mouths of rivers, where salt water and fresh water are mixed.

euthanasia—the humane killing of an animal that is suffering.

eutrophication—excessive nutrient enrichment in water often caused by nitrogen and phosphorus.

eviscerating—removing the internal organs of fish. Also known as *gutting*.

exoskeleton—a skeleton outside the body.

extensive aquaculture—a type of production system that involves low population density, little control over the system, and little intervention by the producer.

external parasite—a parasite that attaches itself to the outside of a fish's body.

eyed eggs—fertile eggs that are beginning to show the development of the fish.

eyespot—a dark spot that shows the developing embryo in each egg. Also called *eye*.

eyestalk ablation—the cutting of one eye of a female shrimp, which in turn causes her to produce eggs.

F

fabricating—preparing fish into suitable pieces. Also called *cutting*.

facility plan—a plan that describes how a site is to be prepared for a recreational aquabusiness.

Fair Labor Standards Act—a federal law that sets minimum wage, overtime pay, equal pay, record-keeping, and child labor standards.

fancy—term used to describe ornamentals that have characteristics which are particularly appealing to people.

fats—substances composed of fatty acids.

feasibility—the potential for carrying out a successful enterprise.

feeder fish—a species of fish used as live food for the production of other species.

fee-lake—a facility where consumers fish for recreational purposes.

female:male ratio—the number of females that can be stocked in a broodfish pond for each male.

fill—soil used to create a levee.

fillet—a cut made by slicing parallel with the backbone of a fish. Also called a *fillet cut*.

filter feeder—an organism that filters small particles of food materials from the water.

filtration—the process of removing solids and dissolved solids from water.

fishing hook—a curved piece of metal for holding bait and for sticking into and holding fish.

fingerling—young fish from 1 to 10 inches long used to stock grow-out facilities.

fishing tackle—the equipment used in sport fishing.

fish keeping—caring for ornamental fish species as a hobby or an avocation.

fish ladder—a stair-stepped structure that allows salmon to negotiate natal stream waters.

fish sacrifice—the killing of female fish to collect eggs.

flavor testing—testing to assure that fish have the desired flavor.

float—a small piece of cork, plastic, or other material lighter than water used to let a fisher see movement of a fishing line.

floating aquatic plant—a plant that floats on the water.

food—any material eaten that contains nutrients needed by animals.

food aquacrop—a crop grown in water and produced almost exclusively for human food.

food chain—the sequence in which organisms feed, starting with the smallest organisms that use dissolved or suspended nutrients and ending at the highest levels with animals that eat meat from other animals.

forage—plants grown for leaves and stems and eaten by aquacrops.

formalin—an aqueous solution of 37 percent formaldehyde that can be used in water for the control of external protozoa and monogenetic trematodes.

free-access feeding—making feed available all the time so that fish or other animals may eat when they wish.

freeboard—the height of a levee minus the normal water level; the distance between the top of a levee and the waterline.

free enterprise—the economic system of the United States that permits individuals to own private property. Also known as *capitalism*.

freshwater aquaculture—the growing of aquacrops in streams, ponds, and lakes not containing salt water.

fry—newly hatched fish with egg sac attached.

fry transfer—the approach of allowing the spawning mats with eggs to remain in the broodfish pond for hatching and then moving the fry to grow-out ponds when they are about $3/4$ inch (2.0 cm) long.

fungal disease—a disease caused by tiny organisms known as fungi.

G

gallons per minute—the measure used to determine the capacity of a well to produce water. Abbreviated *gpm*.

gamete—a sex cell.

ganglia—masses of nerves.

gas bubble disease—a condition resulting from supersaturation in which bubbles form on the surface of an aquatic animal's body or within tissues and the vascular system.

gastropod—a mollusk with a single coiled shell. Also called a *univalve mollusk*.

gene—a segment of a chromosome that contains the hereditary traits of an organism.

general worker—a worker expected to handle a wide variety of tasks rather than specialize in a specific type of job.

genetic code—the sequence of nitrogen bases in the DNA molecule.

genetic engineering—removing genes from DNA, modifying genes, or adding genes to DNA.

genetics—the study of the laws and processes of biological inheritance.

genotype—the genetic makeup of an organism.

geothermal water—water that is naturally heated in the earth.

gills—in fish, the primary organs that oxygenate the blood and exchange carbon dioxide.

gonad releasing hormone—a hormone (usually a synthetic form) given to fish to promote spawning.

grading—sorting fish into batches of uniform size and species for processing.

gravid—pregnant; full of eggs.

gross return—the total money received for an aquacrop.

H

habitat—the environment in which an organism lives and thrives.

handling—in relation to feed, moving it from one place to another.

hapa—a nylon-type net enclosure that allows fry to escape from larger fish in an aquarium or tank.

haploid cell—a cell produced by meiosis.

hardness—the amount of calcium and magnesium in water.

hardy—the ability of fish to survive in a wide range of conditions.

heliciculture—the process of raising or farming snails.

heredity—the passing of traits from parents to offspring.

hermaphrodite—an animal that is both male and female.

heterozygous—having different alleles for a particular trait.

high-density lipoprotein—"good" cholesterol in the blood. Abbreviated *HDL*.

high-density stocking—crowding many more animals into a growing facility than would normally be found in nature.

hollow tail—a nutritional disease of crawfish in which the tails are not filled out.

homozygous—having similar alleles for a particular trait.

hospital tank—a small separate tank where diseased fish are moved for treatment.

host—an organism on which a parasite lives and from which it derives nourishment.

hulis—a taro cutting made of a piece of stem 12 to 18 inches (0.3 to 0.5 m) long and a 2- to 3-inch (5- to 8-cm) section of the corm.

hybridization—the process of breeding individuals that are distinctly different. With fish, it involves using different species that are closely related.

hybrid vigor—a condition in which offspring have greater desired traits than their parents.

hydrometer—an instrument used to measure density. The reading is converted to salinity with the use of a conversion table.

hydroponics—the culture of terrestrial plants whose roots grow in gravel or some other substrate where a shallow current of water constantly flows.

I

impoundment—an enclosure that holds the water and/or an aquacrop.

indefinite treatment—the treatment of fish for long periods by adding low concentrations of therapeutants (chemicals) to the water. Also called prolonged treatment.

indirect loss—a loss that results when the environment in which an aquacrop is living is less than ideal.

industrial effluent—the water released by manufacturing plants.

infectious disease—a disease caused by germs or pathogens (disease-causing organisms) that may be transferred from one fish to another.

infrastructure—the network required for an aquaculture commodity to become commercially important.

ingest—to consume or eat food.

initial cost—a cost involved in beginning an aquaculture enterprise. Also known as *start-up cost*.

injection—the administration of drugs to small numbers of fish with a hypodermic needle and a syringe.

integrated aquaculture-agriculture—the combination of practices to produce traditional crops and livestock products as well as aquaculture crops and products.

intensive aquaculture—the production of aquacrops at a high rate of stocking.

internal parasite—a parasite that lives in the organs or digestive tracts of fish.

intertidal zone—the area covered with water during a high tide but not during a low tide.

isolation tank—an aquarium where new fish are kept for a few days before being put into a large aquarium with other fish.

K

keeping ease—the ease with which a particular species is produced.

koi pond—an ornamental water area used for keeping koi.

L

labyrinth fish—a fish with an air storage chamber above the gills.

large-equipment operator—a person skilled in the efficient and safe operation of bulldozers, front-end loaders, and other heavy equipment.

lateral plates—bony structures along the sides of primitive fish species, such as sturgeon.

lesion—a change in a tissue as a result of injury or disease.

levee-type pond—a pond made by forming an earthen levee on nearly level land.

life cycle—the changes that an organism goes through from a given stage until the same stage recurs in the next generation.

life process—an essential activity for an organism to remain in the living condition and perpetuate its species.

life span—the length of an organism's life.

line—in fishing, the string attached to a pole on one end and with a hook attached to the other.

live hauling—providing live aquacrops to others who will likely use them in recreational fee-lakes.

locomotion—the process of moving from one location to another.

lure—an artificial bait pulled through the water with the notion that the fish will mistake it for something to eat.

M

management—the handling of a wide range of mental tasks to carry out aquaculture successfully.

manager—an individual who is in charge of the everyday operations of a business.

manured pond—a system that involves constructing pens for chickens, hogs, and ducks over the water where fish are being grown so that manure can fall through the slated floor of the pens into the water and the fish can use the manure as food.

mariculture—the production of aquatic crops in salt water. Also called *marine aquaculture.*

marine water—the water in the oceans and gulfs, which is primarily salt water.

marker-assisted selection—a process of selecting broodfish using genetic markers that identify specific genes.

marketing—all the steps needed to get a desired product to the consumer.

marketing channel—the route or procedure followed to get a product to the consumer.

marketing functions—the steps or processes that a product passes through before it reaches the consumer.

marketing plan—a written statement that guides the marketing process.

marketing planning—the process used to develop a marketing plan.

meal—a coarsely ground feed.

mechanical filtration—the passing of aquarium water through materials that remove suspended solids.

mechanical weed control—the physical removal of weeds and algae from the water.

meiosis—cell division in the sexual reproduction of organisms.

merchandising—promoting the sale of processed aquacrops.

milt—fluid containing sperm.

minerals—inorganic earth materials.

misbranded food—a product offered for sale under the name of another product.

mitosis—cell division for growth and repair.

molting—an animal's shedding its outer shell (exoskeleton) and increasing in size as it develops a new one.

monoculture—a production system in which only one species is grown at a time.

monosex culture—growing all fish of the same gender together.

morphology—the study of the form and structure of organisms, including animals and plants.

mouthbrooder—a fish that incubates eggs in its mouth.

multicellular organism—an organism that has many cells.

naiad—a freshwater mussel.

natal stream—the place where salmon were hatched.

nauplii—baby shrimp.

net pen—a large cage-type structure made with nylon or plastic netting over a frame of plastic or other sturdy material.

net return—the amount of money that remains after all expenses for the production of a crop have been subtracted from the gross return.

neutral buoyancy—the quality of neither floating nor sinking.

niche—the location of an organism within a pond and the function of the organism.

niche market—a specialized outlet for a crop.

nitrogen cycle—the natural circulation or cycling of nitrogen through the earth's environment.

NMFS—the National Marine Fisheries Service; a part of NOAA that promotes sound mariculture practices.

NOAA—the National Oceanic and Atmospheric Administration; a federal agency with considerable responsibility for seafood and non-seafood products, including wild and mariculture harvest.

noninfectious disease—a disease that may be due to improper diet, poor environment, chemicals, and/or physiological changes.

non-native species—a species that does not naturally grow in an area.

nutrient—a substance used by organisms to live and grow.

nutritional disease—a disease that results from an inadequate diet.

O

Occupational Safety and Health Administration—an agency of the U.S. Department of Labor that promotes and regulates a safe and healthy work environment. Acronym: *OSHA*.

offshore aquaculture—the use of cages in seawater to produce aquacrops.

omega-3 fatty acids—polyunsaturated fatty acids found in some fish that raise the level of high-density lipoprotein (HDL) ("good" cholesterol) in the blood and reduce the level of low-density lipoprotein (LDL) ("bad" cholesterol).

omnivorous fish—fish that eat foods of both animal and plant origin.

open ocean—the area of the ocean that is away from the shore and is not readily affected by tides and the inflow of fresh water.

open raceway—a raceway in which the water is used once and disposed of.

open system—a system in which the water is pumped in at one place and removed at another.

organ—a collection of tissues that work together to perform a specific function, such as the gills of a fish.

organic aquaculture—the production of fish and other aquacrops without off-farm inputs.

organ system—the association of several organs that work together to perform an activity.

ornamental aquaculture—the keeping of fish, plants, and other species for aesthetic or personal appeal.

ornamental aquatic plant—a plant grown in water for its aesthetic appeal.

Osteichthyes—the class of the kingdom Animalia and the phylum Chordata composed of aquatic organisms, each of which has a skeleton with true bones, a skull with sutures, teeth (if present) usually fused to the bones, nasal openings on each side, premaxillae and maxillae, and a swim bladder or a functional lung.

owner—a person or other entity that owns a business.

oxygenation—the addition of dissolved oxygen (DO) to water.

oxygen depletion—the condition in which the DO level in water is below the level needed to maintain the living condition of the aquacrop being produced.

P

packaging—placing processed fish or other products in containers.

paddy taro—aquatic taro.

pan-dressed—the dressed form of fish in which the internal organs, head, scales or skin, and fins are removed.

parasite—a plant or animal that lives in or on another plant or animal.

partnership—a business owned jointly by two or more people.

pellet—a mixture of ground feed materials that has been compressed to form a feed particle of appropriate size.

pen—a container for aquacrops attached to the earth at the bottom of a water impoundment.

permeability—the rate at which substances infiltrate the soil.

pest—a plant, animal, or other organism that is detrimental to a species.

phenotype—the physical or outward appearance of an organism.

photoperiod—the amount of light organisms are exposed to in one day.

phycocolloid—a gel-like substance extracted from seaweeds that has many applications in science and the food industry.

physiological disease—a disease caused by a malfunction of an organ or other life process.

physiology—the study of the functions of the cells, tissues, organs, and systems of an organism.

phytate—a chemical in feed ingredients that contains phosphorus.

phytoplankton—algae plankton.

planktivorous fish—fish that eat algae or zooplankton.

plankton—the tiny plants and animals that float in pond water.

pollutant—any substance that contaminates water used in aquaculture.

polyculture—a production system in which two or more species are grown together.

polytrophic—eating a variety of animal and plant materials, including detritus.

pond—an artificial impoundment, usually made of earth.

predator—an animal that attacks and feeds on other animals.

preservation—the technique of keeping food from spoiling.

prevention—the practice of keeping fish and other aquacrops healthy and free of disease.

processing—preparing an aquacrop into a convenient form for the consumer.

product form—the form in which an aquacrop is marketed.

production cost—a direct cost involved in producing a crop.

production intensity—the density (crowding together) of the aquacrop being produced.

profit—the money left over after all costs of production have been paid.

prophylactic treatment—a practice used to prevent disease.

proteins—substances formed by simple organic compounds called amino acids.

put-and-take pond—a fee facility stocked with catchable-size fish grown elsewhere.

Q

quarantine—the isolation of fish from each other.

R

raceway—a long, narrow structure that uses flowing water. See also *closed raceway* and *open raceway*.

RAS—recirculating aquaculture systems; the systems filter, clean, and aerate water for circulating back through aquaculture growing facilities.

ration—the feed given an animal each day to meet its nutrient needs.

RBC—rotating biological contactor; a motorized filter that rotates an open canister of material (usually plastic) so that the canister constantly goes from being submerged to being in the open air.

receiving—taking delivery of aquacrops from producers at a processing plant.

recessive trait—a trait that is covered up or masked by the allele for a dominant trait.

recirculating facility—a water enclosure in which the water is recycled.

recreational aquaculture—the raising of fish for sport fishing.

redds—holes filled with fertilized salmon eggs.

refractometer—an instrument used to measure salinity.

regulations—interpretations by agencies of laws that have been enacted.

Regulatory Fish Encyclopedia—a compilation of information that provides accurate identification of fish products in marketing. Abbreviated *RFE.*

reproduction—the process by which new individuals of a species are created.

research—a systematic approach used to answer questions.

restricted feeding—supplementing the fish diet by providing only what the fish need beyond the natural food available.

return—the income from a crop when it is sold.

rhizome—a horizontally creeping, below-the-ground structure that sends up shoots for the reproduction of some plants.

rice-fish culture—the stocking of fish into rice fields to eat the golden snail.

rice pond—an aquaculture facility that is rotated for rice production.

ripe—the condition of a female fish with fully developed eggs in her ovaries.

risk—the possibility of failure or loss.

rooted aquatic plant—a plant that grows with roots in the gravel or other medium at the bottom of an aquarium.

S

salesperson—an individual who promotes products to customers, takes orders for products, and sees that products are sold efficiently and accurately.

salinity—the amount of salt in water.

salmon farming—salmon aquaculture usually involving the use of net pens or sublittoral enclosures.

salmonid—any member of the salmon family.

salmon ranching—salmon aquaculture in which a hatchery releases fingerlings or smolts to the sea and waits until the fish return.

sampling—selecting a small, representative part of an aquacrop to determine if it is up to standard.

sanitation—the practice of keeping water and facilities clean.

scheduled feeding—providing feed each day at specific times.

scientific method—the step-by-step process of solving scientific questions or problems.

seabed zone—the ground always covered by the sea.

seafood—edible marine fish, shellfish, and other aquatic plants and animals, either wild or cultured.

season fee—a fee a fee-lake user pays for a full fishing season or a year.

seine—a long net used to harvest an aquacrop.

seine boat—a small boat used in seining.

selection—the choosing of a male parent and a female parent for mating because of desired qualities, such as coloring in an ornamental fish species.

self-perpetuating—the capability of an organism to reproduce in sufficient numbers to provide an adequate population.

selling—changing the ownership of an aquacrop.

service technician—a skilled individual who provides a variety of services in setting up, adjusting, operating, and servicing equipment and processes.

sex reversal—the changing of an organism from one sex to another.

sexual reproduction—the production of a new individual from the union of a male sex cell and a female sex cell.

shore—the land next to the ocean.

shucking—removing the edible portion from the shell of a mollusk.

sinker—a small weight placed on a fishing line near the hook.

skinning—removing the skin from the flesh of fish.

sluice gate—a structure that allows the flow of seawater in and the flow of fresh water out.

soft crab—a crab that has molted and has not developed another hard shell.

softshell crawfish—crawfish in the 12-hour stage between hard shells that occurs when crawfish molt.

sole proprietorship—a business owned by one person.

spat—larval oysters.

spawning board—a flat board that floats or is suspended on the surface of the brood pond so that fathead minnows can spawn underneath.

spawning container—an artificial nest.

spawning mat—a mat of fibrous material used to control spawning.

spore—a small, seedlike plant part.

sport fishing—an avocational activity of catching fish for fun and relaxation.

spring—a natural opening in the earth that produces water.

stock enhancement—the release of cultured fish into the wild of streams and lakes by state and federal government hatcheries.

storing—in relation to feed, holding or keeping it in a warehouse or bin until it is fed.

strain—a group of organisms developed with similar traits to achieve a desired goal; most often applied to fish and other aquatic animals.

stream—a flowing body of water.

stunning—using an electric shock to paralyze fish.

sublittoral zone—shallow (usually 5- to 100-feet-deep) inshore areas, such as bays and lagoons.

substrate—material that makes up the bottom of the growing facility.

substrate spawning—nesting on the bottom of the water for spawning and hatching.

supersaturation—the condition in which water contains more gas than is soluble at a given temperature.

supervised experience—that part of agricultural education that allows students to practice what they have learned in the classroom and the laboratory. Abbreviated *SE*.

supervisor—an individual who oversees, directs, and evaluates the work of employees.

surface runoff—rain, melted snow, and other types of precipitation in excess of the amounts absorbed into the earth that run off the surface and may be collected in reservoirs for use in aquaculture.

suspended solids—materials that neither float on top nor sink to the bottom.

sustainable aquaculture—the production of aquatic organisms using efficient and cost-effective methods to improve human capacity, utilize and conserve available resources, and protect the environment.

symptom—evidence that a disease exists.

tank—a relatively small water facility.

taxonomic name—the scientific name of an organism based on its genus and species.

taxonomy—a system of arranging organisms into groups. Also called *scientific classification* and *systematics*.

thalli—the stems of algae.

therapeutic benefit—something that provides enjoyment, relaxation, and a feeling of personal well-being.

thermostated heater—a warmer with a thermostat that is suspended in the water.

tissue—a group of cells that are alike in structure and activity.

topography—the slope of the land on which a pond is built.

trade deficit—the situation that occurs when more is imported than exported.

transgenic fish—fish with artificially altered genetics.

transgenic organism—a genetically engineered organism that can pass the altered gene to its offspring.

trash fish—undesirable fish present in a crop of fish.

treatment—the use of therapeutic or management practices to help fish and other aquacrops overcome disease.

turbidity—the presence of suspended particles of soil or plankton in water.

ulcer—an open sore on the skin that festers and contains pus.

univalve mollusk—a mollusk with a single coiled shell. Also called a *gastropod*.

V

variety—a group of related organisms within a species with some unique characteristics but whose differences are not great enough to warrant another species; most often applied to plants, including terrestrial and aquatic plants.

vat—an impoundment much like a tank but usually constructed of concrete or concrete blocks and, therefore, not portable.

veins—vessels that carry blood to the heart.

vigor—the lively movement of fish in water.

viral disease—a disease caused by a virus.

viscera—internal organs, especially the stomach and the intestines.

vitamins—organic substances necessary for proper nutrition.

W

warm-freshwater aquacrop—a species that requires warm fresh water with a temperature range of 70° to 90°F (21° to 32°C).

water aging—collecting an open container of water and allowing it to stand for 24 hours exposed to the open air so that substances may escape.

water biology—the living and nonliving organisms found in water and the processes they carry out.

water chemistry—the composition of water.

water cycle—the never-ending circulation of the earth's water.

water enclosure—a facility in which aquaculture takes place.

water garden—a decorative water area that has a variety of plants and, typically, goldfish.

water management—the use of water in aquaculture to maintain a good environment for the aquacrop.

water pH—the acidity or basicity of water.

water physical characteristics—the conditions of water due to temperature.

water quality—the suitability of water for a particular use.

water recirculation—the pumping of water back through the same water facility.

water reuse—the directing of water to other aquaculture or plant culture systems, which allows for more value to be obtained per unit of water.

watershed pond—a pond created by damming a natural stream or valley.

weight-of-catch fee—a fee a fee-lake user pays based on the pounds of fish caught.

well—an opening made into a water table of the earth to obtain water.

well-being—the state in which an animal's needs are met and it does not suffer.

wooded pond—a natural pond found in a low area where trees and other vegetation are present.

World Aquaculture Society—an international association for the promotion of aquaculture. Abbreviated WAS.

Y

yield—the amount of high-value product remaining after processing.

Z

zoeae—larval crabs.

zooplankton—animal plankton.

zooplankton inoculation—the addition of zooplankton to pond water to promote increased zooplankton growth.

zygote—a cell formed by union of male and female sex cells, followed by meiosis.

Bibliography

Ackefors, Hans, Jay V. Huner, and Mark Konikoff. *Introduction to the General Principles of Aquaculture.* New York: The Haworth Press, Inc., 1994.

Aquaculture: Opportunities for Appalachia. Washington: Appalachian Regional Commission, 1990.

Avault, James W., Jr. *Fundamentals of Aquaculture.* Baton Rouge, LA: AVA Publishing Company, Inc., 1996.

Burtle, Gary J., Larry W. Dorman, and D. Leroy Gray. *Baitfish Production in the United States.* Athens: University of Georgia, College of Agricultural and Environmental Sciences, 1994.

DeVito, Carlo, and Gregory Skomal. *The Everything Tropical Fish Book.* Avon, MA: Adams Media Corporation, 2000.

Everhart, W. Harry, and William D. Youngs. *Principles of Fishery Science,* 2nd ed. London: Cornell University Press, 1989.

Heen, Knut, Robert L. Monahan, and Fred Utter. *Salmon Aquaculture.* New York: John Wiley & Sons, Inc., 1993.

Hinshaw, Jeffrey M. "Trout Production: Feeds and Feeding Methods." Raleigh: North Carolina State University, Southern Regional Aquaculture Center Publication No. 223, 1990.

Hinshaw, Jeffrey M. "Trout Production: Handling Eggs and Fry." Raleigh: North Carolina State University, Southern Regional Aquaculture Center Publication No. 220, January 1990.

Hodson, Ronald G. "Food Fish Production of Hybrid Striped Bass." Raleigh: North Carolina State University, n.d.

Huner, Jay V., ed. *Freshwater Crayfish Aquaculture in North America, Europe, and Australia.* New York: The Haworth Press, Inc., 1994.

James, Barry. *Koi.* Morris Plains, NJ: Tetra Press, 1985.

Jensen, Gary L., Joseph D. Bankston, and John W. Jensen. "Pond Aeration—Types and Uses of Aeration Equipment." Baton Rouge: Louisiana Cooperative Extension Service, Southern Regional Aquaculture Center Publication No. 371, 1989.

Jensen, John W. "Watershed Fish Production Ponds." Auburn: Alabama Cooperative Extension Service, Southern Regional Aquaculture Center Publication No. 102, 1989.

Jolly, Curtis M., and Howard A. Clonts. *Economics of Aquaculture.* New York: The Haworth Press, Inc., 1993.

Kight, Troy. "Hybrid Striped Bass Pros and Cons," *Research Highlights,* Mississippi State: Mississippi Agricultural and Forestry Experiment Station, February 1990.

Killian, H. Steven. "Sample Graded Method for Fingerling Transactions," *The Aquaculture News* (February 1996), p. 15.

Krul, Syd. "Mahimahi Reproduction at the Waikiki Aquarium," *Today's Aquaculturist* (January 1990).

Landau, Matthew. *Introduction to Aquaculture.* New York: John Wiley & Sons, Inc., 1992.

Lee, Jasper S. *Commercial Catfish Farming,* 3rd ed. Danville, IL: Interstate Publishers, Inc., 1991.

Lee, Jasper S., and Diana L. Turner. *AgriScience,* 3rd ed. Danville, IL: Interstate Publishers, Inc., 2003. (Now available from Pearson Prentice Hall Interstate, Upper Saddle River, NJ.)

Lee, Jasper S., Jim Hutter, Rick Rudd, Lyle Westrom, Amanda R. Patrick, and Austin M. Bull. *Introduction to Livestock & Companion Animals.* Upper Saddle River, NJ: Pearson Prentice Hall Interstate, 2004.

Masser, Michael P. "Cage Culture: Cage Construction and Placement." Frankfort: Kentucky State University, Southern Regional Aquaculture Center Publication No. 162, 1988.

Masser, Michael P. "Cage Culture: Handling and Feeding Caged Fish." Frankfort: Kentucky State University, Southern Regional Aquaculture Center Publication No. 164, 1988.

Masser, Michael P. "Cage Culture: Species Suitable for Cage Culture." Frankfort: Kentucky State University, Southern Regional Aquaculture Center Publication No. 163, 1988.

McCoy, Henry D., II. "Aquaculture and the Law: A Primer." *Aquaculture Magazine* (January–February 1996), pp. 38–44.

McHugh, John J., Steven K. Fukuda, and Kenneth Y. Takeda. *Hawaii Watercress Production.* Honolulu: University of Hawaii, College of Tropical Agriculture and Human Resources, 1987.

McLarney, William. *The Freshwater Aquaculture Book.* Point Roberts, WA: Hartley & Marks, 1987.

Morgan, E. Ruth, and Martin W. Brunson. *Toxicities of Agricultural Pesticides to Selected Aquatic Organisms.* Stoneville, MS: Southern Region Aquaculture Center, 2002.

Murphy, Tim R., and James L. Shelton. "Aquatic Weed Management." Athens: University of Georgia, Southern Regional Aquaculture Center Publication No. 361, April 1989.

Nelson, Joseph S. *Fishes of the World,* 2nd ed. New York: John Wiley & Sons, Inc., 1984.

Parker, Rick. *Aquaculture Science,* 2nd ed. Albany, NY: Thomson Delmar Learning, 2002.

Porter, Lynn, Jasper S. Lee, Diana L. Turner, and Malcolm Hillan. *Environmental Science and Technology,* 2nd ed. Danville, IL: Interstate Publishers, Inc., 2003. (Now available from Pearson Prentice Hall Interstate, Upper Saddle River, NJ.)

Salmon and the Sea. Renton, WA: Renton School District, 1988.

Smith, Theodore I. J. "Aquaculture of Striped Bass and Its Hybrids in North America," *Aquaculture Magazine* (January–February 1990), pp. 40–49.

Stickney, Robert R. *Principles of Aquaculture.* New York: John Wiley & Sons, Inc., 1994.

Stickney, Robert R., ed. *Encyclopedia of Aquaculture.* New York: John Wiley & Sons, Inc., 2000.

Stone, Nathan, and Hugh Thomforde. *Common Farm-Raised Baitfish.* Stoneville, MS: Southern Region Aquaculture Center, 2001.

Stutzenbaker, Charles D., Brenda J. Scheil, Michael K. Swan, Jasper S. Lee, and Jeri Mattics Omernik. *Wildlife Management Science & Technology.* Danville, IL: Interstate Publishers, Inc., 2003. (Now available from Pearson Prentice Hall Interstate, Upper Saddle River, NJ.)

Tave, Douglas. "Production of Triploid Mud Loach," *Aquaculture Magazine* (January–February 1996), pp. 82–85.

Tucker, C. S., and Edwin H. Robinson. *Channel Catfish Farming Handbook.* New York: Van Nostrand Reinhold, 1990.

Walker, Susan S. *Aquaculture.* Stillwater, OK: Mid-American Vocational Curriculum Consortium, Inc., 1990.

Wellborn, Thomas L. *Catfish Farmers Handbook.* Mississippi State: Mississippi Cooperative Extension Service, Publication No. 1549, 1989.

Wellborn, Thomas L. "Construction of Levee-Type Fish Production Ponds." Gainesville: University of Florida, Southern Regional Aquaculture Center Publication No. 101, revised 1997.

Wellborn, Thomas L. "Site Selection of Levee-Type Fish Production Ponds." Gainesville: University of Florida, Southern Regional Aquaculture Center Publication No. 100, 1988.

Index

production, 32–34, 471–492
reproduction, 115
univalve, 71
molting, 109, 373
monitoring, 295
monoculture, 15
morphology, 95
mullet, 496–497
municipal water, 195
muskellunge, 440
mussels, 485–487
mutation, 150

N

natal stream, 464
National Marine Fisheries Service, 45
National Oceanic and Atmospheric Administration, 45–46
National Warm Water Aquaculture Center, 84
net pen(s), 270, 285–287
nitrogen, 201
in aquariums, 531
compounds, 220–221
cycle, 207–209
North America, 16–19
nutrition, 120–139
disease, 154

O

oceans, 193–194
offshore aquaculture, 14, 450–453
omega-3 fatty acids, 30
open systems, 14–15
organic aquaculture, 627–629
organs, 101
systems, 102
ornamentals, 62–63, 510–557
oscar, 511
oxygen depletion, 215–220
oysters, 74–75
depuration, 482
morphology and physiology, 110–113
packing, 342
production, 472–482
seeding with helicopter, 621

P

packaging, 339
paddlefish, 406–409
parasites, 158–162
pearls, cultured, 41, 445
pellets, feed, 134
pens, 187–188, 270, 285–287
perches, 430–434
permits, 258–261
pest(s), 142–174
definition, 144
pH, water, 200, 209
aquariums, 530
phenotype, 77
phosphate, 221
phycocolloids, 602–603
physiology, 95
phytate, 616
phytoplankton, 213
pikes, 438–440
piranha, 545
plankton, 213
bloom, 224
plants
aquarium, 548–550
freshwater, 72
nutrition, 121–122
ornamental, 548–550, 578–586
pollution, 200–201
controlling, 231–232
polyculture, 16, 618–620
polytrophic, 376
pompano, 498–499
pond(s), 183
catch-out, 637
drainage, 281
engineering, 280–281
koi, 587
levee-type, 266–267, 273–274, 278–282
rice, 375
size, 278
volume calculation, 225–226
watershed, 267–268, 274–275, 281–282
wooded, 375
ppt, 73
prawn, 38, 379–387
predators, 162–166
preservation, 340–341

processing, 316
fish, 336
procedures, 336–343
product form, 331–332
production, aquaculture, 32–34
freshwater species, 356–409
production systems, 11–16
promotion, 349–350
protected animals, 172
protein, 123
protozoa, 159

Q

quarantine, 155–156, 161

R

raceways, 13, 183–184, 268–269
construction, 283–284
site, 275
volume calculation, 225–226
R&D, 23–26
ration, 121
recirculating facility, 14–15, 298–305
recreation, 22, 325–326, 632–657
recycling
water, 196
red drum, 499–500
redds, 465
refractometer, 447–448
regional aquaculture center, 25
regulations, 258–261, 454, 644–645
Regulatory Fish Encyclopedia, 318–320
reproduction, 94
asexual, 113
decapod, 114–115
fish, 113–114
mollusk, 115
sexual, 113
reptiles, 68
research, 23–25, 43–44
rice-fish culture, 611
runoff
surface, 196–197

S

safety, 646–647